Pam,
Hope you
enjoy these fun
stories and
amazing women!
Robbie Gries

Anomalies

Pioneering Women in Petroleum Geology: 1917 – 2017

by

Robbie Rice Gries

Pioneerwomengeologists@gmail.com

ISBN: 978-1-936499-09-0

Library of Congress Control Number: 2017901359
Petroleum
Oil and Gas
Geologists
Women in science
Women Entrepreneurs
Affirmative action
Women role models
Women managers

Cover Design by Jerry Criddle

Designed by JeWeL Publishing LLC
www.jewelpublishing.com
Denver, CO

Printed by Steuben Press, Longmont, CO

Printed in Unitied States of America

Back cover photo credit: San Diego History Center

Anomalies

Pioneering Women in Petroleum Geology: 1917 – 2017

Anomaly--A departure from the expected or normal;
a geologic feature which is different from the general surrounding
and is often of potential economic value.

Dedication

To

David E. Bailey, my husband

Patient, understanding, supportive, who makes me laugh

and

Dr. Lynn M. Gries, my daughter

Creative, enthusiastic, positive, always.

Table of Contents

Foreword

Foreword—the Inspiration

Prior to the research for this book, my depth of knowledge about female geologists in petroleum geology was limited to my own generation, those of us who were lucky to be job hunting when Affirmative Action affected that pursuit in the mid-1970s. Yes, I knew of a few "pioneering" women—Doris Curtis, Evelyn Wilie Moody, Anny Coury. I had read the Memorials for Fanny Carter Edson and Dollie Radler Hall, and in the 1980s had interviewed Ninetta Davis. But, to me, they were just very rare and exceptional women—which, of course, they were. When Doris died, and, as my generation began to age and retire, I thought, "Oh my, we REALLY need to preserve our stories—mainly thinking about we women who made our 1970s debut into the "no woman's land" of the oil patch.

The impending 100th Anniversary of the American Association of American Geologists (AAPG) in 2017 propelled me into action. About four years ago in 2013, I suggested to the Professional Women in Earth Sciences (PROWESS) Committee, AAPG's evolved diversity committee, that we do something to celebrate the *first 100 women in petroleum*. I asked, "How about identifying the 100 first female members of AAPG and making a banner or decorating a wall to celebrate them at the Centennial Celebration at the Annual Convention and Exhibition (ACE) in Houston?"

I had already begun to collect stories from my generation, and I resolved to identify older pioneers who would be good fodder for my book—someday.

The PROWESS committee embraced the concept wholeheartedly. Carol McGowen, Karin Alyea, and JoAnn Trippett, all three AAPG staff members who had played important roles with the committee for over two years, quickly went into action. They descended into the bowels of the basement of AAPG headquarters in Tulsa, a quiet, dark, damp, dusty chamber enveloped with the incessant hum of the computer system that dominated the space. They rummaged through thousands of 3 X 5 paper membership cards, carefully trying to determine women from men (eliminating male Fays, Hollys, Laras, Shirleys, Lynns, Beverlys, Hilarys, Claires, and Gails). While I had originally thought the first 100 female members would easily stretch into the 1970s, our era, I was shocked, absolutely shocked, to find that we had 100 women identified before the end of World War II. Even more astounding, I saw that our female history of employment in the oil business began the same year as AAPG, 1917. *What a true Centennial celebration this would be.* From this rich resource evolved the concept of creating an AAPG Documentary on Pioneering Women in Petroleum. Vern Stefanic has been the driving force in making this a reality. His work, incorporating the information we uncovered, combined with Matt Randolph's good skills taking video footage, is resulting in a documentary production that will shine a light on these almost forgotten pioneers.

The AAPG hand-written membership cards contain a treasure trove of information about each person, ironically, far more information than is captured with the greater computer power available today. We had a name (plus name changes added with marriages), date of birth, place of birth, schools, degrees, work experience, and other association involvement. The AAPG cards gave the committee and me the basic information for in-depth searches for relatives, friends, and obituaries. The Prowess committee, at that time, divided up the 100 identities and began some basic research: this included the hard work of Amanda Haddad, an amazing force, Kumkum Ray, Lee Avary, Ann Vasko, Elizabeth Petrie, Jessica Moore, Jessica P. Moore, Lauren Cassel. Tania Campbell, and Linda Kyle. I could take their discoveries and run with it, trying to find relatives and stories.

Another great asset to these membership cards was that they allowed me to illustrate numerically and graphically the history of women in the oil business. Though not every female geologist in the oil business was a member of AAPG, most were. Consequently, the progression of women entering petroleum geology could be graphed by using the number of women joining AAPG by year (Graph 1). Though women were working in the industry as early as 1914-15, the first woman employed by an oil company came in 1917, and the first women members of AAPG began in 1919.

The eras covered in this book are obvious on the AAPG membership graph: World War I (WWI), the micropaleontology era; World War II (WWII), the post-war years; and lastly the consequential recruitment of women after Affirmative Action that began prior to the oil embargo of late 1973. The data on this graph were assembled with AAPG Membership Services staff, Vicki Beighle's, patient compilation of lists of women members in various forms.

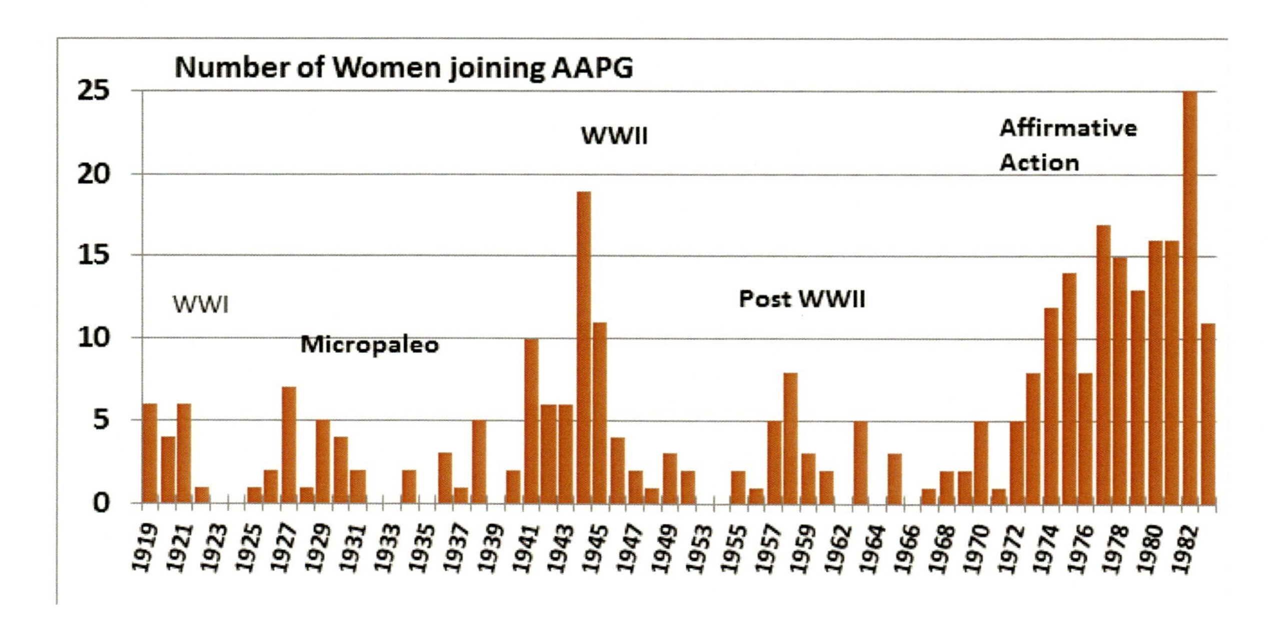

Foreword—the Mission

It is my goal and desire that "those who would have been written out of history, be written in." And, by writing them in, that young people who fall in love with geology, as these women did, will enjoy knowing of their adventures, adversities, successes, and inspirational effect. I also hope that all geoscientists will enjoy venturing into the life and times of these strong and determined women whom we almost lost to history. As I came to know these pioneers through their stories, the stories told by their descendants, the letters they left behind, the friends that recalled their experiences, I was overwhelmed with emotions—admiration, humility, sadness, joy, and pride.

Foreword—the Losses

The most difficult reality I had to face was learning that invaluable, irreplaceable diaries have been lost for key women in this history: Dorothy Aylesbury McCoy's diary through her landmark employment (1918-1924) in the oil business; Julia Gardner's very personal diaries of her experience nursing on the frontlines of France during WWI; Alva Ellisor's several diaries of her entire career doing breakthrough micropaleontology research. Also missing are Alva's priceless photographic scrapbooks. After many disappointing dead end pursuits, I had to admit they were lost forever; it broke my heart.

Foreword—the Joys

On the other side of the quest was the absolute joy I had when after months and months of hunting, I found grandsons, granddaughters, great nieces and nephews, friends, sons and daughters. I would be energized, once again, inspired to continue the days of tedious searches because these people gave me renewed hope.

A remarkable number of women had considerable experience "sitting" oil wells, describing samples as early as 1914, yet the Affirmative Action era of the 1970s had to re-claim the right to do wellsite work. This historic reality had been lost over the years.

A major insight came to me in this research. So many early women were oil finders and loved exploration; however, they downplayed their successes and trials—they were humble and resilient.

They did not, and, likely could not, make a big deal over their oil discoveries so our generation does not think about these early women as "oil finders." More often we associate them with research and paleontology, greatly minimizing their exploration accomplishments. Many not only found oil, but left their descendants with royalties. I stumbled upon their exploration legacies by accident with several of them—Reba Masterson, Dollie Radler Hall, Alva Ellisor, Bess Stiles, Constance Eirich, Linda Green Miller, Hazel Peterson and Mary Cole Robinson. Who knows how many more there are, unknown because of their personal modesty.

Whether with oil revenues, or with salaries, I discovered these pioneers were generous with their money. They were exemplary philanthropists contributing to their universities, their communities, to students, and often to their families when they were in great need—whether offering assistance during the Great Depression or for medical school tuition. And, these early female pioneers, like so many geologists, worked long, long after "retirement."

Dollie Radler, 1919, University of Oklahoma geology field camp, the first year women could major in geology. She is horsing around with one of her classmates. (Photo: Bethan Read, Jackson, Mississippi.)

Acknowledgements

Families

What a treat it was to find and talk to Fanny Carter Edson's granddaughter, Sue Tappeiner in Corvallis, Oregon, and Fanny's grandson, Dale Burtnett of Cage, Oklahoma. Sue had a treasure trove of photographs, letters, news articles, and records of oil and gas interests. Dale's daughter, Kris Ann Moyer, from Fargo, Oklahoma, offered wonderful and legendary stories.

Dollie Radler Hall was legendary before this research began, but when the late Tim Denison of Dallas, Texas, supplied me with correspondence between his father, A. Rodger Denison, and Dollie, I could put myself in Dollie's shoes as she dealt with Sidney Powers when he was ill in 1928. I could sense the deep and supportive friendship between Dollie and Rodger as colleagues in their search for oil and their roles as managers. But, when my research was almost finished, one of my abstracts that included Dollie's name was posted on the internet, and Dollie's cousin, Bethan Read from Jackson, Mississippi, sent me an astounding collection of Dollie's archives—files of photographs and memorabilia, as well as "news to me" information about her involvement in the first reflection seismic survey. I kept thinking, "We could have lost this!" Bethan's memories of Dollie's financial generosity and brilliance (photographic memory) was enlightening. And, through Bethan, I talked to another of Dollie's cousins, Betty Winfrey, who still lives in Broken Arrow, Oklahoma, where Dollie lived.

Reba Masterson's family is rich with stories, with knowledge about her pursuit of oil all over Texas and every state that boasted production at the time. Reba's relatives included Dallam Masterson IV with ConocoPhillips; Amanda Masterson at the Texas Bureau of Economic Geology; Anthony Dallam "Budge" Shepard, retired; Wilber Masterson, a retired lawyer; Dorothy Masterson, a museum director; and her niece, Dr. Lynne Echegaray, from Oklahoma recalled their wonderful Aunt Fefe.

For a while I thought Dorothy Aylesbury McCoy was our first female petroleum geologist because *she was the first woman to join AAPG*. I searched relentlessly and at last found her grandson, Frank "Spank" McCoy, in North Carolina. We mourned together the loss of her priceless diaries to a flooded basement. And, I was thrilled to find her notes on her early oil business experience preserved in the archives at the American Heritage Center in Wyoming, thanks to Edgar Owen, who had a copy and archived it.

Julia Gardner, who had no offspring, treasured her relationship with her niece, Winnie Considine. I was fortunate to locate Winnie's son, Barney Considine of Missoula, Montana, who had a priceless photograph and memories of his mother talking about her beloved aunt. I searched long and hard for any glimmer of hope to find her WWI diaries, but alas, one of her friends apparently destroyed them.

Bob Wynn, of Oklahoma City, has an amazing collection of photographs from his aunt Vita Lee Waters Chase, whom he knew well and shared memories of her travels and work at Amerada.

Anomalies

I almost gave up on the search for the elusive Linda Green Miller, those two last names were too common to gain much from internet searches. But, thanks to Jacque Branch, at ANB Bank in Amarillo, I was able to locate great nephews, Ned Wilson and Lawrence Kelts Green, and through them, Dr. Robert E. Wilson. All shared memories and photographs of this early entrepreneur and oil finder. Becky Livingston, with the panhandle Plains Historical Museum, advised me through the process.

Carl Probst Woods and Ann Maslanka, great nephew and great niece of Fredrica Probst Halley, were helpful to me with their memories of Fredrica and especially helpful putting me in touch with Fredrica's grandson, Alan Rummage of Woodland Hills, California. Alan provided a beautiful photograph and some memories of his grandmother and his mother, Mattie.

Doris Curtis' nieces, Lucy Suchman and Susan Suchman Simone, provided a treasure of photos and stories about their aunt. Doris' colleague and my long-time friend, Ed Picou, was also a valued contributor to her stories with his memories. Ed was also a significant resource on information about the micropaleontology era and the ongoing need for paleontology in oil and gas exploration.

I appreciate Dawn Herrington for her insights on her mother, Louise Houssiere Herrington, and Clay Mizer for his recollections and photos of Joan Finklestein Mizer, and Dan Binkley for photo and memories shared about Margaret Binkley Pack.

John and Tamara Frank, of Louisville, Kentucky, were the perfect hosts for our visit with his mother, Anne Robins Frank. Jane Nelson, wife of Agnes Farrell's nephew, Gregory Farrell Nelson, was helpful with photos, stories, and correspondence.

Mildred Frizzell's son, John, and her niece and nephew, Michelle and Keith Bingham, of Lubbock, Texas, were forthcoming with photographs and great stories of "Old Timer's" adventures. James Peterson of Denver was immensely helpful providing Hazel Peterson's photographs and correspondence, including access to her many oil and gas prospecting files.

Janet Lebow Fahey and her brother, Philip Lebow, contributed their memories, their photos, and information about Ruth Lebow's multi-faceted career, for which I am grateful. Don Lewis is to be thanked for leading me to Mia Alexander and her important story—and for helping me in the search for other "lost" pioneers in California.

I struck gold when I located Patty Kellogg in Gloucester, Virginia. She is the granddaughter of one of our most important micropaleontologists, Esther English Richards Applin. Patty had correspondence, photographs, and an unpublished (and unfinished) autobiography that facilitated an amazing reconstruction of how important discoveries were made using micropaleontology in the 1920s. This is an archive of great historical value. Patty was delightful to talk to about her grandmother and a fantastic resource. Finding the nephew that Alva Ellisor helped to raise, Rik Ellisor, in Oregon was a thrill. It appears that her priceless diaries and scrapbooks are lost (she donated to The University of Texas at Austin—but they cannot be located). However, Rik shared many memories of his profoundly influential, generous, and intelligent aunt. And, to finish off this trio of paleontologists, we were privileged to have direct discussions with Hedwig Kniker's niece, Janice Kniker Lee, in Houston, where Amanda Haddad conducted an interview and discussed Hedwig's archives at the Briscoe Center in Austin.

John Rhoades and his sister, Judy Carriveau, were located and gave us some insight into their geologically passionate aunt, Eleanor Caldwell. Hasan Sarikaya, of Ankara, Turkey, is currently writing a comprehensive biography of Turkey's first woman in petroleum geology, Mehlika Tasman Ribnikar and shared photographs and insights, for which I am very grateful.

Appreciation also goes to the Moody family, Sandy, Misty and, especially, Jennifer Moody, children of Evelyn Wilie Moody. I tried to locate them for two years, only to find them right under my nose in Austin, Texas. Their recollections and photographs were worth the wait. Also in Austin was Kathy Leadford, Bess Stiles' niece. She had a rare photograph of her aunt and information about royalties that were passed down.

For me, it was fun to find in my home town of Denver, men, whom I had known all my career, were sons of amazing pioneers. Ed Wasson, Isabel Wasson's son, provided photos and some stories while we reminisced about our overlapping exploration interests in the Rockies. And another Denver geologist, Chuck Bitgood, came to mind when I read about Ellen Posey Bitgood.

I telephoned Chuck and said, "Are you related?"

What a wonderful surprise to find he has kept a great archive of photos and newspaper stories about his mother.

My Denver friend, Guonong Hu, was a valuable resource for China's first woman in petroleum geology—I only had to ask, and within days he responded with the material from Yang Yi's daughter, Zang Min, and biographer, Ma Zhen.

Back in Houston, Richard Bishop was an immense source of information about his highly respected mother, Margaret Bishop, while Steve and Mara Brachman provided many stories and a photo of Mary Cole Robinson, Mara's oil-finding mother. Marie Antonieta Lorente was such a resource and help with the pioneering women of Venezuela, as was Paty Gomez Ortiz on the first Mexican woman in petroleum geology. I appreciate Monika Gesler from Switzerland providing me with the information about Warda Bleser-Bircher. Many thanks to Alain-Yves Huc and Max Bordenav of Paris, who led me to Dominique and Michel Gubler, sons of the first French woman in petroleum geology, Yvonne Gubler. Henry Pettingill from Houston reached back to his days working in Spain to interview women pioneers in that country.

Matt Hudson from the Geological Society of America provided me with numerous GSA Memorials and accompanying photos as well as publishing advice and encouragement.

Using the internet and genealogy programs, I found Margaret Oros' nephew in Rio Vista, California, Nyle Jordre, and he contributed a wonderful photo of her in her youth. Deeny Haertlein, daughter of Rosamond Haertlein and niece of Jean Allen Ferrin, was a fount of information on the Allen sisters. L. Greer Price generously furnished photographs of Dorothy Echols. James MacDonald in Ohio was a good resource for Constance Eirich and Esther Franz. Pam Howell sent me a rare photo of Grace Hower. Jerry Sides, in Midland, Texas, was very helpful with information and touching stories about Maria Spencer as well as Mary Louise Rhodes.

George Vandersluis, friend and colleague, helped reconstruct Monica Donnellan's history and provided her photos and her priceless well sitting letter. Susan Morrice, Debra Neshida, Neil Hurley, Bob and Phyllis Merrill, Susie Simmons, all helped in many ways, some with lots of work, all with great encouragement.

Melissa Gray, my assistant, at Priority Oil & Gas LLC, who ran the office during my mental absence, who tackled computer problems *ad nauseam*, who put up with my cries of frustration and bellows of distress, she who did the necessary bookkeeping and provided encouragement, patience, and appreciation—she deserves very special thanks, and I remain in her debt.

Editing

When Denise Cox volunteered to help me with editing, I had not a clue what a practiced and expert editor she was. I really appreciate her time and dedication to the project and amazing ability to re-arrange and re-organize for the better. That being said, I take full responsibility for any errors, either with information or with typographical missteps. Gerald Tyler, my brother-in-law, was easy to coerce into editing. He is an experienced writer and kept me thinking and improving the stories as he fell in love with these women, too. Ann Priestman, long-time friend and woman of many talents, patiently read and edited chapter after chapter—after Denise and Gerald and still managed to find some issues. Donna Anderson not only read and edited much of the manuscript, but helped with the citations. Michelle Judson gave me a hand, a much-needed hand, with references. Gwenn Jensen, one of the best resources for "the correct way," provided many edits and pieces of advice. Kumkum Ray also volunteered and helped with early research, references, and additional eyes. I appreciate greatly the efforts these friends made and know that my deadline would never have been reached without their efforts. Here, again, Melissa Gray came to the rescue and even enlisted her sister-in-law, Suzette Lyons, and her son, Billy Gray, for editing. Gratitude abounds. Sandy Lardinois, JeWel Publishing, formatted the book for publication, and was necessarily roped into some editing just because it needed to be done. And, she knows what she is doing.

Librarians

I have benefited greatly from the assistance of Dennis Trombatore, Head Librarian, Jackson School of Geoscience, The University of Texas at Austin, who embraced the project early on and was generous with both research and advice. Katie Dziminski of the DeGolyer Library at Southern Methodist University was a wonderful source of help as well as Jacquelyn Reese at the Western History Collections, University of Oklahoma. Also, before she retired, Jody Bales Foote at the Youngblood Energy Library at the University of Oklahoma was a help finding photos and information about OU Graduates.

John R. Waggener, of the American Heritage Center at the University of Wyoming, was helpful with the Edgar Owen collections, the Elizabeth Watson collection, and other important background material for this research. Michael Foote at the University of Chicago was helpful locating photos and information about the early female geology graduates and provided me with the book on the history of the geology department at Chicago. The staff at the Dolph Briscoe Center for American History, The University of Texas at Austin. Austin, Texas, was very helpful on my several visits and with filling orders. I especially appreciate the extra effort of Aryn Glazier. David Null, at the University of Wisconsin, was a good resource for UW graduates and, in particular, Fredrica Probst.

Mona Lambrecht at the University of Colorado Heritage Center in Boulder, Colorado, was helpful with graduates from that institution, and Dr. Gregory P. Dietl and his staff at the Paleontology Research Institute in Ithaca, New York, were generous with time and effort for Helen Plummer and Helen Hodson. Alex Asal at Smith College and Deb Wales at Middlebury also provided assistance with a few graduates as well as Jim and Kristi Hoban from Texas Christian University. Appreciation to James Stimpert, with Special Collections at the Sheridan Libraries of Johns Hopkins University, who was helpful with material for Julia Anna Gardner.

Financial Contributions to Publication

American Geological Institute

American Association of Petroleum Geologists (AAPG)

Jane Woodward

Petroleum History Institute

Pacific Section AAPG

Rocky Mountain Section AAPG Foundation

Rocky Mountain Association of Geologists Foundation

West Texas Geology Foundation

John Kaldi
Piotr Krzywiec
Elizabeth "Betsy" Campen
John Mason
Janet Fahey
Barbara Tillotson
Maria Antonieta Lorente
Susan Cage
Marvin and Harriett Brittenham
Heidi and Steve MacAlpine

Joseph P. D. Hull Jr.
Connie and Roger Knight
Donna Anderson
Lyn and Gary George
David E. Bailey
Helen Laura Foster
Debra Neshida and Neil Hurley
David R. Cook and Gretchen M. Gillis
Edith Allison
Al and Ione Taylor

Debra Sacrey
Lesli Wood
Jane and Marshall Crouch
Robert Kier
Robert and Carol Gunn
Robert Chambers
Allyson Anderson Book
Sue Tappeiner
John Armentrout
Lauren A. Langford, M.D.
Ripley and Lamina Marks
Denise Mruk Cox
John Dolloff
Fredia Hester
Tony Jackman
Michelle Judson
Ann Molineux
Dallam Masterson IV
Katherine "Lee" Avary
Cindy Yeilding
Ohio Oil & Gas Energy Education Program
Pinar Yilmaz
Richard S. Bishop, PhD
Association of Women Geoscientists
Julie Downey Garvin
Dr. Lynn Margaret Gries

"Wells, like babies, generally "blew in" at night and the thrill of feeling the earth tremble with the sudden release of trapped petroleum by the hard metal spud of the rotary drill was compensation enough for sagging beds and greasy food.".

Bob Burtnett, Fanny Carter Edson's son-in-law, describing her love for being on drilling locations

Cars and people crowd their way to the Daisy Bradford No. 3. Photo: Charles S. Nicks, 1930; Kilgore Historical Preservation Foundation, Archives, Kilgore, Texas.

Prologue

An Exciting Day for the First Female Petroleum Geologist

Imagine what it was like when news of a potential strike came to the ears of a gutsy geologist, anxious to be part of the petroleum world:

Reba Masterson loaded up her 1929 Model A Ford for her trip from San Antonio to Henderson, Texas over 300 miles away in East Texas. She had heard reliable rumors that promising shows had been detected in "Dad" Joiner's third attempt drilling the Daisy Bradford lease. The previous two wells that showed promise ended as failures with stuck pipe or other complications. This one, the Daisy Bradford #3, had been drilling for a year and a half and was plagued with poor equipment and Joiner running out of money. Worse for Joiner, his lease was expiring. He had already managed to get two extensions. The drilling was finally improved with a new drill string, but a drill stem test of an oily zone had failed. In desperation, they had run casing and bailed unsuccessfully for days. Now, they were making one last ditch effort and were swabbing the zone. Thousands of people were camped nearby throughout the testing. Somehow, optimism prevailed despite the discouraging results. Joiner was housed in nearby Overton, Texas, but had apparently rushed back from a Dallas trip for this round of testing. Reba knew there would be no place for her to stay in Overton. She was lucky to book at the Davenport Hotel in Henderson.

It was 5 a.m. and she was not sure if she would get there before dark, especially if there was traffic with other "rubberneckers." Though her new car could make 60 mph, with so many small towns and high traffic, she would be lucky to average 40 mph. Reba had been chasing discoveries for over 20 years off and on, finding that she could often parlay her geology expertise into an interest in leases surrounding discoveries as land owners and investors were hungry for "scientific" opinions. She had already done some scouting around this area, identifying leaseholders that might have interests she could acquire.

She was a tiny woman, maybe 5' 2" and very slim. But at age 48, she was a tough and determined business woman and a very competent geologist—the first professional female petroleum geologist in the country. Though she never thought about that, she just did what she liked to do. She had never worked for a company; she just got her degree and started applying geology to finding oil. Getting that degree, however, was a story in itself!

Usually, she traveled with her good friend and constant companion, Eunice Aden, but on this fine October day in 1930, she would be traveling alone. Eunice was at Medina Lake, taking care of new building at their Kiva Camp for girls. Reba didn't like traveling without Eunice...even with her trusty .32 caliber pistol her father had given her when they were involved in an East Texas lawsuit where she had been threatened if she testified. She rarely went anywhere without her pistol. But, Eunice provided more protection because she had a .38, and, she was taller, larger, and very athletic. Formidable, she was also gregarious and always surrounded by friends. Yes, Reba felt safer when Eunice was with her.

As Reba drove eastward into the rising sun, she let her mind drift back to her Galveston days. Her father frequently entertained visiting oil men. In 1901, he and a few colleagues organized The New York and Texas Oil Company, and it was there that she met Dad Joiner on one of his many Galveston visits. It was not only a nice place for a small vacation, it was a great place to mingle with other oil men and investors. Her only irritating memory was when she let him beat her in a poker game so many years ago—losing an oil lease to him! She hoped that one never came in big, making her feel the fool!

Branch Masterson, her father, had instilled a fascination for the oil business in her, and they often had occasion to learn of abandoned properties that could be bought for back taxes. He made his living in law, but he enjoyed dabbling as a "vacancy hunter" that way, picking up properties and their attached mineral rights for back taxes. Despite his interest in the oil business, she had an awful time fighting with him to let her go to college and study geology. But, he got tired of her nagging every night at the dinner table and, maybe more importantly, realized when she turned 26 she was probably never going to get married and, perhaps, would need a career! She hadn't wanted to study law like her brothers. She liked being in the thick of an oil field. In 1908 when she started at the University of Texas in Austin, she was only the second woman in the geology program. This was a path to give her the excitement of travel, business, and science all rolled into one.

She had been 19 when the 1900 Galveston Hurricane took her mother's life, and the lives of so many other family members, that forced great maturity and responsibility upon her. At the time, Reba remembered being pushed to her limits with the responsibilities of rebuilding the family home, taking over the domestic duties her mother once managed, caring for her 16-year-old brother, Thomas, and, of course, caring for her father. Her older brothers and older sister were long gone from the house. But her sanity was kept in place by the enthusiasm she had earlier shared with her father about the oil business. After the Hurricane, when Spindletop came in a few months later, they welcomed the distraction and speculated about what might be around them. Saratoga field was discovered the next year, Sour Lake in 1902, and Goose Creek in Harris County in 1903. She and her father followed it carefully and took to driving to these places and learning to scout any new drilling. He would check out the possibility of buying properties and minerals as they went along. She learned how to do the same. They were lucky enough or smart enough to acquire leases in the Damon's Mound area after J. M. Guffey's early drilling tests failed in 1901 or 1902. No accident, she was at Damon's Mound when it blew in November 15th of 1915. Had it not been for the August 1915 hurricane bringing her back from Colorado, she would have missed it there...her first time to witness a blow out! Their leases, long considered speculative, proved fruitful indeed for the Masterson family!

As she continued her drive toward Henderson, she thought how much she still missed her father—though he had been dead for ten years. She had a wonderful, but convoluted, relationship with him. Reluctant though he was to let her go to college, he came to appreciate her when she gained so much knowledge in Austin and Boulder. He was proud of her geologic expertise and her business sense.

She remembered when, as a diversion from her studies at the University of Texas, she and her father had visited Colorado and she fell in love with it. She wasn't through with her geology degree, but she knew she could finish while considering oil properties in the Rockies. They had considered acquiring leases around the Boulder oil field—so exciting near the little foothills college town—but the field was in serious decline by the time she moved there in 1911 to start coursework at the University of Colorado.

Her five years of studying and looking at the structural geology of Oklahoma, Louisiana, and Texas were equally trying, but she could, more easily, get back to her home in San Antonio for breaks. She had plenty of resources for her studies by visiting the Bureau of Economic Geology in Austin. She enjoyed a friendly relationship with the geologists there but was glad she did not have to depend on making a living there...living from state budget to budget was not her cup of tea.

As Reba stopped to service her car in College Station, she thought about the college rivalry between UT and Texas A&M. Silly, but fun. She was more attuned that morning to the good fortune of having paved roads. And more service stations. She loved that she did not have to crank the car as she did in her early years of chasing oil discoveries. Nor, did she have to deal with as many flat tires and breakdowns as when she was running around in oil fields after she left the University of Colorado. She had planned to start right away in the oil business when she finished CU but, once again, a hurricane altered her plans. She had to finish her last few credit hours at CU by correspondence and didn't get her geology degree awarded until 1916.

As soon as possible, she started her independent study of oil fields, of new exploration efforts. Traveling was so much more challenging then. Her excursion through Kansas, Illinois, West Virginia, Pennsylvanian, and Kentucky doing reconnaissance work was grueling but wonderful. Driving that old Model T was hard and physical, but the muddy, god-awful roads were really a pain. It was easier in the summer months when Eunice could accompany her. Many times, she would never have made their destination without Eunice's help or without the help of strangers, or both!

Gassed up, she continued her drive toward Henderson. She knew these roads well and the small towns she had to drive through—out of San Antonio and into Seguin where her friend, Hedwig Kniker, came from, a fellow UT student and now successful geology consultant. She drove on through Lockhart, Bastrop, Bryan; ahead of her was Crockett, Weeping Mary, Alto, and Rusk. Traffic was beginning to build, certainly most cars heading to the same place she was going.

Late in the afternoon she pulled into Henderson and found the Davenport Hotel. After checking in, she changed into boots and clothes that would work out on a drilling location. She was glad that women had begun to wear high boots and jodhpurs in the field unlike the old days of formal dresses that she had worn to Damon's Mound when it blew. Could that have just been nine years ago?

Henderson was packed with cars and people, many heading out to check the activity at the Daisy Bradford. The usual oil field trash was in abundance—she was used to dealing with that. She recognized an oil scout she had come to know and he caught her up with news about the testing at the well. He told her the crew had been bailing for almost two days and had started swabbing the well. He thought the well could prove itself very soon, one way or the other. She hurried to her car and headed west out of town. It was easy to find the way—cars packed the roads. When she got as close as possible, nearby landowners were charging people to park and she took advantage of it. "My god!" She thought. "There must be several thousand people here."

As she left her car, she heard the crowd begin to grow silent. She whispered to someone, "What's happened?"

He whispered back, "They heard something in the drill pipe. We're listening." She couldn't see but suddenly heard people yell and shout as a spurt of oil came up the casing and onto the surface! She, and all eight or nine thousand spectators were rewarded as oil began to pulse out of the well bore, then up and over the crown—a gusher! At last! She was happy for Dad Joiner. She watched in awe and pleasure as history was once again being made in Texas. Could there be anything more exciting? She knew she had work to do, too. Could she get a piece of the Ashby lease nearby? She thought about the contacts she had made and started working on her strategy to find a piece of the action. How far to go? Rusk County only? Or move out to Green County? Smith? She had a lot of work ahead of her.

Women geology students, 1910 Burning Mountain, Murray County, Oklahoma. (Photo: #4572, Western History Collections, University of Oklahoma, Norman, Oklahoma.)

Figure 1. Women were "waiting in the wings" for a chance to work as geologists. This geology class was from the University of Oklahoma, 1909, at a time when women were not allowed to major in geology. The first female graduates were in 1919. (Photo: Blakey, 1985, p. 73.)

Chapter 1

World War I Forces the Oil Industry to Hire Female Geologists in 1917

The Backstory: The Early Mindset Against Geologists in Petroleum Exploration

Geology and geologists of any gender were not a welcome sight in the oil industry in the first decade of the 20th century (Fig. 1). Geologists had made inroads to being respected for their scientific expertise and economic viability in a few places of the world such as the Far East and Latin America, but generally, in the United States they were ignored, scorned, or totally rejected. In the U.S., most geologists were employed by geological surveys or universities prior to the first decade of the 20th century (Owen, 1975, pp. 217-223). California oil companies made progress with the acceptance of petroleum geologists in the years from 1892-1911, largely because of the successful integration of the "anticlinal theory" with surface geological mapping. In contrast, oil companies based in the more traditional East Coast debated the anticlinal theory for forty years and reveled in efforts to prove that geology did not work in finding oil. Geologic respect was even slower to materialize for Texas and Mid-Continent oil companies.

Ed Owen, (Fig. 2) past president of the American Association of Petroleum Geologists (AAPG) and author of *Trek of the Oil Finders* remarked, "Petroleum geology, which had been generally ignored by the pioneers in Pennsylvania, became an object of active ridicule in Oklahoma" (Owen, 1975, p. 231).

In 1908, Gulf Oil Corporation's (Gulf) engineering manager, C. H. Markhan, in

Figure 2. Edgar W. Owen, author of Trek of the Oil Finders: Memoir 6*, 1975, the penultimate history of the petroleum business. An oil finder who taught in his retirement at The University of Texas at Austin for a dollar a year, instilling ethics and professionalism in the fortunate students who knew him. Ed was acutely aware of the discrimination against geologists in the early 20th Century and cites multiple incidents in his tome. Ed was president of AAPG in 1941 and the recipient of the Sidney Powers Memorial Award in 1964. (Photo: Blakey, 1985, p. 73)*

Figure 3. William Wrather, 1927, employed in 1908 by Gulf Oil Company, later to become USGS Director (1943-1956), AAPG President (1922-23), and Sidney Powers Memorial Award recipient 1956. (Photo: AAPG archives, Tulsa, Oklahoma.)

Pittsburgh, was forced to employ geologist William E. Wrather (Fig. 3) but prefaced his employment, saying, "Now, young fellow, I'm not hiring you as a geologist. You're a scout. You can use geology if you want to, but the oil companies don't have much to do with geology. They don't have any confidence in it." (Owen, 1975, p. 199). Gulf's production department referred to the newly formed geological department in 1913 derisively as "the zoological department" (Owen, 1975, p., 296).

The manager of Humble Oil & Refining Company's Pacific Northwest affiliate, Carter Oil Company, was forced to hire a geologist and greeted him with the admonition, "I don't think you'll do us much good and I will damn well see that you don't do us any harm." (Owen, 1975, p. 312). After several initial geologic-based successes, Carter Oil's manager reversed his opinion and authorized the hiring of twenty-five more geologists!

The Beaumont-based Texas Company (eventually Texaco) had their own anti-geology prejudice as a manager remarked, "If I had the final say-so none of you fellows would be around here. You can best please me by getting the hell out of here into the brush and staying there." Another Texas Co. manager refused to speak to any of the geologists. And Wallace Pratt's Texas Co. boss in Wichita Falls greeted him with "Mr. Pratt ... we don't think much of geologists around here. Your office is at the end of the hall—the last door. When I want to see you, I will send for you" (Owens, 1975, pp. 315-316). (Fig. 4) Empire Gas and Fuel Company (Cities Service Oil Company) generated the greatest increase in the employment of geologists with its large discoveries in Kansas of Augusta and El Dorado fields using geological mapping. Soon they employed up to 250 geologists. Owen recalls, "... by 1916 almost any warm [male] body with college training in geology could get a job" (Owen, 1975, p. 300). But Empire, too, had a shaky start. The company almost lost its chance at discovering the prolific Augusta field when their recently hired geologist, Everett C. Carpenter, took his first map to his manager and reported that the manager did not "enthuse one iota about the map and report" (Owen, 1975, p. 298).

Figure 4. Wallace Pratt, an AAPG Founder and President (1920-21) who was relegated to the end of the hall in his earliest job as a geologist. Wallace was the first recipient of the prestigious Sidney Powers Memorial Award from AAPG. He was a visionary, who, as the first geologist hired by Humble Oil and Refining Company and through his skill as a geologist, an innovator, and a leader, built the company into the leading producer of oil and the holder of the country's largest oil reserves by the time he retired in 1960. He famously said, "Where oil really is, then, in the final analysis, is in our own heads!" (Salvador, 1982, pp. 1412-1416). (Photo: AAPG Archives, 1927, Dallas, Texas.)

When production in the Mid-Continent increased by 375% directly related to the use of geology, other companies woke up to the value of geologists (Owen, 1975, p. 285). This awakening occurred as the demand for more oil was greatly increased with World War I (WWI) raging in Europe and the automobile boom sweeping the U.S. The number of U.S. automobiles increased from about 640,000 vehicles in 1911 to over 9 million in 1920 (Owen, 1975, p. 284). Geologists gained the respect and the jobs they wanted at a time when the world desperately needed their talents to find more oil and gas (Fig. 5).

The War to End All Wars and the Impetus for Hiring Women

The United States, determined to stay neutral in a war that had been escalating since July 1914, changed its perspective in 1917 when the Germans began sinking U.S. ships in the North Atlantic, and Germany tried to form an alliance with Mexico. Mexico had just resolved the Mexican War conflicts with the U.S., and U.S. troops that had been in Mexico were withdrawn in February 1917. Two months later, on April 6, 1917, the U.S. declared war on Germany; and six months later, on the Austro-Hungarian Empire in December 7, 1917.

An early attempt to create a strong, voluntary U.S. military was unsuccessful and conscription quickly was imposed. Ten million men were enlisted in 1917 and, when their numbers increased to 24 million, the male workforce was decimated. Although American troops began to arrive in France as early as June, 1917, they were few

Figure 5. Empire geologists ready to map surface anticlines with plane table and alidades to prospect for oil. Empire hired the most geologists during the WWI era but did not do a great job of retaining them (Photo: Blakey, 1985, p. 184).

and ill prepared. Not until October, 1917, did they enter the conflict in great numbers. By the Armistice on November 11, 1918, two million American men had served on the battlefields of Western Europe, and more than 50,000 had lost their lives (www.history.com). Some reports suggest 110,000 casualties (www.eyewitnesstohistory.com). Returning American men to the U.S. after the Armistice was a drawn-out, logistical process and further delayed men returning to the civilian workforce (Ellison et al., 1987, p. 27-29).

Participation in World War One (WWI) forced several oil companies to try the experiment of hiring female geologists to fill their positions (Fig. 6). Roxana Petroleum Company (Shell Oil Co.) in Tulsa took the lead and hired the first woman in 1917; eight months later, Empire (Cities Service Oil Company) hired the second. Gypsy Oil Company (Gulf) and Amerada Petroleum Corporation (Hess Corporation), soon thereafter, hired women.

Figure 6. Men in 1918 lined up for enlisting in WWI. (Photo: internet, by Bain News Service, publisher.)

1917-1918: The First Female Employees in Petroleum During WWI

Roxana Hires Women in Petroleum Geology

Figure 7. Richard "Dick" Conkling, first to hire a woman employee in petroleum geology, with Roxana Petroleum in Tulsa. (Photo: Roxoleum, *v. 2, no. 5, p. 14, DeGolyer Library, Southern Methodist University.)*

Richard A. "Dick" Conkling, (Fig. 7) a graduate of the University of Oklahoma (1911), was working on an advanced degree at the University of Chicago (1913-1915) when he quit his studies to go back to work. His professor at Chicago (Dr. Salisbury) had found temporary work for him the year before in Venezuela for eight months with a Philadelphia firm. That work led him to another diversion from getting his master's degree. His position with Royal Dutch Shell in Europe lasted six months until he experienced, first-hand, the beginning of WWI. With the outbreak of the war, Shell returned him to the U.S. with orders to join Roxana Petroleum Company (Roxana) in Tulsa as chief geologist. Dick, in January, 1915, stipulated a month's vacation in his contract to enable him to get married back in Chicago, to Winifred Winne, a recent graduate of the University of Chicago with a master's degree in geology.

While in The Hague, Dick, very likely, heard of Shell's female consultant in paleontology and stratigraphy, Carlotta Joaquina Maury: the first woman hired to consult on paleontological samples for oil and gas. He may have met her while he worked in Venezuela, as they overlapped a few months. Dick was no stranger to women geologists, coming from the environment of University of Oklahoma (OU) where there were many enrolled in geology but not allowed to major in geology at the time. By 1915, the University of Chicago had graduated six women with bachelor's degrees in geology and three with master's degrees.

Roxana, established in Oklahoma in 1912, was the creation of the Royal Dutch/Shell Group (Fig. 8). Roxana entered the American petroleum market to acquire, by purchase and by exploration, crude oil for their refining facilities. Roxana's President Watershoot A.J.M. van der Gracht (Fig. 9), a geologist and respected manager, nurtured a "fair and happy loyal, hardworking, well disciplined...bunch, proud of its reputation and company" (Beaton, 1957, p. 150). The company harmony was disrupted when WWI conscripted 265 male Roxana employees to war, including many of their geologists. Van der Gracht was truly an exceptional manager: he created very progressive employee policies for the departed soldiering men; he started a news magazine, *Roxoleum*, for the men away at war; and, he ensured that salaries to families were maintained by paying the family the difference between their Roxana wage and their service wage.

Figure 8. Roxana's office building in Tulsa, the Mayo building. (Photo: Roxoleum, v. 1, no. 8, p. 15, DeGolyer Library, Southern Methodist University.)

Dick Conkling was part of the group of 50 geologists who met in Tulsa in February, 1917 and founded the Southwest Association of Geologists (soon to be renamed the American Association of Petroleum Geologists). Two months after this meeting, in April, 1917, Dick hired Helen Jeane Skewes to be an assistant to him as an "office" geologist in the subsurface department. Thus, Helen Skewes would make history as the first female geologist hired as an employee (not consultant) geologist in the petroleum industry. How he was acquainted with Helen Skewes, who was working at the Illinois State Geological Survey at the time and was a Northwestern graduate (not the University of Chicago), we will never know. But, Dick had become acquainted with Fred Plummer while at the University of Chicago, and Jean and Fred were soon to marry, so perhaps it was through Fred that Dick learned about Helen. In February 1918, Dick hired Roxana's second female geologist, Margaret Campbell, from the University of Chicago. In May, two more women were hired from the University of Chicago: Esther Franz and Mary Emily Wright. The following month, Dick branched out of the Chicago system and hired Fredrica Probst from the University of Wisconsin—she was the sister of Karl Probst, a Roxana engineer. In June, he added another Chicago graduate to the Mineral Wells, Texas office—Eva Adams. Also for the Roxana Mineral Wells office, Dick hired "the brightest kid in the class of 1919," Linda Green from OU, his own local alma mater.

The American Association of Petroleum Geologists (AAPG), born in 1917, has become the world's largest organization promoting the science of petroleum geology (aapg.org).

Records of earliest membership in the organization are archived in the Tulsa Headquarters of AAPG and provided a remarkable basis for research on the earliest women involved in petroleum geoscience.

Figure 9. Dick and Winnie Conkling (left) and Mrs. and Mr. van der Gracht on a rig in Texas. (Photo: Roxoleum, *v. 1, no. 8, p. 7, DeGolyer Library, Southern Methodist University.)*

Conkling's wife, Winnifred Winne Conkling, unemployable because, like most companies at the time, Roxana did not employ married women, was possibly frustrated by her sideline role (Fig. 10). However, she was present on most business trips and geology field trips discussed in *Roxoleum* (Fig. 11). In May, 1918, *Roxoleum* reported, "Mr. and Mrs. Conkling chaperoned a class from the University of Oklahoma on its spring field trip in the Arbuckles. From there they ran down to Ardmore and spent

Figure 10. Winnie Conkling with a Texas geology field party. She earned her master's degree in geology from the University of Chicago and traveled to the field and to wells with husband, Dick Conkling. (Photo: Roxoleum, *v. 2, no. 5, p. 15, DeGolyer Library, Southern Methodist University.)*

Figure 11. Winnie and Dick Conkling, seated, on a field trip to Elk Basin, Wyoming. (Photo: Roxoleum, *v. 1, no. 7, p. 4, DeGolyer Library, Southern Methodist University.)*

several days going over southern Oklahoma fields with Mr. Merrill. They returned laden with fossils and enthusiasm, and now, after a comparatively brief stay in Tulsa, they are out again; this time in Texas." She was reported to be learning drafting skills in the drafting department, and she spent time in the Texas division office doing quadrangle mapping where she was pronounced "quite a draftsman" (*Roxoleum*, April 1919, p. 16), but she was never on the payroll.

Helen Jeane Skewes Plummer (1890-1951)

Figure 12. Helen Jeane Skewes first female geologist and employee of an oil company. During WWI, in 1917, the loss of men to fight in the war compelled Richard Conkling to hire women for Roxana. (Photo: Helen Plummer archives, Paleontologic Research Institute, Ithaca, New York.)

Helen Jeane Skewes (Fig. 12) attended Northwestern University where she became interested in geology and received a B. A. degree in 1913. She spent two to three years with the Illinois Geological Survey in Urbana before her move to Tulsa. Helen was not only an office geologist, she was "an assistant to Conkling." She and Conkling's wife, Winnie, were devoted volunteers in the war effort—knitting and sewing countless sweaters and hats, and Helen served as an officer in the Roxana Red Cross volunteer effort. She was a Roxana employee for only one year before she married Frederick Plummer, the head geologist of Roxana's Texas Division. Fred knew Dick Conkling from their school days at the University of Chicago. Though the Texas Division was formally a Houston office, Fred lived and worked out of Mineral Wells, Texas, a small town west of Dallas-Fort Worth. After she married, Helen quit her position in Tulsa and moved to Mineral Wells. She traveled with Fred on many of his business trips especially when he visited Tulsa where her old colleagues welcomed her (Fig. 13).

Figure 13. Frederick and Helen Plummer after they married in 1918. Their honeymoon was combined with travel around Texas for work. (Photo: Roxoleum, *v. 1, no. 6, p. 15, DeGolyer Library, Southern Methodist University.)*

Helen continued to contribute to their WWI Red Cross efforts. She did not become a member of AAPG when her Roxana female colleagues did in 1919; likely her "unemployed" status prohibited her from doing so. However, it was noted that she not only attended the meeting but also had drafted Fred's map for his presentation at the meeting (*Roxoleum*, March 1919, p. 8). During a two-year period, about 1920-22, she spent with her husband at Shell's headquarters in The Hague, Holland, she became interested in micropaleontology (in 1920, in Houston, Texas, four oil companies formed a consortium to use macropaleontology for stratigraphic correlations and soon turned to micropaleontology) (see Micropaleontology, Chapter 7). In Europe, she started accumulating her own collections of fossils and literature. Upon returning to the U.S., she completed her graduate degree in 1925 from Northwestern. Her first publication, "Foraminifera of the Midway formation of Texas" was published in 1926 (*Texas University Bulletin* 2644, pp. 1-306). Much of her career was behind-the-scenes as a help to her husband; editing his manuscripts, doing the artistic work for publications, and checking all the data, as well as accompanying him on field trips. During the 1920s and '30s, Helen's field studies and collecting extended over a large part of the Gulf Coastal region, and she used her micropaleontology skills and experience to consult with petroleum companies. (Fig. 14)

Figure 14. People from Roxana's Tulsa office visit the Mineral Wells office in 1918. Left to right: George Lucas, I. J. Broman, Helen Skewes, J. G. Burtt, R. A. Conkling, J. W. Merritt, R. J. Davis, Chester Hammill, E. Floyd Miller, Glen Lasky. (Photo: Roxoleum, *v. 1, no. 4, p. 31, DeGolyer Library, Southern Methodist University.)*

Helen and Fred lived in Houston from 1924-1927 where she developed lifelong friendships with other micropaleontologists: Esther Richards, Alva Ellisor, and Hedwig Kniker. Esther Richards, in her letters to her boss and colleague, E. T. Dumble, told him she was delighted when Helen volunteered to do all the drawings for one of her manuscripts. Helen also became renowned for her social skills and was appreciated for hosting a very lovely wedding brunch for Esther Richards and Paul Applin when they married (from Esther's autobiographical notes).

After a brief sojourn in Fort Worth, Texas, Fred Plummer joined the staff of Bureau of Economic Geology (BEG) at The University of Texas in 1928, and their permanent residence was established in Austin. "Auntie Plummer" allowed neighbor children the run of her house in Austin and tried to instill in them an appreciation for botany and geology. She nurtured and gave generously to them. She was demanding of herself in every endeavor – from gardening to cooking – insisting, even when she did not enjoy something, that it be done to perfection. Her hospitality was legendary.

From 1933 until her death in 1951, Helen consulted for the BEG. During the 1940s, she helped the Petroleos Mexicanos establish a micropaleo laboratory in Mexico. The BEG did not hire Helen "full-time" until after her husband died in 1947. It was also after Fred's death that Helen Plummer joined AAPG and remained a member until her own death.

Figure 15. Helen Jeane Skewes Plummer memorial Photo: (Photo: Adkins, 1954, p. 1854.)

Helen Plummer (Fig. 15) was considered an authority on late Paleozoic, Mesozoic, and Cenozoic foraminiferal assemblages. Over her lifetime, she organized an outstanding private collection of foraminiferal genera, species, and assemblages, and brought together an extremely valuable scientific library pertaining to these fossils. Many well-known paleontologists "contributed comprehensive suites to her collection." But it was not by exchange alone that the Plummers compiled their collections. Helen, always the stickler for detail, visited thousands of localities with her husband, washed samples, and prepared slides of their own collecting. Also, because of drilling activity near Austin, she secured many well samples brought to her by drillers for identifying the formations. Her work is of great significance because she left full and detailed records of type localities. This has permitted workers who followed to collect and to study larger suites of topotypes. Helen Plummer's valuable paleontological collections of a lifetime were donated to the Paleontological Research Institute in Ithaca, New York.

Dick Conkling Hires More Women in 1918

Margaret Campbell Hancock (1891-1980)

Figure 16. Margaret Campbell, second woman hired for Roxana. She knew Conkling at the University of Chicago where she worked in the Geology Museum when he was working on a graduate degree. (Photo: Roxoleum, v. 2, no. 8, p. 11, DeGolyer Library, Southern Methodist University.)

Margaret Campbell was hired in February, 1918, by Dick Conkling to become an "office geologist" for Roxana in Tulsa (Fig. 16). She had been working at the University of Chicago Geology Museum when he was in graduate school. One of her first assignments aside from her geologic duties was to write "news" from the Geological Department for *Roxoleum* (Fig. 17). In May, 1919, the office was moved to St. Louis and Margaret wrote in detail about the trials and tribulations of traveling there, staying in an awful accommodation, and settling there. She and another Roxana office geologist, Esther Franz, shared an apartment.

LADIES' REST ROOM A NOVEL FEATURE OF OUR NEW OFFICES

One of the novel features of Roxana's new suite of offices in the installation of a ladies, rest room. This room is located on the ninth floor. It is exquisite in its appointments, the walls being decorated in a beautiful Tiffany blend. The draperies and rugs harmonize beautifully and the wicker and mahogany furniture is the finest of its kind. Wall lights and a beautiful chandelier makes the lighting plentiful but subdued. Mirrors and pictures adorn the wall and as a whole this room, exclusively for the use of the lady employes, is about as attractive as it could be made.

Figure 17. One of Margaret Campbell's news items from St. Louis—Roxana's new offices ... when women at the workplace were a novelty. Roxoleum, v. 1, no. 8, p. 12, DeGolyer Library, Southern Methodist University.

It appears Margaret Campbell was unhappy with the move to St. Louis because she had a beau named Hancock, who lived in Arkansas. In January of 1920, she returned to St. Louis from a Christmas vacation and learned she was to lose her apartment at the end of the month. Because she was planning to get married sometime soon, she quit her job and moved back to Chicago, Illinois "indefinitely" rather than move again. She then married "Mr. Hancock," and her whereabouts after that are not known (Fig. 18).

Figure 18. Margaret Campbell from the Tulsa, Oklahoma office visits the Graford, Texas warehouse with Earl Oliver (left), John Rick, and John Suman (right). Suman was from the Mineral Wells, Texas office and, later, was Paul and Esther Applin's best man. (Photo: Roxoleum, v. 1, no. 9, p. 14, DeGolyer Library, Southern Methodist University.)

Mary Emily Wright Bottom Taylor (1895-?)

Mary Emily Wright was hired by Roxana in May, 1918, after she completed field work supported by Empire in Bartlesville. She became an AAPG member in 1921 but her records at the University of Chicago are obscure. The Geology Department appears to have not recorded the women who graduated in 1918—most, if not all, are missing from the 1963 history book *The First Seventy Years of the Department of Geology: University of Chicago*. A search of Chicago yearbooks illustrates their presence—in geology.

Roxoleum reports Mary Emily's marriage to William Bottom in October, 1918, and his departure for WWI soon thereafter. Roxana's accepted policy on marriage was for the woman to quit. Roxana must have made a war-time exception with Mary Emily because she continued to work for a year after her marriage even though her husband returned from his enlistment within a few months.

Mary Emily became the lone geologist in the Tulsa office when everyone else moved to St. Louis. She was still with Roxana when they ceased to produce *Roxoleum* in 1920. Naturally, she became the Roxana "Correspondent

Figure 19. "Geology Department Girls," back row: Miss Heads, Eva Adams, and Fredrica Probst; middle row: Esther Franz, Miss Gordon, Linda Green, and Miss Hartman; sitting: Misses Mauldin and Menard. (Photo: Roxoleum, *v. 3, no. 7, p. 13, DeGolyer Library, Southern Methodist University.)*

for News from Tulsa." It can also be noted there were encouraging comments and tones in the magazine about the suffragette movement that passed nationally in 1920. Sometime before 1924, she left Roxana and married again (widowed or divorced unknown); her new husband was Charles B. Taylor and they had a son, Abbott Lawrence Taylor. By 1930, the family had moved to Homewood, Alabama, and she was widowed before 1940. In 1937, she was working at an army post in Atlanta, Georgia, which was noted on her AAPG membership card. Mary Emily Wright Bottom Taylor was an AAPG member for fifteen years, indicating she kept up her interest and perhaps worked as a geologist after she married, but knowledge of her career ends in Atlanta. (Fig. 19, without Emily Wright Bottom)

Esther Franz (1895-1990)

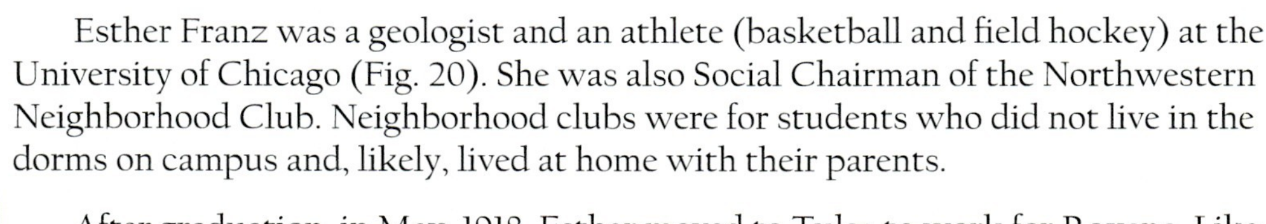

Figure 20. Esther Franz was a subsurface geologist with Roxana and quit when married, returned to Chicago and worked in a family chemical business. (Photo: Cap and Gown *yearbook, 1917, University of Chicago, p. 89.)*

Esther Franz was a geologist and an athlete (basketball and field hockey) at the University of Chicago (Fig. 20). She was also Social Chairman of the Northwestern Neighborhood Club. Neighborhood clubs were for students who did not live in the dorms on campus and, likely, lived at home with their parents.

After graduation, in May, 1918, Esther moved to Tulsa to work for Roxana. Like Margaret Campbell and Mary Emily Wright, she knew Dick Conkling and his wife, Winnie, at the University of Chicago. When the exploration office was moved to St. Louis, Esther transferred with the other Roxana staff geologists. She left Roxana sometime around 1923, moved back to Chicago to live with her parents, and took a job as a secretary at a bank (personal communication, James MacDonald).

In the late 1940s or early 1950s, Esther Franz moved to the St. Joseph, Michigan area south of Kalamazoo and Grand Rapids to work in her sister and brother-in-law's company, East Shore Chemical Company. Both her sister and brother-in-law were chemists. Her brother-in-law was the president of the company, her sister vice-president, and Esther became the company secretary. The company was sold in 1986 and today is known as ESCO, owned by Mitsubishi Corporation (personal communication, James MacDonald).

Fredrica Probst Halley (1893-1964)

Fredrica Probst was one of the few Roxana women hired as a geologist who was not from the University of Chicago; she took her geology degree from the University of Wisconsin (Fig. 21). Fredrica was a sister of a Roxana petroleum engineer, Karl Probst, and likely had her introduction to Roxana through him. Hired in June, 1918, she, too, moved to St. Louis where Roxana had recently completed building a major refinery. Fredrica was described as an "office geologist," but there are many photos of her "in the field" with Paul Applin or with the Conklings (Figs. 22 and 23).

Figure 21. Fredrica Probst graduated from the University of Wisconsin and joined Roxana in Tulsa, where her brother, Karl, was an engineer. She married Harry Halley and ran her own consulting and investing office all her life. (Photo: Alan Reid Rummage, Woodland Hills, California.)

Figure 22. Fredrica with Paul Applin in the field for Roxana doing geological work in Texas. (Photo: Roxoleum, v. 2, no. 5, p. 15, DeGolyer Library, Southern Methodist University.)

At some point, she moved back to Tulsa from St. Louis. Her parents were living in Tulsa, and her father, a former furniture maker in Indiana, had decided to venture into the oil business. He was acquiring properties in Oklahoma and was described as an "oil operator." Shortly thereafter, Fredrica met Harry L. S. Halley, a promising young Tulsa attorney and recent WWI veteran. They married and had one child, Matilda, or Mattie as she was known.

Fredrica stayed involved with oil and gas properties all her life, keeping an office in Oklahoma City. Fredrica was always quietly strong and forceful, though very modest. Her grandson, Alan Reid Rummage of Woodland Hills, California, tells a story of when she was invited to join a Tulsa "social club," possibly when her husband became an Oklahoma Supreme Court Judge. In the interview process, she was asked what her religion was. Annoyed with such a personal question, she answered, "I'm a heretic!"

Figure 23. Tulsa geologists visit a well site in Palo Pinto County Texas. Left to right, Winnie Conkling, Fredrica Probst, Dick Conkling, Eva Adams, Mr. Frankfurt, and Fred Plummer. (Photo: Roxoleum, v. 2, no. 2, p. 16, DeGolyer Library, Southern Methodist University.)

According to Alan, Fredrica expressed disappointment when her daughter did not continue her education beyond her bachelor's degree, and this caused conflict between them for years. After Fredrica died, Mattie went back to school and got her law degree. She was a very accomplished person in her own right—a jazz enthusiast, contributor to the arts, and very active on behalf of battered women and abused children. Mattie inherited oil properties from her mother and traveled frequently to Oklahoma to continue to manage Fredrica's office and properties until her death. Her great nephew, Carl Woods of Broken Arrow, Oklahoma, related that Fredrica's "business" seemed not to be in exploration or development but in consulting, regarding oil and gas royalties. For people who had royalties and did not understand them, she may have educated and advised them. She also spent time investing her own royalty income from the properties inherited from her father in non-oil and gas assets. Fredrica Probst Halley was likely the second female geologist to become an "entrepreneur" in the oil business.

Eva Adams (1898-1983 possibly)

Eva Adams was also a University of Chicago geology graduate from the class of 1918 (Fig. 24). In early October of that year, Eva joined Roxana's staff in Mineral Wells, Texas, where she would work for Frederick Plummer. *Roxoleum* (November 1918, p. 22) reported "Miss Adams hails from the 'windy city,' so she has had a thorough training for withstanding those vigorous northers which blow across northern Texas. As office geologist, Miss Adams will probably be confined indoors more than is good for one of her delicate constitution, but she has visions of field trips which will tend to tickle her appetite and make her feel that she is really getting her money's worth...."

Figure 24. Eva Adams worked in Mineral Wells, Tulsa, and, finally, in St. Louis with Roxana. (Photo: Cap and Gown yearbook, 1918, University of Chicago, p. 22.)

Eva was elected to be on the executive committee of the Roxana Club of Mineral Wells in January, 1919, but, a month later, was transferred to the Tulsa office. When Roxana moved everyone but Emily Bottom to the St. Louis office, Eva moved again and roomed with Margaret Campbell, Esther Franz, and Lucy Raubaugh. She apparently loved to dance and party. It is not known where Eva Adams went after she left Roxana.

The Empire Experiment—Hiring Women in 1918

After Everett Carpenter's immense success in convincing Empire Gas and Fuel Company (Cities Service Oil Company) to hire geologists for field mapping, he hired Alexander Watts McCoy, who was an OU professor and, previously, a geologist for Marland Oil Company (Fig. 25). Alex McCoy brought with him a mission to set up a "subsurface department" in their Bartlesville, Oklahoma headquarters (Fig. 26).

Figure 25. Alexander Watts McCoy, 1927, who hired his sister-in-law, Dorothy Aylesbury, as an "experiment" in 1918—WWI to see if women could replace the men who were off to war. He is credited with inventing and refining the art of subsurface geological technology for the oil industry, creating a scientific approach to subsurface geological practices that set the standard. He pioneered oil-field water sampling, sample logging, shoreline mapping, and many other aspects of good exploration. He was president of AAPG in 1925-26 when Tulsa was selected as the permanent home for AAPG and J.P.D. Hull was selected to be business manager. He was famous for his unorthodox thinking and for tackling problems with "joyous abandon." (Photo: AAPG archives, Tulsa, Oklahoma.)

Today's geologists take for granted subsurface procedures and the value of collecting and analyzing subsurface data – reliable samples, systematically making lithologic logs, recording, analyzing drill times, keeping contour maps current with active drilling, and participating in well completion decisions – but, in 1917, this was a new, novel, and formidable objective. Carpenter and McCoy convinced New York management this was a worthwhile endeavor and robustly developed a "subsurface department." Very capable personnel were hired, co-operation with the drilling and production departments was established, and this remarkable facet of a proper oil and gas company had its birth.

By 1919, McCoy was able to report that his department had every available well log in the Mid-Continent fields (Owen, 1975, p. 302). Field trips were part of the rigor. To put the importance of this newly cultivated scientific technology in perspective, today's geologists who grew up with computers must visualize the working environment PRIOR to the technology of electronic well logs for correlation, and PRIOR to the recognition of macro and micro fossils as useful stratigraphic tools, and before the invention and application of geophysical tools for petroleum exploration. The only tools geologists had for exploration were the rocks and the expertise to identify, correlate, and map a prospect. The lithologic descriptions of well cuttings that were the basis for their subsurface geologic work were, most often, compromised by poor wellsite supervision and exacerbated by the drilling crews' low opinion of demand for consistency and discipline collecting samples.

Figure 26. Bartlesville, Oklahoma, during the early years when Empire had been hiring record numbers of geologists and had started hiring women during WWI. (Photo: Bartlesville Area History Museum.)

McCoy (who would become the 7th president of AAPG) was considered one of the most creative thinking and innovative of petroleum geologists of the times. But, one of his more daring ventures was to hire women to fill-in for the men who went off to war in 1917-1919. Having a geologist sister-in-law gave him an opportunity to try the experiment without much risk or fanfare.

Dorothy Aylesbury McCoy (1896-1975)

Figure 27. Dorothy Aylesbury, 1921, on her wedding day. Empire's first female geologist. She was the second woman to be hired in petroleum geology and wrote about her experiences in "The Pebble Puppies." (Photo: Spank McCoy, Wake Forest, North Carolina.)

Dorothy Aylesbury (Fig. 27) had recently graduated with a bachelor's degree in geology from Washington University in St Louis, Missouri. Alex McCoy dated Dorothy's sister, Helen Aylesbury, also studying at Washington, while he was in graduate school, a short walk away at the University of Missouri. He married Helen in the fall of 1917 and hired Dorothy to work in his subsurface department a few months later, beginning January 4, 1918.

Dorothy recalled, "Lest this sounds like a high degree of nepotism, it must be remembered that this employment was frankly experimental, and if the experiment proved unsuccessful the error could be corrected quietly and with little embarrassment." She was put to work "posting scout data pertaining to the sub-surface work, posting oil well logs, keeping maps up to date, and all the other tasks common to the activity of a geological office." Dorothy wrote about her employment at Empire at the request of Everett Carpenter in 1963, and her stories were called "The Saga of the Pebble Puppies." These papers are preserved within E. W. Owen's archives, University of Wyoming.

Apparently, the "experiment was successful," and McCoy hired three more women graduates from the University of Chicago a few months later in June 1918. It can be no coincidence that they, too, came from the University of Chicago where Roxana had recruited three women. Though Empire and Roxana offices were 60 miles apart, it is likely that McCoy had conversations with Dick and Winnie Conkling about female geologists soon to graduate.

Dorothy Aylesbury wrote, "Aside from the regular office routine, the girls were required to take extra training in the form of several field training trips to give them first-hand knowledge of geology as applied to the petroleum industry; also, they were required to take instruction in practical pursuits such as map-making, beginning with the use of rod and transit in field problems" (Fig. 28). Their office covered Oklahoma and Kansas, and the four "girls" were assigned to a part of the two-state area. They were also enrolled in a motor mechanics course "... instituted as a war measure; in those days, many men, and very few women, knew nothing about driving an automobile!" It might be safe to assume there was some travel to the field because they were required to learn not only to drive but also to "fix" the car if it ran into trouble (Fig. 29). Everett Carpenter described the experiment: "...which was almost unprecedented in the oil industry, turned out very satisfactorily and helped to open new careers for women" (McMurry, 1968, p. 1803).

Figure 28. Female geologists learning "rod and transit" mapping in Oklahoma. (Photo: Blakey, 1985, p. 17.)

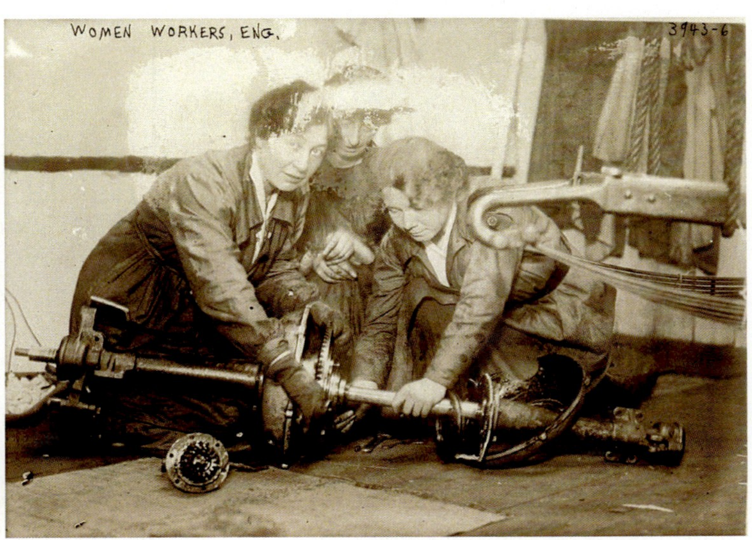

Figure 29. Women at Empire were required to learn to drive and repair automobiles so they were mobile for company business. (Photo: http://www.loc.gov/pictures/collection/ggbain/item/ggb2005022484/, accessed 1/22/2017.)

Dorothy also recalled that she and her female colleagues attended the 4th Annual AAPG meeting in Dallas, Texas 1919, and became "Associate Members" of the fledgling organization of which both Alex McCoy and Everett Carpenter were founding members. Their membership application cards are still in the AAPG archives as are most of the cards for the pioneering women in AAPG. That same year, Empire provided support for Mary Emily Wright to do field work for her master's degree at Chicago (refer to previous Roxana section).

Dorothy quit Empire on March 1, 1920, when Alex McCoy left and worked with him in his new consulting office in Bartlesville, Oklahoma. Dorothy married Lewis McCoy (no relation to Alex) in June, 1921, and resigned from AAPG in 1923. Dorothy's grandson, Spank McCoy, believes that Dorothy may have met Lewis McCoy in Denver, implying that Dorothy also moved to Denver when Alex and Helen McCoy moved there to open an office. There are no records to verify how long she worked for her brother-in-law.

Figure 30. Dorothy Aylesbury McCoy, 1963, the year she wrote, "The Saga of the Pebble Puppies," unpublished memories of her employment at Empire in Bartlesville. (Photo: Spank McCoy, Wake Forest, North Carolina.)

In truth, Empire, though notable for hiring great numbers of geologists, seems to have had a difficult time keeping any geologists. Edgar Owen quit the company in 1917 (before he was conscripted to go to war) because the company would not pay his men in the field their daily expenses. Owen paid them out of his own pocket, then quit. Owen states "Only a few members of Empire's geological organization of 1917 remained with the company though 1919" (Ellison et al., 1987, p. 21). This may also explain why Mary Emily Wright, whose graduate field work was supported by Empire, chose to work for Roxana.

Dorothy Aylesbury McCoy highlighted in her notes that the nickname around Bartlesville for the female geologists was the "Pebble Puppies" (Fig. 30). She said it was derived from the practice in the business of calling the male geologists "Rock Hounds" and perhaps indicated something about women not being equivalent to a "Rock Hound."

Helen Souther Boettler (1895-1979)

Figure 31. Helen Souther joined Empire in May, 1918, and resigned when she married Empire engineer, Joe Boettler. (Photo: Cap and Gown *yearbook, 1918, University of Chicago, p. 48.)*

Helen Souther came to work on May 1, 1918, as a subsurface geologist for Alex McCoy as soon as she finished her University of Chicago bachelor's degree (Fig. 31). Helen resigned from Empire in 1920 when she married Empire valuation engineer, Joe S. Boettler. She also resigned from AAPG soon thereafter. No further history is known.

Barbara A. Hendry Holman (1897-1970)

Barbara Hendry, also a graduate of the University of Chicago, was hired by Empire as a "sub-surface" geologist in June 1918 (Fig. 32). In January 1921, Barbara Hendry was the last of the women hired as geologists by Empire to resign. She left to work for Phillips Petroleum, also in Bartlesville, Oklahoma. Two years later, in 1923, she quit Phillips (or was let go) when she married Empire valuation engineer, Newton D. Holman. Barbara Hendry Holman resigned the same year from AAPG in April 1923. The practice of having women quit their jobs when they married was not unique to the oil and gas business; notably, school teachers were required by contract to quit when/if they married ... or if they "stepped out" with unsavory men.

Figure 32. Barbara Hendry joined Empire in June, 1918, fresh from the University of Chicago. She quit in 1921 to work for Phillips Petroleum until she married Empire engineer, N. D. Holman, in 1923. (Photo: Cap and Gown *yearbook, 1918, University of Chicago, p. 34.)*

Florence Travis
(DOB and DOD not known; education not known)

Florence Travis was hired by Empire in August 1918. She was from Chicago, Illinois, too, but her university affiliation could not be verified. In June 1919, less than a year after she started, Florence was the first woman to quit Empire to work for another company. Knowledge of her life after she left Bartlesville is unknown and there is no record that she ever joined AAPG. Dorothy Aylesbury wrote about her employment in "Pebble Puppies"; otherwise, her identity and geologic career remain a mystery.

1919 AAPG Convention in Dallas, Texas

The American Association of Petroleum Geologists enlisted their first female members at the 1919 Convention in Dallas, Texas where Roxana sent Esther Franz, Fredrica Probst, Margaret Campbell, Eva Adams, and Winnie Conkling. Helen Plummer was also at the meeting but did not join AAPG. Emily Wright Bottom seems not to have attended; she is not in the "University of Chicago alums from Roxana" photograph taken at the convention (Fig. 33). One of Emily's charges in the Tulsa office was to "keep the home fires burning" when others were out of the office and may explain her absence. Emily joined AAPG in 1921.

There are no records that Eva Adams and Linda Green attended the 1919 AAPG Convention in Dallas. Linda Green's story will be told in the next section as an early female entrepreneur. Empire sent Dorothy Aylesbury, Helen Souther, and Barbara Hendry to the 1919 Convention and all three joined AAPG at that time. This meeting was also where Sidney Powers observed Dollie Radler Hall and decided to interview her for a job with Amerada (See Chapter 2, Earliest Managers).

Figure 33. AAPG 4th Annual meeting in Dallas, 1919, and a gathering of University of Chicago alums including new AAPG members Franz, Souther, and Campbell as well as Winnie Conkling and Eva Adams [not identified in order]. (Photo: Roxoleum, *v. 2, no. 6, p. 14, DeGolyer Library, Southern Methodist University.)*

Of these earliest female employees for Roxana and Empire, all married and were required to quit their jobs. Only Plummer, Probst, and Green would take initiatives to remain in the industry for the rest of their working lives.

Carlotta Joaquina Maury

(1874-1938)

One of the initial women to consult for oil and gas interests was Carlotta Joaquina Maury (Fig. 34) who began that work as early as 1906, working with her professor, G. D. Harris, of Cornell University in Louisiana, and later, as she became aligned with the Geological and Mineral Survey of Brazil, she continued some of her consulting for Royal Dutch Shell Petroleum Company. Carlotta was an extraordinary macro paleontologist and forged amazing paths for women in geology—collaborating in oil field mapping in Louisiana; teaching in South Africa; organizing and leading a geologic survey to the Dominican Republic; and diving into the paleontology and stratigraphy of Trinidad, Venezuela, and Brazil. Carlotta did all this before AAPG founders Sidney Powers graduated from Harvard; before George Matson entered the oil business; before Everette DeGolyer organized Amerada Petroleum; and before Wallace Pratt returned to the U.S. from his first geology job—US government mapping in the Philippines. And, all before the American Association of Petroleum Geologists (AAPG) was formed in 1917. She was an excellent paleontologist and a woman of independent means.

Figure 34. Carlotta Joaquina Maury, consultant to Royal Shell and others, worked for the Brazilian government most of her career. (Photo: Reeds, 1939, GSA Proceedings*, p. 156.)*

Carlotta never became a member of AAPG and made her career as an academic; however, her work with her professor in Louisiana on Miocene biostratigraphy (Jennings Oil Field, Louisiana salt dome discovery, 1906-1908) can be considered groundbreaking for women. She was also the first woman paleontologist/stratigrapher hired to consult for Royal Dutch Shell Petroleum Company on Venezuelan projects from about 1910 or 11 and continued occasional consulting for twenty years resulting in sixteen confidential reports. Simultaneously, she worked with the Geological and Mineral Survey of Brazil. Not a "petroleum geologist" per se, she provided the paleontology to others for this purpose.

Born in Hastings-on-Hudson, New York, her destiny to work some day in Brazil might have been "sealed with a kiss" in 1876 when Brazil's emperor, Dom Pedro II, visited New York and the Maury home and kissed this baby girl. Carlotta's grandfather, Daniel Gardner, was the Emperor's physician, and Carlotta's maternal side of the family had lineage to Portuguese nobility. Carlotta attended Radcliffe College, Columbia University, the Sorbonne in Paris, and, lastly, took her geology PhD at Cornell in 1902. It was after teaching at Cornell for a few years that she joined Dr. Harris to help sort out the stratigraphy of salt deposits in Louisiana. She published this work with Harris and soon was publishing on her own.

Her work in Venezuela began as paleontologist for the Veatch Expedition (1909-1911). She had a three-year sojourn to South Africa (1912-15) where she taught and published one paper about a possible salt structure north of Cape Town. Highly unusual for a woman, in 1916, she organized and led an expedition to the Dominican Republic and soon published her work on the stratigraphy and fauna; then, she ventured into mapping and delineating strata and faunas of Puerto Rico.

She became associated with the Geological and Mineral Survey of Brazil and continued that association until 1934, conducting exhaustive research on the fossil faunas of Brazil and combining that with stratigraphic delineations. Much of her work after 1923 was conducted out of her Yonkers, New York apartment where she had set up her private lab. She was financially independent and invested in her own publishing: she engaged skilled draftsmen and engravers to prepare her plates for her many monographs; she hired other specialists when she needed assistance in identifications when she was not the expert; and she provided the initial expense of preparing these large governmental publications while awaiting the slow return of an honorarium after they were published. She had unique and superior published fossil plates, using white on black illustrations instead of black on white, the more common way to illustrate.

Extraordinary in many ways, Carlotta Juaquina Maury was a pioneer in every way. (Biographical material from Reeds, 1939, pp. 156-168).

An aside that is indicative of the status of women at this time: Carlotta's sister, Antonia Coetana de Paiva Maury, became an astronomer and one of the unusual group of women who, at the turn of the century (late 1800s to early 1900s), worked tirelessly as scientists and mathematicians ("computers") in the Harvard Observatory. One of Antonia's colleagues, widow Mrs. Mina Flemings, complained, "He [her boss, Edward Pickering] seems to think that no work is too much or too hard for me, no matter what the responsibility nor long the hours. But let me raise the question of salary and I am immediately told that I receive an excellent salary as women's salaries stand. If he would only take some step to find out how much he is mistaken in regard to this he would learn a few facts that would open his eyes and set him thinking. Sometimes I feel tempted to give up and let him try some one else, or some of the men to do my work, in order to have him find out what he is getting for $1500 a year from me, compared with $2500 from some of the other [male] assistants. Does he ever think that I have a home to keep and a family to take care of as well as the men? But I suppose a woman has no claim to such comforts. And this is considered an enlightened age!" (Sobel, 2016, p. 96) Carlotta and Antonia were both nieces of Henry and Margaret Draper, whose private funding of the Harvard Observatory brought it world renown stature and acclaim.

Chapter 1: Sources and References

AAPG Executive Committee. 1946. "Alexander Watts McCoy Memorial." *AAPG Bulletin,* vol. 30, no. 2, pp. 292-296.

Adkins, Mary Grace Muse. 1954. "Helen Jeane Plummer 1891-1951." AAPG Bulletin, vol. 38, no. 8, pp. 1854-55.

Applin, Esther Richards. Autobiographical notes. Courtesy of Patty Kellogg, Gloucester, Virginia, granddaughter of Esther and Paul Applin.

Aylesbury McCoy, Dorothy. 1963. "The Saga of the Pebble Puppies." Notes written at the request of Everett Carpenter. E. W. Owen Collection #6558, Box 3A, American Heritage Center, University of Wyoming, Laramie, Wyoming.

Bain News Service. Young men registering for military conscription, New York City, June 5, 1917. Photograph. United States Library of Congress's Prints and Photographs Division, digital ID ggbain.24572. Wikimedia Commons. https://commons.wikimedia.org/w/index.php?curid=18464012. Accessed 12/30/2016.

Bartlesville, Main Street. Circa 1920. Photograph. Bartlesville Area History Museum, Bartlesville, Oklahoma.

Blakey, Ellen Sue. Oil on Their Shoes: Petroleum Geology to 1918. Tulsa, Okla.: American Association of Petroleum Geologists, 1985. 192 pp.

Beaton, Kendall. *Enterprise in Oil: A history of Shell in the United States.* New York: Appleton-Century-Crofts, 1957. 815 pp.

Ellison, Samuel. P., Jr., Joseph J. Jones, and Mirva Owen, eds., *The Flavor of Ed Owen—a geologist looks back*, Austin: Geology Foundation, The University of Texas at Austin, 1987. 142 pp.

Fisher, Daniel Jerome. *The Seventy Years of the Department of Geology, University of Chicago*: *1892-1961*. Chicago: University of Chicago, 1963. 147 pp.

History.com Staff. 2010. "World War I Ends." *History .com.* http://www.history.com/this-day-in-history/world-war-i-ends. A+E Networks. Accessed 12/17/2016.

MacDonald, James, Columbus Ohio. Interview with Robbie Gries, February, 2015.

McCoy, Spank, Wake Forest, North Carolina, grandson of Dorothy Aylesbury McCoy. Interview with Robbie Gries, March 2015; source of wedding day and 1963 photographs for Dorothy Aylesbury McCoy.

McMurry, Wallace E. 1968. "Everett Carpenter Memorial." *AAPG Bulletin*, vol. 52, no. 9, pp. 1799-1800.

Owen, Edgar Wesley. *Trek of the Oil Finders: A History of Exploration for Petroleum.* Memoir 6. Tulsa, Okla.: American Association of Petroleum Geologists, 1975. 1647 pp.

Owen, Edgar Wesley. Archives. American Heritage Center, University of Wyoming, Laramie, Wyoming.

Plummer, Helen. *Foraminifera of the Midway Formation of Texas.* University of Texas Bulletin, no. 2644, Austin, Tex.: The University of Texas at Austin, 1926. 206 pp.

Plummer, Helen. n.d. Photograph. Helen Plummer Archives, Paleontological Research Institute, Ithaca, New York.

Reeds, Chester, A. "Memorial to Carlotta Juaquina Maury." *Proceedings of the Geological Society of America for 1938*, May 1939, pp. 156-168.

Roxoleum. [Including photographs cited in text]: Volumes 1, 2, and 3. DeGolyer Library, Southern Methodist University, Dallas, Texas.

Rummage, Alan Reid, Woodland Hills, California, grandson of Fredrica Probst Halley. Interview with Robbie Gries, February 2015; source of college graduation photograph of Fredrica Probst Halley.

Salvador, Amos. 1982. "Wallace Pratt Memorial." *AAPG Bulletin*, vol. 66, no. 9, pp. 1412-1416.

Sobel, Dava. *The Glass Universe: How the Ladies of the Harvard Observatory Took the Measure of the Stars.* New York, New York: Viking, an imprint of Penguin Random House LLC, 2016. 324 pp.

University of Chicago. *Eva Adams*. 1918. Photograph. *Cap and Gown* yearbook. Chicago, Illinois. p. 22.

———. *Esther Franz*. 1917. Photograph. *Cap and Gown* yearbook. Chicago, Illinois, p. 89.

———. *Barbara Hendry.* 1918. Photograph. *Cap and Gown* yearbook. Chicago, Illinois, p. 34.

———. *Helen Souther.* 1918, Photograph. *Cap and Gown* yearbook. Chicago, Illinois, p. 48.

William Wrather. 1927. Photograph. American Association of Petroleum Geologists Archives. Tulsa, Oklahoma.

Woods, Carl, Broken Arrow, Oklahoma, great nephew of Fredrica Probst Halley. Interview with Robbie Gries, February 2015.

"World War I Casualties." Wikipedia, The Free Encyclopedia, https://en.wikipedia.org/wiki/World_War_I_casualties. Accessed 12/17/2016.

World War I. Eyewitness to History.com. www.eyewitnesstohistory.com/w1frm.htm. Accessed 12/17/2016.

Chapter 2

The First Women to Be Entrepreneurial Geologists

Rebecca "Reba" Byrd Masterson (1882-1969)
The First Female Petroleum Geologist

Rebecca ("Reba") Byrd Masterson (Fig. 1) was born in Galveston, Texas in 1882 to Branch Tanner Masterson and Anne Wilmer Dallam. Her father was a lawyer and eventually became a judge in Galveston.

Figure 1. Reba Masterson circa 1900, near the time of the Great Galveston hurricane. (Photo: Dallam Masterson IV, Houston, Texas.)

Early in Reba's life, tragedy struck when her mother and nine other family members died on September 8, 1900 during the Great Galveston Hurricane. Reba was 18 at the time and she and two brothers barely escaped with their lives. She and her mother, brothers, and future brother-in-law, Lewis Fisher, left their home (Fig. 2), four blocks from the shoreline in a small boat, attempting to get to the safety of their aunt's home located next door and higher by five feet. When the small boat overturned, they were in trouble with the crashing debris-laden surf. Her mother struck out for a tree which escaped her grasp; she was swept seven miles downstream to her death. Reba, however, managed to grab onto another tree and made her way to a pile of debris caught between her house and her aunt's. From there, she scrambled onto the front porch and made it to relative safety inside. Her brothers, also, made it independently to the aunt's house. But, in the two-story house, they were still not safe from the pounding waves and ultimate storm surge of 15 feet. The resourceful family cut large holes in the floors to relieve the pressure of the waves and prevented the house from being swept away. Reba's father, older sister, and older brother were on the mainland during the storm and returned a day later to the island and the devastating news. Reba's mother's body was not found until some months later. (Refer to Appendix 1 for Reba's brother's account of the hurricane.)

Reba was 26 years old when she finally fulfilled her dream to go to college and enrolled at The University of Texas (UT). Her great niece, Dr. Lynne Echegaray (personal communication), tells about her delayed education: "At the dining room table, time after time, as her brothers went off to college, she would pester her father to let her go, also. He would say 'no', stating, 'young women did *not* attend college.' At last, he gave in. Probably from exhaustion."

Figure 2. The Masterson home in Galveston, 1900, after the hurricane. (Photo: Dallam Masterson IV, Houston, Texas.)

In 1908, her father, Branch T. Masterson, filed a lawsuit on the family's behalf over his late wife's inheritance. Masterson had studied and practiced law with John W Harris, a wealthy Galveston lawyer who had an "adopted" daughter, Anne Wilmer_Dallam, whom Branch married. At the time, no one thought Anne's adoption was a legal adoption, just a generous offer from Harris to take in an orphan and raise her. However, several years after Harris, by then Judge John Harris, had died and his probate had been settled in favor of his natural children, Masterson found official adoption papers. This meant Reba's mother should have inherited her portion of Judge Harris' estate.

Coincidentally, 1908 was the same year that Reba finally began her studies in geology at UT. Meanwhile, the lawsuit rumbled on. Once a close family, the suit with the Harrises turned everything on end and the lawsuit persisted for nine years, taking its toll on everyone. While at UT, Reba missed several semesters in 1910, 1911, and 1912—possibly returning to Galveston for long months to help her father with the legal proceedings which were not finally settled until 1917. The *Houston Post* carried details of the settlement agreement whereby Reba and other family members were beneficiaries to the settlement involving properties in 60 Texas counties plus shares in the Galveston Wharf (total value of all properties at $2,233,860). Reba and her siblings would not have to struggle to get ahead if they were wise—and they were. For Reba's father, this may have been the opportunity he hoped for to become more involved in the oil business. He had been a director in The New York and Texas Oil Company which had offices in Galveston, Houston, Beaumont, and New York (The Atlanta Constitution, 1901).

Figure 3. Reba Masterson at the University of Colorado, 1916, where she may have been the first woman to graduate in geology. She was 34 years old. The yearbook states about Reba's Texas roots: "Her accents mild betray her." (Photo: The Coloradan *yearbook, 1916, University of Colorado, with permission from CU Heritage Center, Boulder, Colorado.)*

Reba was the second female geology undergraduate student at the University of Texas, and studied from 1908 to 1912. She was active in the Kappa Gamma sorority. Her most important relationship forged in Austin started when she joined the Young Women's Christian Association (YWCA) Club. The faculty sponsor was Eunice Aden, daughter of a wealthy San Antonio family and instructor for physical education at UT. She was soon to become UT's Director of Physical Activities. Everyone who met Eunice loved her vivacious personality and her devotion to the outdoors. Eunice was determined that girls should be exposed to camping and physical activities. She must have been enthralled with Reba, too, an older student, charting a course in a man's field—geology, a ground-breaking choice for a woman. Though Reba was a student, they were colleagues, almost the same age, and became friends for life.

Reba's great nephew, "Budge" (Anthony Dallam) Sheppard recalled that Eunice traveled with Reba everywhere and in many ways, could be described as her "body guard" and protector. Budge recalled that Reba was a tiny woman with a fierce passion for business while Eunice was a large, strong, gregarious woman who readily made friends. They were both suffragettes and active with local efforts in San Antonio to acquire voting rights for women in Texas. The Texas effort was led by San Antonio native, Eleanor Brackenridge, undoubtedly a friend of Reba and Eunice.

It was during those first years in Austin that Reba felt fortunate to have found the Kappa Kappa Gamma "fraternity" (so called at the time) where she would have met Eleanor Brackenridge, the City Member of the fraternity and a notable activist for the rights of women. Eleanor was working on her pamphlet "The Legal Status of Texas Women" that would be published in 1911. She was greatly influential with all the young Kappa Kappa Gammas. Reba was likely responsible for Eleanor's trip to Galveston in 1910 where she spoke and agitated for women's suffrage. Before suffrage became the law nationally, Eleanor was the first woman to vote in Bexar County when Texas granted women voting rights in 1918, two years ahead of national suffrage. Reba may well have introduced her young Galveston protégé, Alva Ellisor, to Eleanor Brackenridge. Alva was likely captivated with these independent women and, in the fall of 1910, she followed Reba's lead to The University of Texas (UT) and majored in geology.

Reba did not complete her degree at UT but left in 1912, moving to Colorado and resuming her studies at the University of Colorado (CU). What led to her move—and the consequential three-year delay in acquiring her degree—is not known. It could be that her father, Branch Masterson, a "vacancy hunter" who picked up abandoned mineral and oil and gas properties and farming properties throughout the west, influenced Reba to move there and oversee and/or acquire properties. Her pursuit of geology, from the beginning, may have been fueled by the need to evaluate lands she and other family members owned for oil and gas as well as mineral potential. She attended classes at CU from 1912 to 1915 (Fig. 3).

It was likely difficult being away from her friends in Austin, and though she joined Kappa Kappa Gamma and became active in the YWCA again, it was not the same. Students and teachers alike teased her about her Texas speech; the yearbook indicates "Her accents mild betray her!" But, the geology in Colorado was amazing, and Reba must have been fascinated with the structures and exposures along the Front Range. Professor Russel George, known for being friendly with students both inside and outside the classroom, provided the guidance she needed. The faculty was small with only three instructors. Not nearly the strength and diversity she was used to at UT, but she could finish her degree there, and CU readily accepted all her credits from Texas. Reba was awarded her Bachelor of Science in 1916. She was 34 years old.

Reba left Colorado in 1915 and finished her last few hours for her degree by correspondence (CU transcripts). This was possibly because another hurricane hit Galveston in August 1915—preceding her final Fall Semester at CU. In addition, she was already involved in ac-

Figure 4. Discovery at Damon Mound Field, 1915. Reba was on site when the oil well came in. (Photo: Anthony Dallam "Budge" Sheppard, Houston, Texas.)

Figure 5. Female observers in their Ford Model T Touring Car after initial development at Damon Mound field. (Photo: Spencer, 2015, p. 3.)

quiring and overseeing oil and gas properties in Texas. Reba's great nephew, Budge, related that Reba was present in November 1915 when the discovery well for Damon's Mound field "blew in" about 50 miles west of Galveston. She was, in fact, an investor in Damon's Mound wells located about 30 miles west of Galveston. (Figs. 4 and 5). Family members enjoyed royalties from that field for years, and still own several half-acre lots at Damon's Mound, a salt dome and highest geographic point in Brazoria County, Texas.

Figure 6. C. M. "Dad" Joiner, (third from left) shakes the hand of geologist A. D. "Doc" Lloyd at the 1930 discovery well of the East Texas oilfield. Haroldson Lafayette "H. L." Hunt (third from right). Did Reba lose an oil lease to him in a poker game? (Internet image http://aoghs.org/petroleum-pioneers/east-texas-oilfield/, accessed, 12/1/2016.)

Reba usually bought land with minerals but was not interested in the land—the surface uses, only the minerals, Budge recalled. When opportunities arose to sell, she would sell the surface and retain at least half of the mineral rights, using a very sophisticated minerals clause for the time, possibly developed by her brother, Thomas, a lawyer who was also involved in acquiring mineral properties. Budge remembers that, when Reba died, she had properties with mineral rights in 20 counties in Texas.

There is a family tale about Reba having lost an oil and gas lease to Dad Joiner in a poker game (Fig. 6). The family, naturally, takes the story with a grain of salt, but we have learned that Joiner liked to spend time in Galveston. A small town at that time, it is easy to imagine two "oil men" like Joiner and Branch Masterson knowing each other. And, easy to imagine Dad Joiner visiting the Masterson home and Reba joining in on a friendly poker game (see Prologue).

Budge Sheppard recounted another story about Reba being involved as a witness in a lawsuit against an historic operator. She received several threats trying to persuade her not to testify at the trial. Her father bought a .32-caliber pistol to provide her with some protection as she traveled to the trial and testified (Fig. 7). Eunice, who often traveled with Reba, acquired her own gun, a .38-caliber pistol, and Budge remembered that Eunice was a very good shot.

Figure 7. The .32-caliber pistol bought by Reba's father for her to use for protection when she was threatened for testifying at a lawsuit. (Photo: Anthony Dallam "Budge" Sheppard, Houston, Texas.)

Reba joined AAPG in 1923, a few years after her father's death in 1920 in Colorado. On her membership application card, she wrote she was a "student of geology" and that she had spent a year doing reconnaissance work on the oil fields of Kansas, Illinois, West Virginia, Pennsylvania, Indiana, and Kentucky. She continued listing her experience on the AAPG card saying she spent five years studying the structural geology of Oklahoma, Louisiana, and Texas. Between leaving Boulder, Colorado in 1915 and her membership application in 1923 were six to eight years when she was investigating and evaluating the geology of oil properties. Reba must have been working the oil patch starting soon after she left Boulder in the summer of 1915. It is easy to imagine that, during the hiatus between her coursework at UT - Austin (1911) and enrolling in Colorado, she was also doing reconnaissance work. Budge Sheppard says that whenever there was an announcement of an oil discovery, Reba would take off, driving to the area, Eunice always with her, to see what she could accomplish there. He believes she was able to parlay her geologic knowledge into deals, trading for an interest and buying where she could. Imagining these two women traveling around the country in a Model T Ford puts their exploits in perspective. It was no easy accomplishment.

In 1923, when the Houston Geological Society was formed to host AAPG's 9th Annual Meeting, Reba and six other women (her young protégé, Alva Ellisor, Esther Richards Applin, Hedwig Knicker, Laura Lane, Emma Jane

Figure 8. 1922 Southwestern Geological Society, Sept. 15-16. Top row, left to right: Drue D. Christner, Chester A. Hammil, Harold K. Shearer, Carroll E. Cook, E. H. Sellards, F. W. Simonds, L. T. Barrow, E. W. Bracks, Lyman C. Reed, Wm. R. Poague, Phillip S. Justice and Fred H. Lahee. Middle row, H. P. Bybee, E. L. DeGolyer, J. P. D. Hull, Rebecca B. Masterson, Laura Lee Lane, Dorothy Shoaf, Laura E. Thomson, Unidentified (maybe Bess Stiles), Lulu Pace, W. M. Winson, Charles N. Gould, Leon C. Pepperberg, David P. Donaghue, and F. L. Whitney. Bottom row. V. V. Waite, Willis Storm, Robert C. Gaskill, R. L. Cannon, G. M. Knebel, Ward. C. Bean, E. B. Stiles, J. W. Beede, unidentified, Charles D. Vertrees, Clarence E. Elwell, Gayle Scott. (Photo: Newsletter, University of Texas at Austin, Department of Geological Sciences, no. 13, 1964 p. 40.)

Coffman, and Bess Stiles) were amongst the 74 founding members; 10% women (Fig. 8). At that time, and for the rest of her life, she was a resident of San Antonio.

Another of Reba's great nephews, Bill Masterson of Dallas, says he, like cousin Budge, spent two summers with her in Colorado working on her tungsten mine near Nederland, Colorado where she had her gun handy, and she robustly protected her tailings from night time pilferers. During the Great Depression, she, with her usual good business acumen, purchased this property along with its rustic and beautiful large lodge for a song; she added to its value considerably. She continued to mine the property during WWII when tungsten prices were very high. Bill Masterson recalls what an independent woman she was all her life. The family still has her gun, which they show when they tell another story. "She heard a noise one night, went downstairs gun in hand, thought she saw a human figure moving, so she shot at it and broke a full-size mirror in which she had seen her own reflection."

Budge and Bill remember working on the mine one summer after WWII when tungsten prices had dropped. The mine needed to produce a certain tonnage each year for the claim not to revert. They would "mine" some ore, then add enough dirt to whatever they mined to make up the necessary tonnage, and take it to the smelter in Nederland, fulfilling the requirements and allowing their aunt to retain the claim.

Budge described himself as Reba's "aide" or "butler" during those summers, performing chores for her because she was losing her eyesight (Reba refused to see a doctor or medicate for her eyesight because she was a Christian Scientist). In her later years, Reba was known to the family as "Feefee" and Budge speculates the name referred to her full head of white fluffy hair, similar to a poodle. He recalled she looked like a sweet little grandmother, but, she was anything but! She continued to be a strong and tough business woman all her life. Working for her was both a pleasure and a challenge to Budge and the other nephews. The family fondly referred to Eunice as "Eunie" and says that, when Reba and Eunice visited, it was like having another set of grandparents.

Reba and Eunice started a girl's camp (Camp Kiva), which became very popular, at Medina Lake, 30 miles west of San Antonio. Eunice quit her job at the UT in 1921 to run the camp. They both dedicated significant time and money to make it successful, and it was. Reba and Eunice were frequently written about in the *San Antonio Express* and other Texas newspapers regarding their travels and participation in society events, including notices about Camp Kiva. Reba eventually set up a scholarship at UT in Eunice's name for physical education students, honoring Eunice's years there as a physical education innovator.

Reba Masterson's influence on her family and their continued love of petroleum geology is enduring. Reba's great niece, Amanda Masterson, has spent her career at the Texas Bureau of Economic Geology. Amanda uncovered a prospect map of a structure south of Castroville near the Medina-Bexar county line that Reba, then 49, had submitted to the Bureau while consulting for them in 1931.

Reba's great-great nephew, Wilmer Dallam Masterson IV, is also a UT geology graduate and is in the petroleum business. His daughter, Kathleen, is starting her career with a geology degree from Colorado State University.

Rebecca "Reba" Byrd Masterson was a member of AAPG for 48 years until her death in 1969. She always described herself as a "consulting geologist" (Fig. 9). She was the first female geologist working fully in the oil patch. She was an incredible lifelong entrepreneur who used her geologic education and business acumen to become the first female independent oil woman.

Figure 9. Reba Masterson, 1926, at AAPG Denver meeting. (Photo: AAPG archives, Tulsa, Oklahoma.)

Fredrica Probst Halley (1893-1964)

Fredrica Probst Halley (see Chapter 1) was an early entrepreneur/consultant and independent. She was concurrent in the oil and gas business with her Roxana colleague, Linda Green. Fredrica lived and worked in Tulsa, Oklahoma after she quit Roxana as required when she married, but she maintained an office and consulted the rest of her life. She was involved in managing oil and gas royalties, income, and advising people on royalties, according to her nephew, Carl Probst Woods of Broken Arrow, Oklahoma.

Linda Lucille Green Miller (1892-1986)

Figure 10. Linda Lucille Green graduated in 1919 from the University of Oklahoma with a perfect grade point average. An older student, she was one of the two first women geology graduates. (Photo, 1926, from AAPG archives, Tulsa, Oklahoma.)

Linda Lucille Green was one of the first two women to graduate with geology degrees from University of Oklahoma (OU) in 1919 and was proud of her "perfect grade point average" (obit, *Amarillo Globe-Times*, 10-2-1986) (Fig. 10). She, like Reba Masterson, was an older student, graduating at age 28. Interestingly, Linda showed her entrepreneurial spirit in her college days and belonged to the "Business Opportunity Club" at OU. She was hired by Roxana in June of 1919 immediately following the war and went to work in Mineral Wells, Texas where Fred Plummer was head geologist (Fig. 11). She must have known both Fred and Helen quite well in those early years before the Plummers moved to Houston in April of 1920. Records of Linda Green's membership in AAPG are lost, but she, like most of Roxana's women geologists, no doubt joined and was known to have attended AAPG annual meetings (*Sooner Magazine*, 1938, p. 190).

Like Margaret Campbell and Mary Emily Bottom before her, Linda took over writing the "News" for *Roxoleum* relieving Fred Plummer of that duty. (Fig. 12) In her column, she makes mention of a colleague, Ned O. Miller, and his travels for the company. Ned took over writing the news when Linda was transferred to St. Louis in June, 1920. The magazine went extinct shortly thereafter through no fault of his; the war had ended and the purpose of the magazine was eliminated. Before the year was out, Linda quit Roxana and moved back to Texas—and married Ned.

Figure 11. Part of the Roxana team from Mineral Wells, Texas, Linda Green is on the right in the back seat. (Photo: Roxoleum, *1920, v. 3, no. 2, p. 11, DeGolyer Library, Southern Methodist University.)*

Ned invented a special method for completing gas wells in the Texas Panhandle. Linda's great nephew, Ned Wilson (named after Linda's husband), remembers her telling stories about her and Ned driving all over north Texas and Oklahoma selling their "Miller Method" and trying to build their company. Imagine the state of the roads and the unreliability of cars in the 1920's as they traveled their dusty trail.

Ned Otis Miller died in January 1929 from one of the tragedies of medicine at the time. What seemed a simple operation for "apparent gallstones" turned fatal because he actually had cholestatic hepatitis and he died from complications. Linda was bitter about the poor diagnosis all her life (Personal communication, Dr. Robert Wilson, husband of Linda's niece, LuLynn Green Wilson).

The value of the Miller Method technology is described in the *Pampa Daily News*, January 29, 1932, "Miller Head is Widely Used Now," page 10, which reported, "Many gas wells in the Panhandle are using the Miller head, made by the Miller Method company. The head is becoming popular now that the railway commission has started a gas conservation fight...The Miller head gives gas control by equalizing the gas pressure with water. There is no flow of gas too large to be controlled. Had the Miller head been in use several years ago, the Bayshore well would have been tamed instead of killed, in the opinion of Muck Berentz of Borger who visited here this morning."

Dollie Radler Hall wrote, "After the death of her husband, she assumed the management of Miller Services in Amarillo. Her husband invented a special method for drilling gas wells in the Texas Panhandle. This service was expanded and widely used. Besides her active management of the company she was very successful in developing production of her own" (1965, p. 297).

Ned's patent was filed in 1927 but not approved until after his death (April 8, 1930, Patent # 1,753,440). Linda's management of the company was not without challenges; she had to deal with efforts to steal the patent (personal communication, Dr. Robert "Bob" Wilson), and sometimes, she had difficulties with business partners.

From Ned Otis Miller's patent #1,753,440: "This invention relates to the drilling of deep wells where gas formations are encountered or are expected to be encountered, and is a method for cutting off controlling and conserving the gas which is tapped during the drilling operations while at the same time permitting drilling to continue. It frequently happens where gas formations are found that, unless adequate means for control are provided, large quantities of gas escape and are wasted, and often blow outs occur with consequent loss or damaging of tools, casing and equipment together with the more serious misfortune of dangerous fires and injuries to the workers. It is the primary object of the present invention to make it possible to avoid these conditions and thoroughly control the gas flow when encountered."

Linda's life was always challenging. As a young woman, she was diagnosed with cervical cancer and had surgery, which created not only some life-long medical/physical problems, but also gave her a fear that "death was imminent" recalls her great nephew, Ned Wilson. However, she lived to be 94.

Figure 12. Linda Green during her days with Roxana in Mineral Wells, Texas looking fairly content. (Photo: Roxoleum, *1920, v. 3, No. 2, p. 10, DeGolyer Library, Southern Methodist University.)*

Another tragic circumstance in Linda's life came from the young engineer, H. E. Rodgers, who worked with her, helping to promote the Miller Method. He presented a paper on the Miller Method at the American Petroleum Institute (*Pampa Daily News*, 1935), and she formed the company Martex Petroleum with him. In 1939, Rodgers committed suicide and it is not known what became of that partnership. Linda's loss of this friend and business partner must have been sad indeed.

Tragedy seemed to be a constant in Linda's life. During her childhood, tragedies were abundant. Her mother was an orphan and just 14 years old when she married Linda's father, a widower, 27 years old. Linda's mother had five children by the time she was 24; Linda was the fourth (Fig. 13a and 13b). Linda wrote the story about her brothers and the woman whose name she bore, relating that her mother had lost one boy before she was born and then a second, a three-year-old, when he accidentally toppled a pot of boiling water onto himself (personal papers provided by Lawrence Kelts Green). Her mother's friend, Linda Bolton, sat with her for 13 long days and nights until the little boy finally died. When baby Linda Green was born shortly thereafter, she was named after "Linda," her mother's loyal friend.

Figure 13a. Linda Lucille, the middle child, with her brother, Darsie Andrew Green on her right and her sister Esther Green on her left. Her mother, Emma (behind the fence on the right), was 14 and John Henry Green (back, left) was 31 when they married. John Henry committed suicide when Linda was 13, and her mother died when she was 23. (Photo: Ned Wilson, Missoula, Montana.)

Figure 13b. Linda Lucille with her brother, Darsie Andrew Green (enlarged from previous photo).

Linda and her younger brother, Darsie Andrew Green, lost their father to suicide when they were in their early 20s. Left to their own means, they worked to put each other through OU, both as geologists. Linda's brother, Darsie, went to work for Pure Oil Co. out of college and moved all over the country with his job. He and his wife, Neola Kelts, had two children, William Kelts and LuLynn. They became Linda's surrogate children, especially LuLynn, whom she treated like a daughter. When Darsie settled in Colorado, Linda, already a widow, frequently drove up from Amarillo for visits. Ned recalls her short little body peering through the steering wheel of her Oldsmobile. Bob Wilson remembers that Linda and Darsie often argued over his choice to remain with Pure Oil when she insisted he should become "independent." Linda had wells drilled in Yoakum County, Texas on property she and Ned owned. (Oil is still produced from some of these wells in the Wasson Field—the "Mrs. N. O. Miller No. 1" and "No. 2.") Darsie, feeling the responsibility of children and a wife, did not want to leave their futures to chance and refused. He thought that Linda, comfortable with oil pumping into her account and no family to support, was not very understanding. More than once she left in a huff and drove all the way back to Amarillo (personal communication, Bob Wilson).

Figure 14. Linda Green Miller on her horse. She was a founder of the Amarillo Club for horsemanship in 1941. (Photo: Lawrence Kelts Green, Fort Benning, Georgia.)

In addition to running her company, Linda was active in the Amarillo Garden Club and the Amarillo Horseman's Association, which she helped found in 1941 (Fig. 14). Among many talents she exhibited, she wrote poetry ... and mostly to and about her husband, Ned. The poems quoted next are from several stages in their relationship including the joy of love, the anguish of doubt, and the crushing blow of death.

To Ned

I love him in the morning.
I love him noon and night.
I love him when the days are short,
Or long into the night.

I love him when he's feeble.
I love him when he's strong.
I love him when I know he's right
Or when he's very wrong.

I've loved him for a long, long time.
I'll love him all my life
For better or for worse – what comes,
You see, I am his wife.

At the Herring Hotel in Amarillo

I loved you once
But, I do not know.
Life, in its moving orbit,
Changes so.

I craved you once.
I could not let you go.
You were my moon, my stars
And all below.

You left my love
To wither and decay,
And I have cleared a path,
To find another way.

(On the Herring Hotel envelope, which contained the poem to the left was a note: "Yesterday I walked in shadows, Today I walk in light!" Her mood had lifted.)

After Ned's death, written March, 1929.

I laid him there in his casket
That all of the world might see.
They came and they looked –
But they knew not
That they were looking at me.

My heart had gone out with his heart.
My soul he took with his own.
My love and my life, they were with him
'Twas only my body stayed on.

Her poem questioning...

I wonder, God,
If you grieved
For your Son
Who died.

I wonder, oh, God!
If your sorrow
Was less
Because it was
Sanctified.

It is remarkable that these poems survived. Many pioneering women wrote diaries, many must have written poetry, too, as a way educated people dealt with hard times in those days. Often personal writings were lost or destroyed.

During WWII, Linda was appointed to the Petroleum Administration for War (PAW) and took the role seriously (Fig. 15a and 15b). She was the rare woman on this council. She moved to Washington D.C. for two years and took her niece, LuLynn, with her, enrolling her in a finishing school. Even with her beloved niece, Linda did not escape tragedy. Linda Lucille's namesake, LuLynn Green Wilson, preceded her aunt in death.

LuLynn had married Robert Wilson while he was in medical school, and they had four children: Mike, Catherine Carmen, Rebecca Lynn, and Ned Andrew. Linda treated them like her own grandchildren (Fig. 16). She joined Bob Wilson and the family when they built a Trail Hut in the Rockies in LuLynn's honor. Darsie and Neola's son, Bill, moved to California, and married Carolyn Hughes; he did not see as much of Aunt Linda, but their children, Lawrence Kelts, Linda Katherine (named after Linda), and James Andrew had fond memories of their great aunt.

Linda was generous with others and frugal with herself. Her family tells stories of her being courted by the local Cadillac franchise. She liked to string them along, then she would go out and buy an Oldsmobile, saying she didn't need to waste money on a luxury car. Ned Wilson says his great Aunt Linda paid his way through medical school and helped the other nieces and nephews where she could. Linda is buried in Colorado near her niece, LuLynn, on Bob and LuLynn's mountain property, the "Halloween" mining claim.

Linda left $1 million to the Cal Farley's Boys Ranch in north Texas decades after her husband's death (worth about $10 million today) and had it earmarked to build the Ned Otis Miller Auditorium. In 2014, when I asked people at the Cal Farley Ranch about Linda Green Miller, no one there knew anything about her. She also set up a scholarship, the "Linda G. Miller Leadership Scholarship," at West Texas A&M University specifically for female students who exhibit leadership skills, transferring from Amarillo College. Sadly, few people in Amarillo, today, know much about her.

Linda Lucille Green Miller was more than a pioneer woman in geology; she was the first woman geologist known to own and run her own oil and gas company and develop production for her own account. She was a true entrepreneur and a pioneering independent oil woman.

Figure 15a. The Petroleum Industry War Council in Washington DC, 1942, where Linda Green Miller served for two years during the war, one of very few women. (Photo: the Bernard L. Majewski papers, University of Wyoming, American Heritage History Center.)

Figure 15b. Linda (enlarged part of previous photo), Petroleum War Council.

Figure 16. Linda Green Miller with great nephew, Michael Wilson, in 1951. (Photo: Ned Wilson, Missoula, Montana.)

A Day Imprinted on Memory

By Wilmer Dallam Masterson (1884 - 1974)
Reba Masterson's Brother's Account of the 1900 Hurricane

Here I am, in the early twilight of day, and of life. That problem age, just beyond the horizon of three score and ten, with not enough to do to keep the mind properly busy, so it just seems to drift into events of long ago.

Comfortably reclining in a deck chair, on the beautiful beach at Galveston, the "Coney Island of Texas," I love to watch the continuous roll of the gulf waves as they break with whitecaps at varying distances from the shore, seemingly angry at the resistance encountered in their efforts to reach the sun bathers and strollers.

How peaceful a scene it is with an occasional large steamer moving lazily into port, just beyond the rock jetties, protecting the entrance channel a mile or so to the east and some shrimp boats, with all sails flying as they wend their way back to port with the days catch of shrimp and fish.

This scene is close by, but my mind wanders to another scene on this same island, when the same gulf rolled shoreward in a very different and ferocious mood. The date was September 8, 1900. A date that goes down in history as marking the most destructive hurricane ever to enter the Gulf of Mexico and one of the most destructive measured in lives lost ever recorded. It is to the events of that day, as they affected my life, that my mind returns and though more than a half century of time has elapsed, the picture is as clear now as though the happenings were only yesterday.

I was just turned sixteen years of age the day before and on the morning of the eighth I was stretched out on a cot on the wide front porch that encircled the south half of our rambling ten room cottage home. I wasn't asleep but just thinking of the many things I had received for my birthday and making plans to enjoy them as soon as day had grown a little older. My brother T. W. had promised to go with me for an early gulf swim but I was not to call him before seven o'clock. The weather was perfect and, except for some high clusters of clouds that seemed to be moving much faster than normal, there was no hint of impending danger. I noticed more people than usual, strolling past our home toward the beach, about four or five blocks to the south, so I walked to the fence to inquire the reason for so many early bathers, and I was told there was an unusually high tide, which was strange since the wind at the time was quite brisk from the north which would generally oppose the normal tide. I called my brother and we joined the march to the beach only to learn when we arrived that there was no beach. The waves were already pounding against the long line of sand hills which acted as a barrier to ordinary high tide and every wave made additional inroads on this barrier. Small private bath houses on the gulf side of this line of sand hills had already collapsed and wreckage from these and other unprotected structures was accumulating in the sand hills, with the strong north wind seemingly trying to force the waves back, and thus causing spray to go high in the air. The scene was spectacular but also very frightening.

We did not linger long for we knew there was much to be done at home and my brother also wanted to get to town as soon as possible to get the latest weather information. On my mother's advice, the yard man and I started preparations in the yard for possible flood water, since she had experienced one storm and knew how the cow and horses and chickens had to be taken care of, and she and my sister had much to do in the house. She thought we might have to contend with two or three feet of water for that was about the maximum during the previous storm she remembered.

My brother came home from town about noon and reported that situation was very serious. Indications were right in the line of as very severe storm and salt water was already in ditches beside our home and he had to wade in some places on his way home. This was back water from the bay, but indicated already a tide of at least four feet above normal and wind velocity was increasing and coming in gusts so typical of a hurricane storm.

A few hours later a friend of ours, Lewis Fisher, came in from his office on foot since by that time there was no other means of transportation to our end of town. My father and older brother were on the mainland on a business trip and my older sister was also on the mainland visiting friends.

Our home occupied the east one-third of a four square block area. My grandmother, Mrs. Harris and a daughter Miss Rebecca and another daughter, Mrs. Walter Fisher and her husband and three children, occupied the west one-third and lived in a large two story home. The middle one-third of the four block area was occupied by another of Mrs. Harris' daughters, Mrs. Davenport, was also lived in a large two story home with her husband and three children. That home rested on high brick pillars, so that the first floor was eleven feet above the average ground level. Our cottage was only raised about six feet above ground level.

When Mr. Fisher reached our home, he and my brother decided that with the depth of water steadily increasing in our yard, it seemed advisable to make plans to leave our home if the water level reached some predetermined depth that might dislodge the house from its foundation pillars. They made their way through water about waist deep to a nearby amusement park where they secured a large flat bottom rowboat which they brought home and tied to the side entrance steps, the idea being to use the boat to take us to the Davenport's home next door if the water should rise to such a depth as to really threaten our home.

There was a picket fence five feet high which the boat would have to clear, so a mark was made on our side steps indicating a five-foot depth. When the water reached that mark, my mother and sister [Reba] were helped into the boat, my brother and Mr. Fisher took the oars, and I sat in the bow to check clearance over the picket fence.

We were to return for the three servants as soon as possible. The water was not rough at this time, since it was principally back water from the bay, as the sand hills and debris collected by them was protecting against direct attack by the gulf. It was about six PM when we left our home in the boat. My mother was not well and had very poor eyesight, I remember she handed me a small package which she urged me to be sure and preserve. I was never to know the contents of that package.

The first half of that eventful boat trip was smooth riding and we successfully passed over the picket fence but just then the gulf waves began rolling in, as the protecting sand hills had finally given away. I grabbed an overhanging branch of a tree to steady the boat, now out of control and drifting sharply away from the intended goal. Heavy drifts of debris, wreckage of houses nearer the gulf than ours, were piling up against the trees. My brother called for me to let go in hopes that one pull on the oars might get us to the house and safety. The boat just spun around and dived to the bottom in one of the waves. My brother caught my mother and got her safely into one of the trees. I reached the same tree and my sister and Mr. Fisher reached one a short way to the west. My brother told me to get into position to steady my mother and he would attempt to swim to the house. I did not think that he could possibly make it, but he did, and with many helping hands a rope was made of all the curtains in the house and with one end tied to his waist he was back in the water for the return swim of the tree which he succeeded in reaching, only to find that when he gave the signal pull, that the rope was broken and of no value. Debris was now jammed against our row of trees and we knew that they would go down very soon. I was pretty well fogged trying to keep my mother from falling, so after my brother had a brief rest he took my place and I moved to another branch of the tree.

Only a few minutes later the tree went down and piles of debris swept over us. Somehow under the water he lost my mother. A few months later her body was found about seven miles distant on the mainland. I too went down under the debris and my pants leg got caught on a nail and in scrambling to get to the surface I had to get out of my pants and it was then that I lost the precious package my mother had given me for safekeeping. I was nearly exhausted now but managed to get hold of a section of roof that was floating by and this gave me a brief rest before another less kind piece of debris cracked me on the head after which I was unconscious for over an hour. When I came to I was still half on that section of roof and it was now jammed between a tree and a house. It was now pitch dark except for frequent streaks of lightning with the aid of which I found my way from the roof across a short stretch of water to the front porch of the house. The water here on the porch was only waist deep so I made my way to the front door which was swinging loose on one hinge, and as I entered the front hall amid floating chairs and other furniture I heard, above the roar of wind and thunder, the scream of a child for help. I hurried to the rescue and to my surprise it was my own ten-year-old cousin Wharton Davenport. I then knew for the first time that I was now in my grandmother's house. I carried the boy upstairs and found my two aunts Rebecca Harris and Mrs. Walter Fisher together with the other two Davenport children and the three Fisher children, one of whom was in its nurse's arms. They were all in a bedroom as far away from the storm side of the house as possible and the children were on the bed covered with a comforter to protect them from flying debris.

Just after I placed my little cousin on the bed with them I heard, above the noise of the storm a crashing of timber and I knew this huge old house was collapsing. The bed came sliding down on me and pushed me partly through a door before the ceiling and roof crashed down upon us all.

I was pinned down in the wreckage and I either heard or dreamed I heard calls for help from those who were in that room but can't be sure, for the next thing I clearly remember was that I was being kicked by some man who only wanted to know if I was alive or dead. Other than myself, there were only three in that house who survived – the nurse and baby, and one of the Davenport children. The man helped me up from the wreckage and, though pretty badly cut and bruised, I had no broken bones. The man said that he had found nine dead in the ruins and there might be more. A clock he picked up indicated that house had collapsed at nine PM and now at five AM the water had subsided to only a depth of about two feet.

I made my way back to the Davenport home, which we had tried so hard to reach by boat and there I was reunited with my brother and sister [Reba] and Mr. Fisher, all of whom had given me up for lost, just as I had despaired of ever seeing them again. It seems that with the help of the mass of debris between trees and houses they had finally made it, though of course very exhausted. My aunt Mrs. Davenport was of course near collapse when I told her of the death of their two children and two sisters in the wreckage of my grandmothers' home and also her brother-in-law Mr. Walter Fisher who died trying to get home to his family. Dead bodies were seen in all directions, even hanging from trees, and later estimates placed the number of dead as between six and eight thousand. Many more would have been lost except for a protecting wall of debris that acted like a seawall in protecting thousands of homes from the direct force of the storm. Though the Davenport home stood eleven feet above ground, my brother said it would have been lost if they had not cut large holes in the floors to relieve the waves' pressure which many times during the night forced large volumes of water through the floor up to the ceilings. The house shifted on its foundation about two inches.

As soon as daylight came in spite of fatigue and soreness we visited the wreckage of our home and found about two-thirds of it gone and the remainder jammed in some trees a short distance from its original location. Two of the servants had been saved on the roof of this section but the cook was too large to get through the trap door and was lost. Our little pet dog that had always been afraid of water came jumping to meet us. How it got saved is still a mystery.

My older brother, father, and sister made their way back to the island by boat since the only bridge connecting the island to the mainland was washed away. We all left the city for a time since conditions from a health standpoint were very serious with dead bodies everywhere in the piles of debris, in temporary shallow graves, or being burned or hauled out to sea in large barge loads.

Conveniences were all out and food and water very scarce. Many in the downtown area and the north residence section were fortunate to avoid much suffering and loss, and they did a wonderful job of cleaning up the wreckage. Books have been written describing the horror of those recovery days, months, and years. Yes, it took years to remove the scars of the catastrophes and make the city safe, but it was done. The efficiency of the steps taken in the recovery were proven when in 1915 another storm of equal if not greater severity hit the city and only a few deaths in unprotected areas were reported, and property damage, though heavy, was by comparison very light. The seawall, grade raising, and new causeway to the mainland and many other major improvements have created a port and pleasure island for all to use and enjoy in safety.

Now my early twilight dreaming comes to an end and a beautiful full moon has risen from the far off ocean horizon and its sparkling shaft of light playing on the whitecap waves makes me marvel how such a peaceful, enticing ocean can become so ferocious.

The bathing parties have deserted the beach so I will bring my mind back to today's' realities and wend my way homeward.

Chapter 2: Sources and References

AAPG Convention Denver, Colorado [enlarged picture Linda Lucille Green and Reba Masterson]. 1926. Photograph. American Association of Petroleum Geologists Archives, Tulsa, Oklahoma.

Amarillo Globe-Times. "H. E. Rodgers Found Dead." October 9, 1939. p. 1 and 5.

Amarillo Globe-Times. "Linda Lucille Green Miller." Obituaries. October 20, 1986. p. 6.

The Atlanta Constitution. "The New York and Texas Oil Company (Branch Masterson attorney of Galveston)." Advertisement. May 11, 1901. https://www.newspapers.com/newspage/26825821/. Accessed 12/17/2016.

Echegaray, Lynne, Stillwater, Oklahoma, great niece of Reba Masterson. Personal communication with Robbie Gries, 2015.

Green, Lawrence Kelts, Fort Benning, Georgia, great-nephew of Linda Green Miller. Interview with Robbie Gries, August 2015; source of photograph of Linda Green Miller at the Amarillo Club.

Hall, Dollie Radler. 1965. "Women in Exploration." *Tulsa Geological Society Digest*, vol. 33, pp. 295-298.

Haroldson Lafayette "H. L." Hunt, C. M. "Dad" Joiner, geologist A. D. "Doc" Lloyd on Daisy Bradford discovery well. 1930. Photograph. American Oil & Gas Historical Society, Washington, D.C. http://aoghs.org/petroleum-pioneers/east-texas-oilfield/. Accessed 01/23/2017.*Masterson, Reba.* circa 1926. Photograph. American Association of Petroleum Geologists Archives, Tulsa, Oklahoma.

Masterson, Wilmer Dallam. "A Day Imprinted on Memory." Personal notes on the Galveston Hurricane of 1900 by the brother of Reba Masterson. Reprinted with permission by Wilmer Dallam IV, Houston, Texas.

Masterson, Wilmer Dallam IV, Houston, Texas, great great nephew of Reba Masterson. Personal communication with Robbie Gries, 2015-2016; source of circa 1900 photographs for Reba Masterson and the Masterson house in Galveston after the hurricane.

Masterson, Wilmer Dallam III, Dallas, Texas, great nephew of Reba Masterson. Personal communication with Robbie Gries, April and May 2015.

Miller, Otis Ned. Method of Drilling Wells in Gas Formations. US Patent 1,753,440. Filed May 17, 1927, and Issued April 8, 1930. United States Patent and Trademark Office. http://patft.uspto.gov/. Accessed 11/2016.

Pampa Daily News. "Miller Head Is Widely Used Now." January 29, 1932, p. 10.

Pampa Daily News. "API Program Takes Form." [References the talk by H. E. Rogers "Panhandle Drilling and Use of the Miller Method in Balancing Gas Pressure," vol. 28, no. 288, p. 1.] March 10, 1935, p. 1.

Petroleum Industry War Council in Washington, D.C. 1942. Photograph. Bernard L. Majewski papers, University of Wyoming, American Heritage Center, Laramie, Wyoming.

Roxoleum. [Including photographs cited in text]: Volumes 1, 2, and 3, 1918-1920. DeGolyer Library, Southern Methodist University, Dallas Texas.

Sheppard, Anthony Dallam "Budge," Houston, Texas, great nephew of Reba Masterson. Personal communication with Robbie Gries, December 2015; source of the photograph of Reba Masterson's .32-caliber pistol.

Sooner Magazine. "Sooner Geologists at Tulsa Meeting" [Linda Green Miller attended AAPG Annual meeting]. May 1936. https://digital.libraries.ou.edu/sooner/articles/p190_1936v8n8_OCR.pdf.

Spencer, Jeff. *Female observers at Damon Moundfield.* 2015. Photograph. SIPES-Houston Chapter Newsletter, March 2015, p. 3.

The University of Texas at Austin. "Southwestern Geological Society meeting 1922." Photograph. Department of Geological Sciences newsletter, no. 13, 1964 p. 40. http://www.lib.utexas.edu/books/landscapes/publications/txu-oclc-10062456-13/txu-oclc-10062456-13.pdf.

University of Colorado. "Rebecca (Reba) Byrd Masterson." 1916. Photograph. *Coloradan* yearbook. CU Heritage Center, Boulder, Colorado.

University of Oklahoma. "Linda Lucille Green." 1918. Photograph. Sooner yearbook. Western History Collections, University of Oklahoma, Norman, Oklahoma. p. 18.

Wilson, Ned, Missoula, Montana, great nephew of Linda Green Miller. Personal communication with Robbie Gries, August 2015; source of photographs for Linda Green Miller with family members.

Wilson, Dr. Robert, Denver, Colorado, husband of Linda Green Miller's niece, LuLynn Green. Personal communication with Robbie Gries August 2015.

Chapter 3

The First Women to Become Geology Managers

It was early in the employment of women as petroleum geologists that a few became managers. Happily, it is possible to highlight the careers of three of them: Dollie Radler Hall can claim to be the first to attain management status, serving for nearly 30 years with Amerada Petroleum Corporation; Constance Grace Eirich was employed by Gypsy Oil Company for nearly 35 years; and Alice Langlois spent 20 years with Alder Oil Company. Each of them represented a lifetime of service with their respective companies. All three were career women choosing not to start a family. Only Dollie married at the age of 36, considered relatively late in life in the 1930s. She was very involved with her extended family. Common themes for these women included their technical expertise as professional geologists and dedication to the oil industry as well as to their respective companies. All faced similar difficulties and challenges, but their respective careers are stories of hard work, persistence, and patient fortitude. Interestingly, they were hired by some of the most legendary men in the field of petroleum geology – Sidney Powers, Everette DeGolyer, and George Matson – which may be a commentary on the men's enlightened regard for women as well as the hard work of these women pioneers.

Figure 1. Dollie Radler, foreground, circa 1919-20, at the University of Oklahoma (OU) geology field camp collecting samples. Dr. Charles Decker, who promoted and mentored many female students, is behind her on the right. Dollie was the first woman to earn a master's degree at OU and the third to earn her bachelor's. She worked on her master's while working fulltime at Amerada. (Photo: Bethan Read, Jackson, Mississippi.)

Dollie Radler Hall (1897-1995)

Amerada Petroleum Corporation (now Hess), based in Tulsa, Oklahoma, hired their first woman during the WWI male geologist shortage. We don't know her name, but she is mentioned as "just leaving" in Dollie Radler's biographical notes when Dollie started work for the company immediately after the war in 1920—the year women attained the right to vote. Two very well-known geologists and AAPG leaders were involved in Dollie's career. Everett DeGolyer, who had taken charge of Amerada in 1919 and Sidney Powers, who became its chief geologist were surprisingly progressive when it came to hiring, promoting, and retaining women.

Dollie was raised in western Oklahoma. Her cousin, Betty Winfrey, of Broken Arrow and 20 years her junior, recently spoke more about Dollie's early childhood (personal communication). Betty said Dollie's mother was a single mom; her father abandoned his family. When Dollie was a teenager, and her mother was scraping by, working at a "Five and Dime" store in western Oklahoma, Dollie would, occasionally, be sent to eastern Oklahoma to spend time with her mother's family and numerous cousins. Betty recalled that Dollie never wanted to leave but had to return to western Oklahoma when school started. Despite these hardships, she persevered, studied, and, after acquiring a teaching degree, she was admitted to the University of Oklahoma (OU) in1916 to study for a bachelor's degree in Geology. (Fig. 1), By just a few months, Dollie followed the first two female students to graduate in geology at OU: Linda Green and Jennie Livingston.

Dollie was never thwarted by hard work and worked her way through college, carrying 18 hours a semester and working 40 hours a week to pay for it. Her college jobs included everything from dishwashing, house cleaning, laundry work, and, eventually, she had a job in the geology library. This was a double bonus for her. She would wait until the end of the day, check out the textbooks she needed to study that night and return them in the morning, saving her the expense of buying geology books.

Dollie also assisted her professor, Dr. Charles Decker, a founder of AAPG and Secretary-Treasurer, in his volunteer efforts for the budding organization. (Fig. 2) This led to her presence at an AAPG meeting in Tulsa where Sidney Powers (Fig. 3) "sized her up" and wired her to schedule an interview. The story of how Sidney Powers hired her amused Dollie all her life. The interview was in 1919 just before she graduated. She was 21 and later remembered that "We met in a geology office in Oklahoma City. Dr. Powers asked me if I was in mourning. I said, 'no.' He recalled that I wore a black dress in Tulsa at the AAPG meeting, and still was wearing a black dress. I told him it was the only good dress I owned. He said that, if I came to work for him, I should never wear black. I haven't worn the color in years" (Parker, 1993).

Figure 2a. Dollie in the field in Oklahoma, circa 1922. (Photo: Fanny Carter Edson family, Sue Tappeiner, Corvallis, Oregon.)

Figure 2b. Close up with Dollie's charming crooked smile.

Figure 3. Sidney Powers, who hired and relied on Dollie Radler to run Amerada's Exploration Department. (Photo: Dollie Radler's papers provided by Bethan Read)

When Dollie joined Amerada, (Fig. 4) she worked fulltime but continued her graduate studies at OU. Upon graduation in 1921, she became the first woman to receive a master's degree in Geology from OU.

After three years of initial training and gaining experience of the oil business, Sidney Powers deemed Dollie capable enough to be assigned to subsurface work in eastern Oklahoma. Two years later, in 1923, she was promoted to management and took over much of Powers' management responsibilities in the Tulsa office.

Figure 4. Dollie Radler, when she graduated from the University of Oklahoma in 1919. (Photo: Bethan Read)

In 1926, Dollie was promoted to "administrative geologist" and, twelve months later at the age of 30, she received a further promotion, giving her responsibility for

Figure 5. Dollie in the field with well-dressed colleagues, circa 1930. F. W. Simonds is beside her. Rodger Denison is to the left behind Dollie in the photo. The photo shows Dollie's delightful leadership, even on a field excursion. (Photo: Bethan Read)

directing operations and making recommendations for exploration, leasing, and drilling with a staff of 100 employees in her department and an annual budget of $500,000. (Fig. 5)

Powers was then fully able to pursue his scientific efforts with his typical passion, becoming influential in the geologic organizations he nurtured as president of AAPG, Executive with GSA, and as a major contributor to the International Geologic Congress. Even there we see evidence of the great contribution Dollie made to his endeavors, which he gratefully acknowledged in several of his publications recognizing that she had supplied the data he used.

From 1927 to 1928, Dollie played a significant role in the early discoveries using seismic reflection technology (see Chapter 8).

One of her favorite memories was the role she played in Amerada finding a partner in their large undrilled Kansas and Oklahoma leases in 1929. The vice president called her in and requested maps showing this acreage in the best possible light. The deadline was close so she had to work in a flurry, utilizing everyone at her disposal. She said, "I was mad though, because I thought they were going to sell the company. They hadn't told me why they wanted the maps. Still, I did my job."

With maps in hand, Dollie and the vice president went to Chicago to try to interest Stanolind (Amoco) in a partnership. She recalled, "I did the best selling job I could."

The deal resulted in the sale of an undivided one-half interest in certain undeveloped leases for a cash consideration of $5 million and an oil payment of $5 million from Stanolind's interest. Twenty-five years later, when she was again negotiating a Stanolind deal, she was informed that the Kansas-Oklahoma deal was one of the best Stanolind had ever made.

Figure 6. Dollie and three colleagues possibly checking out a drill site, circa 1935. (Photo: Bethan Read)

One of Dollie's many exploration contributions was having the foresight to develop the hitherto unpromising Fitts pool in Oklahoma. Success in that field increased the company's income by about $1 million a year (Parker, 1993). That value at a time when oil was selling for 67 cents a barrel, is today equivalent to $14 million per year. (Fig. 6)

Figure 7. A. R. (Rodger) Denison, protégé, confidante, colleague, and, eventually, boss. He was president of AAPG 1943-44. (Photo: Ferguson, 1964, p. 239.)

A. Rodger Denison, whom Dollie had first met at OU in 1919 when he had started back to college, was one of Dollie's lifelong friends (Fig. 7). When he finished his degree in 1922, she hired him to work with her in Amerada's Tulsa office. They became close work colleagues and intimate correspondents, writing to each other regularly. Rodger's son, the late Tim Denison of Dallas, provided copies of Dollie's correspondence when his father was managing Amerada's north Texas office. Excerpts from these letters provide

Figure 8. One of Dollie's photos of an oil well coming in. (Photo: Bethan Read)

insight, not only into her close relationship with Powers, but her management style, company issues, and her very personal feelings for Powers as well as her worries about his health.

Some letters capture her excitement and thrill over exploration success and new finds:

"We have three new Seminole (Texas) pools. That and the fact that we gave away the forty in Kansas which is now offset by a 3000 bbl. well is all we have to worry about." (Fig. 8)

"The test at Anthony should core the Stalnaker tonight ... running seventy feet higher than the old dry hold. Our second well at Oxford will drill in tomorrow ... the IAIO well ... is running 12 ft. higher than expected. Looks very much like an oil well."

"We have a well in the Hoover series on our Oxford forty. If we keep on we will have as many sands producing there as on the Galtry."

"We finally secured samples on the Okla City well and find that it is still in Pennsylvanian [geologic age of rocks] at 6830. Dr. Gould wasn't so far wrong when he said some 20 years ago, that there was 7000 ft. of Pennsylvanian at Oklahoma City." (Fig. 9)

In 1928, Sidney Powers became seriously ill and confined to bed, which caused enormous problems at work for Dollie and Rodger, who had been promoted to manage Amerada's North Texas office.

On January 29, 1928, she wrote:

Dear Rodger: Just returned from a visit to Mr. Powers. He is better but rather tired, having had a continuous stream of visitors since ten this morning. His temperature has gone up the last couple of hours and I feel sure the nurse has already brought an end to all visits today. She is very efficient in spite of Sidney's "Crabbing."

An Xray will be taken Thursday if he continues to improve. Until then I intend to humor him in all his plans for field trips etc. but when I find out the opinion of the doctors I imagine I'll be ready to say a few things.

The 'bombshell' about royalties has certainly caused a great deal of discussion ... it will be my unpleasant duty to tell Sidney of this. He has, I believe, sold a part of his and has a deal on now to sell some more. After talking to Mrs. Powers this afternoon she has decided that I shall break the news to him in the morning before he gives his word on something that he will be unable to carry out.

I am feeling much better today and have managed to get some real rest. Realizing my own limits, I visited a doctor Friday and Saturday and as a result am almost normal again. I think my reaction to this whole affair was due to the fact that Sidney's worst hallucinations concerned the G.R.C. [DeGolyer's geophysical company] and things I had said a day or two before he became ill. Of course, I unloaded at the wrong time and all this being the last of his great worries was the one that bothered him most. Mr. Porter, bless his heart, consoled me by saying that if it hadn't been this, it would have been his house or something else. Nevertheless, you can

Figure 9. Amerada Field trip, car bogged in mud. Photo taken by Dollie's geologist employee, Vita Lee Waters Chase, 1932. (Photo: Bob Wynn, Oklahoma City.)

imagine how I felt. I am hoping that the next eleven months bring me something more pleasant than January has brought.

A few days later she wrote of some improvement in Powers' condition:

Dear Rodger: Have a little time tonight and will endeavor to write you the latest happenings. Did not send you a daily bulletin yesterday as Sidney wasn't nearly so well and I didn't know what to think of the case. However, he is much better today. Has been up the greater part of the day but is still quite weak ... I have gotten thoroughly disgusted these past two days with Mr. DeG's [DeGolyer] (Fig. 10) attitude about Sidney's illness. Such a lordly, high and mighty attitude ... Mr. DeG left tonight for the East. Maybe I'll have a chance to recover now from a part of the strain.

Figure 10. Everette DeGolyer who became president of Amerada and promoted Dollie to "acting chief geologist." (Photo: DeGolyer Library, Southern Methodist University.)

A week later she continued with mounting concern: "... He worries all the time now about me getting sick and wants me to let the work go etc. I don't know what I would do if it were not for the work. I can bury myself in work and quit thinking about what might be the trouble with him."

The strain of work pressures and deep concern for her mentor and friend inevitably began to tell on her to the extent that she needed a break and took a month away from Tulsa. On her return towards the end of May 1928 she confessed her feelings to Denison:

... it is a good thing for me that I had a month away from here. If it hadn't been for that I don't see how I could have struggled through some of the trying situations I have found myself in the last two or three weeks. However, being blessed with a hearty constitution I can't see that I have suffered any ill effects. Everything at the office has been going just fine. That, of course, has been my salvation.

Three days later, she asked Denison to write to

... Sidney at Barnes Hospital St Louis giving him a résumé of all things happening or that have happened in your division since you talked to him. He is taking quite an interest in the oil business again and in the organization as a whole ...."

It is clear that the frustrations and serious effect of Powers' health issues was the subject of frequent discussion between Dollie and Rodger. On July 12, she wrote,

I suppose you have wondered what was the outcome of many of our discussions the other night. So, thought I would drop you a line and satisfy your curiosity. I am still at very much of a loss to know what is the best method to use in handling our esteemed boss. He is certainly a puzzle to me—Spend seven years learning how best to get along with a person and then have them change in so many ways certainly is food for thought.

When Sidney Powers died in 1932, not only did she lose a wise boss and esteemed colleague but also a mentor who had guided her footsteps for over a decade and who, in turn, had trusted her and relied on her judgment and expertise. A rewarding work partnership had ended and Dollie, no doubt, felt the loss keenly.

Figure 11. Charlie Hall, about 1932, Dollie's husband and partner in hosting many company parties with his music and good humor. (Photo: Bethan Read)

Although she had known Charles S. Hall (Fig. 11) since they were children, it was not until 1933 that they decided to get married. She was then 36 years old with Charlie five years her junior. Maybe with the loss of Sidney and the daunting task ahead, she felt the need for Charlie's companionship and support. Career wise, they were poles apart with him in the livestock business and her in the more intense oil business, but that very difference may have been one of the factors bringing them together. The couple later acquired a small ranchette in Broken Arrow where Charlie could pursue his interest in livestock. Both loved to entertain and especially enjoyed having her Amerada employees over to their house. The basement was turned into a "party room," and many social gatherings were held there. Charlie was quite a musician and played for many of the gatherings with his friends, Dickie Hess and Jack Strong. Children of her employees were welcome and several have related their great memories of visiting their place (personal communication with Bob Wynn and Bill Sinclair). (Fig. 12)

Figure 12. Charlie Hall and Dollie Radler were wed in 1933. (Photo: Bethan Read)

Amerada was the only company that seemed to have a policy retaining women when they married, probably owing to Dollie and her important role. Consequently, the company, with her at the helm, hired many female geologists and geophysicists (more than 15 in Amerada's first 50 years)—single and married. No other company of this era was known to employ as many women, and all were in exploration geology and geophysics. She was also very fortunate being employed by Amerada, because they never reduced the salaries of their employees during the Depression (as Shell did in Tulsa, see Fanny Carter Edson Chapter 4).

Throughout her career, she accrued royalty interests from many of the properties she explored, some through her work with Amerada and some on her own. (Fig. 13) Her niece, Bethan Read of Jackson, Mississippi, tells of Dollie assigning one of her royalty interests in Gaines County, Texas to Charlie "for spending money." Bethan eventually inherited Charlie's spending money royalties and says it continued to be a significant source of income for the family and, in fact, is still producing. When Dollie died, she left royalty interests to her family and a few friends from eighteen producing leases and eighteen non-producing leases in Dewey, Seminole, Stephens, Bryan, Okmulgee, Creek, Atoka, Caddo, Coal, Grady, Hughes, Kay, Lincoln, Pottawatomie, and Pushmataha Counties.

Later, during the Depression, she was very generous with her extended family, letting cousins live with her when they had no place to go and providing financial assistance as needed. They described Dollie as the "kindest" person they had ever known, never ever raising her voice and always generous.

Figure 13. Dollie at work at Amerada where she was responsible for directing operations and making recommendations for exploring, leasing, geophysical programs, and drilling. (Photo: Bethan Read)

After Sidney Powers' death, Everette DeGolyer continued as President of the company and promoted Dollie to be the "acting chief geologist." Powers' passing and the position left open in the management structure, which, by rights, should have been hers to fill presented a dilemma to DeGolyer. Granting her the title did not transpire as she later recalled:

"I was called in by the vice president. He said they didn't know what they were going to do with the newly vacated position, but until a decision was made, I was to have the title of acting chief geologist and carry on. Those were the only instructions I ever received." (*AAPG Explorer*, 1979, p. 3).

Her cousin, Hazel Schlegel later wrote of the difficulties Dollie had as a manager, "...some of the men would not talk to her at first. But she earned their respect ... She did the work, ... but they wouldn't make her the permanent chief geologist because she was a woman" (*Tulsa World*, 1995).

Also in that obituary, long-time Amerada fellow co-worker, Rolla Hudson, recalled some of Dollie's difficulties, "Men from other companies sometimes chided our geologists because they took orders from a woman. But she was one of the best subsurface geologists, man or woman, in the state of Oklahoma."

When Dollie resigned, Hudson thought, "...she was concerned that her sex was creating embarrassing situations for the geologists working for her."

In addition to the men at Amerada, Dollie hired and supervised several women geologists, married and unmarried, including Vita Lee Waters Chase, Grace Hower, Elva Tate Hasher, Lenora May Williams Hunt, and Bertha Tepper. Selections from the correspondence between Dollie and Rodger provide a perspective of Dollie's characteristics as a manager. For example, her sensitivity and extreme helpfulness with a new hire in the office: "Our new girl Miss Tepper [Bertha Mayer nee Tepper was a 1927 graduate of the University of Chicago in geology. She later would be the Managing Editor of the Journal of Geology] arrived on the scene last Monday. I believe she will be very good. She is a little dark complexioned southern girl about Marjorie's size, is very quiet and seems to be very willing. She will need to be taught a great many things but I can't expect too much from one just out of school that never saw an oil company office before. I am going through all the files and separating everything myself, then she puts them in order and makes new files. As a result, our having to do a lot of work at night, but it will be such a relief to have them all straightened out that I don't mind the work. The joy of having a willing worker is the main thing."

Dollie was also compassionate and expressed her concern over employees that were being let go: "He wired that he had no further use for Carlson. Surely do hate it and don't know what John will do now. Have been unable to think of anything else for him.

"I wonder if a personal letter from me to Jack would do any good? ... Knowing the landman exceptionally well, as well as knowing Jack's greatest fault, I think I can understand the situation. I have always talked very plain to Jack and I know he will not resent anything I might say ... It is certainly up to Jack now to either make or break himself as far as the Amerada is concerned."

On the other hand, Dollie could be tough with employees when needed, as she demonstrates: "I am moving S______ to Shreveport to help Kisling. Have a thorough understanding with Mr. Blow that if he doesn't make good I can get rid of him. I put it squarely up to S_____. ... Birk almost had a fit because I was moving S_____ while Dickson was away. I guess he thought I could get wells shut down in Champagnelle to await his pleasure. I may have made him sore but I imagine he knows now who is running this department."

"I know that before Jan 1st I am going to do my best to get rid of four land men either by turning them back to their department or by dismissal."

"Should you or any of the district men find any discrepancies in H___'s work please let me know immediately. Have found in checking up that I haven't done a very good job of "nursing" the last few months and he has gone astray on a few things. Have adopted a system of keeping him under my thumb and <u>hope</u> to keep straight on samples."

The letters also preserved a treasure of a comment about Amerada's bias with respect to geologists and geophysicists: "Besides that, DeGolyer wants us to work as many members of the geological department into geophysical methods as possible. He refuses to let a party work at the Amerada without a geologist in charge."

Dollie was not only the first female geologist manager in the oil business, *she was also the first to hit the "glass ceiling."* (Fig. 14) After being "Acting Chief Geologist" for five years, Amerada still refused to make the position permanent and, instead, brought her protégé and close friend, Rodger Denison, to Tulsa over her head as "Chief Geologist." Their roles were now reversed with him as her boss. She had always been supportive of Rodger, as can be judged from remarks made in one of her letters to him in 1928 while she was his boss: "You have received your check before now and I am sure you have survived the shock [he received a raise]. No,

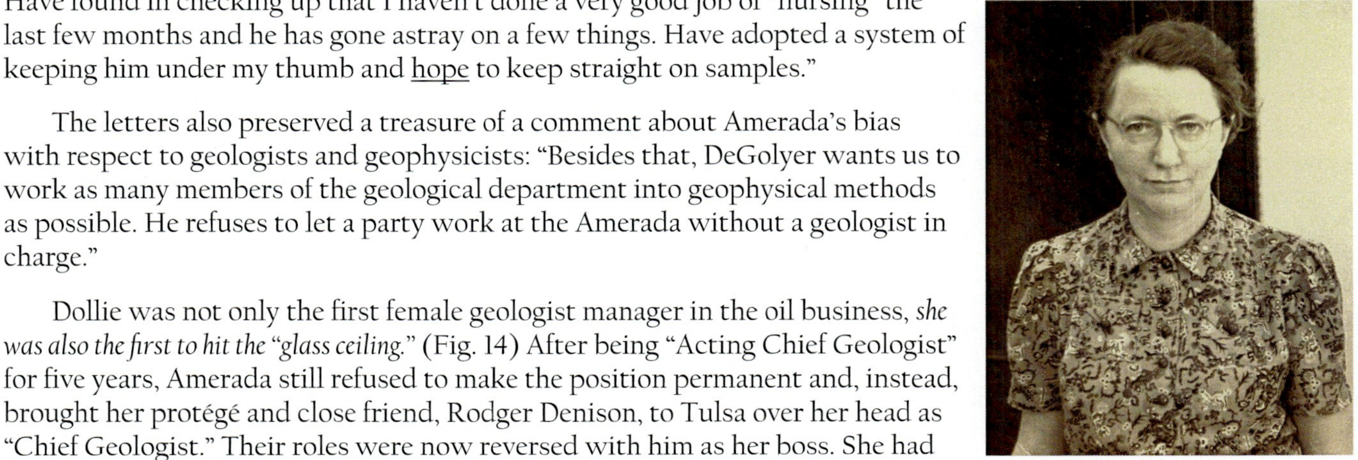

Figure 14. Dollie was a manager, mentor, and company trainer with over 100 employees reporting to her. (Photo: Bethan Read)

Figure 15. Dollie retired from Amerada in 1949 and set up her consulting office in Tulsa. One of her more exciting projects was an intensive and comprehensive study of Cuban geology in the early 1950s. (Photo: Bethan Read)

the *'Powers that Be'* did not see fit to increase my check, but that is just another of the penalties I pay for being a woman in a man's profession. That, however, does not lessen my pride and joy in your achievements. I always have the satisfaction of knowing that I have already accomplished more than my wildest dreams when I started on my geologic career, and that I have also accomplished as much as any woman in the same kind of work. So, this isn't such a bad world after all."

Perhaps it is typical of Dollie that she continued working for Rodger for ten years or more, after his promotion. After she retired from "the Amerada" he became Amerada's Corporate Vice President.

Dollie's husband, Charlie, died in 1947 aged only 65, leaving her alone at their small ranchette in Broken Arrow. Two years later, in1949, she retired from Amerada and moved to Tulsa where she set up a consulting business, saying she never could imagine "really retiring" but, instead, would work until she died; she enjoyed it too much (Fig. 15). One of her more unusual projects was significant work in Cuba. Ruth Sheldon Knowles, writing in *World Oil*, March 1956, says, "Mrs. Dollie Radler Hall, consulting geologist of Tulsa ... has made one of the most intensive and comprehensive studies of Cuba's geology. She states, 'There is evidence that some form of petroleum is present in every province of Cuba, that there is a very thick section of sedimentary rocks from Jurassic to recent time that has not been explored ... there is ample proof that these rocks under proper conditions could form excellent reservoirs and there is also present plenty of source material'.... Mrs. Hall points out that one of the greatest obstacles to exploration in Cuba has been 'everybody has called everything green, serpentine, and everything hard, granite.'"

Sheldon continues that, prior to the 1954 discovery of heavy oil in Upper Cretaceous sandstone, previous oil finds had come from serpentine rocks. Sheldon quotes Dollie saying, "The oil obviously did not originate in the serpentine. Therefore, it is thought that the oil now found in the serpentine was originally trapped at depth and was carried to its present position during the igneous activity that disturbed the original reservoir ... there should be large reservoirs at depth."

The article on Cuban exploration included enthusiasm for Cuba's prospectivity from DeGolyer, Wallace Pratt, and others. It is altogether likely that Dollie was consulting for DeGolyer, who, by then, was in a partnership—DeGolyer and McNaughton in Dallas. (Fig. 16)

Years later, in 1974, Rodger Denison's son, Tim Denison, offered to send Dollie copies of the correspondence between her and his father, which had captured how difficult Sidney Powers had been. She responded, "Dear Tim: It was a pleasant surprise to hear from you. I would be very pleased to have copies of the correspondence you refer to. I am not surprised to learn of Mr. Powers' pessimism in 1928. You know hindsight is much better than foresight. Your father and I had many discussions about Mr. Powers' attitude but we couldn't come to any conclusion until his spleen operation in 1929. Then we realized that he had been suffering intensely for many months. After the operation, he was like a different person. Turned the running of the department to the two of us and spent almost his entire time looking into the geology of basins that had not yet been drilled. You might be

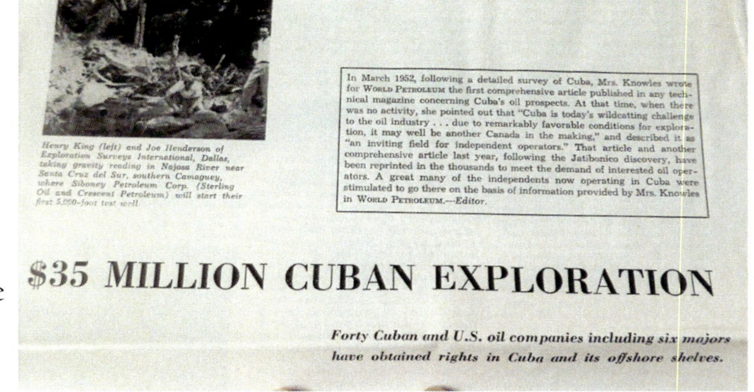

Henry King (left) and Joe Henderson of Exploration Surveys International, Dallas, taking gravity reading in Najosa River near Santa Cruz del Sur, southern Camaguey, where Siboney Petroleum Corp. (Sterling Oil and Crescent Petroleum) will start their first 5,000-foot test well.

In March 1952, following a detailed survey of Cuba, Mrs. Knowles wrote for World Petroleum the first comprehensive article published in any technical magazine concerning Cuba's oil prospects. At that time, when there was no activity, she pointed out that "Cuba is today's wildcatting challenge to the oil industry . . . due to remarkably favorable conditions for exploration, it may well be another Canada in the making," and described it as "an inviting field for independent operators." That article and another comprehensive article last year, following the Jatibonico discovery, have been reprinted in the thousands to meet the demand of interested oil operators. A great many of the independents now operating in Cuba were stimulated to go there on the basis of information provided by Mrs. Knowles in World Petroleum.—Editor.

$35 MILLION CUBAN EXPLORATION

Forty Cuban and U.S. oil companies including six majors have obtained rights in Cuba and its offshore shelves.

Figure 16. Ruth Sheldon Knowles' article about Dollie's consulting work in Cuba, World Oil, *October 1955. (Reprint in Dollie Radler Hall's papers at the American Heritage Center, University of Wyoming. With permission from* World Oil, *Houston, Texas.)*

interested to know that he recommended seven for prospecting if and when the depression was over and Amerada could use the seismograph and exploration know how in developing oil. Six of these are now oil provinces. Only one remains to be developed. Best of luck to you on your own. Hope you will be as happy as I have been since leaving Co [Amerada]."

Figure 18. Dollie Radler Hall affected Amerada Petroleum profoundly. She was the earliest female exploration manager, promoting, hiring, and retaining married women and mentoring many male and female colleagues and students. (Photo: Bethan Read)

Figure 17. Dollie and Hollywood celebrity, Bob Hope, in Tulsa at a fund-raising event, about 1958. (Photo: Bethan Read)

Dollie Radler Hall is also remembered as a great mentor to students at University of Oklahoma throughout her career as well as being active in professional societies. She was a Member and Governor of the Pilot Club of Tulsa (a service nonprofit organization founded by business women) and was involved in countless other civic activities in Tulsa. (Fig. 17) She had a particular fondness for helping with education and children. She was the first female Honorary Member of the Tulsa Geological Society. (Fig. 18) Notably, in 1963, she was the *first woman to become an Honorary Member of AAPG*. It would be 20 years before another woman, Doris Curtis, became an Honorary Member. Dollie was also a founder of the AAPG Energy Minerals Division and maintained her AAPG membership for 74 years until her death in 1995 at the age of 97. (Fig. 19)

Figure 19. Tulsa, Oklahoma during the days that Dollie Radler Hall was Exploration Manager for Amerada Petroleum and Constance Eirich was manager at Gypsy Oil. http://www.okhistory.org/shpo/architsurveys/ILSofdowntownTulsa.pdf, accessed 1/6/2017.

Constance Grace Eirich (1887-1973)

Figure 20. Constance Eirich graduated from the University of Michigan in 1911. Hired during WWI in 1918, she was the second female geologist to become a manager in an oil and gas company—Gypsy Oil Co. (Photo: the Michiganensian yearbook, 1911, p. 58.)

One year after the founding of AAPG, on September 1, 1918, Gypsy Oil Co (later Gulf Oil) hired Constance Eirich as a "petroleum geologist" (Fig. 20). Interestingly, she was hired by George Matson, Chief Geologist for Gypsy Oil and an AAPG legend himself (Fig. 21). George Matson, with Stanley Herold and J.V. Howell, further demonstrated his support for women in geology when he sponsored Constance Eirich for membership in the American Institute of Mining and Metallurgical Engineers in 1919.

Figure 21. George Matson, who hired Constance Eirich in 1918. She quickly proved herself as an oil finder and manager. Matson was the 5th AAPG President in 1921. (Photo: Wilson, 1940, p. 606.)

Constance was born in 1888 in Van Wert, Ohio and received her master's degree from the University of Michigan in 1913. She took several teaching jobs in Arkansas, Ohio, and Michigan and was considering a job in Kansas City when she heard through friends about a job in Tulsa with Gypsy Oil (Fig. 22). Her professionalism and skill led her to a management/executive position at Gypsy in ap-

Figure 22. A Gypsy Oil Company vehicle with a young girl playing at the wheel of her daddy's company car circa 1915. She would later become a geologist—Mildred Armor Frizzell. She lived in Tulsa most assuredly, knew Constance Eirich, and, perhaps, was inspired by her to be a geologist. (Photo: Mildred Frizzell's collection provided to AAPG, for A Century Special Issue of Explorer, 2000 publication, p.26.)

proximately 1928, making her the second female geologist to attain that position (Fig. 23).

In addition to being the second woman manager, Constance has the distinction of possibly being the first woman geologist who could take direct credit for finding oil as an explorationist. She discovered at least four oil fields in Oklahoma: Cheyarha, Garcreek, Rosenwald, and Payson East. As a manager for Gulf, Constance was responsible for pivotal decisions that led to other discoveries, but these were "hers." (Fig. 24)

Figure 23b. Close-up of Gypsy sign above the door. (Photos by Matt Randolph, Tulsa, Oklahoma)

Figure 23a. Gypsy Oil Company office in Tulsa, Oklahoma, 303 MLK Blvd, now a coffee shop and salon. (Photos: Matt Randolph, Tulsa, Oklahoma)

She stayed with Gulf Oil in Tulsa for 34 years. During a visit to the "Gypsy Building" in Tulsa in 2017 it was discovered that until the building was renovated in the 21st century, there was not a "ladies room" in the building. Constance and other women working there had to use "outside" facilities behind the building.

Writing about Eirich in *Scribner's Commentator*, (May 1941, "The Ladies Find Oil") Ruth Sheldon said, "Because Gulf Oil Corporation suffers from a hangover of the passionate aversion to publicity of its

Figure 24. Men (said to be geologists) working for Gypsy Oil, likely under the supervision of Constance Eirich, in the 1920s or 1930s. (Photo: Bradley René Garcia, building owner, who shared the comments about geologists. He found the photo when he bought the Gypsy building and renovated it. January, 2017.)

creative genius, the late Andrew Mellon, no Gulf employee is allowed to speak of his or her activities with the company ... Consequently, it is impossible to credit Eirich, executive geologist for Gulf in Tulsa, Oklahoma, with specific accomplishments. But neither could prominent women geologists be catalogued without including her. Her thirteen-year record as an executive geologist for one of the world's great oil companies – and its only woman geologist – and the respect in which the geological profession holds her, must speak for themselves ... Eirich herself said, "I gave up my right to individuality when I joined a big corporation."

Figure 25. Constance Eirich after she retired and began consulting in Tulsa. She eventually moved back to her hometown of Van Wert, Ohio. (Photo courtesy of the Van Wert County Foundation.)

Constance (Fig. 25) retired years later, and carried her legacy career back to her hometown, Van Wert, Ohio, where she was a notable philanthropist for her community.

Constance Eirich was the first female member of the Tulsa Geological Society. She was also the first woman to be awarded Honorary Membership in the Ohio Geological Society (1973) in which she maintained her membership during her Oklahoma years. Dollie Radler Hall commented, "She has probably found more oil with subsurface mapping than any other woman ..." (1965, p. 297).

Alice Langlois (1911- ?)

Figure 26. Alice Langlois, 1927, (Photo: Pittsburg High School yearbook, with permission.)

Born in Minnesota, Alice Langlois (Fig. 26) moved all over the south and west and even to South America as a child with her French-Canadian father who was a railroad scheduler. She became fluent in English and French.

She worked for Alder Oil Company (a subsidiary of Newmont Mining Corporation) from 1934-37, in their New York office, before attending Columbia University. Going to school while working for Alder, she acquired her bachelor's in geology at Columbia in 1941 and worked in the Land and Geology Department. In 1945, she moved over to Newmont Mining's other affiliate, Newmont Oil Company, before the two oil affiliates merged in 1946. She became the Secretary and Treasurer of Newmont Oil and in February 1946, she was elected to Vice President.

In the first four years after Newmont was formed, it invested $1.5 million and had royalty income that ranged from $900,000 to $1.5 million. Between 1949 and 1956, while Alice was Vice President, Newmont invested $3 million more on royalty acquisitions. Alice's boss, Phil Kraft, who had been responsible for her promotion, negotiated a deal with Magnolia Petroleum Company (Mobil) for half interest in one of their offshore ventures, which obligated them to share exploration and development costs ranging up to $4.1 million by 1957. Their share of production in the venture climbed from a token $19,000 in 1950 to $6

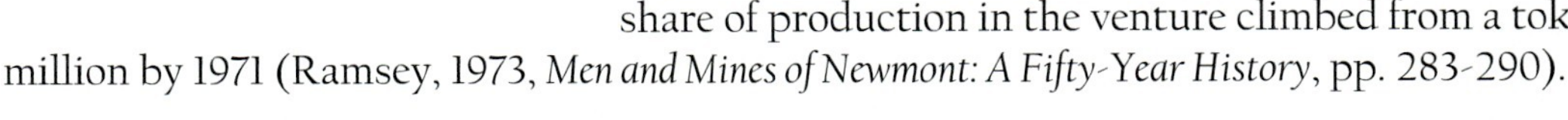

million by 1971 (Ramsey, 1973, *Men and Mines of Newmont: A Fifty-Year History*, pp. 283-290).

Ramsey comments on Alice, saying, "Not many companies, even today, can boast of having a woman as an officer, yet Newmont Oil Company felt such feminine influence as long ago as 1945, long before today's Women's Liberation Movement. ... A competent and attractive woman, as Vice President Alice Langlois ran the office and participated in, and kept track of, all the acquisitions of mineral and royalty interests of Newmont Oil during her tenure. When Newmont Oil Company moved its office to Houston in September, 1954, Alice Langlois chose to resign as vice president and to move abroad with the Mobil Oil Corporation in order to live in Paris, which she had always wanted to do."

Alice was only 45 when she moved to Paris with Mobil (she apparently had developed a good relationship with their Gulf Coast partner) and no records of her have been located beyond that move. She was a member of AAPG from 1941 to about 1948 or longer.

Chapter 3: Sources and References

Everette DeGolyer. Photograph. n.d. DeGolyer Library, Southern Methodist University, Dallas, Texas.

Edmond, Rebekah. "Dollie Radler Hall – Still Practicing at 82." *AAPG Explorer*, 1979, p. 3.

Eirich, Constance after retirement. n.d. Photograph. *Van Wert County Foundation Newsletter.* 2012, Spring issue, p. 3.

Frizzell, Mildred Armor. n.d. Photograph. *AAPG Explorer Special Issue*, 2000, p. 26.

Ferguson, John L. 1964. "Albert Rodger Denison Memorial." *AAPG Bulletin*, vol. 42, no. 2, pp. 239-251.

Garcia, Bradley René, Tulsa, Oklahoma. Personal communication with Robbie Gries January 22, 2017; source of photograph, *Men working for Gypsy Oil*. n.d.

Hall, Dollie Oklahoma with Fanny Carter Edson. circa 1922. Photograph. Tappeiner, Sue, Corvallis, Oregon, Fanny Carter Edson granddaughter.

Hall, Dollie Radler. 1965. "Women in Exploration: Abstract." *Tulsa Geological Society Digest*, vol. 33, pp. 295-298.

Hall, Dollie Radler. Letters to A. R. Denison, January through July, 1928 and Tim Denison, 1974. [Copies provided to Robbie Gries by Tim Denison, 2014.]

Knowles, Ruth Sheldon. "$35 Million Cuban Exploration." *World Oil,* October 1955, reprint no page numbers. [Available through Dollie Radler Hall, personal papers, American Heritage Center, University of Wyoming, Laramie, Wyoming.]

Knowles, Ruth Sheldon. "Cuban Oil Search." *World Oil*, March 1956, reprint, no page numbers. [Available through Dollie Radler Hall, personal papers, American Heritage Center, University of Wyoming, Laramie, Wyoming. With permission from *World Oil*, Houston, Texas.

Parker, Roberta. "Dollie Earned Her Place in a Man's World of Oil." *Broken Arrow Scout*, Thursday, October 18, 1973, p. 2.

Parker, Roberta. "Happy Birthday, Dollie." *Broken Arrow Scout*, Wednesday, June 2, 1993, p. 6A.

Petzet, G. Alan. "Four Here Recall First Reflection Seismograph Find 50 Years Ago: Amerada-GRC Opened Era at Oklahoma Wildcat." *Tulsa World*, December 24, 1978, p. 8G.

Pittsburg High School. *Alice Langlois.* 1927. Photograph. *Purple and White* yearbook. Pittsburg, Kansas, p. 55.

Ramsey, Robert H. 1973. *Men and Mines of Newmont: A Fifty-Year History.* New York: Hippocrene Books pp. 283-290.

Randolph, Mathew. *Gypsy Oil Company office and sign.* 2017. Photograph. Tulsa, Oklahoma.

Read, Bethan, Jackson, Mississippi, Dollie Radler Hall's niece. Personal communication with Robbie Gries, September and October 2016; source of Dollie Radler Hall's personal collection of photographs, newspaper articles, letters, and other memorabilia.

Rose, Joan. "City, State Loses 'Pioneer' Lady Hall." *Tulsa World*, May 1995, p. 1, 4A.

Sheldon, Ruth. 1941. "The Ladies Find Oil." *Scribner's Commentator*, vol. 10, pp. 28-32.

Sinclair, Bill, Denton, Texas, son of an Amerada employee who worked with Dollie. Personal communication with Robbie Gries, 2015.

Tulsa Mainstreet, Historic. n.d. Photograph. In *Downtown Tulsa Intensive-Level Historic Resources Survey,* Cathy Ambler and Elizabeth Rosin, Rosin Preservation, LLC, October 7, 2009. http://www.okhistory.org/shpo/architsurveys/ILSofdowntownTulsa.pdf. Accessed 01/7/2017.

University of Michigan. *Constance Eirich.* 1911. Photograph. "*Michiganensian* yearbook." p. 58.

Wilson, W. B. 1940. "Memorial George Charlton Matson." *AAPG Bulletin*, vol. 24, no. 3, pp. 606-609.

Wynn, Bob, Oklahoma City, Oklahoma, nephew of Vita Lee Waters Chase. Personal communication with Robbie Gries, September 2015; source of photographs as cited in figure captions.

Chapter 4

Heavy Minerals Oil Finder

Fanny Carter Edson (1887-1952)

Fanny Carter Edson made her stratigraphic, petrographic, and paleontologic contributions to petroleum geology working the difficult and puzzling lower Paleozoic section of the Midcontinent region. In 1910, she was the first woman to graduate with a B.A. in geology from the University of Wisconsin. (Fig. 1). Her college yearbook quote forespoke her life's attitude:

"He's a fool who thinks by force or skill to turn the current of a woman's will."

Figure 1. Fanny Carter about the time she graduated from the University of Wisconsin in 1910. (Photo: Sue Tappeiner, granddaughter, Corvallis, Oregon.)

Fanny, who always hated her name because it was a common name for a mare in those days, married fellow geologist, Frank Aaron Edson, also from the University of Wisconsin, soon after her graduation. He entered the iron-ore exploration business, starting his own company in Minnesota. Fanny's role in their mining company was as an "advisory geologist" as well as secretary-treasurer for their business. Not confined to the office, she would later write about overseeing drilling and core examination as well as making structure maps of Precambrian rocks encountered from the core data. She was responsible for recommending locations for future core holes. Fanny also used magnetic data, a newly developing geophysical technology, as a mapping tool (Fanny's personal papers). Through this work, she became very interested in the Precambrian rocks of Minnesota's iron ore region, and decided she needed to know more about "hard rocks." She went back to Wisconsin for her master's degree in 1913-14.

Figure 2. Fanny and baby "El," born in 1917,when Frank Edson left to serve in WWI. (Photo: Sue Tappeiner.)

In 1917, with the outbreak of WWI, Frank and Fanny moved to Duluth, Minnesota where, at age 30, she gave birth to her only child, Eleanor (she had suffered two still births previously) (Fig. 2). Frank, a Quaker and Pacifist, left his family for service in Europe in acceptable support roles, first with the YMCA Field Service and, later, as a chaplain's assistant while Fanny kept the home fires burning in Duluth. Fanny kept busy with various clerical jobs and teaching junior high science; she was never one to be idle and to "stay home." "Married" school teachers were not allowed in almost all school systems in the U.S. at that time so she could only teach, officially, as a "substitute"; however, she taught fulltime for a semester. Fanny also contributed to the war effort with an assignment in Washington, D.C. as part of the Minerals Division of the War Trade Board leaving baby "El," as she was called, with a maid in Duluth while she was away.

Figure 3a. Fanny and young "El" traveled by train to Oklahoma, to Mexico, and to California. Fanny often ducked into a baggage car to smoke a cigarette during their journeys. (Passport Photo: Sue Tappeiner.)

Figure 3b. Frank Edson (left) with baby "El" at 3 months on her first outing to Crosby Mountain, Minnesota. Fanny on far right and her parents.

Returning from the war, Frank Edson took a job in Norman, Oklahoma, with the Oklahoma Geological Survey in 1920 and was joined in January 1921 by Fanny and Eleanor. Before moving, she took Eleanor by train to Mexico City for a three-month visit with her sister, Doris, whose husband was working there. Eleanor, at four years old, had memories of leaving the Pullman coach occasionally to go to the baggage coach with her mother so Fanny could smoke a cigarette (Figs. 3a and 3b).

Upon arrival in Norman, Fanny immediately recognized that, to work in Oklahoma, she needed to remake herself into a petroleum geologist and prudently enrolled in classes at the University of Oklahoma (OU). After one semester, she was enlisted to teach beginning geology students and to work with graduate students. At OU, she developed a lifelong friendship with Dollie Radler, who was studying for her master's degree while working fulltime at Amerada (Fig. 4).

Figure 4. Fanny (left) and Dollie Radler Hall, about 1923, Norman, Oklahoma, in their field clothes. (Photo: Sue Tappeiner.)

In June of 1923, Fanny and Eleanor again boarded a train and went to Palo Alto so she could complete studies for a PhD. At age 36, with years of professional experience on her résumé, Fanny felt more like a contemporary of the faculty than a young coed. Rules for the female students at the time included not smoking nor having bobbed hair, two rules Fanny chose to ignore (Fig. 5). One day, the dean invited her for a visit to his office and was having what she regarded as a "friendly" conversation with her when he pulled out his cigarettes and offered her one. She accepted. He then proceeded to expel her for breaking a coed school rule, crushing her chances for her PhD after she had completed most of her research. Ten years later, when she had published and developed an excellent professional reputation, Stanford offered Fanny an "honorary" PhD, which she enjoyed refusing. Upon leaving Palo Alto, with her dreams of a PhD dashed, Fanny started

Figure 5. At Stanford studying for her PhD, Fanny "bobbed" her hair and would not quit smoking ... gets expelled for both. (Photo: Sue Tappeiner.)

Figure 6. Tulsa, Oklahoma in the early 1920s, photo taken by Fanny soon after her arrival in the "Oil Capital of the World." (Photo: Sue Tappeiner.)

to look for work in the oil business in Los Angeles. Unexpectedly, she was offered a position with Roxana (Shell) back in Tulsa. (Fig. 6)

Before the move, it became obvious to Fanny that her marriage had failed. Her daughter later wrote that the years of 1921 to 1923 in Norman, before they left for Palo Alto, were the only times that the Edsons were "almost a family" though her father was gone a great deal of that time, too (Eleanor's personal papers). Roxana did not keep women on their staff after they married so Fanny's employment with them in 1924 must have come with the recognition that she was soon to be "unmarried."

Fanny and Frank divorced in 1925. The Edsons' divorce settlement was surprisingly more like those of the 21st century than for the 1920s with an agreement stating that young Eleanor (age eight) would have an alternating year with each parent, and both parents would have frequent visitation rights on weekends. That being agreed upon, life's circumstances didn't cooperate. Eleanor spent the first year of the divorce with her father in Norman while her mother started her job with Shell in Tulsa. It was Eleanor who would take the overnight train to Tulsa for weekends to be with her mother. Eleanor wrote, "Early Saturday morning my mother would be standing in the Tulsa station to help me down the giant steps. She had to work on Saturday mornings so I played with beakers and test core samples and famous oil bearing sands in her laboratory until we had lunch in a restaurant ...." (Eleanor's personal papers).

After that first year, Eleanor lived only with her mother. Fanny had the trials of a single mother and provided almost all the support for Eleanor financially; Frank was not as resourceful with money as Fanny (personal communication, Eleanor's daughter, Sue Tappeiner of Corvallis, Oregon). Decades later, when Fanny's younger sister, Persis, (Fig. 7) was separating from her husband, Fanny wrote to her older sister Doris, "...to say the least, I am sorry she [Persis] is having to go through that same experience of disgrace and repudiation I did. It leaves scars from which I, at least, have never recovered" (Fanny's personal correspondence).

Figure 7. Fanny Edson and her sisters, Doris on the left and Persis on the right. Fanny, rather thin from a difficult year in college in 1910. (Photo: Sue Tappeiner.)

Fanny had to work long hours (Monday through Friday plus Saturday morning) for Roxana/Shell. She managed her single parenthood by having a maid come in every day when Eleanor was due home from school, about 4 p.m., and stay until 6 p.m. when Fanny got home, including preparing the evening meals. Fanny's great granddaughter, Kris Ann Moyer of Fargo, Oklahoma, related that, on Sunday evenings when their maid had the night off, Fanny would cook supper, sometimes throwing caution to the wind and make a big chocolate cake. Fanny loved to bake and was good at it. This took its toll with Fanny—she had a lifelong struggle with her weight. (Fig. 8)

Figure 8. Fanny and Eleanor, who would often dress like a boy when not in school. (Photo: Sue Tappeiner.)

Kris Ann also shared a story from Eleanor that Fanny was gone so much to the office or in the field that, sometimes, she did not notice things going on with Eleanor at school. At one point, Eleanor's teacher offered to find Eleanor a coat to wear to school because she did not appear to have one. When Eleanor related this to her mother, Fanny was incensed at the implication and immediately took Eleanor down to the "posh-est" store in Tulsa and bought her a velvet coat with white mink trim and white mink buttons and sent her to school dressed "appropriately" the next day (Eleanor's personal papers). At other times, when Fanny needed to attend to a well or go on a field trip, she did not have anyone to care for Eleanor. Kris Ann recalls, "She took Grandma Burtnett—Eleanor, age seven years, to a hotel and checked her into a room, gave her cash and told her it had to last her a week, so to be careful not to spend it all quickly. Little Eleanor said goodbye to her mother and promptly went to the candy store and to the movie and spent everything. One of the things she bought was a box of Fenamint gum [a chewing gum laxative]. Eleanor had always liked the taste but her mother would only give her one small piece on rare occasions (she apparently didn't associate the chewing gum with constipation). Anyway, without supervision she chewed as much as she wanted. Grandmother Burtnett said she got horrible diarrhea and passed out on the bathroom floor. She came to, weak and dehydrated. At the end of the week, when Fanny came back and retrieved Eleanor, she was a much more compliant kid."

Fanny later described her early days with Roxana as the "horse and buggy" days for subsurface geology because the science was in its infancy (Eleanor's personal papers). She began working with well cuttings from cable-drilled wells and developed heavy mineral/stratigraphic correlation techniques. With the onset of rotary drilling, this proved invaluable as the samples became much more contaminated and much more difficult to work.

For fourteen years, Fanny managed and trained people for her Roxana laboratory in conjunction with working out the much-needed pre-Mississippian stratigraphy for Roxana's Kansas and Oklahoma exploration. She diligently integrated her well sample work with field work. Her son-in-law, Bob Burtnett (Eleanor's personal papers) wrote of her, "She also had to 'sit on wells,' that meant, she had to be on hand when the drilling rig was penetrating the formation usually associated with the critical oil sands. She stayed in village inns or boarding houses close to the crew. There were no fancy motels in those days. Wells, like babies, generally "blew in" at night and the thrill of feeling the earth tremble with the sudden release of trapped petroleum by the hard metal spud of the rotary drill was compensation enough for sagging beds and greasy food."

Burtnett continued, "Several times a year she joined field trips, to which geologists from all over the nation assembled (Fig. 9). They would compose a caravan of twenty, or so, open touring cars following a leader to the Black Hills in South Dakota or one of the newly discovered western Texas oil fields. (Fig. 10) She recalls a southern trip, probably as far away as Mississippi, which was a succession of fried chicken with cream gravy as each small town on the route attempted to cope with such a hoard of visitors eating on the run. These trips would generally last two weeks and those sitting toward the tail of the string of cars would get completely coated with dust because

Figure 9. Arbuckle field trip, 1927, Fanny the only woman present. (Photo: Sue Tappeiner.)

Figure 10. A typical Mid-Continent geological field trip caravan, 1921 or 1922, to see the Fayettville shale. (Photo: taken by Fanny, provided by Sue Tappeiner.)

Figure 11. Arbuckle field trip, 1933 (Photo: taken by Fanny, provided by Sue Tappeiner.)

so few roads were paved. Fanny Edson was one of the boys and extended no special consideration because of her womanliness." (Fig. 11)

Burtnett commented on Fanny's ingenuity, "One might recall the absence of air conditioning at that time. Mrs. Edson suffered mightily from the heat of Oklahoma summers. She rigged up a sheet with the bottom edge dipped into a tub of water and a pedestal electric fan positioned behind it by the open window to try to reduce the laboratory room to a workable temperature. Much of her desk work was drawing detailed maps of sub-surface geologic structures. Her moist arm would smear the colored pencil lines so she utilized blotting paper and talcum powder."

J. B. Leiser wrote (1953, pp. 1182-1186) that she was often in the field examining outcrops. He discussed her contributions to solving the continuing problems in Oklahoma stratigraphy (Fig. 12): "Fanny's correlation charts (Fig. 13) kept pace with the amassing detail and her research; the frequency of revision at times led her to laughingly refer to them as 'late editions'. A medium for exchanging ideas and open information between stratigraphers of several oil companies was formed in 1927 as the Tulsa Stratigraphic Society, and Fanny Edson was a charter

Figure 12. Fanny (in the center of photo in a dress) on another field trip, her favorite recreation. (Photo: Sue Tappeiner.)

member ... her determinations and mapping of the subsurface pre-Mississippian rocks yielded for her company an accurate outline of the newly recognized Central Kansas Uplift ... Fanny Edson's able planning had organized the processing of samples and the training of new employees which now began. Under her administration and training supervision the laboratory staff of assistants grew to seven in number and became recognized ... as one of the most efficient in the region."

Figure 13. Fanny showing her stratigraphic correlations. (Photo: Sue Tappeiner.)

Burtnett continued his remarks about Fanny: "She belonged to technical societies and was much in demand as a speaker. She was restricted in writing very much about her work because it was confidential property of her employer, but she managed to publish subjects of a general nature that were reprinted in many languages and earned her worldwide recognition."

Ruth Sheldon wrote about Fanny's stratigraphic prowess and 1927 discovery (1941, pp 29-31). "Jewels have been made famous as tools to aid the search for oil by Mrs. Fanny Carter Edson research stratigrapher and geologist for Shell Petroleum Corporation for 16 years and now chief geologist of Cimarron Petroleum Corporation, Tulsa, Oklahoma ... If she had not originally studied mining geology, the oil industry might still be puzzling over a number of riddles. In studying samples of oil-well drillings under the microscope, Mrs. Edson noticed the appearance of various heavy minerals—minute particles of semi-precious stones such as zircon, tourmaline, garnet and topaz. Intrigued, she wondered if it would be possible to identify oil-producing formations and correlate then by these minerals—that is, if the same amount and the same type of minerals could be found in a single formation wherever it appeared. After long hours of studying these diminutive fairylands of color and shape she found that her surmises were true.

"Her greatest triumph with this method was the opening of a $15,000,000 oil pool and the solution of a riddle. She had found that many different sandstones separated in some places by a hundred feet or more of sediments were all called the Wilcox sands, the oil sand symbolizing Happy Hunting Grounds for Oklahoma oil men. These so-called Wilcox sands had different porosities and produced varying quantities of oil. Oil men were puzzled and discouraged, as one would have a Wilcox well producing thousands of barrels of oil a day, whereas another's would produce only a hundred.

"Under Mrs. Edson's microscope it developed that each of these 'Wilcox' sands had a different heavy mineral analysis, so in reality they were different sands. One, the most prolific oil producing sands of all, had a definite, easily recognizable analysis. She called this the 'True Wilcox' sand.

Figure 14. Fanny loved the field and often went to wells while drilling to examine samples as they surfaced to identify the "True Wilcox" sand. (Photo: Sue Tappeiner.)

"Her company was drilling a wildcat well in Oklahoma, and when the sand was reached which was supposedly the 'Wilcox' a small amount of oil was found. She analyzed the sand sample, and said this was not the 'True Wilcox' but a higher sand. She urged them to drill deeper. They did, with increasing reluctance and to the accompanying oaths of the drillers, for the sand hardened, become quartzitic and the heavy drilling bit, backed by thousands of pounds of weight, could pound its way through at the rate of a only a foot a day. As each sand sample was brought up, Mrs. Edson [*at the wellsite*] analyzed it and advised going deeper. (Fig. 14) They were ready to abandon the attempt and plug back to the oil sand already discovered, but Mrs. Edson put up strong opposition and they continued. When the well was drilled about eighty feet into the sand body they hit the "True Wilcox" and the well gushed. Oil flowed in such tremendous quantities that it was impossible to remove the tools from the hole. So, this well, which flowed 1,400,000 barrels of oil, was never officially completed and the tools remained in the hole for several years. This was the discovery well of the Marshall pool which has produced 15,000,000 barrels of oil and is still producing." [T19N R4W Logan County, OK] "Further north, the Marshall field became the first 6,000-foot depth pool in Oklahoma. Shell petroleum completed its discovery well, Shell No. 1 McCully, on 8 May 1927 ... the Marshall field yielded over 12 million barrels of petroleum by 1941." (1991, Oklahoma Historic Preservation Society).

Burtnett remarked further, "Slackening of operations at the onset of the great depression brought consolidation of the Shell Company's Mid-Continent field district sample laboratory work into the Tulsa office directly under [Fanny]. For one thing, she was a woman working for less than a man with a comparable job. She needed the job because she had a daughter to support. She took subsequent cuts in salary as the depression worsened, but she continued to work and to do research which brought her to the attention of the Geological Society of America."

Fanny's nomination by Sidney Powers to be a GSA Fellow (awarded in 1932) was a source of great pride to her, making her the first woman in industry to be honored as a GSA Fellow. She relished the achievement for the rest of her life. Shell sent her to Philadelphia to accept the award—the first Shell employee to receive this award, they were proud of her. Bob Burtnett related that, as she walked along the halls at Harvard to find the auditorium where she was to receive her award, "...a gentleman stopped her to ask if she was the new cleaning lady!" (Fig. 15)

Figure 15. Fanny in the 1930s, a professional photograph. (Photo: Sue Tappeiner.)

He recalled, though she got a kick out of her work, she did not recommend it for other women. In fact, when she was interviewed in March, 1933, at the AAPG convention, she told the reporter that women who are engaged in work that usually is done by men must have a particular quality of temperament to succeed in their work. "Perhaps it isn't right, but there is no question but that sex is a handicap in geological work .... When we women do the right thing it is taken for granted. That is what we are paid to do. When we make a mistake, as everyone does occasionally, the mistakes are magnified." She continued, "I am speaking generally, of course. Personally, my connection is a most happy one. I am accepted as 'one of the gang.' But that

Figure 16. Fanny and her memorialist, J. B. Leiser, on a field trip in 1927." (Photo: Sue Tappeiner.)

is because I realized long ago that I need not expect any extra concessions because I am a woman ... I am constantly receiving letters from high school and college girls who want my advice about choosing geology as a profession ... My advice is always no. That isn't because I don't believe women make just as capable geologists as men, but because I know they can't make a success at it unless they are willing to discard all the advantages their sex gives them—and so few of them are willing to do that." (*Houston Post*, 1933).

Fanny, in fact, discouraged her daughter from getting a geology degree and tried to point her in the direction of medicine. Eleanor, however, felt that medicine was just as prohibitive as geology and she proceeded to get her degree in geology.

After Eleanor graduated from Tulsa High School in 1935, Fanny sent her to Texas State Teachers College for Women in Denton where her sister, Persis, taught. This year gave Eleanor a chance to make up some math requirements as well as give Fanny time to get the funds together for El to attend the University of Wisconsin, where all the Carter women had matriculated. Eleanor joked all her life of the memory of the Texas college teachers greeting the young women each day with "Future wives and mothers of Texas!" (Eleanor's personal papers).

El worked for her mother, briefly after her degree, in her consulting business, but once married, never continued geological work. Eleanor's daughter, Sue Tappeiner, speculated that Eleanor's view of a successful marriage was shaped in her childhood to think that being a wife and mother did not mix well with a professional life.

Shell's attitude about Fanny and her professional life also changed with the times and with different management. In his tribute to Fanny, Bob Burtnett related (Bob Burtnett personal papers) that, in 1938, Shell hired a cost accountant to streamline Shell operations, and Fanny's job seemed unproductive to him so she was consequently fired. Fanny had been instrumental in finding the 15-million barrel Marshall Field for Shell as well as many others, but corporate memories can be short, and they can also overlook or fail to understand the value of fundamental stratigraphic work.

Interestingly, in Shell's 800-page volume of company history in the United States (Beaton, 1957, p. 332), no mention is made of the Shell laboratory in Tulsa or Fanny Carter Edson or heavy minerals or micropaleontology. And, though it was mentioned that women were hired for refineries, field pumping, and marketing during WWI and WWII, no mention is made of women hired for geological exploration even though there were many. Chapters are written about the onset of geophysics, well logging, coring, and many other tools that helped exploration, but nothing about the use of heavy minerals or paleontology. The only reference that can be tied, and without any credit where credit was due, was on page 332 in a discussion about Shell needing to "Feed the Big Expansion" of its sales operation and the important development of new oil fields. There it was said "the company discovered the Lovell pool and a new pool in the Marshall district." (Fig. 16)

After Shell "laid her off" in 1938, Fanny set up and ran an independent consulting practice in Tulsa for several years before moving to Denton, Texas to help take care of her aging parents. After their deaths, during WWII (1943-45), she worked briefly for the U.S. Geological Survey, then continued consulting with clients in Wichita, Kansas. At age 58, she fully retired to her many hobbies, including her noteworthy gem and mineral collection and jewelry making. She moved to Chillicothe, Illinois where she lived with her daughter and son-in-law, Bob. One hobby treasured by her family was her interest in researching family history, which led to embroidering a five-foot-high family tree beginning in England, 1480.

Figure 17. Pretty Boy Floyd, an acquaintance of Fanny's. (Photo with permission from The Pueblo Chieftain *& Star-Journal Publishing Corp., Pueblo, Colorado.)*

On Fanny's hobbies, Ruth Sheldon relates, "Mrs. Edson's work with this [heavy mineral] method developed [into] a personal hobby. The semi-precious stones, though small, were so beautiful that she began to collect them as jewels. She now has a unique and valuable jewel collection. Just as she became an authority on the analysis of semiprecious stones in relation to oil, so she has become an authority on their appraisal as jewels. Not only amateurs, but even professional jewelry dealers bring stones for Mrs. Edson to examine."

Kris Ann recounts delightful memories of a woman like few others. Kris Ann's stories were told to her by "Grandma Burtnett" (Eleanor), and she remembers her saying that Fanny was on very cordial terms with the "gangs" of Tulsa. It was in the Prohibition years so the gangs were very likely bootleggers or involved in bootlegging. In fact, Eleanor liked to tell about Fanny personally knowing Pretty Boy Floyd (Fig. 17), who jokingly wrote a check to her once for $100,000 or some outrageous figure. She threw it away, but years later, after he gained so much notoriety, the family lamented about what that check might have been worth.

Tulsa was one of the worst offenders of prohibition laws in Oklahoma. (Fig. 18) "In 1930, Tulsa had a population of 180,000. Considered the "Oil Capital of the World," this city on the Arkansas River prided itself for allegedly having more millionaires per capita than any other city in the United States. Liquor flowed as freely in Tulsa as the black gold, which often yielded profits lucrative enough to invite the envy of those less fortunate. Since statehood, Tulsa had been rightly termed by many as "wide open," and those with any perspective entertained no illusions that the Eighteenth Amendment would change the city's drinking and gambling habits or significantly alter the personal entrepreneurial arrangements of the "ladies ..." (Franklin, 1971, pp. 93, 94).

Figure 18. Bootleggers and gangs were a problem for Tulsa, the Oil Capital of the World, where Prohibition was largely ignored. (Photo: http://skyscraperpage.com/forum/show)

Grandma Burtnett told Kris Ann that Fanny "associated" with these tough guys to the point that she sometimes took young Eleanor to a hotel and had her wait in the balcony quietly while she went to the lobby and completed some kind of transaction ... possibly just buying alcohol. That leads to another family legend when two opposing gangs in Tulsa were feuding, and it was extremely unpleasant around Tulsa. The gang leaders wanted to negotiate a truce, and an exchange would be made to seal the deal. When they tried to identify someone trusted to be a go-between, they agreed that Fanny Carter Edson would be trusted by both. She did what they requested, generating at least a temporary lull in hostilities.

Fanny had a long and distinguished career in petroleum geology. She was a member of AAPG for 30 years and remained active in her professional societies until her death in 1952. J. B. Leiser, in his 1953 AAPG memorial for Fanny, wrote "The vigor and humor of her personality included a trenchant scorn in her contempt aroused by hypocrisy. But her laugh, in merriment was infectious and especially characteristic, for she found much at which to laugh." (Fig. 19)

Figure 19. Fanny's self-portrait in a Season's Greeting card she made and sent later in life. (From Sue Tappeiner.)

After Fanny's death in 1952, her first Shell lab assistant, Ted Peters, wrote to Eleanor saying "She coursed the field like a pointer, sniffing out the few solid chunks of Truth concealed in all the forest of Error, and when she got hold of some of these chunks she sunk her teeth in it and held on in spite of hell, harassment, and high water. That attitude doesn't make for an easy, peaceful life; but now that I am nearing the end of my own professional career, I can testify that it gives me a feeling of inward satisfaction that no compromise with Truth will ever purchase. She was a stout-hearted fighter for the truth as the truth was revealed to her; she never compromised; she never retreated; she never surrendered" (Eleanor's personal papers).

Chapter 4: Sources and References

Beaton, Kendall. *Enterprise in Oil, A History of Shell in the United States.* New York: Appleton-Century-Crofts, Inc., 1957. 332 pp.

Bootleggers and gangs. http://skyscraperpage.com/forum/showthread.php?t=170279&page=1301. Accessed 12/15/2016.)

Burtnett, Eleanor Edson, daughter of Fanny Carter Edson. Personal papers. Courtesy of Sue Tappeiner, Corvallis, Oregon.

Burtnett, Bob, son-in-law of Fanny Carter Edson, Personal papers and correspondence. Courtesy of Sue Tappeiner, Corvallis, Oregon.

Edson, Fanny Carter. Personal papers and correspondence. Courtesy of Sue Tappeiner, Corvallis, Oregon.

Franklin, Jimmie Lewis. *Born Sober; Prohibition in Oklahoma 1907-1959.* Norman, Oklahoma: University of Oklahoma Press, 1971. 212 pp.

Houston Post. "Women attend Convention of Oil Geologists." March 25, 1933.

Leiser, J. B. 1953. "Memorial-Fanny Carter Edson." *AAPG Bulletin*, vol. 37, no. 5, pp. 1182-1186.

Moyer, Kris Anne, Fargo, Oklahoma, great grand daughter of Fanny Carter Edson. Personal communication with Robbie Gries, October 2015.

Oklahoma Historic Preservation Society. 1991, "The Energy Theme in Management Region Six 1912-1951, 40-90-2.003." Oklahoma State University, Department of History, Stillwater, Oklahoma. http://www.okhistory.org/shpo/contexts/Region6Energy.pdf.

Peters, Ted, Shell Lab Assistant to Fanny Carter. Correspondence to Eleanor Burtnett. Eleanor Burtnett personal papers. Courtesy of Sue Tappeiner, Corvallis, Oregon.

Pretty Boy Floyd. n.d. Photograph. The Pueblo Chieftain and Star-Journal Publishing Corp., Pueblo, Colorado.

Sheldon, Ruth. 1941. "The Ladies Find Oil." Scribner's Commentator, vol. p. 28-32.

Tappeiner, Sue, Corvallis, Oregon, granddaughter of Fanny Carter Edson. Personal communication with Robbie Gries, March 20, 2016; source of Fanny Carter Edson and daughter Eleanor Edson Burtnett's personal papers, correspondence, photos, and newspaper articles.

University of Wisconsin. *Fanny Carter.* 1911. Photograph. *Badger* yearbook, Madison, Wisconsin. p. 43.

Chapter 5

Post WWI: Earliest Women Sitting Wells

We learned that Fanny Carter Edson (Chapter 4) was no stranger to the wellsite and was often on location when samples were taken to verify if they reached their stratigraphic objective and tell the drillers whether to keep drilling or to stop. She also was out on rigs studying samples when she and her husband were in the iron ore business between 1910 and 1917; it is likely she was *the first woman to "sit wells."* Several other oil companies in addition to Roxana also sent their female geologists out to do wellsite work though it was not common. Ruth Sheldon (1941, p. 31, 32) describes Constance Leatherock was a common sight on drilling wells in the 1920s and 1930s. In Chapter 6 on the earliest micropaleontologists, Esther Applin spent considerable time looking at samples while wells were drilling. However, when women came into the oil and gas business in the flush of Affirmative Action hiring in 1973-77 (Chapters 13-17) the history of women being present and competent on wellsites had been completely lost and forgotten. A new generation of women had to "fight for" the right to well sit—for the opportunity to have a complete exploration geologist's experience and set of responsibilities.

The Importance of Wellsite Work

So, why was wellsite work an important part of a petroleum geologist's career? Why have we taken notice of early female geologists "going out on a well?" (Fig. 1)

The wellsite geologist bears the major responsibility for properly drilling and evaluating a prospect for oil and gas. Prospects (ideas of where oil and gas can be discovered) are developed primarily in the office, using data from previously drilled oil and gas wells, seismic data, and other information such as coordinating that data with the rocks on the surface. When a "prospect" has been developed, the company will buy the land rights to drill that prospect, which can be extremely expensive. These rights are usually in the form of a "lease," which gives the company

Figure 1. Young women in the 1920s on a mining location. Fanny Carter Edson got her introduction to drilling while in mining in about 1914 as she supervised drilling core holes and examined the cores for iron-ore exploration in Minnesota. (Photo: AAPG archives, Tulsa, Oklahoma.)

the right to drill on that land. The oil and gas rights (called mineral rights) are usually held privately in the United States or can be owned by the state or the federal government.

The oil company agrees to "carry" the mineral owners for all the expenses of exploring and drilling. The mineral owners, whether an individual, a group of individuals, the state, or the federal government will be entitled to a percentage of all hydrocarbons found without having to pay any of the expenses or being liable for any problems. This can range from a common 12.5% to 30%. Or, sometimes more. The oil company (the operator) pays 100% of the expenses and takes economic and legal risks, for 70% to 87.5% of the revenue. In addition, after oil is found, the operator will pay 100% of the expenses to operate the well—well heads, pumps, storage tanks, gas lines, monitoring equipment, pipelines, electricity, protections for wildlife, protections for water sources, the salaries of all the field personnel, most of the taxes, etc.

Given this financial commitment, the operating company needs to be absolutely certain they have a fully qualified geologist on location who will ensure that the target formation will be properly drilled and evaluated. *That is the job of the wellsite geologist.*

The company engineer takes on most of the mechanical oversight, making sure the rig is performing correctly and the drillers, roughnecks, and crew are doing their jobs safely and with good equipment. But, it is the geologist who says, "drill deeper," "drill slower," "stop drilling and circulate" (meaning to move the drilling fluids that are in the pipe back to the surface, bringing up all the "cut" rock [cuttings] from the bottom of the hole). The geologist may also say, "change the drill bit (the part of the drill string that actually cuts the rock, sometimes with industrial diamonds embedded in them—they are expensive) when it appears the change is needed. The rig crew and engineer will do as the geologist directs; she may say, "Catch samples every twenty feet, or every five feet." There are dozens of instructions that the wellsite geologist can use and will use to ensure that this prospect is adequately evaluated. Ideally, the geologist, the company engineer, and the toolpusher work as a team. However, *the wellsite geologist is the boss.*

Imagine when this was strictly a man's world with women rarely or never approaching a wellsite (wellsite superstition claimed "women were unlucky") what it must have been like for a young woman to show up at the location and "run the show." It was not an easy transition for anyone. But, human beings are flexible and resilient. Within a very short period, a matter of a few years, companies dictated new policies and said this is the way it will be, and women became accepted. The environment at the wellsite changed to accommodate both genders. The world did not end. Superstitions were put aside.

Why did women want to be out there on a wellsite? It was cold, or hot, and dirty, and noisy, and smelly. There is little privacy, and sleepless nights are the norm. The talk can be crude; the food can be disgusting; and, *if* there are sleeping accommodations, they can be rank. The job is physically taxing. Her hands are constantly in dirty water, washing and preparing samples that have come up from the muddy drill hole. They get chapped and red, and drilling mud gets into the fingernails and the cuticles and on any exposed surface—her face, her clothes, and her hair.

Figure 2. A drilling rig with drill pipe being lifted by the elevators. This is an older, small truck-mounted rig much like those used in the early days of drilling with pioneering women. The "doghouse" is the white cabin-like structure. (Photo: Robbie Gries, Denver, Colorado.)

The inside of the doghouse (the small cabin on the derrick floor (Fig. 2) where the recording machinery resides and where the crew goes to get out of weather, or change clothes) can be dirty and greasy; everything she touches leaves dirt or grease on her hands, which gets wiped on her pants or shirt. Things are soon grimy and black, just like the coffee in the doghouse that is usually about 20 hours old and has a burnt pot smell and taste. The fellows are chewing tobac-

Figure 3. Drilling is inherently a "dirty" business with mud and grease in abundance. (Photo: Robbie Gries.)

co or sunflower seeds, making a further mess. Yes, *why* would anyone want to be on a wellsite? (Fig. 3)

For a petroleum geologist, *there is nothing more rewarding than actually being on the location when an idea is being tested, when a prospect is being drilled.* All the discomforts magically fade away when she hits the horizon she predicted and it is full of oil or gas. The thrill is like that of being rewarded with a newborn baby. We, not just the women but the men, too, often call these prospects "our babies."

Oversight of that whole process, from spudding the well (beginning to drill), through completion (either putting on equipment to produce the oil and gas or plugging the well with cement if it is a dry hole) is fraught with possibilities for things to go wrong. The geologist almost never rests. She is looking at samples as they come up from the bottom of the well bore (hole) and trying to determine if the expected layers of rock are "coming in" at the right depth. This is crucial because it can give her a good idea if the well is going to be successful long before the prospective layer is drilled. Often, the rocks are not penetrated where expected, and then she is re-calculating and informing everyone at the office, with extra concerns. Then, she will try to reevaluate and make new predictions on the job. Every morning, the wellsite geologist calls the office (the operating company and sometimes she must call several partners, too) with a report on what was drilled. She reports her rock descriptions, whether there were any oil and gas shows, and how the well is drilling—fast or slow, as expected. Is the crew taking all the safety precautions? The geologist makes a report of everything seen, heard, smelled, and tasted for the previous 24 hours.

When drilling is in the early stages, a typical day (before many of the modern digital equipment was introduced) might start with the geologist getting up hours before dawn and going to the doghouse; collecting the geolograph records (a recording of the feet drilled overnight and the time it took to drill each foot); and collecting samples (cuttings) the crew captured all night—probably a bag for every ten, twenty, or thirty feet. These samples are often dumped out of the wellbore onto a flat, screened surface called the "shale shaker," which vibrates and partially cleans the cuttings—small pieces of rock that are flushed to the surface from the drill bit as it grinds its way through the rocks.

Figure 4. Sample trays with cuttings from the bottom of the well bore are examined using the binocular microscope. Robbie Gries shows a budding geologist, Henry Andrews, how cuttings "fizz" when 10% hydrocloric acid is applied to them—testing for chalky rocks. (Photo: Robbie Gries.)

She takes these to her trailer if she is lucky enough to have a trailer (Ellen Posey often did the work on the hood of her car or truck); she washes the samples more (the crew washed them during the night to get most of the mud off); and puts them in trays to dry, one tray for every ten-foot interval (Fig. 4). That done, she will plot the geolograph footage, making a graph of depth versus feet drilled per minute or five minutes, etc. This graph is very revealing to the geologist: the slower the drilling can mean the drilling is in "tighter" rock, and a common tight rock is shale. A change in drilling rate might be significant, indicating the drill bit has crossed a fault or drilled into an unexpected sandstone or a volcanic flow, or a bed of coal, or a layer of salt. Those different lithologies (rock types) will drill at noticeably different speeds, and the wellsite geologist builds up experience to know which rock types correlate to drill times.

The geologist then looks at the dried samples in a binocular microscope and describes them: "shale, dark gray, calcareous, with microfossils, etc." She looks for signs of oil and gas—does it have any odor? Is there oil "bleeding" out of the rock or out of fractures in the rock? She adds water to the tray and looks to see if gas is bubbling out of rock. And, then she puts the sample under a black light—an ultra violet light. Bright yellow, green, or vivid light blue—several varieties of color indicate their presence. She will carefully describe the colors, the abundance, and the movement of any hydrocarbons in the tiny rock samples. All the information is plotted, by depth, on the "sample log" for the day. Usually the geologist had been up late the night before, "running the samples" that were drilled before she went to bed, so she only has a few to describe in the morning. Time is of the essence. Everyone back in the office expects that call by 7 a.m., sometimes earlier.

Today, she would just grab her cell phone and call in. But, not too long ago, the convenience of cell phones didn't exist. Sometimes, the rig was close enough to a landline to have a phone on the rig or in the trailer, but for decades, the geologist had to drive to a phone to make the morning call. That meant waking even earlier in the morning to get the samples described before driving to access a phone, most likely a pay phone booth where you needed coins, and frequently in windy, rainy, or blizzard conditions.

There is a rhythm and routine on the wellsite most days. The long steel sting of pipe attached to the drill bit is built by "joints" of 30-foot length pipe. The first five or more joints are extra heavyweight "drill collars" providing the weight for the rotating drill bit to cut through the rock making the borehole. Drilling into the rock layers, each joint grinds its way down its 30-foot length. At the end of the joint, the driller stops the process, and his roughnecks surround the "rotary table" on the rig floor as he mechanically lifts the drill string with "elevators" or clamps that men then place around the top of the highest joint in the drill string. (Fig. 5) They will prepare to put big heavy-duty tongs (wrenches) around each side of the connection between the upper joint and the lower joint. The driller turns the rotary table to unscrew the drill string and allow the roughnecks to add another joint of pipe to the drill string. They use the tongs (or on older rigs a wrap chain) to screw the joints back together. Before the joints are screwed together, the crew smears heavy-duty grease onto the threads of each exposed joint to keep the connections lubricated and rust free. This thick, viscous lubricant has a way of insinuating itself around the rig.

But there are the extraordinary days, that often begin in the middle of the night, when the wellsite geologist is awakened by the "screaming" of the brakes on the rig. When the drill bit hits porous rock like a sandstone, it often starts drilling very rapidly, faster than more resistant shale. The driller notices immediately and puts on the brake, slowing down the drilling, and the brakes make a very audible screech of protest. Everyone within earshot knows that "something" different has been penetrated.

Figure 5. Young Henry Andrews watches from the doghouse door as the roughnecks adds another joint of drill pipe to the drill string so the well can be drilled deeper. (Photo: Robbie Gries.)

The weight of the long steel string of drill pipe is constantly monitored by the driller. The geologist tells the driller when to expect to encounter fast drilling porous rock, or potential oil or gas saturated "pay." The driller operating the machinery on the rig floor stays close to the console that controls the drawworks (the hoisting machinery for the pipe) and brakes as the drill bit approaches the crucial zones so that the brakes can quickly be applied.

Commonly, the minute the "pay zone" has been penetrated, the geologist wants the drilling to stop and "circulate up" the rock samples from the bottom of the hole. The drill string keeps rotating, but the weight of the drill string is lifted off. The brakes are on. This allows the drilling fluid, usually a mud made from water and a thickening agent like bentonite (a natural ground-up shale product), which has been pumped down through the inside of the pipe, to come back up to the surface on the outside of the pipe (between the pipe and the surrounding rock). The thick mud carries the "cuttings" or samples of the rock from the bottom of the hole and, depending on the depth, might take 10 to 30 minutes or longer before the samples make it to the surface. Waiting is an exercise in patience while everyone speculates what the rocks in the zone look like; excitement builds.

As soon as the samples are up, the geologist prepares them and examines them under the microscope and with the black light. Soon, if she can report they have hit the prospective zone, she will describe the samples and the "shows" if there are any. She will quickly prepare a report and a recommendation and rush to the phone to alert the office. The wellsite geologist can make several recommendations: continue to drill, take a core, or run a DST.

If the wellsite geologist and her company have decided in advance they want to "core" the pay zone, the coring service company would be alerted to be on standby when she knows she is close to the zone. She confirms the service company is ready with the core equipment and on location as the rig crew trips out of the hole to exchange the drill bit for a coring bit. The core bit is a drilling tool that has the cutting edge (usually industrial diamonds) around the perimeter of the drilling collars and cuts a length of rock in one solid piece instead of grinding the rock into tiny pieces with the regular rotary drill bit. (Fig. 6) These cores, when pulled to the surface, are analyzed much more thoroughly and provide far more geologic information. So, why not core the entire well bore? It is extremely expensive because drilling with a core apparatus is very slow, and rig time is charged by the hour when coring. This also means she must be very astute and accurate in picking the layers to core because drilling the wrong zone is a costly mistake. And, embarrassing!

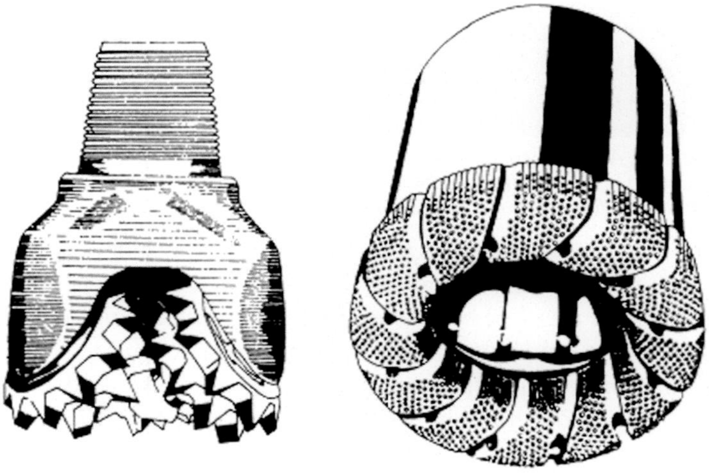

If the decision is to run a test of the fluids in the pay zone, a "drill stem test" (DST), the well-site geologist calls out the location to the service company that has been chosen. She has, no doubt, already alerted this service company, too, to be on standby. When everyone is informed, she will instruct the driller to, perhaps, drill a few feet further into the zone to test more of the reservoir rock, or she will have him continue to circulate, because that action helps make the walls of the hole more stable and resistant to caving in while they run the test.

Figure 6. Diagrams of two drill bits; on the left is a "rotary bit" with "teeth that cut the rock into small pieces or cuttings." On the right is a coring bit, where solid rock remains intact in the center of the core barrel and the diamond teeth on the outside cut the rock. (Kansas Geological Survey, http://www.kgs.ku.edu/Publications/Oil/primer12.html, accessed 1/15/2017.)

Everything must be prepared for the hours that the testers are operating and performing the DST. After the hole is "conditioned," the crew pulls the drill pipe out of the hole (called "tripping out"), an arduous and lengthy process. Depending on the size of the rig, the drill pipe is pulled out in one to three 30-foot joint lengths (stands) and stacked vertically on the rig floor in a designated area on the rig floor. The drilling rig has a pulley system built in to pull up these lengths of pipe. One roughneck places himself near the top of the derrick on a platform called the monkey board while two others are at the bottom to disconnect the pipe. Together, all three men will "stack" the 90-foot length of pipe to the side, leaving them vertical, resting until they "trip" back in the hole.

In the early days, oil scouts – people who would gather information on what was happening at a wildcat drilling site – would sit some distance away with binoculars, undetected by the people on the rig and "count" those joints as they came out of the hole. They could then report to their offices that the operator of this well was testing a zone at a depth of about 6000 feet because they counted out 67 joints 90 feet long. And, the scout probably learned from gossip in town that the testing service had been called out to the well. Scouting information was very valuable if a company had offsetting leases and wanted to know as quickly as possible whether the well will shed light, *for free*, on the potential of their leases. Dollie Radler Hall (Chapter 8) wrote that her employees needed to be more careful about "scouts." She reminded her colleague that scouts were "not as dumb as we would like [to believe]" and that Amerada personnel needed to be careful what they said and what they did.

Activity increases with the arrival of the service company and the DST equipment, which consists of a chambered tool (bottom hole assembly) with valves that can be opened or closed from the surface and recorders to document pressure changes during the test. The tool is lowered down the well bore on a cable from the top of the derrick or run into the hole on drill pipe. It can have single or double "packers" that balloon out to isolate the zone

Figure 7. A service company female engineer prepares to run "wireline" logging equipment into the wellbore. (Photo: Robbie Gries.)

being tested from the pressure of the viscous drilling mud in the hole. A single packer can be set above the zone if the hole does not penetrate a deeper formation; double packers are set above and below the zone for a "straddle test."

With the pay zone isolated, the fluid in the prospective rock can flow into the isolated space in the wellbore where the natural "pressure" within the formation can be measured and a sample of the fluid from those rocks collected; it could be oil, gas, or natural formation water.

Figure 8. Logging requires not only technical skills but a fair share of physical strength. (Photo: Robbie Gries.)

The wellsite geologist discusses the rock properties with the service company and recommends the length of flow times for the test. The test begins with the tool chamber shut-in, meaning nothing can flow into the chamber or to the surface. Then, the tool is opened briefly to get some idea of the pressure by how easily the formation fluids can flow to the surface: is it slow? fast? And, at what pressure? what kind of volume? Then, the tools are shut in again, possibly for an hour, to allow the pressure from the formation to build up again; then it is opened once again so the fluid can flow to the surface. Sometimes it has a flow period of several hours to allow the geologist and engineers to estimate what kind of flows are possible from that zone. DSTs are opened to the surface only in the daytime, and all precautions are more readily put into place for any oil or gas coming up to the surface. Frequently, the preparations are made during the night and the test is run at daybreak.

The wellsite geologist is on location through the entire DST process; her job does not end until the well has been "logged." Also termed borehole or wireline logging, it is the practice of making physical measurements by instruments lowered into the hole (on a "wire line"). Data often includes measurements of the conductivity of the rock and any contained fluids to electric currents (water is conductive, oil is resistive). The electrical measurements provide the geologist with information about the types of rock in the layers from the bottom of the hole to the surface. The logs can also indicate if the pore space in the rocks contain water, gas, or oil. (Figs. 7 and 8)

Other measurements with "wireline tools" help refine those ideas about the types of rock and the fluids in those rocks. These tools might measure the natural radioactivity of the rocks, the ability of the rock to carry sound waves, the porosity of the rock, the permeability, and many other attributes.

The geologist supervises the "logging run" to be sure the equipment is calibrated and performing correctly throughout the logging process. In the early days, she reviewed the output inked onto paper and, more recently, watches a computer screen in the logging truck to make these judgments, comparing the output with a set of logs from a previously drilled well in the area. When she agrees with the service company employees that everything is calibrated correctly and the tools are functioning correctly, the service company begins logging, with the tools at the bottom of the hole, the measurements are taken from the bottom to top.

Figure 9. It is good news when the "casing" is brought in, meaning the well will be completed as a "producer." (Photo: Robbie Gries.)

After the well is logged, the wellsite geologist takes those logs and makes further calculations to determine the thickness of the "pay zone," the quality of each foot of pay (porosity), and the hydrocarbon saturation (percent of oil vs water) of the rocks. With those calculations, she makes a recommendation to the office to "complete the well," meaning to run casing (steel casing), or she recommends "plugging" the well, meaning, sadly, that it won't produce economical quantities of hydrocarbons. A "cement truck" is called to the location to fill the wellbore with cement. When her recommendations are approved, she communicates with the company man to instruct the drilling crew to take the necessary actions.

When all the evaluations are complete and the well is considered a "producer," the driller will be instructed to "trip" back into the hole with the drill bit and drill string to drill deeper for enough "rathole" so wellsite information can be collected through the entire producing zone. "Casing" can be set below the zone to accommodate production equipment. Casing is steel pipe that will carry the hydrocarbons to the surface. (Fig. 9) When it is in place, cement is pumped in to fill the space between the rock layers and the pipe. When set, the cement and casing prevent contamination from the produced fluids from getting into rock layers above the producing zone. As part of the drilling process, the shallowest zones in the well (near the surface that might have fresh water reservoirs) are protected by two or more strings of casing and cement.

Figure 10. The equipment for a gas well is installed after the drilling rig is removed. The well is then tied in to an interstate pipeline. (Photo: Robbie Gries.)

When the casing is cemented and the well is completed, the entire derrick is moved off the well bore. In its place, much smaller "production" facilities are installed. (Fig. 10) Gauges, housing, meters, and some type of production equipment like a 'pump jack' to lift the fluids" are put in place." Gas wells usually have just pipes and meter gauges that have a small closet-sized building over them to protect the meters from the elements.

The wellsite geologist's work in done. (Fig. 11) Back in the office, armed with the good or bad news, she might use the new data to develop more drill sites, perhaps a new prospect, or she might recommend a different strategy to her company.

Figure 11. These Kansas wells were operated and overseen by women in the field: owner/operator, Robbie Gries, and colleagues, Jessica Andrews and Amy McLean. (Photo: Robbie Gries.)

[This description of wellsite work was based on drilling shallow onshore vertical wells similar to those overseen by the early pioneers in wellsite work, where older drilling rigs and basic equipment are prevalent (the photos in this chapter are from shallow wells drilled in 2001 through 2015). Drilling in the 21st Century is much more technically advanced and sophisticated but not always needed to get the job done.] (Fig. 12)

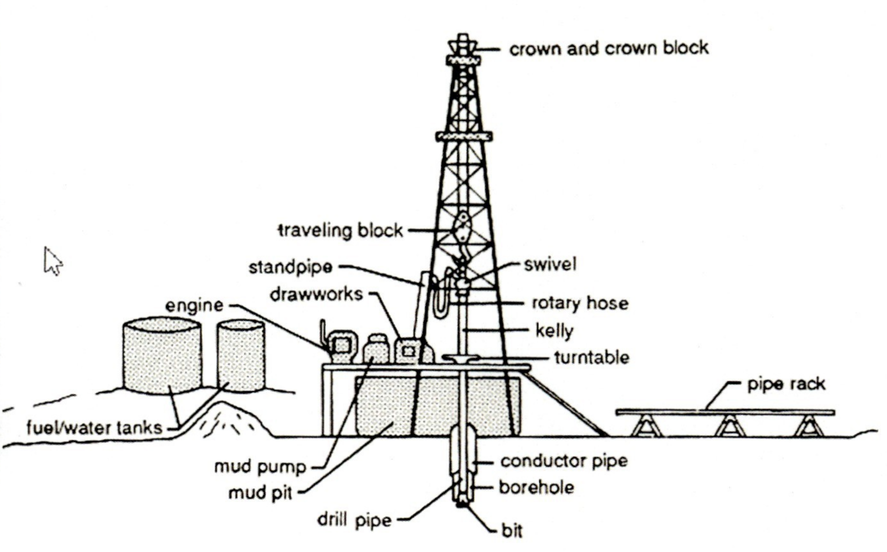

Figure 12. Drilling rig and its components (Diagram from the Kansas Geological Survey, http://www.kgs.ku.edu/Publications/Oil/primer12.html, accessed 1/15/2017.)

Ellen Nora Posey Bitgood Roblin (1905-1974)

Figure 13. Ellen Posey doing field work in the Arbuckles of Oklahoma. She is visited by John Fitts (a self-taught geologist and oil finder, who often visited geologists in the field to learn what he could). Writing on the photo, "Summer—Ellen Posey and I [Fanny Carter Edson] camped in Arbuckles below the spring on Falls Creek." (Photo taken by Mildred Armor Frizzell and provided by Charles Bitgood, Denver, Colorado.)

Ellen Nora Posey was the penultimate wellsite geologist of the early pioneering years. She was born in the shadow of an oil derrick in the Paola, Kansas oil field where her father, Fred Posey, was a cable tool driller (Fig. 13). "Life was very nomadic," Ellen told John Purnell when he wrote about her in the Cities Service company magazine, Earth Scientist, (1952, p.22-23). "I went to 13 different grade schools and we never lived in the same house longer than 18 months."

When the larder was low and money scarce, "the girls" (Ellen and her sister) would hire out to chop weeds in a neighboring farmer's corn patch. Once, they earned 15 cents and walked six miles to town to buy a box of .22 shells "So Dad could go out and shoot rabbits for stew." When they were living in the oil patch near Farmington, New Mexico, they went to a county fair and there was a "turkey shoot," 10 cents a shot. Her dad had only 10 cents in his pocket, but, even though he was firing a strange gun, he hit the target's bull's eye. The family had turkey for Thanksgiving, and he invited the drillers to eat with them.

Figure 14. Ellen with her baby son, "Chuck," in the field where she preferred to be. (Photo: Charles Bitgood.)

Ellen's mother thought her interest in rocks started during a sojourn to New Mexico when she was ten years old. She liked to gather "pretty rocks." When they were expected to move back to Texas, Ellen and her sister, Irene, were willing to leave all their toys behind if they could take a suitcase full of the "specimens" they had gathered.

Ellen's son, Charles Decker Bitgood, of Denver, Colorado, or "Chuck" as he prefers, remembers, "Her uncle, J. P. Wolfe, then superintendent of the company's [Cities Service] Kansas office, influenced her choice of career."

Chuck said that Ellen's cable-tool-driller father was furious with her for choosing geology as a major and tried very hard to change her mind. He recollects she had been planning to study journalism, then adds, "But her uncle talked to a male geologist he knew and was assured there was a great future of women in the field."

Ellen enrolled at University of Oklahoma (OU), working to cover most of her expenses and graduated in 1928 with her B.A. She went on to complete her M.S. in 1932. Her first job would be with Cities Service, formerly Empire Oil, in Bartlesville, Oklahoma where she became enamored with wellsite work in those early years. John Purcell quotes Cities Service superintendent of production, Earl Dowse, recalling her days working with him: "She was a sharp one, even then. Of course, it was a new experience for the boys, having a woman out on the rig, and some of them had to try a few practical jokes. They'd doctor her samples; once, someone went down to the river and got a little sand and slipped it into a sample bag, just to see what would happen. In a few minutes, we heard her whistle – she could whistle so you could hear it half a mile – and saw her wave her arms. She looked up from her microscope and said, 'Well, boys, I don't know what you can do about it, but the Arkansas River bed has just moved into the bottom of that hole.' No matter what tricks the men tried, they never tripped her. So, pretty soon they gave up trying."

Ellen worked for four years before company policy required her to quit when she married Fred S. Bitgood in 1936. They moved to the west coast where he found a job and, in 1940, Charles Decker was born, named after her OU geology professor and mentor, Dr. Charles Decker. When WWII broke out, she worked as a chemist in a war plant in Las Vegas.

Figure 15. "Mrs. Bitgood, who lives here [Wichita Falls, Texas], is one of the nation's leading geologists and specializes in locating likely drilling sites for oil wells." Lubbock Evening Journal, March 11, 1953, p. 21. (Photo: Charles Bitgood.)

Toward the end of the war, in 1944, Ellen was divorced and became a single parent. She moved to Wichita Falls, Texas, with her young son (Fig. 14) and bought a binocular microscope for $114. She started sharing an office with another consulting geologist, John A. Kay, who described her work ethic: "She'll jump in that car of hers, drive three or four hundred miles and then do a day's work that would flatten most men .... She never heard of a time-clock and can rough it with the best. When she goes out on a well, she takes a bedroll along and catches naps (Fig. 15) .... Mrs. Bitgood was sitting on a West Texas well in the deep of winter. A sudden blizzard swept down; snow choked the makeshift trail to the highway and isolated the crew without food or means of transportation. The crew members decided the only way to avert starving or freezing was to try to walk out to the highway, nearly three miles across country. One of the roughnecks jerked a thumb toward Mrs. Bitgood 'How'll we get her out?' he asked.

"'Never mind me,' Mrs. Bitgood retorted, 'You just worry about yourself.'

"'It was snowing pretty hard when we set out,' the roughneck reported later, "'and for a while nobody paid much attention to anybody else. Then I happened to look up and there was Miss Ellen topping a rise half a mile ahead. It was the last time we saw her 'til we got to town.' It was her work ethic, good humor, and kindness that won her wellsite respect."

John A. Kay said he long since became accustomed to seeing a big, two-fisted derrick worker come into the office looking for "Miss Ellen." "After a little foot-shuffling," Kay said, "...he will usually say something like this, 'Miss Ellen, we want to know when you're going to be on another well with us. We ain't had a good cup of coffee on the rig since last time.'" (Purcell, 1952, p. 23). (Fig. 16)

Figure 16. Microscope on the hood of her car, Ellen was sought after for her north Texas expertise. (Photo: Charles Bitgood; used in Cities Service company magazine, Purcell, April, 1952, p. 22-23.)

It was not only on the wellsite but, also, back in the office that Ellen's high standards and technical excellence were recognized: "She's one of the few women doing the job that men long have monopolized, and with good reason. Searching for oil is a demanding occupation—for it takes years of scientific training, lots of scrambling over rough country, and an encyclopedic knowledge of rocks and fossils."

Edward Kadane, of Wichita Falls said of Ellen, "She's the equal of any man I ever saw and better than most ... we've employed her for the last six or eight years and I wish she'd work for us full-time" (Purcell, 1952, p. 22).

Figure 17. Ellen with Chuck when he was 8 or 9 years old on a wellsite, a very common occurrence as he grew up. (Photo: Charles Bitgood, Denver, Colorado.)

But Ellen would not give up her independence and Dollie Radler Hall (1965, p. 297) wrote of her, "Her knowledge of the stratigraphy of the area is unsurpassed and she probably has had as many successful completions as most men."

This sentiment was reiterated when Ellen was written about in the *Lubbock Evening Journal*, (1953, p. 21): she "...gets as much kick out of seeing an oil well 'come in' as if she owned it. The gush of the black fuel means that she has scored another success at her unusual job."

Figure 18. Ellen and her granddaughter, Kimberly Anne Bitgood, in about 1961 on a Kadane Oil Company well near Crowell, Texas. (Photo: Charles Bitgood.)

Ellen inspired her family by example. She often took young Chuck to wells with her after he turned 8 or 9 though she fretted about his safety around the equipment (Figs. 17 and 18). Chuck followed in the footsteps of his mother as well as the man for whom he was named, Dr. Charles Decker, and became a geologist.

Ellen Posey Bitgood remarried in 1965 to Ormond W. Roblin. She was president of the North Texas Geological Society in 1954-55 and a member of AAPG for 41 years.

Constance Leatherock Nieschmidt (1904-1965)

Constance Leatherock was born in Indiana but moved to Oklahoma for much of her early life (Fig. 19). Her Oklahoma City High School (OHS) yearbook comments about her "...a Hoosier; she originated in Indiana, the land of all bright and scintillating wit. At OHS she cast in her lot in the Girls' Debating Club and soon became well known for her flowery eloquence—indeed she could spout oratory with the very best of them" (OHS yearbook, 1916, p. 53). Constance graduated from the University of Oklahoma (OU) in 1928 and immediately went to work for Twin State Oil in Tulsa. Ruth Sheldon wrote in *Scribner's Commentator* (1941, p. 31-32), "Constance Leatherock, paleontologist for Tidewater Oil Company, Tulsa, Oklahoma, spends more of her time at her microscope than any of the other women, as her work consists entirely of examining samples of all important wells drilled in Oklahoma. Tidewater depends upon her for its information regarding drilling discoveries in the State. Although she does most of the work in her office, on many occasions she spends long hours in the oil fields, watching the drilling of an important well to analyze the samples as they are brought up from the hole. The danger and hardships of spending time on a rig floor in all kinds of weather are considered so essentially a man's job that even oil men are surprised to see a woman quietly doing it as routine work."

Figure 19. Constance Leatherock at Oklahoma City (Central) High School where she could "debate with the best of them." (From Cardinal yearbook, 1916, p. 53.)

Six years later in 1934, she left Twin State Oil and began work for Superior Oil. In1936, Constance would work briefly with the U.S. Geological Survey (USGS) in Tulsa where she published with N. Wood Bass; then a year later, returned to the oil business with Tide Water Associated Oil Company. Constance traveled to the Panama Canal in 1937, but the impetus is not known— if the travel was for business or pleasure.

Ruth Sheldon, in her article "The Ladies Find Oil" provides some insight into the difficulty that women may have had finding and retaining employment as geologists. "The geological departments of schools and universities throughout the country graduate every year an increasing number of young women eager to find a place in the oil industry. Oil companies offer them little encouragement. Many accept positions as secretaries in geological departments, where their training makes them invaluable, but where there is no chance for advancement. Many resort to teaching. Some are lucky enough to become geologists with small independent oil companies." (Sheldon, 1941, p. 32)

Sometime before 1947, she went back to work with the USGS and moved to Billings, Montana, where both her professional and personal life changed significantly. She published on the Bighorn Dolomite, the Heath Shale, the Amsden Formation, subsurface stratigraphy of southeast Montana. She would also marry, at age 46, Ernest A. Nieschmidt, a widower who was a forestry and soil science professional with a 16-year-old son. Constance Leatherock Nieschmidt retired after 1958, possibly as late as the early 1960s.

Maria Frances Spencer (1907-2003)

Maria F. Spencer graduated with her B.A. from University of Oklahoma (OU) in 1928, her M.S. in 1930, and went to work for Superior Oil Company in Dallas, Texas (Fig. 20). In a 2015 interview, her Superior Oil colleague, Jerry Sides, related, "In 1930 Bill Keck, Sr., CEO of Superior Oil contacted the head of the OU geology department, Dr. V. B. Monnett, and said he wanted to hire their brightest student, particularly to work the Pennsylvanian carbonates in the Permian Basin. Monnett said, 'Well, what if the brightest student I have is a girl?' After gasping and pausing a bit, he took a deep breath and reportedly told Monnett that 'If she can work like a man, I will hire her!'"

Figure 20. Maria Spencer, as a geology student at the University of Oklahoma. (Photo: Sooner *yearbook, 1928, p. 53, Western History Collections, University of Oklahoma Libraries.)*

Maria was hired and moved to Tulsa with Superior in 1931, then to Oklahoma City in 1932, and finally, to Midland, Texas, in 1934. Jerry Sides, who was considerably younger than Maria, went to her for advice and counsel because she was the most respected and experienced hand in the Midland office.

Sides also remembered, "Maria did all of the usual duties geologists did in the early days—wellsitting, running samples on countless wildcats, developing prospects. At the time, Superior was the number one independent oil company in the country and they had their own company rigs. Geologists were expected to run samples and wellsit. For a woman, this would be an uncomfortable assignment as the men on the rig did not appreciate women 'invading' their space. The roughnecks would go out of their way to be vulgar and sexist. Marie was constantly given the difficult assignments and soon learned to handle herself around the roughnecks. An example was that the roughnecks would deliberately urinate off the rig floor when she was around. She took it in stride, had to do her 'business' out in the field with as much grace as possible and always managed. She gained Bill Keck Sr.'s total confidence and by 1936 was promoted to District Geologist [Maria was 29 years old]. While her regular job for 31 years was prospecting for oil and getting her wells drilled, he [Bill] also would assign her to take on new and difficult tasks and new ventures."

Ruth Sheldon writes in *Scribner's Commentator* (1941, p.31), "Maria Spencer, of the Superior Oil Company of California, is second in charge of their Midland, Texas, office. She not only follows the progress of every well drilled in West Texas and New Mexico, but it is through her research work that Superior knows where to drill its own wells. She is proud of the fact that she has saved her company great sums of money. On one occasion Superior wanted to lease all of Edward's Plateau in Texas, which covers about six counties, intending to spend half a million dollars in development. Miss Spencer advised against it stating that her findings did not indicate that oil would be found in commercial quantities. The Company fortunately took her advice, for since then other companies have drilled wells there, and all have been dry holes."

Sides told of Maria's travels when she worked in California for a while and often had to drive back and forth from Midland. This was before the interstate highway system and before cars were air-conditioned. She developed a travel technique driving at night and sleeping in a hotel in the day. Before leaving Midland, she would buy a 100-lb. block of ice and put it in the car to cool it. It was at least a two-night drive, so she would buy another block for the second night on the road.

Shortly after the end of WWII in 1946, Keck sent her to sit a well Superior was drilling in the Bahamas. Superior had developed a prospect and drilled a deep wildcat on the northern end of Andros Island. (Figs. 21a and 21b). Having no roads from Nassau to the wellsite, Maria took a boat every day to the north end of the island where the well was being drilled. Maria, in her report on the well, (Spencer, 1967) said, "The loss of circulation throughout the extremely porous section above 4200 feet retarded drilling operations. Caverns between 10,600 and 10,709 feet caused a prolonged fishing operation, and later forced abandonment of the test when approximately 8000 feet of drill pipe was lost in one of the caverns through a break in the 7-inch casing. No shows of oil and gas were found."

She was also involved in an Aero Magnetic survey of the islands and a marine gravity survey. The highlight of the assignment was being able to study living reefs (*Midland Reporter Telegram*, 2003).

Maria's next international assignment would take her from the Pleistocene carbonates of the Bahamas to the Devonian carbonates of Canada. Sides continued his discourse about Maria, "She moved to Calgary in 1949 to assist in opening an office for Superior's Canadian company."

Sides added, "Another of Maria's Superior assignments was to lead the exploration program in Oldham and nearby counties [in Texas] where Superior put together over about 600,000 acres. Much of the acreage was on the Matador Ranch that later the [well known West Texas]

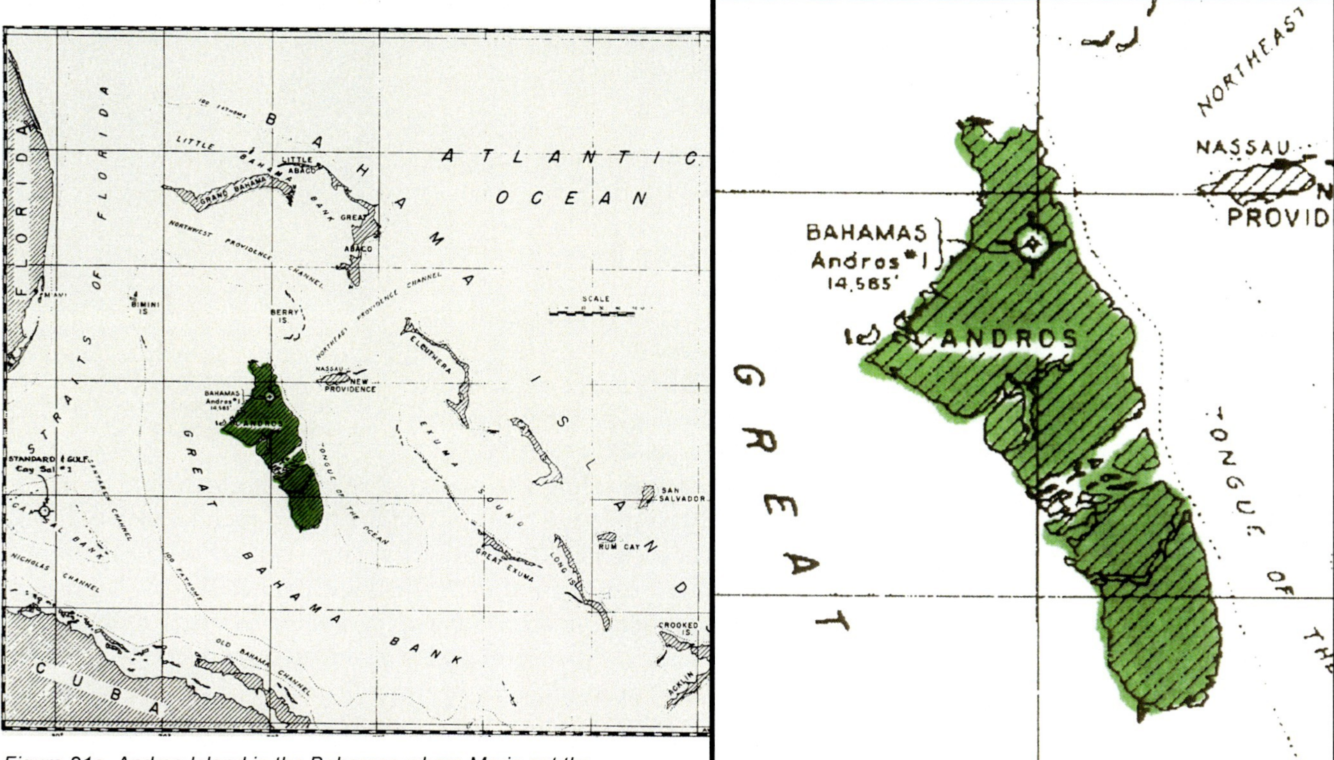

Figure 21a. Andros Island in the Bahamas where Maria sat the exploration well Superior drilled in 1949. The location was determined by its accessibility from the river; it was necessary to bring equipment by barge to the north end of the island where the "stratigraphic" test might encounter a complete geologic section. (From Spencer, 1967, p. 263-268.)

Figure 21b. Close-up of Figure 21a showing the location of the Superior Andros #1 on the north end of Andros Island. Drilled to 14,565 feet; it was a dry hole. Maria had to take a boat to the location every day because there were no roads. She spent a full year overseeing the operations.

Scharbauer family bought a portion of along the Canadian River. She was moved to Amarillo to run the project along with several other geologists to work for her. They drilled six or seven wildcats, took core, and ran a seismic program. All the wells were dry holes but they provided information toward a later productive prospect. Unfortunately, then, because Bill Keck Sr. died, and young 'playboy' Howard Keck (as described by Maria later) took over, Superior walked away from the deal."

Maria was confident that Bill Keck, Sr. would take care of her in her retirement; she had served him well and was loyal to the company, Sides recalled. When Keck, Sr. died, she continued to feel confident that she would always have a job with Superior, and likely, she would have if Bill Keck, Jr. had continued as the CEO. However, Howard Keck took over the company from his brother and summarily shut down many of the projects that brother, Bill Keck Jr., was pursuing, such as the Matador Ranch. Then, he let several of the key staff members go—offering a package, at first. Marie did not take the package because she wanted to continue to work and thought her record of success and loyalty would be recognized. It was not. Howard fired her and she was left without a package or a job at a very difficult time to get a new job (1961). She had been in exploration all her life, was 54 years old, and unable to find a new position with an oil company. She eventually found a job as an elementary school teacher and, then later, as a high school teacher, which she continued until retirement. She ended her days living off a small teacher's pension in Midland. A person known all her life as never saying a bad word about anyone, she was understandably bitter towards Howard Keck.

Figure 22. Maria Spencer in 1958. She lost her job when she was in her fifties and resorted to teaching to earn her living. (Photo: West Texas Geological Society Directory.*)*

In her spare time, Maria loved to tend to her flowers. She could be found in her yard on "I" street in Midland planting and growing beautiful flowers. She was also active in the League of Women Voters, the Daughters of the American Republic, American Association of University Women, and a Camera Club in Midland. She helped establish the now extensive geological branch of the Midland County Library. She was active in the West Texas Geological Society and received the Pioneer Award for 1991-92. She was a member of AAPG for 71 years (Fig. 22).

Mary Louise Rhodes (1916-1987)

Mary Louise Rhodes loved "kicking iron," as she described her wonderful days doing wellsite work (Fig. 23). Mary Louise fell in love with geology at the University of Missouri and acquired her B.S. in 1938 and master's in 1939. The time spent at field camp in Lander, Wyoming, was very special to her and cemented her dedication to a career in geology. Mary Louise found employment in the oil business only because of and during WWII. She started with the Standard Oil Company of Texas (later Chevron) in Houston and was soon transferred to Midland, Texas, with the production department. She examined well samples, constructed sample logs, and recommended development well locations, including the preparation of all the necessary subsurface maps and cross sections (Reese and Cheatham, 1988).

Figure 23. Mary Louise Rhodes at the University of Missouri where she fell in love with geology and acquired her B.S. (1938) and M.S. (1939). WWII provided an opportunity to enter the oil and gas business. (Photo: The Savitary yearbook, 1935, courtesy of Uni*versity of Missouri, MU Libraries, p. 94.)*

In 1946, immediately after the war, Mary Louise was transferred from production to exploration and she remained in exploration for the rest of her career. She worked in the Texas cities of Abilene, San Angelo, Amarillo, and Corpus Christi and in Denver, Colorado and became a senior stratigrapher for Chevron. Mary Louise's expertise was in carbonate stratigraphy and she was considered an outstanding scientist in that field. Donald Reese and Bruce Cheatham praised her highly for scientific contributions and her penchant for freely sharing her thoughts and ideas with colleagues and students.

When she retired, Mary Louise moved back to her beloved Midland, Texas, and continued her work with lifelong friend, John Emery Adams. Their paper, "Dolomitization by Seepage Refluxion" (Adams, J.E, and Rhodes, M.L, 1960) is considered a seminal publication on the topic. Their collaborations resulted in several joint papers and many contributions to students at the Permian Basin Graduate Center (PBGC). Mary Louise taught several classes at the Permian Basin Graduate Center in the late 1970s.

Figure 24. Mary Louise Rhodes, who loved "kicking iron" or sitting on wells; she was an Honorary Member in the Permian Basin SEPM. (Photo: Reese and Cheatham, 1988, p. 92.)

Jerry Sides of Midland remembers that "Mary Louise was a favorite of everyone. She had a very effervescent personality and worked hard for the West Texas Geological Society (WTGS), especially with field trips and the *Oil and Gas Field* [in West Texas] *Volumes*." The field trip publications and *Oil and Gas Volumes* are indispensable references for anyone working conventional plays of the Permian Basin. She was awarded Honorary Life Membership in the Permian Basin Section of SEPM in 1978 and, also, from the West Texas Geological Society in 1978.

Mary was a world traveler, enjoying global travels as well as her special love of the Guadalupe Mountains and Big Bend in Texas (Fig. 24). She was an AAPG member for 44 years.

Margaret Delano Binkley Pack (1917-1995)

Margaret "Mickey" Delano was born in Miami, Arizona, and loved visiting oil and mining camps with her Irish immigrant father, who was a site manager. Much of her early schooling was in Peru (when she was five and again when she was eleven) because her father was assigned there. Later, she spent her freshman year in high school in Peru. As a result, she was fluent in Spanish. Her father was also a collector of ore samples and minerals and she became fascinated. She liked to know the "what, how, and where" of things.

Margaret Delano Binkley graduated from University of California Berkeley in 1938 (Fig. 25); she was married to fellow geologist, William Binkley, while she was still in college. He found a job with Royal Dutch Shell in the Dutch East Indies, and they were based there in 1940 when WWII started. They quickly returned to California with their one-year-old daughter, Mary.

Her husband volunteered for the Army Air Corps and headed to the South Pacific. Mickey went to work for Standard Oil in Taft, California, but had to quit when she contracted Valley Fever. After she recovered, she heard the California Division of Oil and Gas was looking for an inspector for their Taft office. After interviewing, she was told she could have the job if she could pass an examination. It was fortunate she had taken some petroleum engineering courses. She later joked that with the WWII shortage of geologists, probably a green gorilla could pass the test. Mickey passed and became the first woman in the Division doing petroleum geology (Rintoul, 1990).

Figure 25. Margaret Delano Binkley, married during university years, at the University of California Berkeley. (Photo: Courtesy of Blue and Gold *yearbook, 1938, p. 140, University of California, Berkeley.)*

But the war changed the job considerably. The Petroleum Administration for Defense became the Petroleum Administration for War (where pioneer Linda Green Miller served during the war) and the oil business was made over to serve the war efforts. One of the concepts introduced was "maximum efficient rates" (MER) for oil production, and new rates were established. The Conservation Committee of California Oil Producers got busy classifying the pools in the state to define their "maximum efficient" production rate. When Mickey joined the Division in 1943. Her duties as an inspector involved oversight of drilling operations ensuring that wells were drilled, completed, and abandoned according to state regulations. She witnessed the cementing of surface casing and downhole cement squeeze jobs to prevent contamination of oil, gas, and water sands. She also witnessed water shut-off tests, the placement of abandonment plugs in wells, and inspected blowout prevention equipment.

Mickey was a tiny woman, only five feet one or two inches tall and small-framed in those days. Because she worked for the state, she found the stringent rules that governed how long women could work did not apply to her and that, like the working men, she worked much longer hours. The 40-hour week was somewhat academic and she often found herself working closer to 80 hours (Rintoul, 1990).

In her interview with Rintoul, Mickey explained what it was like to be in what had, up to then, always been a man's world, "I think what made it possible for me was that I was anxious to succeed and people were very helpful. And the men in the oil fields were just kind people. They were just good ... But, of course, it was a fortuitous time to break into the field. My husband was overseas. Everyone felt it was important to get on with the war. There was a manpower shortage, and it was clear I wasn't taking anybody's job."

Her son, Dr. Daniel Binkley, of Honolulu, Hawaii, recalls that she was very fortunate the men she worked with took on a protective role and tried to watch out for her amongst the rough and tough personnel. But, she was cautious and always carried a .32-caliber pistol with her on her solitary journeys. Mickey shared her perspective of working in the field: "Few really young men worked in the oil fields then. They were in the armed services or headed for greener pastures in shipyards or in other wartime projects. The oilfield men I dealt with [were all older and] were a special kind of people with a special kind of Pride. Some had little formal education. But you don't work your way up from rig hand, to driller, to toolpusher, to drilling foreman or drilling superintendent or to other positions of trust by being behind the door when God passes out brains.

"Oilmen preferred to help people who make an effort to help themselves. They worked hard and expected other people to do the same. They had a strong set of moral values and their own rules of acceptable behavior. But, they were kind. They could have run me off, and they knew it. But they didn't.

"I don't think being a woman was an advantage. Once the men were sure it wouldn't hurt my feelings, they'd say things like, 'We don't approve of women working, and we don't approve of women working in the oil fields, but you're different.' But of course, I wasn't different. They just knew me; that was all. Eventually, I think we just took each other for granted. I thoroughly enjoyed those days. They were a marvelous experience." (Rintoul, 1990)

Mickey met few other women professionally. She said, "During the war some oil companies hired women as pumpers, gaugers and for other [production] jobs traditionally held by men. In addition, I knew one other female geologist nearby, a woman from Berkeley who worked for a major oil company, but I never ran into her in the field."

The same year Mickey joined the Division's Taft office, notices to drill new wells in District 4 reached an all-time high with 849 new notices compared with 416 in 1942. Most of the activity took place in the Midway-Sunset and South Belridge fields, which fell within the jurisdiction of the Taft office. Abandonments, too, almost doubled the preceding year, representing an effort to salvage steel casing for use in drilling more wells. "I don't think I've ever worked as hard. And we were so busy. We had about 40 rigs drilling, 17 in Elk Hills alone." The West Side of the district was a big area. It'd be nothing unusual to make two or three trips to Elk Hills, and probably go to Belridge or Lost Hills and all around in one day. "Of course, there was nobody on the road except you and a few others ...."

To get the field experience she acquired during the war, she reflected, would have taken perhaps 10 years under other circumstances, "We had so many companies drilling, using every type of rig including cable tools. I was on all of them, many times. We just chased so many holes. It isn't that I was all that smart. But everyone was very helpful, and I did work hard. It was fun."

While most of the wells that were drilled in the Taft area were development wells, at least one was an exploratory well that commanded some attention. California took the record for the world's depth away from Texas (15,279 feet) by drilling to a depth of 16,246 feet near the South Coles Levee field. Unfortunately, it was a dry hole.

When the war ended in 1945, California had produced one billion barrels of oil for the war effort, increasing production from about 130 million barrels in 1941 to 328 million barrels in 1945 (Rintoul, 1990).

Mickey's son, Daniel, recalls many nights that he and his older sister, Mary, traveled out to well locations, especially in the Kettleman Hills, with their mother as she monitored and supervised activities. He confessed that having a mother so involved in her career set him apart from many of his school mates of the 1950s. He recognized that at that time moms were "supposed to" put their kids and homes first, not careers. His mother did not choose to live like that and was a far cry from the "typical mother." One consolation for him and Mary occurred in those early days of television. Daniel was at a friend's house watching TV (his mom and dad refused to have one in the house) and a program came on about a recent earthquake and there was his mother. On TV! Being interviewed for her geologic expertise. To have a mother on TV was astonishing and, suddenly, his school mates gained a new appreciation for him. It was heightened even further when he went to the Saturday movies with friends and the "newsreel" played—there, again, was his mother on screen. No one else had a mother that was on TV or the movie theater. He was a star with the other kids, at least, for a while. (Fig. 26)

Figure 26. Margaret Binkley Pack, exhaustingly, performed her regulatory duties overseeing the plethora of drilling in California during WWII. She often took her children with her to the drill sites. Subsequently, she worked for independent oil companies and, finally, in Washington, D.C., she worked for the IRS, specializing in oil and gas issues. (Photo: Daniel Binkley, Honolulu, Hawaii.)

Mickey and her husband were often separated by their job locations and their marriage ended in divorce in 1963. For a while, she continued her career as a petroleum geologist and, before leaving the Taft Division, she supervised the drilling of a borehole for the Atomic Energy Commission (AEC) in Nevada. In 1953, she left the Taft Division and joined Oceanic Oil Company in Bakersfield. In 1966, she married geologist Phillip Pack, and her career took several new turns as they moved about, accommodating both careers. She worked with the AEC in New Mexico and in Denver when Phillip's career led them to those locations. His final job was in Washington, D.C. where she found interesting employment with the IRS. According to her son, Daniel, her oil and gas experience placed her in the unique position of being the go-to expert on tax returns that declared oil and gas depletions and other production tax claims.

Daniel, thinking of his mother's complete dedication to her profession, muses that there could not be many female geologists who had also married two brilliant male geologists. Margaret Delano Binkley Pack was a member of AAPG for 56 years.

Ruth Young Lebow (1919-2007)

Ruth Lebow was hired for her first job by Richfield in 1941, winning out over several male applicants, which apparently rankled them a bit (personal communication, Philip Lebow). Ruth earned her bachelor's and master's degrees from the University of Chicago (1940, 1941). (Fig. 27) While a student at Chicago, she had a fascinating non-geology project the summer of 1938. She worked on the original "sleep study" conducted in Mammoth Cave in Kentucky by University of Chicago physiology professor, Nathaniel Kleitman. She tracked the data on his and a colleague's experiences for 30 days in the dark in the cave.

Figure 27. Ruth Young in geology field Camp, Baraboo, Wisconsin, 1939. (Photo: Janet Lebow Fahey.)

She left Richfield before 1943 and worked for the U. S. Geological Survey briefly when she married Myer Lebow. The Lebow family in Los Angeles had a small oil and gas company—Lebow-McNee Oil Company (later Lebow Oil Company). Her husband was a petroleum engineer and eventually took over the company from his father. Ruth did the wellsite and geologic work for the company for decades (Fig. 28).

Her children, Janet Lebow Fahey and Philip Lebow, remember Ruth often taking them with her throughout their childhoods to the drilling sites while she evaluated the pay zones, looked at samples, and calculated the pay from electric logs. Janet and Philip loved playing in and around the mud pits and the rig (Fig. 29). Phil recalls going out about once a week to various drill sites during what was usually a four-month drilling program and remembers sleeping on the back seat of the car many of those nights. One night, he woke up and looked out the window to see the glowing eyes of a huge jackrabbit staring at him. Then, he noticed a drove of additional jackrabbits around the car. It was surreal to be surrounded by what, as a young boy, he thought of as "not-so-friendly" jackrabbits.

Figure 28. A budding scientist, Ruth Young, age 15 circa 1934. She became the geologist and wellsite supervisor for Lebow Oil Company. (Photo: Janet Lebow Fahey.)

Ruth talked to her kids about what she was doing geologically and what she was seeing in the samples. Phil remembers her estimates of where they would pierce the anticlines and faults. When she found a well to be "wet" and not a producer, she would describe it as "a long skinny swimming pool."

The wellsite terminology became so familiar that, "by the time I was an early teen, I could discuss drilling, drilling rigs, drill bits from Hughes and others, drill pipe, surface pipe, cellars, casing, drilling muds, mud pumps, and sumps. I could tell you how drilling proceeded, how the drill table, kelly, and chain tongs all worked, how they were powered, and what their dangers were (broken pipe, stuck pipe, and fishing tools). I had seen blowout valves, blowout preventers, and casing collars up close. I could also discuss from firsthand experience, cementing, gravel packers and packing, pumps, pumping units, down hole pumps, tubing, sucker rods, rod boxes, perforators, and wells sanding up and going to water. And I knew about, and had been sprayed with casing head gas, light gravity oil, heavy gravity oil, and thick paraffin oils! Once, I was dragooned into going into a crude oil storage tank (emptied, mostly) to pull out defective heating coils."

Figure 29. Young Philip Lebow, 1953, not enjoying the sounds on the wellsite as he sits on drill pipe in southern California. (Photo: Janet Lebow Fahey.)

Phil continues, "The company activities dominated dinner table discussion and expanded to the more geological oriented topics of rocks, layers, shales (especially), and crust deformation—my mom's special favorites. Most vacations were driving trips, where we went to see "natural wonders," which were mostly rock formations and mountains of different rock types that my mother found interesting. She would rhapsodize about folding and faults revealed in highway rock cuts. If there was one drawback to her enthusiasm it was that she was extremely competitive about her academic specialty, even with me, a young kid. She, too often, would make it a point to illustrate how little I knew about her favorite topic or how superior her own knowledge was to my own. This drove me from any interest in what her passions about petroleum and the earth sciences were. But she did instill in me a love for nature and animal life, while I had to leave her to her own enjoyments and find other areas where I could grow my own interests. Later, when she taught geology and earth sciences in Junior High School, and Junior College, her interests in sea floor drilling expanded into oceanography, I once again became interested in her passions for the seas, sea life, and to an extent, the geology of the sea floor and continental drift. Over time she became more of a naturalist."

Philip paints other lesser known aspects of Ruth. She was a huge fan of the arts—opera, where she participated as an amateur opera singer herself; ballet; classical music; and languages (she and daughter Janet would speak to each other in French a good deal of the time). She was an exceptional cook and entertainer. He recalls having people like Pete Seeger and Lee Marvin over for dinner and entertainment. She made lasagna while Myer made martinis and they would play "drunken charades."

When Phil was a young man, he made his own contribution to their entertainment. He had made a batch of homemade beer and knew he had accidentally spilled too much sugar into the brew, causing it to have a much higher alcohol content than usual. He came into the house late one night and realized Ruth had been serving his brew to her faculty colleagues when he saw an Irish friend standing on the kitchen table singing Irish ballads.

Philip and Janet also had many hours with their father in the oil patch. Janet remembers when her resourceful father was getting ready to drill, he would head to Taft, California, where Standard Oil of California was located and visit the local bars to find roughnecks for his projects.

When Myer died in 1982, far too young, Ruth ran the company and eventually had to deal with the depletion of the wells and the new Environmental Protection Agency (EPA) regulations for plugging, which required almost a quarter of a million dollars per well. At this time, she and Philip became much closer; she came to rely on him to negotiate with all the aspects toward finding a new owner for the company. While she was a strong and independent woman and had excellent relationships with their operations people in Bakersfield and Torrance, she was surprisingly more intimidated by men outside her circle, especially men who bullied, Philip remembered. She leaned on him greatly in those years to act as a go-between.

Figure 30. Ruth Lebow with her Emmy Award in 1980 for the documentary Oceana. *(Photo: Janet Lebow Fahey.)*

In her later years, she became much more involved in education and taught math and science at Pierce College. Eventually, she was teaching geological courses at UCLA and, during this time, she produced two educational videos for television, *Oceana* and *The Earth Revealed*. She won an Emmy for Oceana in 1980, the documentary where her daughter, Janet, worked with her and both enjoyed its success (Fig. 30). Along with the videos, she created and provided workbooks and exams. She taught courses in geology for both UCLA and the Los Angeles Natural History Museum and Page Museum, covering not only Southern California but, also, Hawaii, Alaska, and Mexico. Janet says that her mother inspired her to pursue a career in science and she acquired a degree in biology and went on for her PhD, specializing in ichthyology. Janet is retired from a career where she consulted widely on environmental issues and muses about her *first job* being at the Sewage Treatment Plant in Taft, California—full circle back to the family roots.

Ruth Lebow was a member of AAPG for 17 years and a registered geologist in the state of California.

Chapter 5: Sources and References

Adams, J. E., and M. L. Rhodes. 1960. "Dolomitization by Seepage Refluxion." *AAPG Bulletin,* vol. 44, no. 12, pp. 1912-1920.

Baars, D. L., W. Lynn Watney, Don W. Steeples, and Erling A. Brostuen. *Figure 25. Diagram of drill bits and drilling rig.* 2001. Photograph. Petroleum: a primer for Kansas. Kansas Geological Survey, Lawrence, Kansas. http://www.kgs.ku.edu/Publications/Oil/primer12.html. Accessed 01/15/2017.

Binkley, Dr. Daniel, Honolulu, Hawaii, son of Margaret Binkley Pack. Personal communication with Robbie Gries, November 12, 2016; source of photograph of Margaret Binkley Pack.

Bitgood, Charles "Chuck" Decker, Denver, Colorado, son of Ellen Posey Bitgood. Personal communication with Robbie Gries, March 25, 2015 through December 16, 2016; source of photographs of Ellen Posey Bitgood Roblin.

Fahey, Janet Lebow, Altadena, California, daughter of Ruth Lebow. Personal communication with Robbie Gries, July 4, 2016 through October 1, 2016; source of photographs for Ruth Lebow.

Hall, Dollie Radler. 1965. "Women in Exploration: Abstract." *Tulsa Geological Society Digest*, vol. 33, pp. 295-298.

Kansas Geological Survey, diagram of drill bits and drilling rig: http://www.kgs.ku.edu/Publications/Oil/primer12.html, accessed 1/15/2017.

Lebow, Philip, Los Angeles, California, son of Ruth Lebow. Personal communication with Robbie Gries, October 13, 2016.

Lebow, Ruth Y. 1992. "Study Guide for Earth Revealed, Introductory Geology." Earth Revealed is a television-based course produced by the *Southern California Consortium*. Copyright by The Corporation for Community College Television and the Corporation for Public Broadcasting.

Lebow, Ruth, 1980, "Oceanus: The Marine Environment, Study Guide." Copyright by Los Angeles County Superintendent of Schools. Prepared for *INTELECOM Intelligent Communications*, as a companion for the Emmy Award-winning educational television series *Oceanus*. Copyright by Corporation for Community College Television. Published by Wadsworth Publishing Company, Belmont, CA 94002.

Lubbock Evening Journal. "Wichita Falls Woman Gets Kick Out of Seeing Oil Well 'Come In.'" Photograph. 11 March, 1953. p. 21.

Midland Reporter Telegram. "Maria Frances Spencer." Obituary. March 27, 2003.

Oklahoma City (Central) High School. *Constance Leatherock.* 1916. Photograph. *The Cardinal* yearbook. Oklahoma City, Oklahoma. p 53.

Purcell, John H. 1952. "She's Got Rocks in Her Head, One of the Smartest Women in Texas." *Earth Scientist.* Cities Service, April Issue, p. 22-23.

Reese, Donald L., and Bruce N. Cheatham. 1988. "Mary Louise Rhodes Memorial." *AAPG Bulletin*, vol. 72, no. 1, pp. 92-93.

Rintoul, William. 1990. *Drilling Through Time: 75 years with California's Division of Oil and Gas.* Sacramento, Calif.: Department of Conservation Division of Oil and Gas, 1990. 178 pp.

Sheldon, Ruth. 1941. "The Ladies Find Oil." *Scribner's Commentator*, vol. 10, pp. 28-32.

Sides, Jerry, Midland, Texas. Personal communication with Robbie Gries, November 2015.

Spencer, Maria. 1967. "GEOLOGICAL NOTES: Bahamas Deep Test." *AAPG Bulletin*, vol. 51, pp. 263-268.

University of California Berkeley, *Margaret Delano Binkley*, 1938. Photograph. *Blue and Gold* yearbook, p. 140, with permission of UC Berkeley.

University of Missouri. *Mary Louise Rhodes*. 1935. Photograph, *The Savitary* yearbook, p. 94,ith permission of University of Missouri.

University of Oklahoma. *Maria Spencer.* 1928. Photograph. *Sooner* yearbook, p. 53. Western History Collections, University of Oklahoma Libraries, Norman, Oklahoma.

West Texas Geological Society. *Maria Spencer.* 1958. Photograph. *WTGS Directory.* Midland, Texas.

Mrs. Mattie M. Lair, Pumper on the Mullen Lease at Hamilton, for Roxana Petroleum, March, 1918, during WWI. (Photo: Roxoleum, *v. 1, no. 3., p. 9. DeGolyer Library, Southern Methodist University, Dallas, Texas.)*

Chapter 6

Julia Anna Gardner (1882-1960)

The First Oil and Gas Biostratigrapher and a War Heroine

Julia Anna Gardner was a remarkable woman, not only for being an avid scientist, doing geologic field work *on her own* along the U.S. Atlantic Coast, Gulf Coast, Texas interior, and in Mexico, but also, for actively participating in WWI and WWII. Her AAPG memorial by U.S. Geological Survey (U.S.G.S.) colleague, A. Nelson Sayre, describes her contributions to be of "inestimable value to all geologists interested in the development of the mineral and human resources of the Atlantic and Gulf Coastal Plains; a host of friends and admirers from all walks of life; and an example of perseverance and courage, tempered by kindliness, that is rarely equaled (Sayre, 1961)."

Julia Anna Gardner spent her early years in South Dakota as an only child with a single mom; her father died when she was ten years old. At 14, she moved with her mother to Massachusetts where she attended and graduated from the prestigious Drury Academy. She wisely chose to attend Bryn Mawr College where she studied under the legendary Frances Bascom and achieved her bachelor's and master's degrees by 1907. (Fig. 1)

Figure 1. Julia Anna Gardner, approximately 1900, seated on the ground with her favorite cousin Winnie Brackett (Married name: Considine) and Julia's mother, also "Julia Gardner," is seated to the right. Behind Mrs. Gardner is Julia's Aunt, Ella Bates Brackett with, likely, her twin daughters, Carrie and Mary Brackett on either side. Julie left a third of her estate to her niece Winnie. (Photo: Barry Considine, Missoula, Montana.)

Following Bascom's lead, Julia went to Johns Hopkins for her PhD in 1911. She was the first woman "regularly" admitted to the Department of Geology to receive her PhD;

Figure 2. Julia Anna Gardner, possibly in 1915, when she joined the U. S. National Museum in Washington, D.C. (Photo: Dutro, 2004, p. 179.)

Bascom's admission was "conditional" including the stipulation that she sit in a corner behind a screen to not disturb the men. After receiving her degree, Julia remained in Baltimore to work at Johns Hopkins and the Maryland Geological Survey on molluscan faunas of the Upper Cretaceous (Molluscan faunas are basically clams and snails in the fossil record). Her time there resulted in her first highly touted publications.

Julia continued her coastal studies with the U.S. National Museum under contract to the U.S. Geological Survey between 1915 and WWI. (Fig. 2) She used molluscan fauna for biostratigraphy. (Biostratigraphy is the art and science of identifying which fossils – biological evidence of life – are present in various strata or rock layers. These correlations of fossils with rock layers allow for geologists to relate strata all over the world to each other.) The time-life span of a mollusk is short enough in geological time, counted in millions of years, that one particular mollusk identified in a layer of rock will likely not be found in rocks above or below that layer but can be correlated with rocks tens of miles, hundreds of miles, away as the "same age."

World War I Impels Her to France

Figure 3. Nurses helping on the front line in France attending to the thousands of wounded WWI. (Photo: Wilson, H. W. and J. A. Hammerton, eds., 1915).

As dedicated as she was to her geology, with the onset of WWI, "She was horrified by the thought of the terrible waste of life and the destruction which seemed to her so useless. She felt that in some way she must make a personal sacrifice to help alleviate the suffering of the millions of people who were caught up in this disaster which had engulfed all of Europe" (Ladd, 1962).

Following her heart, she joined the Red Cross in 1917 at age 32 and was in France before the end of the year. (Fig. 3) At first, she worked with the American Canteen Service and, later, would work as an auxiliary nurse with the ambulance service and in the hospitals. (Fig. 4) Harry S. Ladd, a career USGS geologist who worked with Julia and wrote her AAPG memorial, added, "It was nigh impossible to make Julia talk about her war experiences, although once, when pressed, she did admit that her Unit was under fire and that on one occasion a bullet did land beneath the cot she occupied."

Figure 4. Typical American Field Service ambulance used on the Front in WWI France where Julia Gardner volunteered. (Photo: http://www.mtfca.com/discus/messages/331880/357183.html?1366579105, accessed 1/12/2017.)

"Years later in 1931, C. W. Merriam went to France to do some geological work. He carried a letter of introduction from Julia Gardner addressed to a M. Laire, an archeologist and highly respected citizen in the once war-torn town of Epernay. Merriam was enthusiastically received when Julia Gardner's letter was presented. There was a virtual parade and a reception with some of the participants in uniform. Miss Gardner's war services were well remembered" (Ladd, 1962).

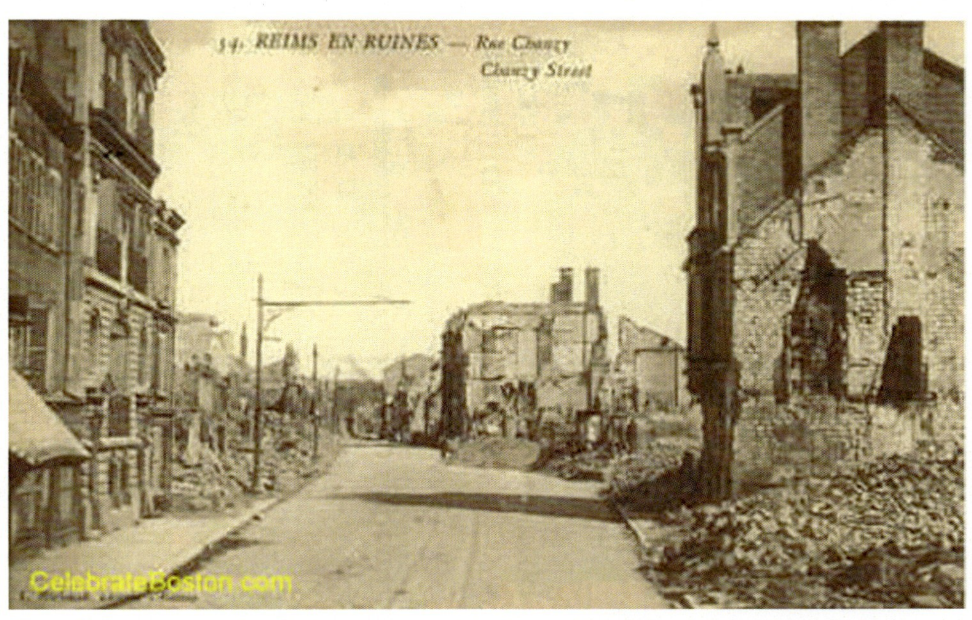

Figure 5. Postcard showing Rheims after more bombing in WWI where Julia was injured after the war. (Photo: http://www.celebrateboston.com/postcard/ww1-destruction.htm, accessed 1/12/2017.)

Sayre said, "Julia Gardner loved people and with rare tact and skill was able to make them talk about themselves, their families, and their activities, but she rarely volunteered any information about herself or her achievements. This was particularly true of her war experience. Almost the only information on this part of her life is taken from her diary in which she wrote of her day-to-day activities. However, it is clear that she was no rear-area non-combatant, but was often in or near the front lines where the going was rough. After the Armistice, she worked with American Friends Service in the devastated areas of France until 1919, when she was hospitalized in Rheims injured in the line of duty ... her small unit was decorated by the French Government for its service with distinction and valor." (Fig. 5)

Julia's priceless diaries of her time in France have been lost or destroyed. Reference is made to their whereabouts at the Smithsonian archives, which places them in "Box 1," but they are missing.

However, an excerpt from another nurse's diary describing her experience on the front during WWI can illustrate the profound existence these volunteers survived.

> *Front Belge, Oct 7 Don't worry if you don't hear from me Darlings – This offensive is taking up all our time. I've never seen anything like it since the beginning of the war. Ambulances for miles almost touching each other, a continual stream. Hundreds come in and are operated on and are sent on every hour. I've never seen such wounds and so many deaths. Dying on the stretchers before they can be attended to. The mud is so impossible. Food had to be gotten to the troops by airmen and some of the wounded lay on their [sic] 4 or 5 days before an ambulance could get to them. Sometimes the men get stuck waist deep in the mud and it is impossible to get them out food has to be taken to them for a day or two if they haven't died from exposure in the mean time and then sometimes they are shot to get them out of their misery. It seems incredible but this mud is almost like quicksand - it clings and sucks down so. Went into Ypres yesterday the first time I've been outside the sheds and operating room for 3 weeks. So beautiful and so sad - full of soldiers and [illegible] very picturesque there lovely old ruins - but breaks your heart. Had tea on the ramparts where so much blood has been shed. Only an occasional shell going over as a reminder the war was still on. The ramparts look rather like the palisades up the Hudson. Went to the top of Mt. Kimmel too - it was clear enough to see miles – Lille - and lots of places. The end prob[ably] nearer but not too soon as they seem to think I'm afraid. We are advancing to Poelcappell at present - man and mud and blackened tree trunks it still gets shelled heavily so a gay life is ahead of us. I wish I'd been at your dinner party. Vinton wrote me about it. Tell her to please send me some records she got them but found that they had to be sent via Red X. Send them to me c/o" (Hancock, 1918).*

Julia Returns to her Career in Geology

Figure 6. The hazards of driving in Florida in the 1920s. (Photo: Florida Memory, State Library and Archives, Florida photogravic collection, John Kunkel Small Collection, #SMX0106 .)

Sayre (p. 1420) continues discussing Julia's geologic career history: "Miss Gardner, after her return to the States, joined the U.S. Geological Survey and resumed her studies of the Coastal Plain ... all of her work concerned with the Tertiary beds ... Virginia and North Carolina ... Florida. (Fig. 6) ... westward to the Mississippi Embayment and thence westward into Texas ... Although the fauna was much more limited, she covered it with her usual thoroughness. *Her studies were aided by the loan of fossil collections and maps from practically all the oil companies in Texas* [emphasis by the author]. She worked out the stratigraphy and showed the correlations of the Midway [Formation] with rocks of similar age, both in this country and abroad. Finally, Miss Gardner's work took her across the Rio Grande Embayment into Mexico where, with the aid of hundreds of collections from oil geologists and a grant from the Geological Society of America, she could correlate the Tertiary faunas of northern Mexico with other Gulf Coast faunas, despite the major facies change caused by the Rio Grande Embayment" (Sayre, 1961).

Sayre comments further on Julia's field work capabilities: "In the field, she usually traveled alone. If there were no hotel accommodations she stayed at the nearest farmhouse, and more than once when she was out in the boondocks at nightfall she slept in her car which, she drove with more daring than skill, although she always seemed to get through. She seemed to be almost without the sense of fear." [For Julia's account of her early field work, her 1940 description is included.]

Julia Gardner was a key biostratigrapher for the oil and gas business from 1924 up to WWII (1941). Biostratigraphy for oil and gas exploration means using fossils to determine the geologic age of a rock formation and to correlate them with rock outcropping or wells drilled some distance away. Geologists looking for oil in similar rocks to those Julia was mapping, had only rock descriptions to correlate, and because rocks can change their character laterally, this commonly failed to work for them. Using fossils or biostratigraphy to identify what layer was being drilled, oil companies would know to continue to drill deeper to find the correlative "pay" zone, or would need to abandon the well, knowing that the wildcat well did not have an oil reservoir present in that location. This was a crucial time in oil and gas exploration when micropaleontology, electric logs, and seismic tools were not developed or available for these purposes; Julia became a profound contributor to the success of untold numbers of companies.

In 1920, Sidney Powers sent fossil samples from a salt dome quarry to Dr. L. W. Stephenson at the Smithsonian Institute, Washington, D.C. for identification. The immediate response Powers received was that Miss Julia Gardner was assigned to examine them and he was sending Sidney her results. The relationship between Amerada and the National Museum had been forged by Everett DeGolyer in 1912 when he sent samples from his work in Mexico to Dr. Dall in Washington, D.C. for identification and for their "mutual benefit." Eight years later in 1920, after DeGolyer had formed Amerada Petroleum, his chief geologist, Sidney Powers, took advantage of this relationship and sent samples from Louisiana and Texas to Stephenson for identification (Julia Gardner correspondence, Smithsonian Institute).

Powers, happy with the work done by Julia, whom he almost always addressed as "My Dear Miss Gardner," recommended to a great number of geologists that they consult with and take advantage of Julia's expertise (Fig. 7). The relationships he cultivated lasted well beyond his shortened life (he died in 1932) into the late 1940s when other tools for biostratigraphy became the *modus operandi*. Powers, too, often opened doors for Julia, recommending oil and gas people for her to visit when she was doing fieldwork in Louisiana and Texas. She frequently met these men in the field or joined them on a field trip. (Fig. 8)

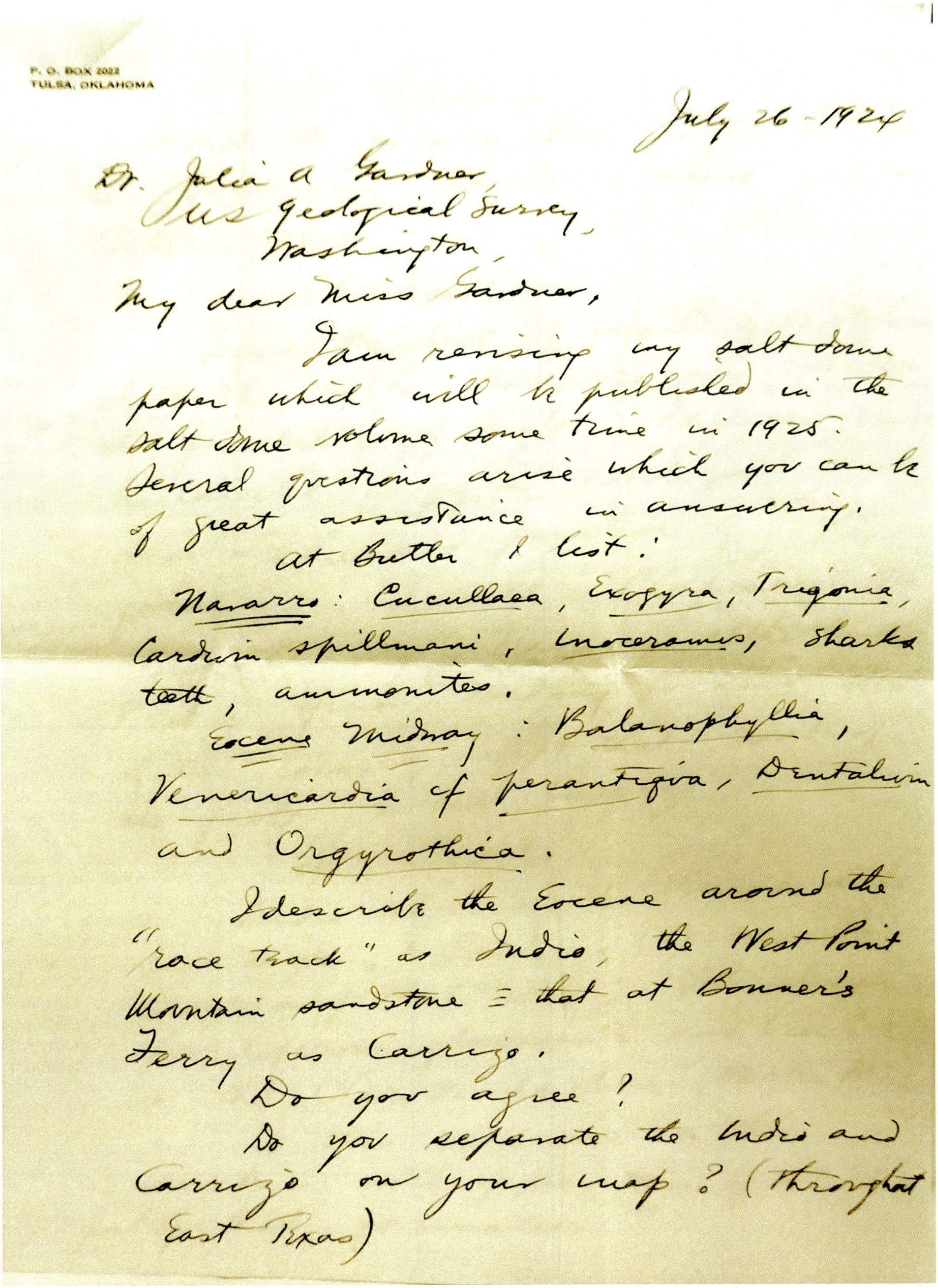

P. O. BOX 2022
TULSA, OKLAHOMA

July 26 - 1924

Dr. Julia A Gardner
US Geological Survey,
Washington,

My dear Miss Gardner,

I am revising my salt dome paper which will be published in the salt dome volume some time in 1925. Several questions arise which you can be of great assistance in answering.

At Butler I list:

Navarro: Cucullaea, Exogyra, Trigonia, Cardium spillmani, Inoceramus, Sharks teeth, ammonites.

Eocene Midway: Balanophyllia, Venericardia cf perantigua, Dentalium and Orgyrothica.

I describe the Eocene around the "race track" as Indio, the West Point Mountain sandstone = that at Bonner's Ferry as Carrizo.

Do you agree?

Do you separate the Indio and Carrizo on your map? (throughout East Texas)

Figure 7. 1924 letter from Sidney Powers to Julia Gardner. (From Julia Gardner archives, Smithsonian Institution Archives, RU 73, Box 12, Washington, D.C.)

Figure 8. Julia joins oil men in the field, 1924. Note her hand lens in her shirt pocket. Top: L. P. Teas, H. J. Howe, Julia Gardner, W. Ray? Young, M. C. Lucky, Bottom: W. E. Howe, J. P. D. Hull, J. W. Bostick, W. C. Spencer. Southwest Texas Geological Society (SWTGS) field trip, Arkadelphia, Hempstead County, Arkansas. (Photo: J. P. D. 'Joe" Hull, Jr., Denver, Colorado.).

Powers' initial request to examine salt dome samples was the beginning of 20 years of intense work on Julia's part, identifying, developing correlations, and generally assisting oil and gas companies in their exploration efforts. Julia Gardner's correspondence that has been preserved at the Smithsonian indicates she performed identification work for at least 60 companies and more than 20 consultants.

Insight into the heavy competition between some of these companies for their biostratigraphic correlations is illustrated by an excerpt of correspondence from William A. Baker, Jr., of Compañia de Petroleo Mercedes, S.A., in December, 1927 (Gardner correspondence, Smithsonian Institute).

Companies that accessed Gardner's expertise included Amerada Petroleum Corporation, Compañia Mexicana de Petroleo "El Aguila" S. A., American Texas Oil Company, Arkansas Natural Gas Corporation, Atlantic Oil Producing Company, Bureau of Economic Geology, Caracas Petroleum Corporation, Compañia de Petroleo Mercedes, Compañia Petrolera Titania, S. A., Conroe Drillers Incorporated, Continental Oil Company of Mexico, S. A., Dixie Oil Company, Gulf Production Company, Huesteca Petroleum Co., Humble Oil & Refining Company, Louisiana Oil Refining Corporation, Magnolia Petroleum Company, Mid-Kansas Oil and Gas Company, Nueces Royalty Company, Peninsular Oil and Refining Company, Pure Oil Company, The Texas Co., Rio Bravo Oil Co., Rycade Oil Corporation, Shell Petroleum Corporation, Sheppard Mound Development Co., The California Company, United Gas System, United North and South Oil Company, Inc. and Wellington Oil Company.

"Dr. Gardner, I am going to request you to please consider any remarks which I made to you or which Dr. Reeside discussed with you relative to Dr. Cushman as strictly confidential ... We have reason to feel safe in saying or rather discussing our ideas and problems with you folks on the Survey, where we would not consider a similar discussion with the geological department of any of the oil companies. You people at the Survey have always been so generous in offering us your assistance when called upon, that I felt it my duty to hint to you the probability that Dr. Cushman's present ideas on the Alazar and Velasco formations are not considered by us as being correct ... whereas we agree with yourself, Drs. Vaughan and Wold that its age is clearly Vicksburg.

"As regards Dr. Cushman's work on the Velasco (uppermost Cretaceous?) Formations. This work was done for the . The Marland had hopes of locating structures by drilling shallow [holes] in the Velasco—which covers the surface of a greater part of their Mexican holdings. Naturally the Marland desired to keep the results of their work on the Velasco as [confidential]. Dr. Cushman, however, claimed that he could publish the results of his studies on the Velasco by the agreement entered into with the Marland. Apparently, therefore, the only way in which the Marland could protect their work was to intentionally garble the well samples sent to Cushman so that what he published would not assist compeditory [sic] oil companies. Cushman was not to know of this. It was told to me in return for a favor done for the Marland. ... Where pure science meets business competition contamination sometimes enters in."

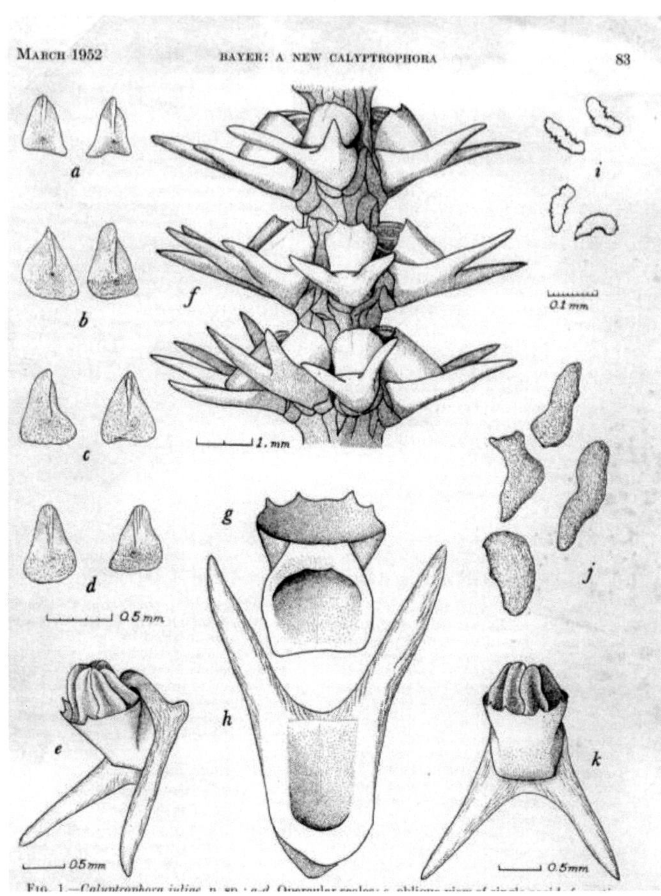

Figure 9. Calyptrophora julia. F. M. Bayer (1952) named this fossil for Julia. (Photo: Bayer, 1952, p. 82.)

Figure 10. Ecphora gardnerae, Maryland's state fossil, named by D. Wilson, 1987, after Julia Gardner. (Photo: Wilson, Paleobiology, p. 23).

Between 1924 and 1941, Julia's correspondence indicated she was helping oil and gas company geologists with up to ten requests per year. At this time, she was also doing her own field work, intensive studies, and publishing prodigiously. The introduction of micropaleontology advances for biostratigraphy in the late 1920s and 1930s began a new collaboration with Applin, Dorothy Palmer, Helen Plummer, and other micropaleontologists (refer to Chapter 7) as revealed in her correspondence.

In addition to the profound publications through the USGS Professional Papers and the GSA's Memoir 11, "Mollusca of the Tertiary Formations of Northeastern Mexico," Julia Gardner published more than 40 papers, where more than 30 were without any co-authors. She was so respected in the macropaleontologic community, she had at least three fossil species named after her: a coral, *Calyptrophora julia* (Bayer, 1952) (Fig. 9), and a gastropod, *Ecphora gardnerae*—the Maryland state fossil (Wilson, 1987) (Fig. 10), and another gastropod, *Chicoreus juliagardnerae*, (Vokes, 1970) has undergone some taxonomic discourse, but stands and is another tribute to Julia.

She spent considerable time in the 1930s both mapping for and working on the Geologic Map of Texas, (Darton et al, 1937).

The Ultimate Field Geologist

Records of Julia Gardner's expense accounts for work she did for the joint USGS and Texas Bureau of Economic Geology (BEG) mapping project have been archived at the Dolph Briscoe Library in Austin, Texas. (Fig. 11) Reviewing them for *just one six-month period out of years of work*, January to mid-July, 1927, provides an idea of the intensity of her travel and the conditions of transportation in the field with whatever Model Ford or train transportation was available to her. Places covered during this six-month period of field work, many she visited multiple times, included: Uvalde, Seguin, San Saba, Austin, Houston, Taylor, and Dallas, Texas; Washington, D.C. by train; Austin, Fort Worth, Bartlett, Teague, San Augustine, and Marshall, Texas; Shreveport, Louisiana; Jefferson, Nacadoches, Jefferson, Atlanta, Naples, Hemphill, Timpson, Garrison, Canter, Athens, Corsicana, Thornton, Tehuacana, f, Fairfield, Trinity, Mineola, Petersburg, and Longview, Texas.

Repairs on the car: twenty-four total in that six-month period ... greasing often, crankshafts repair, starting the car, pulling car out of the mud, repairing the radiator, the radiator hose, the brakes, changing tires and "vulcanizing" [remolding] them, relining brakes, hub caps replaced, gas tank cap replaced, and repairing crank handle. (Remember, she had to crank her car to start it.) She paid for "storage" of the car six times during this period when she went back to Washington, D.C. or took the train to Houston or someplace away from her field work. (Fig. 11)

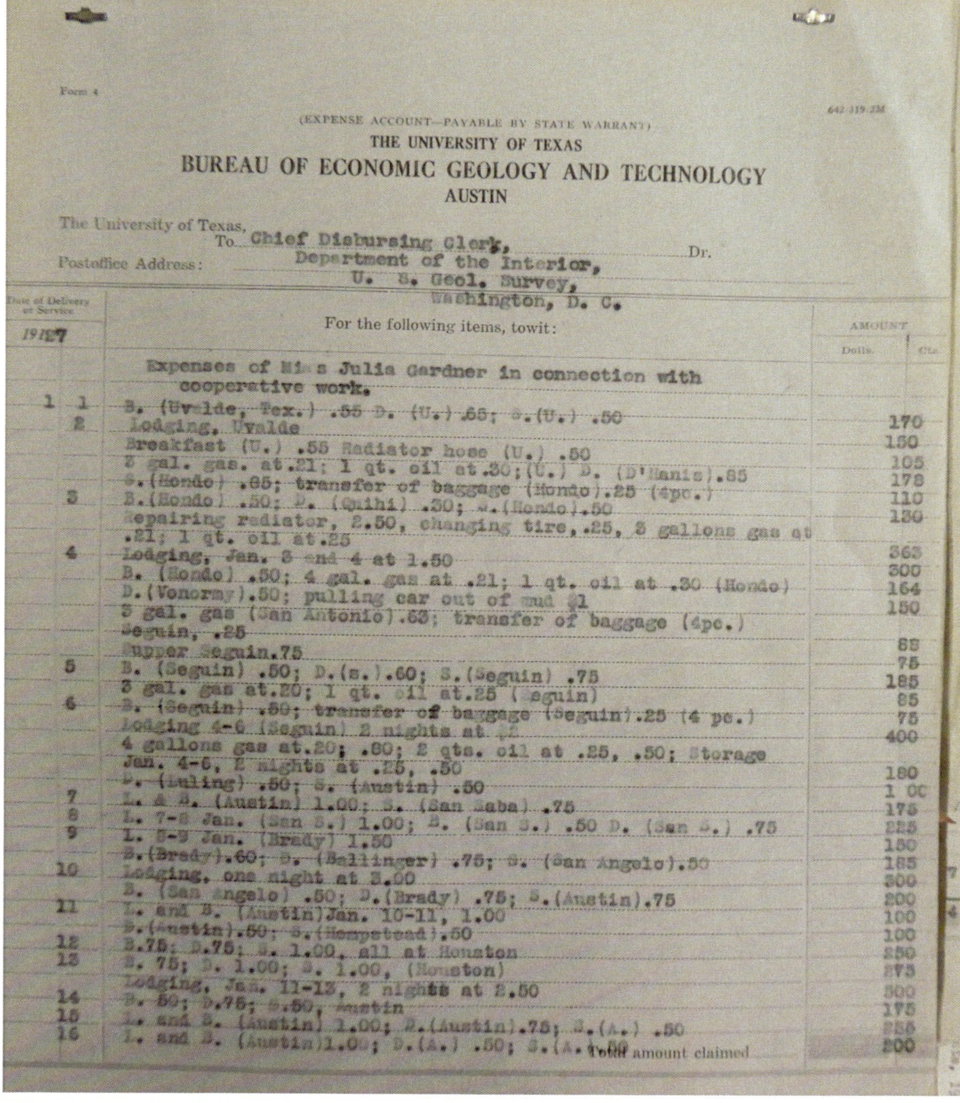

Form 4

642-119-2M

(EXPENSE ACCOUNT—PAYABLE BY STATE WARRANT)

THE UNIVERSITY OF TEXAS

BUREAU OF ECONOMIC GEOLOGY AND TECHNOLOGY

AUSTIN

The University of Texas,
To Chief Disbursing Clerk, Dr.
Postoffice Address: Department of the Interior,
U. S. Geol. Survey,
Washington, D. C.

Date of Delivery or Service 1927	For the following items, towit:	Amount
	Expenses of Miss Julia Gardner in connection with cooperative work.	
1 1	B. (Uvalde, Tex.) .55 D. (U.) .65; S.(U.) .50	
2	Lodging, Uvalde	170
	Breakfast (U.) .55 Radiator hose (U.) .50	150
	5 gal. gas. at .21; 1 qt. oil at .30; (U.) D. (D'Hanis).85	105
	S.(Hondo) .85; transfer of baggage (Hondo).25 (4pc.)	178
3	B.(Hondo) .50; D. (Quihi) .30; S.(Hondo).50	110
	Repairing radiator, 2.50, changing tire, .25, 3 gallons gas at	130
	.21; 1 qt. oil at .25	
4	Lodging, Jan. 3 and 4 at 1.50	363
	B. (Hondo) .50; 4 gal. gas at .21; 1 qt. oil at .30 (Hondo)	300
	D.(Vonormy).50; pulling car out of mud $1	164
	3 gal. gas (San Antonio).63; transfer of baggage (4pc.)	150
	Seguin, .25	
	Supper Seguin.75	88
5	B. (Seguin) .50; D.(S.).60; S.(Seguin) .75	75
	3 gal. gas at .20; 1 qt. oil at .25 (Seguin)	185
6	B. (Seguin) .50; transfer of baggage (Seguin).25 (4 pc.)	85
	Lodging 4-6 (Seguin) 2 nights at $2	75
	4 gallons gas at .20; .80; 2 qts. oil at .25, .50; Storage	400
	Jan. 4-6, 2 nights at .25, .50	
	D. (Luling) .50; S. (Austin) .50	180
7	L. & B. (Austin) 1.00; S. (San Saba) .75	1 00
8	L. 7-8 Jan. (San S.) 1.00; B. (San S.) .50 D. (San S.) .75	175
9	L. 8-9 Jan. (Brady) 1.50	225
	B.(Brady).60; D. (Ballinger) .75; S. (San Angelo).50	150
10	Lodging, one night at 3.00	185
	B. (San Angelo) .50; D.(Brady) .75; S.(Austin).75	300
11	L. and B. (Austin)Jan. 10-11, 1.00	200
	D.(Austin).50; S.(Hempstead).50	100
12	B.75; D.75; S. 1.00, all at Houston	100
13	B. 75; D. 1.00; S. 1.00, (Houston)	250
	Lodging, Jan. 11-13, 2 nights at 2.50	275
14	B. 50; D.75; S.50, Austin	300
15	L. and B. (Austin) 1.00; D.(Austin).75; S.(A.) .50	175
16	L. and B. (Austin)1.00; D.(A.) .50; S.(A.) 1.00	255
	Total amount claimed	200

Figure 11. Example of one of numerous Expense Reports from the Texas Bureau of Economic Geology from the 1920s to the early 1940s which illustrate the frustrations and chores of keeping a field vehicle maintained and contending with delays. Despite the transportation challenges, Julia's field mapping achievements were phenomenal. (Bureau of Economic Geology Records, 1874-1988, The Dolph Briscoe Center for American History, The University of Texas.)

Julia Gardner did field work, almost always alone, for over 20 years. Her correspondence and stories indicate she spent much of her time in the field from 1920 and into 1940s. The nature of her field work changed considerably with the onset of WWII and after that war.

WWII, Julia Gardner in the Military Geology Unit

When World War II descended upon the world in the mid-1940s, Julia was, once again, involved. This time she joined the Military Geology Unit of the Survey where she was describing terrain conditions and geologic factors involved in planning, establishing, and maintaining beachheads in many parts of the world. (Fig. 12) To the task she brought knowledge obtained in her travels overseas and the ability to read fluently in several languages. In his tribute to her, Sayre said, "Although she was now nearing retirement age, she worked as hard as any of this over taxed unit, putting in long hours, sometimes around the clock, and was always ready to lend a helping hand to her younger fellow workers with translations, ideas, and encouragement. Her maps were beautifully prepared, and her texts were superior ... Although it was the custom among this group to use first names only, she inspired such respect and devotion that she was known to all as 'Miss Julia.'"

Figure 12. Woman mapping during WWII when Julia was in the Military Geology Unit. (Photo: Library of Congress, Office of War Information, 1943, (Photo: Marjory Collins, Camouflage class at NY University, where men and women are preparing for jobs in the Army or in industry, New York, N.Y. Retrieved from the Library of Congress. https://www.loc.gov.item/fsa1992001532/PP/. Accessed 01/12/2017.)

Incredibly, Julia also used her paleontological skills and pinpointed specific beaches in Japan from where balloon-borne incendiary bombs (Fig. 13) were targeting the Pacific Northwest forests of the U.S. She did this by identifying the origin of the shells in the sand ballast of the balloons (Lavoie, 2005, p. 39).

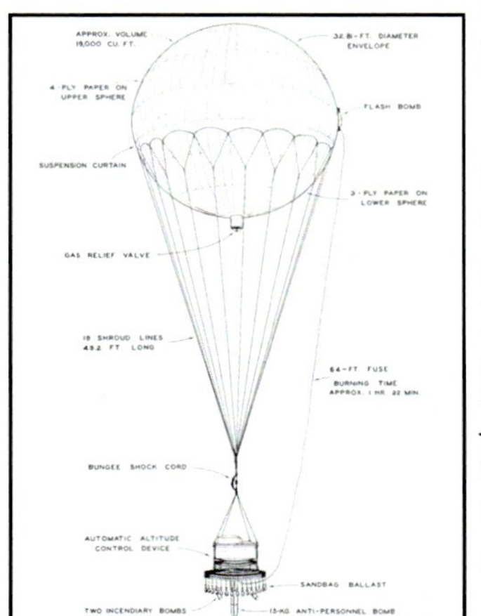

Figure 13. Diagram of a Japanese incendiary balloon bomb with sand ballast that Julia studied to determine that these originated in Japan. One bomb killed 6 people in Eastern Oregon (Photo: Mikesh, 1973, p. 39.)

After the war, Julia went for a tour of duty in Japan with the Natural Resources Section of the Headquarters, Supreme Allied Command in Japan where she worked with geologists and biologists. Headquartered in Tokyo, she traveled widely, visiting universities, and making friends with Japanese scientists and their families. (Fig. 14) Helen Foster (Chapter 11), a young geologist recently from the University of Michigan, who, like Julia, loved field work, joined the Post Hostilities Mapping Program in Japan and recalls, with a bit of humor, that Julia's service in Japan was cut short because she would not follow the rules imposed by her military superiors. One example of her misbehavior was that Julia would acquire her cigarette ration, though she did not smoke, and give them to her Japanese colleagues, which was strictly forbidden.

In her short service in Japan, Gardner forged warm friendships. Sayre said she helped to restore normal relations between our countries by winning respect and admiration as a scientist, and affection as a most charming lady." Her expertise on Japan is preserved in her post-war correspondence, where A. S. Bishop, Chairman of the Committee for Foreign Correspondence, Association of Scientists for Atomic Education Inc. in Berkeley, California wrote to her,

Figure 14. American geologists working with Japanese geologists in the WWII Post Hostilities period of mapping. Helen Foster, another primary geologic mapper who arrived after Julia had been "sent home," is the lone woman in the room. (Photo: Helen Foster, Carson City, Nevada.)

> I should be greatly interested to hear of your trip to Japan, and to learn of the thoughts and attitudes of Japanese scientists on the subject of atomic energy and its control (Smithsonian Institute, Gardner archives).

Sayre also provided perspective on her life outside her work:

> Any memorial to Julia Gardner, the scientist, would be incomplete without a word about Julia Gardner, the woman. She was no 'ivory-tower' scientist, although her standards were high and exacting. She achieved a remarkable balance between her work and her social life. For many years, she lived at the Arts Club of Washington, of which she was a charter member, and often entertained her friends in the attractive rooms whose walls were hung with the latest works of Washington artists. Her guests included scientists, writers, painters, teachers, businessmen, and many others, but despite the wide differences in the interests of her guests, her parties were always delightful. (Fig. 15)
>
> When in the Museum, Miss Julia took a coffee break in the middle of the afternoon. Guests and colleagues alike were most welcome. It was doubtless the strongest, blackest coffee in Washington. On one occasion, when she was busy with something else, I undertook to make the coffee according to my usual recipe. When she had time, she took one look at it, doubled the amount of coffee and poured out half the water. It was big medicine and it awakened and refreshed her guests, dispelled any drowsiness, and restored the staff to their morning vigor. For relaxation, Miss Julia read omnivorously and remembered what she read, seeming to have almost total recall of everything from philosophy to the latest fiction.

Figure 15. Arts Club of Washington which Julia helped to found and where she lived until the illness preceding her death. (Photo: http://culturecapital.com/organization/607/arts-club-of-washington, accessed 1/15/2017.)

Sayre concluded his tribute with the depth of Julia Gardner's character.

Wherever she went she made friends with young and old, the prosperous, and the 'not so prosperous.' In South Texas, the Mexicans affectionately called her 'Tia Julia' ... The most outstanding characteristic of this remarkable woman was her deep sense of humanity. She was forever unobtrusively, almost stealthily, performing acts of kindness—some small, but many of them large. For example, when T. Wayland Vaughan became ill and finally blind, she spent several evenings each week reading to him aloud from his favorite books ... her views on professional and personal behavior and on political matters were strong and firm, and she expressed them well and generally wittily. If the situation demanded, she could criticize concisely and succinctly, but never unkindly."

Figure 16. Julia Anna Gardner, AAPG Memorial. (Photo: Sayre, 1961, p. 1418.)

Julia did not join AAPG until 1927, three years after she started working with oil and gas companies—she was 45 years old. She maintained her membership for 33 years until her death at age 78. (Fig. 16) She was the recipient of countless awards during her career in which she was a charter member of the Society of Economic Paleontologists and Mineralogists (SEPM), a Fellow of the Geological Society of America (GSA), and Vice President of GSA in 1953, a Fellow with American Association for the Advancement of Science (AAAS), and received the U. S. Department of the Interior's Distinguished Service Award. It cannot help but be lamented that Dr. Julia Anna Gardner failed to be selected as a recipient of the Sidney Powers Award of AAPG, established 25 years before her death because her résumé strongly recommends her. However, in 2017, at the AAPG Centennial Meeting, Dr. Julia Anna Gardner will be recognized posthumously as the recipient of the Harrison Schmidt Award for her profound contributions to geoscience and to humanity.

"Notes on Travel and Life"

by Julia Gardner, PhD '11, fac. '17

The *Johns Hopkins Alumni Magazine* Volume, 1940, XXVIII Number 2, pp. 37-42 *(Reprinted with permission from Ferdinand Hamburger Archives, Sheridan Libraries, Johns Hopkins University)*

Miss Gardner, a graduate of Bryn Mawr College, has met successfully the vigorous demands of the life of an open-air geologist and is outstanding among the small but growing number of competent woman geologists. Extensive travels in search of scientific data have brought varied incidents, some trying, some pleasant; but most worth telling about, as Miss Gardner graciously does here for readers of the Magazine. She says she pirated the title from the writings of a 19th century woman traveler.

Late in March, 1920, I entered the port of New York after an absence of more than two years in a foreign land. During that time, I had lived in the present, neither looking back upon the years of training at Hopkins nor forward to the necessity of finding a job in the country basically changed by the World War. The dense fog which paralyzed the shipping in the harbor for more than 12 hours, seemed no good omen and unpleasantly symbolic. I shall never cease to be grateful to Dr. T. Wayland Vaughn, at that time chief of the coastal plain section of the Geological Survey, for the wire which welcomed me to America and opened the door to the federal Survey. I reported in Washington at the office in the old building on F Street the following morning and, as a former director ruefully remarked of those receiving appointments to the government bureau, "Few die and none resign."

Figure 17. Model T Ford, changing tire with inner tube on the road, ca 1923-25. This is what Julia dealt with constantly in her fieldwork days, done primarily alone. Notice the hand crank to start the engine. Julia needed the strength to do it alone in her first years as a field geologist. (Photo: SmokStak.com; repost on Forums.fourtitude.com.)

Geology is the science of the earth and, like Antaeus, the geologist can maintain his strength only by holding one foot upon the ground. My first field trip, however, was after the manner of those of Thomas Cook and Son, perfectly guided and full of interest and material comfort. But on that first trip I learned the vice of many of the profession, always to leave something unfinished to which you are recalled by love of country and of science. Though the Maryland countryside was familiar to me, I had never wandered far afield and had never driven a car.

But drive a car I must, if I was to have more than a nuisance value and so, a few months later, with a more or less theoretical knowledge of a Model T Ford, I set out for Savannah. There the car which I was to use in the Florida field work had been stored for many months. I remember a slight sense of disappointment and apprehension as I looked at it, a pickup truck which some former driver had long ago converted into a covered wagon. The canvas was worn and beginning to flap but it afforded a certain amount of protection and privacy for baggage and field collections. The garage presumably spent the greater part of the day in checking over the car before it was delivered to me in mid-afternoon. I realized the comparative lateness of the hour and the long stretch of Okeechobee swamp road between Savannah and Darien and Brunswick but there were still three or four hours of daylight and surely some settlement could be reached in the meantime. The garage attendant cranked the engine, I went through the motions learned in my half dozen driving lessons and the car began to move toward Florida.

Somehow, I covered the first fifteen miles without remembered incident, but soon after I had passed the bamboo grove of the Agricultural Experiment Station, a landmark in my life, a front tire blew out. The city traffic was behind me and there was no help at hand. So with fumbling awkward movements and a great expenditure of time and energy I changed my first tire. Within the next mile a second tire blew out. I had no second spare only a new realization of the effect upon rubber of long storage in a warm climate. (Fig. 17)

Here the luck that rarely fails me at the last ditch appeared in the form of a large truck. This all happened in those far away days before every hitchhiker was a potential hold up man and the lady in distress upon the road, the criminal's accomplice. So not only did the truck stop, but the driver had two new casings of the proper size and was persuaded to sell them. He also put them on, a service which more than doubled their value at the moment. By the time the ceremony was over, the sun was low and the seventy or eighty miles to Darien and Brunswick were not more than well begun. The truck driver cranked my engine and then his own, for self starters were not standard equipment, and he rolled off toward Savannah and I toward Brunswick.

The road was getting narrow and sandy and on either side was the Okeechobee Swamp. There were no settlements and no passing cars. The sights and sounds of approaching night were all about me. The road showed up like a pale gray ribbon even where the trees on either side were hung with moss, and I hesitated to turn on the car lights and thus black out the beauty of the scene around me. When at last I turned the switch, nothing happened. I had no lights. As in many other unpleasant situations, there was very little to be done about it. I had no conception of the mechanics of the lights and not even a pocket flashlight. The air swarmed with mosquitoes and the only refuge was in motion. The light sandy road could still be followed with frequent stalls at the bridges which were narrow and dark, some with and some without side railings. When the half moon rose, the sandy road caught the dim light. A big cat screamed off in the swamp and, far away, I could hear men shouting. I half hoped, half feared, they would come nearer.

After a very long time, I saw, in the road ahead, a blur of light, which slowly disintegrated into the head-

lights of two parked cars and the lantern which came wavering down the road and was swung in my face. The man behind the lantern said "Oh, my God, it's a woman." He was the driver of one of the two automobiles from some point in the Middle West. One of the cars had a short circuit which was eventually repaired, and I trailed them to Midway, at that time a filling station and cross roads store under a single roof. With my car parked in its shadow and my feet on the seat, I slept the rest of my first night in the field. My mileage for that first day was thirty-one. They told me the next morning that the shouts I had heard were those of men hunting some escaped convicts. It seemed incredible last year, when I drove over U.S. 17, that so long a chapter in my life could have been lived in those thirty-one miles.

The rest of the field season was relatively uneventful. I gradually learned to come to terms with my means of transportation and to park it, as winter came on, headed down grade. The living pattern is much the same throughout the area in which I have worked from Florida to Texas: a room in a country hotel of varying degrees of comfort, with or without heat in winter, usually but not always with screens in the summer, but almost invariably with food I like and with friendly people.

Each area in which I have worked has presented some particular interest other than geological. In northern Florida, it was my so-called poor white friends; in Alabama, the river towns, that many years ago before the railroads went through, were cities of importance in the commercial and political life of the country. Claiborne still a lodestone whenever I come with its sphere of influence, was first known as the John Weatherford Plantation but was renamed in 1813 in honor of Gen. Ferdinand Leigh Claiborne who fortified the high bluff on the east side of the Alabama River. The federal road crossed the river by ferry at that point and connected Milledgeville, the old capital of Georgia, and St. Stephens, the territorial capital of Alabama. Judge Tait, a former senator from Georgia, established himself at Claiborne in 1819 and became forthwith Claiborne's first citizen. At that time, a census indicated that the population of Mobile numbered a little less than 2000, that of Claiborne a little more. So the eminence of the city as well as that of Judge Tait was a probable factor in the election of three out of ten governors of Alabama from Claiborne before 1837. (Fig. 18)

Figure 18. Claiborne, Alabama in the 1930s. (Photo: Library of Congress, Historic American Buildings Survey, HABS ALA, 50-CLAB,1-. http://www.loc.gov/rr/print/res/114_habs.html, accessed 1/12/2017.)

Not a habitation remains at the site of old St. Stephens, the territorial capital of Alabama from 1817 to 1819. It was set on a high bluff commanding the Tombigbee but we could not find even the tablet hidden in the undergrowth; only a few scattered bricks and crepe myrtle bushes.

My work in the later years has been in that part of the country that Texans are pleased to call the Empire of Texas. Although I have spent several seasons in east and central Texas, it is not until I hit the stretch of brush between Moore and Pearsall on the San Antonio - Laredo road that I am roused to yippi-yis (Fig. 19). It used to be that I could leave the highway at Moore and, by a devious route which included all manner of lumber gates and few wire gaps, could arrive at the end of twenty or twenty-five miles at Frio Town, to me one of the last citadels of the old cattle country. Frio town was the county seat of Frio County for ten years after its organization in 1871 but the railroad came through 16 miles to the east and all that is left of the town now is the courthouse with its iron balcony askew, and a few abandoned buildings,

Figure 19. Laredo, Texas during the 1920s, when Julia was field mapping from New England to Mexico. Postcard: Laredo Public Library https://texashistory.unt.edu/ark:/67531/metapth13266/, accessed 1/12/2017.

including the jail and the church and the big white Roberts ranch house.

But Frio Town to me is Mrs. Roberts. Small and slight and dark, with gentle voice and manner and completely unafraid, Mrs. Roberts has lived alone in the big house since her husband's death almost ten years ago. Her son and his family are less than two miles away and there are Mexicans nearby but not within call. She bears her full share of responsibility for the management of the ranch, acts as postmistress in the little fourth class office which serves the nearby ranches, sells sugar and tobacco and other staples at the courthouse store and answers all the questions on the early history of Frio, Atascosa and La Salle Counties. (Fig. 20)

Figure 20. Sal and Lillie Armstrong on Frio County Ranch near Pearsall in Texas, 1906. (Photo: Bill Armstrong, http://www.texasescapes.com/SouthTexasTowns/Big-Wells-Texas.htm.)

All about them the ranches have passed into the hands of strangers, and the families have "moved into town." The sons, untrained for anything but life on the range, have been able to find work only in the garage or filling station and their state recalls that of the Indians on the reservation. But Mrs. Roberts, clear headed, tenacious, with a feeling for the land as strong as that of any peasant on European soil, firm in her refusal to accept defeat in the face of collapsing markets, bank failures, alternating drouths and floods, continues to stand, facing the past perhaps, but a path of greater distinction and dignity than anything offered in the ordinary little towns with filling station motifs that have sprung up in recent years along the Highway.

I have worked much of late below Laredo, in Zapata County, which by an accident in geography happens to be on the Texas side of the Rio Grande instead of in Mexico. During last May and a part of June my base was San Ygnacio, where the Battle of San Ygnacio was fought in June, 1916. The American soldiers were camped on the wide flat terrace of the Rio Grande on the edge of the town. One night a detachment of ragged Mexican soldiers on starved horses crossed the river which was very low and concealed themselves in an arroyo near San Ygnacio. They circulated about the town the following day, secured food for themselves and their horses and boasted that they would attack that night. Only the San Ygnacians understood them but the American sentries were on duty when the attack was made and the battle was quickly over. Six of the Mexicans were killed and are buried near the spot where they fell. Nothing has happened in San Ignacio since that engagement. It is still a staple subject of conversation; that, and what to do with the butter the WPA gives them, for butter is not in the diet of a Mexican household.

To live in San Ygnacio one must go native, and go native I did. Senora Audelia Dominguez de Rodriguez, who neither spoke nor understood my native tongue, took me in with some misgivings which she overcame because I was recommended by a cousin of hers in Zapata. Senora's house had a high gabled roof and was whitewashed both inside and out. The walls were almost as thick as those of the governor's palace in San Antonio. My room was literally a "cuarto" for the house was cut into four rooms by partitions of not entirely opaque flowered material stretched tightly from the floor almost halfway up to the high ceiling. There was one small window, high up and barred. The door which opened on to a narrow gallery flush with the street was of mesquite, hand carved with wooden pegs for nails and a key as large as that to the Bastille.

The first night I noted that preparations for retiring included the closing and locking of all openings to the outer world. Taking refuge in my ignorance of the language and the customs, and feeling that suffocation was one of the more difficult deaths, I open the outer door to my room. When I wakened in the morning it was closed. The next night I reopened the door without comment and it was not closed again excepting at my wish.

The kitchen at Senora Rodriguez' was an arched opening about shoulder high in the thick walls of the chimney. Before that opening Senora stood, small and erect, and deftly performed the simpler arts of cooking on a plate of sheet iron raised on legs over a mesquite wood fire. My tortillas and frijoles were placed upon the best China and born to another room where I ate in solitude. Senora and the small granddaughter, ate at eight, and the visiting grandchildren dined at the table near the kitchen chimney. Dolores was a sweet child, singing with the carelessness of a mockingbird and with the peculiar timbre of the Mexican voice. One of her favorite songs being translated ran something like this: "I was not born in Guatemala, neither was I born in New York. I am 'pure mexicana' and there is nothing Spanish about me.

I said goodbye to Senora Rodriguez and little Dolores and Rosanda, her constant companion, with a catch in my voice. Even though I was, at times, thoroughly uncomfortable, they had given me the best they had to offer, and I have learned something of the Mexicans living in their own Pueblo, not in a quarter on the wrong side of the railroad track in a town controlled by those of another race. I found no evidence in San Ygnacio of some of the unfortunate traits commonly associated with the Mexicans and other towns and cities. My possessions, although I was unable to lock my bags, were never touched and, poor as the people were, they asked nothing from me nor did they expect gifts of any kind. And, poor as they were, they were far more fortunate than their cousins on the other side of the Rio Grande and they knew it.

Late in June I realized a long cherished ambition – I saw the Grand Cañon. There was an old map in the laboratory at Bryn Mawr, so old that the colors which originally must have been a bit gaudy were softer and weathered to a semblance of the Arizona colors. The map is contoured and the proportions of the Cañon where indicated with a fair degree of accuracy. All in all it was a challenge to my imagination and the Cañon became to me the apotheosis of the science of geology. But the dream of seeing it was unrealized until this year. At the end of the third day at El Tovar, I left lamenting that I was not the Indian who used to live on the rim, in the cave with an opening that seemed from the road no bigger than the entrance to a rabbit hole. I had seen only one sunrise from Hopi Point and two never-to-be-forgotten sunsets. He could watch the changing lights in every time and season. In these days when all Europe seems about to crash, even the memory of the color and the carved expanse that Grand Cañon of the Colorado makes the terror of the present weeks seem more fugitive.

Chapter 6: Sources and References

American Ambulance Field Service. 1916. Photograph. "In the American Ambulance Field Service, 1916." EyeWitness to History. www.eyewitnesstohistory.com (2008). http://www.eyewitnesstohistory.com/ambulanceservice.htm. Accessed 01/12/2017.

Armstrong, Bill. *Frio County Ranch, Texas.* 1906. Photograph. http://www.texasescapes.com/SouthTexasTowns/Big-Wells-Texas.htm. Accessed 01/23/2017.

Arts Club of Washington. n.d. Photograph. Culture Capital.com Your Link to the Arts in Metro DC. Washington, D.C. http://culturecapital.com/organization/607/arts-club-of-washington; accessed 01/14/2017.

Bayer, F. M. 1952. "A *new* Calyptrophora (Coelenterata: Octocorallia) from the Philippine Islands." *Journal Washington Academy of Sciences.* vol. 42, no. 3, pp. 82-83.

Car in Florida swamp-changing tire, 1942, photograph, Florida Memory, State Library and Archives, Florida photographic collection, John Kunkel Small Collection, # SMX0106.

Collins, Marjory, Camouflage class at NY University, where men and women are preparing for jobs in the Army or in industry, New York, N.Y.…The girl is correcting oversights detected in the camouflaging of a model defense plant. 1943.Photograph. Retrieved from the Library of Congress. https://www.loc.gov.item/fsa1992001532/PP/. Accessed 01/12/2017.

Considine, Barney, Missoula, Montana, great nephew of Julia Gardner (Winnie Brackett Considine's son). Personal communication with Robbie Gries June 20, 2015 through November 19, 2016; source of photograph of Julia Gardner and her family.

Darton, Nelson Horatio, Lloyd William Stephenson, Julia Anna Gardner, and George Stone. *Geologic Map of Texas.* Washington, D.C.: Department of the Interior, United States Geological Survey. 1937. Map.

Dutro, J. Thomas, Jr. *Julia Gardner circa 1915*. 2005. Photograph. "A National Research Laboratory in the Late 20th Century: U.S. Geological Survey's Paleontology and Stratigraphy Branch as a Case Study." *Proceedings of the California Academy of Sciences,* vol. 55, Supplement I, no. 7, p. 179.

Expenses of Miss Julia Gardner in connection with cooperative work. 1920s. Image. Bureau of Economic Geology Records, 1874-1988. Box 4S259. Dolph Briscoe Center for American History. The University of Texas at Austin, Austin, Texas.

Foster, Helen, Carson City, Nevada. Personal communication with Robbie Gries, June 1, 2015 through January 15, 2017; source of Helen Foster photographs.

Gardner, Julia Anna. 1940. "Notes on Travel and Life." *Johns Hopkins Alumni Magazine*, vol. XXVII, no. 2, pp. 37-42. Ferdinand Hamburger Archives, Sheridan Libraries, Johns Hopkins University.

Gardner, Julia Anna. *Mollusca of the Tertiary Formations of Northeastern Mexico.* Geological Society of America Memoir 11. Baltimore, Md: Waverly Press, 1945. 332 pp.

Hancock, Glory. 1918. "Letters to her family, 10-7-1918." Betty H. Carter Women Veterans Historical Project, WV0181. Martha Blakeney Hodges Special Collections and University Archives. The University of North Carolina at Greensboro, North Carolina.

Hull, J.P.D. *Julia Gardner joins oil men in the field.* 1924. Photograph. Photo courtesy of J. P.D. "Joe" Hull Jr., Denver, Colorado. July 2016.

Ladd, Harry S. 1962. "Memorial to Julia Anna Gardner (1882-1960)." *Geological Society of America Proceedings for 1960,* pp. 87-92.

Lavoie, Dawn, and Deborah Hutchinson. 2005. "The U. S. Geological Survey: Sea-going Women." *Oceanography*, v. 18, no. 1, p. 39.

Manning, W. N., Deer's Store, U.S. Highway 84 (State Highway 12), Claiborne County, AL. 1934. Photograph. Historic American Buildings Survey. Library of Congress Prints and Photographs Division. Washington, D.C. HABS ALA, 50-CLAB,1-1. http://www.loc.gov/pictures/item/al0636.photos.005855p/resource/. Accessed 01/12/2017.

Mikesh, Robert. Japan's World War II Balloon Bomb Attacks on North America. Smithsonian Annals of Flight No. 9. Washington, D.C.: Smithsonian Institution Press. 1973. 85 pp. http://library.uoregon.edu/ec/e-asia/read/balloon.pdf. Accessed 01/12/2017.

Model T Ford, changing tire with inner tube on the road.ca 1923-25. This is what Julia dealt with constantly in her fieldwork days, done primarily alone. Photograph. Web. Original post: SmokStak.com Repost on forums.fourtitude.com by kashah 11/10/2011.

Sayre, A. Nelson. 1961. "Julia Anna Gardner Memorial." *AAPG Bulletin*, vol. 44, no. 8, p. 1418-1421.

Small, John, Kunkel. 1869-1938. *John Soar's Ford Stuck in Everglades.* 1915. Photograph. State Archives of Florida, Florida Memory. Image Number SMX0106. https://www.floridamemory.com/items/show/50790. Accessed 01/17/2017.

Smithsonian Institution Archives. Accession 08-141. Gardner, Julia Anna, b. 1882. Julia Anna Gardner Papers, 1894-1956 and undated, professional correspondence, 1925-1950.

Smithsonian Institution Archives. Record Unit 7327 and Box 12. Geological Survey, Branch of Paleontology and Stratigraphy. Records. Gardner, Julia Anna, b. 1882.

Vokes, E. H. 1970. "*Chicoreus (Siratus) juliagardnerae*, New Name for *Murex gardnerae* Vokes NON Dall with Observations on the Species." *Tulane Studies in Geology and Paleontology*, v. 8, no. 1, pp. 51-52.

Wilson, D. 1987. "Species of Ecphora in the Pungo River formation." in C. E. Ray, ed. *Geology and Paleontology of the Lee Creek Mine, North Carolina*, II. Smithsonian Contributions to Paleobiology, vol. 61, p. 21-29. Washington: Smithsonian Institution Press, 1963.

Wilson, Herbert Wrigley and Hammerton, John Alexander, Sir. eds. The Great War: The Standard History of the All Europe Conflict. Vol. 4. London: Amalgamated Press. http://www.firstworldwar.com/photos/graphics/gws_pgasvictimsruss_01.jpg. Accessed 01/12/2017.

Chapter 7

1920s to 1940s: The Micropaleontology Era

Micropaleontologists in petroleum geology history do not garner the respect they once had because modern geologists fail to fully appreciate their crucial role in the history of petroleum exploration and development (Saucier, AAPG Explorer, March 2015). Many geologists, today, look upon paleontology as mostly an academic pursuit and fail to appreciate the relevance to "real" exploration. Dry holes, particularly, abound in frontier basins when paleontology is ignored and exploration relies on seismic alone.

Put into historical perspective, *micropaleontology* was a technological breakthrough of revolutionary standing. *It was the most important subsurface correlation tool available for decades and, even today, it continues to contribute to better geologic science.* As mentioned in the biography of Julia Gardner (Chapter 6), electric and other geophysical well logs were in their infancy, and seismic was either not yet developed, or, when it was developed, it was limited in its geographic application for decades. The limitations of **macro**paleontology; using larger fossils like mollusk shell remnants as in Julia Gardner's work, were obviously greater when dealing with well cuttings because the shells would be ground to pieces with the drill bit. Micropaleontology, commercially developed in the 1920s, involved the identification of the tiny, microscopic fossilized shells of the most primitive, single-celled animals—foraminifera. Prior to the breakthrough work discussed in this Chapter, foraminifera were thought to be such "lower forms of life" they would not have the diversity of shell structure in short ranges of geologic time; thus, they would not be useful as a correlation tool. If a species of foraminifera lived and died over a period of 100 million years, it was useless to correlate rock layers deposited over a million years with another layer. But, if the foraminifera evolved quickly and had a life span of less than a million to five million years, THIS could be used to "brand" a rock layer and correlate it elsewhere. These early female micropaleontologists proved this was true with foraminifera and created an entire new technology for rock correlations. Very quickly, micropaleontology became essential for all companies doing serious exploration; they developed special micropaleontology laboratories and started hiring these paleontologists as quickly as universities could produce them.

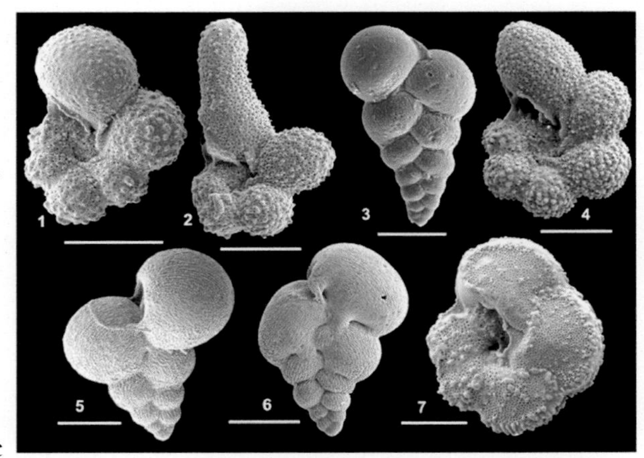

Figure 1. Micro fossils, especially foraminifera were ideal for stratigraphic identifications in well cuttings. Scale: each bar is 50 micrometers. (Photo: Geological Society of America, http://geology.gsapubs.org/content/30/7/607/F1.large.jpg, accessed 1/19/2017.)

Microfauna were ideally suited in oil and gas exploration because they survived the destruction of the drill bit. When the small fragments of rock were dredged up from the well bore, the foraminifera remained intact. They became signatures for geologic formations (Fig. 1).

Figure 2. Houston skyline in the 1920s, a booming oil town and home to Humble Oil, the Texas Company, Rio Bravo, Gulf Oil and many other growing companies. (Photo: "Downtown Houston composite panorama, approximately 1928," Special Collections, University of Houston Libraries, http://digital.lib.uh.edu/collection/p15195coll2/item/197, accessed 1/18/2017).

In 1920, E. T. Dumble, former Director of the Texas Bureau of Economic Geology and Chief Geologist of Rio Bravo Oil Company, was convinced that **macro**-paleo could be effective in working out the chaotic Gulf Coast stratigraphy, and he put together a consortium of four Houston-based companies starting with the Rio Bravo Oil Company, Humble Oil Company, Gulf Oil Company, and the Texas Company (Fig. 2) to try to accomplish this. The companies agreed that Dumble would hire a paleontologist and provide a lab and oversight to the project, sharing the information. Dumble "vetted" Esther Richards for the job in the summer of 1918 and then hired her to set up the paleontology lab at Rio Bravo. Much to Dumble's surprise, the cooperating companies soon decided to set up their own laboratories—though still participating in the consortium. A month after Esther was hired, Wallace Pratt, who had just left the Texas Company to work for Humble Oil in Houston, hired a University of Texas (UT) paleontology graduate, Alva Ellisor, to set up a lab for Humble in Houston. The Texas Company followed suit months later and hired another UT student, Hedwig Kniker, to set up their laboratory, also in Houston. These three single women, who would bear the burden of proving the usefulness of paleontology in oil and gas exploration, soon determined they needed to change the focus from macropaleontology to micropaleontology.

Alva Christine Ellisor (1892-1964)

Figure 3. Alva Ellisor in college; she was the second woman to earn a bachelor's degree from The University of Texas at Austin. (Photo: The Cactus *yearbook, The University of Texas at Austin, 1915, p. 221.)*

Alva Christine Ellisor (Fig. 3) was a phenomenon early on, having survived the Galveston Hurricane of 1900 at age eight when she saw two younger brothers "swept away from her mother's arms" to their tragic deaths (Fig. 4) (1965, L. P. Teas, p 471). The Ellisor family must have known the Masterson family in Galveston (see Reba Masterson, Chapter 2).

Figure 4. The devastation of the 1900 Galveston hurricane claimed the lives of Alva Ellisor's brothers. This photo shows survivors seeking valuables in the wreckage. (Photo: Library of Congress, Prints and Photographs Division, Washington, D.C., # LC-USZ62-120389, http://hdl.loc.gov/loc.pnp/cph.3c20389, accessed 1/19/2017.)

If Alva did not know Reba Masterson well as a neighbor in Galveston, she surely had the chance at The University of Texas in Austin (UT) where, in 1910, Alva Ellisor was the third female undergraduate geology student in the department's history. Reba, ten years older than Alva, had been at UT for two years and, perhaps, even inspired Alva to try geology. Alva earned her B.A. degree in 1915 to become the second woman to graduate with an undergraduate degree in geology from UT and continued her

Figure 5. Wallace Pratt, legendary oil man, hired Alva Ellisor to set up a micropaleontology lab for Humble Oil and Refining in Houston in 1920. He was thrilled with her discovery of using coastal foraminifera for more accurate stratigraphic correlation. (Photo: AAPG Archives, Tulsa Oklahoma.

post graduate work at UT from 1916 to 1918. During WWI, she was hired to fill a vacancy in the Geology Department because several young professors had gone off to war. Hattie V. Whitten, the first woman to acquire a bachelor's and master's degree in geology at UT in 1890, 1900, was listed as an instructor 1901 to 1903, (from 1983, Newsletter, UT, Department of Geology, no 32, p.3, and 1905 *Cactus* yearbook).

In the summer of 1918, Alva took a temporary job with her future employer, Humble Oil, to examine well cuttings. That same year she also published some of her research on Turritella, a Cretaceous gastropod from the Buda and Georgetown Limestones of Texas while studying for her master's degree. In 1919 to 1920, she continued her paleontology studies at the Kansas State Geological Survey. Her early work and recognition of the value of fossils in stratigraphic correlations led the legendary Wallace Pratt to hire her in the fall of 1920 to build the research laboratory at Humble Oil and Refining in Houston (Fig. 5). While Humble was participating in the consortium with Rio Bravo and others looking for better paleontologic assistance in correlating strata on the Gulf Coast, Pratt appears to have decided to create his own lab and hire his own expertise.

Alva Ellisor is credited with making the first major breakthrough for micropaleontology in the subsurface when she recognized the correlative potential of foraminifera. Showing her correlation results to Pratt, her thrill and enthusiasm was matched by his and she liked to tell the story:

> Mr. Pratt was very excited about this discovery. He decided that such an amazing find should be kept a company secret, and gave me instructions not to say a word to anyone about it. At the time, I was living with two other women geologists who were employed by competitor oil companies. When I got home, Esther Richards ... greeted me with the news of my discovery. It seems Mr. Pratt couldn't keep the secret and chose to tell Esther's boss .... Of course, the news of the Foraminifera was then out. (1962, "Alva C. Ellisor, Distinguished Geology Alumna," University of Texas Bulletin, July, p. 2).

Thomas D. (Tom) Barrow (Fig. 6), another legendary oil man and president of Humble Oil remarked at the presentation of her Distinguished Geology Alumna award:

> During the first few years as this work in the Houston Laboratories gradually became known, prejudice and opposition to the validity was expressed not only by petroleum geologists, but by quite a few prominent geologists and paleontologists in the academic world. Miss Ellisor not only had to prove [to] her company, but also to convince the rest of the geologic profession, that micropaleontology was important. Many times, she had to work well samples as unknowns—not being given the name and location of the wells. This was not just to test her during the proving stage, but because some [of the Humble] geologists wanted to be certain that the determination were based entirely on what was found in the samples, and not on the other information as to what the age should be ... I get the impression that as these early workers look back, they think of the prejudice and opposition as being amusing. However, unless they were far more confident than most young geologists are, I doubt much of it was amusing at the time ... she was not only the right person at the right place at the right time, she had the 'industry, alertness, tenacity and ability.'

Figure 6. Tom Barrow, Humble Oil executive, praised Ellisor's work for years. (Photo: The University of Texas at Austin, Jackson School of Geoscience. https://cns.utexas.edu/about/hall-of-honor/past-recipients, accessed 1/23/2017.)

Three of the four Houston companies, Rio Bravo Oil Company, Humble, and the Texas Company, encouraged their female lab managers to collaborate, which led to much faster and more profound progress in the stratigraphic world (Fig. 7). The three women jointly published what is still considered a seminal paper in 1925: "Subsurface Stratigraphy of the Coastal Plain of Texas and Louisiana" (*AAPG Bulletin*, pp. 79-122). Their work successfully began sorting out the chaotic Gulf Coast stratigraphy. Soon after the 1925 paper, B. H. Harlton of Amerada wrote,

> ... Practically every correlation is made by means of micropaleontology. Nearly 75 per cent of all drilling wells depend on micropaleontology for completion and pipe-setting." (Reed, 1931, p. 737).

Figure 7. Houston, Texas in the 1920s. (Photo: "600 block of Main Street facing south at Texas Avenue.1923," Special Collections, University of Houston Libraries, http://digital.lib.uh.edu/collection/p15195coll2/item/185, accessed 1/19/2017.)

Alva Ellisor's major contributions to paleontology and its use in petroleum geology were recognized in 1929 by none other than Sidney Powers, one of the most proficient geologists in the petroleum industry and a founding member of AAPG, when he nominated her to Fellowship at the Geological Society of America.

R. D. Reed in his 1931 paper, "Microscopic Subsurface Work" (AAPG Bulletin, p. 746-747), relayed these comments from Ellisor:

> Ten years ago, it was believed that no Foraminifera existed in the salt dome region of the Gulf Coast because the wells up to that time did not go much below 3,000 feet. In 1920 the first Foraminifera were discovered in the Gulf Coast by the Humble Company, when their wells reached the Oligocene in Goose Creek and West Columbia.
>
> At first the Foraminifera were used to mark the contacts of the formations, particularly in wells on the salt domes. Later Foraminifera were used to determine the age of the formations in the wells of the Cretaceous along the Balcones Escarpment. After a while we began to divide the formations into zones on the basis of Foraminifera. Then we began to correlate surface formations with the aid of Foraminifera.
>
> After ten years of detailed study we find that Foraminifera have a very limited vertical range in the geologic column, and a wide geographic range. Faunal associations remain constant over wide areas so that zones and members of a formation can be traced across the state of Texas into Mexico on one hand or the other.

Alva was as committed to professional societies as she was to her technical work. In 1923, Alva Ellisor, with eight other women, helped to found the Houston Geological Society (HGS) so Houston could host the 1924 AAPG Convention. In addition to Ellisor, those founding members included Esther Applin (née Richards), Emma Jane Coffman, Hedwig Kniker, Helen Plummer (née Skewes), Laura Weinzierl (née Lane), Reba Masterson, Grace Newman, and Elizabeth Stiles. This meant that 12% of the founding members of HGS were women. Alva was twice the Vice President of the HGS. Alva would later write a book on the history of geologists in Houston, which included the history of the HGS and was titled *Rockhounds of Houston*. According to Teas in her Memorial,

> She early recognized the necessity for fieldwork to correlate the subsurface and surface sections, and in 1924 began a series of field trips over a period of 10 years or more, with the writer [Teas] and many other Humble geologists, to sample and study the Tertiary and Cretaceous sections. (Fig. 8)

Figure 8. Alva, organized many field trips to collect samples, believing surface work was necessary to understand the subsurface. From left to right in the photo: Esther Richards, John Suman, Ballard, Alva Ellisor, and colleagues possibly William A. Baker and W. F. Bowman at Hidalgo Bluff near the Brazos River Bottom. (Photo: Applin family, Patty Kellogg, Gloucester, Virginia.)

Alva Ellisor spent her entire career with Humble (ExxonMobil), retiring in 1947 after 27 years. When she started the Humble lab, she and a sample washer comprised the lab staff. By 1946, there were

Figure 9. Alva Ellisor, preparing foraminifera for her microscopic work and identification, 1946, the year before she retired. (Photo: F. W. Rolshausen and R. D. Woods, 1946, p. 2.)

12 micropaleontologists, 2 paleontologists, 20 sample washers, and several clerks handling 220,000 samples annually (Rolshausen, 1946, p. 20). She continued to work, consult, and, eventually when a consultant, acquire leases and production revenue for her own account. (Fig. 9)

Her nephew, Rik Ellisor of Seaside, Oregon, remembers her being substantially well off when she died and owning mineral interests near Plano and Uvalde, Texas, as well as many other places. Rik was raised by Alva in Galveston; he was the precocious sibling of six born to Alva's nephew, Woody Ellisor and his wife, Marie. Woody was a career Navy man and absent most of the time, and Marie was not a healthy person and died in 1960. Often, while Rik was growing up, Marie Ellisor was forced to put her children into a Catholic orphanage because she was too ill to care for them and her husband was absent. Alva and her sister-in-law, Inez Ellisor, would drive to the east coast and retrieve some of the children. Alva favored Rik because he was very curious about science. She home-schooled him for quite a while and indulged in his science projects.

Rik has great memories of his Aunt Alva, who never married, and eventually retired back to the family home in Galveston. He especially enjoyed her tales of the oil business. She delighted in telling him about crashing the Petroleum Club, which was an all-male club, in Houston on numerous occasions. He describes her as a very smiley, upbeat, and happy person except when she encountered ignorance, cruelty, and narrow-mindedness. Then, she could rage for hours.

Her generosity with Rik and some of his siblings included creating a Trust that helped them through college. She was also active in the Altrusa club which was dedicated to public service and she founded the Altrusa Chapter in Galveston.

She accrued distinctions including, the GSA Fellow and Honorary Member of the Houston Geological Society. Alva gave her valuable and remarkable geologic library (3000 volumes) to UT and was a generous contributor to the UT geology department program. She remained active in her professional societies and kept her AAPG membership for 43 years until her death in 1964. (Fig. 10)

Teas (1965), writing her memorial said,

> Hers was surely an inquiring spirit of research. When she had an idea she never gave it up until it had been settled one way or another to her satisfaction. She was supremely confident and persistent in her pursuit of the solution of a problem. Her industry, alertness, and tenacity kept her hammering at an idea until a geologist took her to see what she wanted to see. Her clear thinking and analytical mind at times seemed to out-run that of geologists who had spent much more time on the same field problems with which she worked. She possessed an unusual acumen in working with forams in that she seemed able to recognize, almost at a glance, the proper stratigraphic position of a fauna. Surely we geologists have much for which to be grateful to this brilliant woman."

Figure 10. Alva Ellisor near her retirement. (Photo: Teas, 1965, p. 467.)

Esther English Richards Applin (1895-1972)

Esther Richards was the best paleontology student at the University of California Berkeley and worked as a paleontology assistant for three years while completing her degrees (Fig. 11). She gained her B.A. in geology in December 1918 and immediately started to work on her master's degree.

In the summer of 1919, E. T. Dumble, former director of the Bureau of Economic Geology in Texas and, at that time, the Chief Geologist for Southern Pacific (Rio Bravo) Oil Company, which had offices both in Houston and in San Francisco, called the Berkeley Geology Department and said he wanted to hire a paleontology expert (Fig. 12). Dr. Bruce Clark said, "We haven't a man, will a woman do?"

Figure 11. Esther Richards as a young woman, circa 1914. (Photo: Richard Lawless, grandson, Longview, Texas.)

Figure 12. Esther Richards when she graduated with her master's from the University of California, Berkeley, 1920. (Photo: Patty Kellogg.)

Dumble said, "I don't see why a woman couldn't do it better than a man."

And, Esther was hired for the summer job in Houston (from Esther Applins autobiographical notes). Little did she know that Dumble was "testing" her out for a project he was putting together with several other companies in Houston that would begin the following year.

Esther wrote in her memoirs (provided by her granddaughter, Patty Kellogg), "... he wanted me to work over his collection of macro-fossils ... in the Rio Bravo Oil Co. office ... I liked the work and as usual put everything I had into it."

In August, at the end of her summer employment, Esther had a difficult time getting back to California to finish her master's degree because yet another hurricane had hit Texas. It was not one as devastating as in 1900, but it disrupted rail travel enough to cause her to take a long, long "zig zagging" return route across country that made her late to start classes in Berkeley.

After finishing her M.A. degree in 1920, Dumble hired Esther to set up a Houston paleontology laboratory at Southern Pacific which soon became Rio Bravo Oil Company. (Fig. 13) Esther wrote,

> Mr. Dumble had drilled a well near Galveston, a few years earlier, that had been called the "Galveston deep well" about 3,000' deep ... they got a lot of small shells and shell fragments at one level, and a very fine paleontologist then on his staff determined the age of the beds thru a study of the fossils. I found they were a part of the Miocene formation. This was the first time the age of any buried or subsurface formation in the Gulf Coast area had been determined. Mr. Dumble hoped to apply the same method to the study of other wells drilling about the various salt domes. He had therefore talked over the project with several of the major oil Company geologists, (the Gulf, the Humble, the Texas company, and I believe a few others) and the three mentioned agreed to contribute money to the project and also furnish sets of well samples and other necessary data. The work was to be carried on in the Rio Bravo Co. offices and I arrived on Labor Day in 1920 to start the project.
>
> My job was to determine the age of the producing horizons, their relationship to each other, the angle of tilt, and work out the other complicated data involved in the problem.

Figure 13. Edwin T. Dumble, visionary on the use of fossils in exploration. He hired Esther Richards to work for a consortium in Houston using macro fossils to correlate well cuttings and became a life-long friend. Dumble facilitated match-making between Esther and Paul Applin. (Photo: the Jackson School Museum of Earth History, http://www.jsg.utexas.edu/vpl/history/, accessed 8/2/2016.)

It was rather typical of the Humble Co. and their trend toward the secretive methods they favored, that a month after I arrived they hired another woman geologist, Alva C. Ellisor, to set up a similar project in their offices. They agreed, however, to continue to cooperate in every respect with the Rio Bravo and the Texas and the Gulf companies according to the original plan.

I believe I mentioned earlier that all of the women specializing in geology and paleontology knew about each other, and Alva was one of the two at the Univ. of Texas. I had had some correspondence with her; so, when she arrived in Houston I was delighted to meet her. I had been living in the boarding house where I had stayed the summer before, but Alva and I found a nice apartment in the home of a Mrs. Brownee just off the main street and not too far from the center of town, and we moved in together. It was a splendid arrangement. We spent most of our evenings talking over the day's accomplishments and problems. Weekends we often went down to Galveston where Alva's mother lived and we went swimming in the Bay. Her mother was a dear and never seemed to mind having an extra girl around. (Fig. 14)

Figure 14. Hedwig Kniker, Esther Applin (by then), and Alva Ellisor in front of the apartment house they had shared before Esther's marriage. The three micropaleontologists would talk shop at night, have dinner parties, and trips to the beaches of Galveston for a break from work. (Photo: Patty Kellogg.)

Those little fun breaks helped to give added zest to the work of the following week. Dr. Dumble's idea had been to use fragments and young specimens of macrofossils (shells of various kinds) to determine the ages of the several formations ... of the materials being drilled into. I mentioned that he had successfully used this method in a study of samples taken from the "Galveston Deep well." However, Alva and I soon found that shells were extremely rare in any of the samples, and on the few occasions when we did find them, they were so badly broken by the drill that they couldn't be identified. However, Dr. Dumble, realizing that, at best, we would get only broken or very young specimens, decided to send me on a collecting tour to some of the well know places (called type localities) on the eastern Gulf Coast where several of the formations that might be expected to be present cropped out at the surface ...

I had discussed my plans for the trip with Mr. Dumble and mentioned that I would have a brief stopover [in New Orleans] between trains and he said, "I want to make one change. You will reach New Orleans one day and leave the next. You will need a day there just to rest and see the city."

Esther went on,

...to Vicksburg and Jackson in Miss., several small towns in the panhandle area of Fla and down the Fla peninsula to a little town way down in the Everglades, called LaBelle. The train only went as far south as Ft. Myers and there was a bus to take me the rest of the way. A man on the train who was going to Ft. Myers asked me where I was going and when I said LaBelle he said, "That's pretty wild country over there." LaBelle is on the Caloosahatchee River and near the center of the southern part of the peninsula, a little west of Lake Okeechoobee. The hotel was a rather plain wooden building but clean, freshly painted and airy. But when I went to the desk to register, the proprietor looking quite pale, was sitting in a rocking chair and apologized for not getting up saying, "I was shot last night." I thought my friend on the train wasn't so far off after all ... (Fig. 15)

Figure 15. Esther in the field, 1923, near Meridian, Mississippi. She is wearing her "puffy panties" and high leather boots. (Photo: Patty Kellogg.)

Pigs wandered about thru the town and the alligators, which were numerous, would come out at night and gobble up some of them. I found a nice woman, who took me in a row boat to collect my fossils along the banks of the Caloosahatchee. Snakes were also plentiful and I had a close call with a moccasin while collecting one outcrop... There was a party of government engineers also staying at the hotel ... they took me out with them on a few of their trips into the Everglades ... thru an area they said no white woman had ever been before. It was quite an experience. The Seminole Indians live in the Everglades and we saw a long line of them cross our path at one place—their costumes are very colorful and different from any other Indian group, and I remember being impressed with the utter silence of the passing of that great group. It seemed mysterious and rather spooky ....

Soon after I returned to Houston, both Alva and I had studied a sufficient number of well samples to know that determinable macro-fossils were very rare in the salt dome area we were working on. We had made a careful study of the lithology...and made up a table showing the relative time-relationships of the several units. But we still didn't know the age of the formations represented.

I was sent up to Austin to see some of the Geologists at the University of Texas and Dr. Udden, head of the Texas Bureau of Economic Geol. Dr. Udden's interest was confined mainly to the rocks. He was only incidentally interested in any fossils they might contain, but he had several graduate students working for him and their main job was to wash down the softer rocks, shale, etc., and save the residues. In doing this, some had noticed that in what was left after the mud had all been decanted off, there were groups of minute shells. They also noticed that from several formations which cropped out near Austin, they always got a group of these microscopic fossils mixed with a little sand and some other materials. They had also noticed that these groups were always reasonably alike in samples of the same formations and recognizably different in different formations.

The materials they had worked with were much older, geologically, than any we would expect to find in sub-surface deposits in our Houston area, but when I got back to my office, I began to try out their mud-washing techniques on the well samples I was working with (Fig. 16). Of course, I told Alva and she began to try it too. After what seemed to us to be a very long time, we hit pay dirt. It so happened that both Alva and I were working on samples from the same well on the same day, and found a nice collection of forams independently and at approximately the same time.

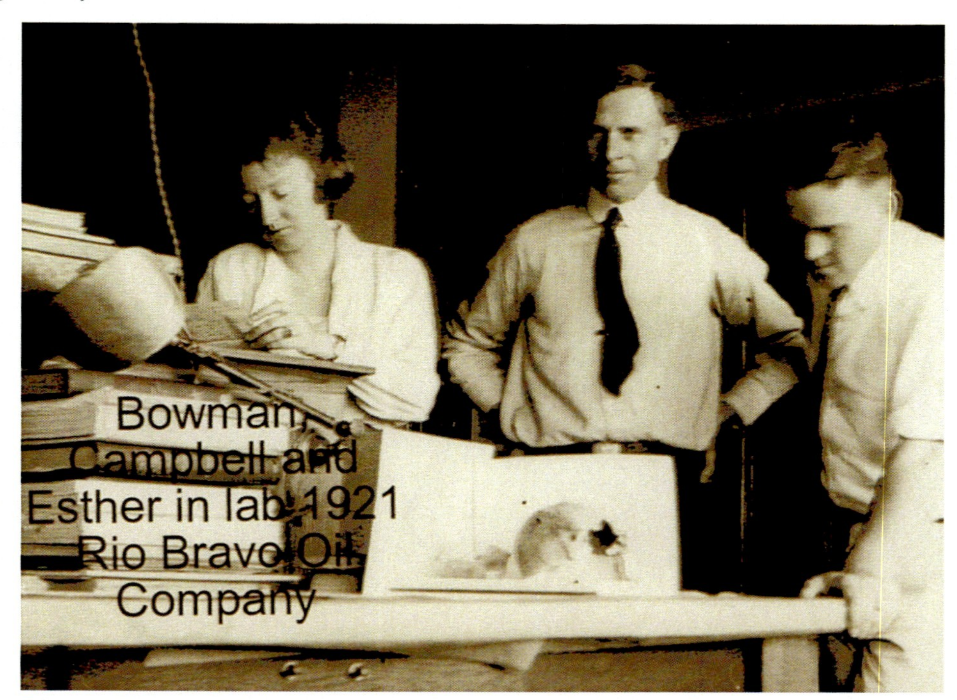

Figure 16. Esther, 1921, sorting out her first laboratory with colleagues Bowman and Campbell at Rio Bravo Oil in Houston. (Photo: Patty Kellogg.)

Dr. Dumble had a very good library which was adjacent to my office. Fortunately, it included several books on foraminifera, written mainly by Cushman, who was the only person in the U.S. then specializing on that group, but working mainly on recent species. But there was one book by T. W. Vaughan on some collections from Panama and one common species in the group of forams I had found was described and figured in Vaughan's article. It was *Heterostegina* and came from material that was definitely Oligocene in age. That was the first time any beds of Oligocene age had ever been recognized, on a faunal basis in Texas. So all in all it was a great day.

... We soon found that fauna in other wells on other salt domes. Then we found two other faunal units, one above and one below the first one we had discovered and were able to trace these also from well to well and record the changes in depth position. Then in a faulted well I discovered an older formation, the Jackson, and we knew our project was a success. Dr. Dumble and geologists in the other companies who had helped to get it started were delighted ... However, geologists and paleontologists in other parts of the country were a bit skeptical because it was a common belief at that time that "the simpler the organism was biologically, the longer its range stratigraphically ... Dr. Dumble wanted to spread the news that this wasn't true and that these simple organisms did change as rapidly in time as their more organically complicated macro-fossil relatives. So he wrote a short paper stating what we had accomplished and sent me up to the annual meeting of the prestigious Geological Society of America. The meeting was in Amherst, just after Xmas in Dec. 1921 and believe me that was an awe inspiring group of scientists. All of the big names from all the Ivy League colleges were there in force and all of the tops from the USGS in Washington. There were a few women, heads of Geol. Departments of Vassar, Bryn Mawr, etc.

Alva had gone with me and since neither of us knew much about what cold northern weather would be like we took all the heavy clothes we thought we might need. This included sets of 'long johns,', which we put on just before we reached New York, our first stop over. We soon learned that we didn't need that type of under garment, as we dashed around the big town. It snowed all day while we were in Boston and for two southern gals that was a lot of fun. I don't think we missed any of the well-known points of interest there from the famous and beautiful glass flowers at Harvard, to tombstones on Boston common. Alva was a very thorough sightseer and tried to make sure we didn't miss anything. We got a lot of fun, too, out of the strange accent and had some trouble in understanding what people were saying to us, and they were equally bothered by trying to understand us ...

... That was my first attempt at being a speaker, and when I got up to read Dr. Dumble's paper before that distinguished group, I was properly scared. I think I squeeked [sic] at first. For reasons given earlier, I knew that it would take a while to convince people in regard to the value and usefulness of our work. So, I wasn't too surprised when Prof. Galloway (of Columbia) got up just after I had finished and said, 'Gentlemen, here is this chit of a girl right out of college, telling us that we can use Foraminifera to determine the age of formation. Gentlemen, you know it can't be done.' ... However, a year later Galloway was telling the world that our idea was O.K. and he was one of the best on the subject of foraminifera and their usefulness as stratigraphic markers. Dr. Cushman ... came up to Alva and me after the meeting and invited us to come down to Boston and spend a day with him in his laboratory which we did. That was the beginning of a very fine friendship ...

... I can't progress beyond that trip to the Amherst meeting without mentioning a few other – to me – important events. I had met Paul [Applin], who had stopped over in Houston on his way to Panuco (Mexico) where he was to be a geologist for East Coast Oil Co. [another Rio Bravo company]. We became good friends and he wrote often after he got down there. In that way, he learned about my trip to New England and since he knew that I would be there over New Years, he wrote to his family in Keene [Mass] and said that a young woman he had met in Houston would be up in that area and he thought it would be nice if they found it convenient to invite me to spend New Year's in their home. I heard much later that Paul's family thought that if he was sufficiently interested in "'the young lady' to make the suggestion, they'd better take a good long look at her, and I got the invitation ... Alva went down to New York to spend New Year's with a friend who lived there. [The Applins] met me at the train and I thought they were great, and mother Applin was so sweet and hospitable ... they all made me feel as welcome, and so at home ... after dinner, when we were settled in the living room, mother said rather quietly, "Esther, a letter came today that I believe must be for you, its addressed to "Mrs. Paul Applin." [She was Mrs. Oscar Applin] I was stunned! Paul and I weren't even engaged.

The letter was actually meant for Alva containing the sad message that her father had passed away. Alva's boss, Wallace Pratt, did not know how to reach her and knew Esther was visiting Paul Applin's parents, so he just addressed the envelope to 'Mrs. Paul Applin,' thinking that was likely Paul's MOTHER's name. It caused a bit of shocking confusion!

Esther continues that Alva and she:

... visited about in the U.S. National Museum, met the U.S. Geol. Survey geologists there and had a most interesting, instructive and pleasant few days there. It was there that I met Julia Gardner of the USGS She was a well-known Paleontologist, working mainly with Miocene macro-fossils and later made a number of visits to Texas on collecting trips. So, I came to know her very well and always spent some time with her when I was in Washington. She had much charm and lots of quiet humor and a most interesting and unusual personality. She always lived at the Arts Club on I Street in Washington and Alva and I stayed with her while we were there on that first trip.

...Back in Houston again, we went on with our work and made steady progress on all aspects of the project. A year after the work began in my office, the Texas Co. decided to set up their own laboratory. The project had progressed so well and the work had increased to the point that they felt the change was justified. Hedwig Kniker, also from the Univ. of Texas, was put in charge of the Texas Co. laboratory and she moved into the apartment with Alva and me. The Texas Co. agreed to cooperate in the development of the project as originally planned and Alva, Hedwig and I spent most of our evenings studying the few books available on foraminifera and discussing our problems.

One of my jobs during this early development period was to talk to the drillers who were brought into my office, and explain why it was necessary for them to cooperate by getting the best samples possible and furnishing the most accurate data as to the depth, etc. and that helped us too. At one time, we went with a group of other top company geologists on a trip to study the outcrop (surface) exposures of the formations we had already determined to be present in the subsurface coastal area. Hedwig and I also made several collecting trips in and around Austin to get data and material from surface exposure of much older formations. This helped me at that time in my Mexican well sample work, and all of us later, when the companies started drilling in E. Texas and in more western and southern parts of the Gulf Coast.

... Not long after Hedwig [Kniker, see next section] came to work for the Texas Co., Grace Newman, my good friend from San Francisco, came to be my assistant in the Rio Bravo Oil Co. Lab. And she too moved in with Hedwig, Alva and me. We each took turns with the cooking, dish-washing and housecleaning jobs and, with a little manipulating by Grace and me, all went smoothly and well. There was a tendency toward some friction between Alva and Hedwig because of some job snatching deal Alva had pulled on Hedwig while they were in College together, but Grace and I managed to keep it under control. We all went down to Galveston on many week-ends, had some of the geologists and their wives and some of the younger geologists from our companies in for dinners now and then, went to movies and generally managed to have a happy time, when we weren't deeply buried in our work. And that was a joy too. I

Figure 17. One mode of travel during Esther's field work, being ferried across rivers and bayous. This is a 1923 crossing of the Alabama River. (Photo: Patty Kellogg.)

loved it and I know the others did ...

... Not long after Grace arrived, Dr. Dumble sent us on another collecting trip to what are called type localities, in Vicksburg and Jackson and Shuburta, Miss., Jackson, Ala. And several small cities in the panhandle region of W. Fla...we traveled by train and, in part, by automobile, and of course had to collect in pretty rough and out of the way places ... (Fig. 17)

A funny thing happened on that trip when we were in Shubuta in eastern Miss. Because of the kind of terrain we would be walking and crawling over, we needed pants and boots, and such articles of clothing were hard to come by at that time [1922] and Grace and I sent to Roose Brothers in San Francisco for our outfits. Mine was a heavy linen finished khaki-colored cotton, with a coat that came down about 2/3rds of the way to my knees, and what I called 'puffy panties,' tight below the knees and fitting into high leather boots [jodhpurs]. We went into the little town of Shabuta and walked down the main business street. There was not a soul in sight, as we walked past the stores, but we seemed to be followed by a sort of rustling murmur and when we looked back from near the end of the street, there was a bunch of heads sticking out of every doorway. When we got back to the hotel, which was really more like a boarding house, as in many small towns at that time, we changed into our regular clothes and went out to cool off and rest on the porch. Lots of cars came by, driving slowly, and in one of them a young boy hung out of the window and yelled, "Ma, they ain't either got on pants." On the same trip, in another town, Jackson, a man sitting next to Grace in the small hotel lobby asked her what we were advertising. It's hard to believe that there were such reactions to women in pants, in what seems to me to be not so very long ago.

Esther writes about how her personal life was an extension of her work life:

... I know you must be wondering about Paul and me during those very early Houston days. He came back from Mexico shortly after I returned from the Amherst trip and was a geologist for the Rio Bravo Oil Co. and we became very good friends. I remember that Alva went home with me on my summer vacation [to Alcatraz] that year and told my father that she was sure that that young man would someday be his son-in-law. I poo-pooed the idea, saying we were just good friends ... Paul was out of town a great deal, doing "field-work" ... he worked near San Antonio and near Austin and down around Laredo, and fairly often Dr. Dumble would send me out to spend the week-end in one of those cities and talk over the geology of the area with him (Fig. 18). Dr. Dumble admitted, a number of years later, that he was intentionally fostering the romance. That is why Wegi [Esther and Paul's daughter Louise] heard me say that Paul and I did most of our courting in the field. She interpreted that as, "corn fields" ...

Paul had a car and we would ride about and have dinner at interesting places and talk, of course, and we both came to realize how companionable we were and how much we enjoyed being together ... I recall too, a trip to Laredo when we went across into Mexico for dinner. There was a Mexican orchestra and another patio and I danced in the light rain which none of us really noticed. Julia Gardner was there too and acted as a sort of chaperone. A most pleasant one. Julia and I managed to smuggle a bottle of tequila back across the border. We got it for a friend in La., and on the train-trip back to Houston we both would pretend to be asleep whenever the conductor wandered up and down the aisle. They were on the lookout for such items which were verboten.

Figure 18. Paul and Esther Applin, left, 1925, on a field trip with two other geologists at Sabine Springs, Texas. (Photo: Patty Kellogg.)

So, after a while Paul and I became engaged and planned our marriage for Oct. 3rd, 1923. We kept it a secret for a while, but of course the girls knew about it and by that time there were 6 of us in the house. Bess Stiles who was secretary and assistant to the Chief Geologists of the Gulf Company—Dilworth Hager, and Laura Lane, another recent girl-graduate in geology from the Univ. of Texas, who had been hired as another assistant in my laboratory. Laura, Bess, and Laura's mother took another apartment on the upper floor of Mrs. Brownee's house ...

... Paul and I ... decided to be married in the smaller, Trinity Episcopal church out on Main Street .... Grace Newman was my bridesmaid and John Suman was Paul's best man ... we invited only our closest friends and had a morning wedding. Of course, the girls in the house helped me dress .... It was small but I have always thought, a very lovely wedding. Afterward Helen Plummer gave a beautiful wedding breakfast for us and the members of the wedding party. It was perfect, as everything she ever did always was ... On our honeymoon we went out to Los Angeles where we stayed a few days and then on up the coast to San Francisco and over to Alcatraz where Paul and dad met for the first time....

Esther and her family had moved to San Francisco in 1907 from Ohio, the year after the San Francisco Earthquake. Esther was twelve and had a younger sister about eight. Her father, an architect, directed the construction of the prison on Alcatraz Island (Fig. 19), and their home was on the island. At first, they lived in the old fort and Esther thought it was like living in an old castle. The family had a routine of shore trips every weekend to enjoy all that San Francisco and California had to offer. When she was a junior in high school, Esther's mother died, and she assumed responsibilities for taking care of both her younger sister and her father. She and her sister were also commuting by ferry to the city for school and, later, she commuted to San Francisco for college courses before she started at UC Berkeley.

Esther continues her autobiographical notes:

Paul and I had bought a little cottage ... some distance west of Rice Institute ... we received lots of beautiful wedding gifts .... The girls, Grace, Alva, Hedwig, Bess and Laura, all went together to get me my silver coffee service and tray ... I forgot to mention that the cloisonne tray was a wedding gift from two older women geologist friends, Rebba *[sic]* Masterson and Eunice Aden. Wegi may remember Eunice. She had a girls' camp on a lake near San Antonio that she and Rebba *[sic]* managed in the summer time, and when Wegi was quite little, she took her down there for a couple of weeks, taught her to swim, ride surf-boards etc. ....

Paul was gone a good deal, doing geological work in various parts of Texas and I went back to my work for the Rio Bravo Oil Co., I didn't like being alone at night and Grace moved in with us a short time after we returned.

For a period, both Paul and Esther battled illnesses. Esther had the flu (a death possibility in those days) and Paul fought equally life-threating scarlet fever and ilio-colitis. Esther also had inflammatory rheumatism. When they were well again, Paul returned to the field. Esther would sometimes meet him over the weekend, taking a train wherever that might be,

Figure 19. Alcatraz Island where Esther Richards grew up, taking the ferry to San Francisco for school. When she married Paul Applin in 1923, they spent part of their honeymoon on the island, to meet Esther's father, who helped build Alcatraz prison. (Postcard from the public domain, with Esther's family home circled by Alcatraz historian, John Martini, Fairfax, California.)

... so, I dressed for the day's activities that morning in my berth [into her field jodhpurs] ... a big-eyed porter looking at me said "Lawdee, Miss, I thought I put a woman in that berth.

... In 1924, the AAPG ... held their annual meeting in Houston. That was a most important meeting for Alva, Hedwig and me. Together, we were to present a paper discussing the several formations and their subdivisions, that we had established thru the use of the groups of foraminifera that each formation contained. The Houston geologists thought that it was time for a public announcement, and wanted those who had done the work to write up the report—I was asked to deliver the paper .... In our paper Alva wanted to do the Pliocene, Hedwig was equally anxious to do the Jackson, and I took the leftover Miocene. The preparations for the meetings, as well as the meeting itself made for very, very busy times for all of us. Geologists came from all over the U.S. .... To me, and to many others the most important one was Prof. Charles Schurchert, whom Paul had known and studied under at Yale ...

During the next two years things went along much as usual. New foram groups were being studied ... and I made a number of collecting trips in Texas ... spent occasional weekends with Paul in San Antonio and Austin .... In the late spring of '25 I learned that I was pregnant and that was really a great piece of news ... both Paul and I were very happy. I stayed well, and busy as usual. With Laura Lane Wienzel [she had married] I was working on a paper of the forams of the Yegua of Texas ... in fact we were working on that project until almost midnight of the night Wegi was born. Paul had left Rio Bravo to become chief geologist for J. S. Cosden in Ft Worth ... but because of mix-ups in communication and Wegi's fast arrival, Paul did not get the news for over 24 hours. When he finally called, Helen Plummer answered the phone and would not tell him if it was a boy or a girl, saying, "... you get down here and find out for yourself."

Esther continues,

I had a very good colored maid. A dear old lady, Molly, who was very competent and thoroughly reliable ... she was wonderful with Wegi and Wegi returned her affection. [Wegi was the Applins' nickname for daughter Louise] I went back to the office for part time each day not long after Wegi was born but did a great many things for her myself ... there were no prepared baby foods at that time, so I cooked and mashed the carrots, apple sauce and soups, etc. it was joyous work.

...I remember another unusual incident from Wegi's baby days. It was during the Xmas holidays. Paul was back in Ft. Worth and Grace had gone home to San Francisco as usual, so I was alone. Wegi got the colic in the night and I picked her up and carried her into the living room, and was trying to soothe her with some warm water and the extra warmth of the fire. There was a knock on the door, and holding Wegi, I went to answer it. A man was standing there with a mask over his face. Wegi was crying and we just looked at each other for a minute. Then he said, "I must have the wrong house" and left. I went back to my chair by the fire, but glanced at the clock. It was 3 o'clock. That was one robber who wasn't all bad.

Esther started working samples for Paul's exploration in Florida before she left Houston for Ft. Worth. That began a rich and rewarding package of historic research that lasted for decades, often publishing jointly with Paul, but ultimately helping to find oil and gas when it made a difference to them economically. In 1926, she resigned from Rio Bravo and joined Paul in Ft. Worth. Within months she set up an office in her home and started consulting in micropaleontology and subsurface geology and worked for companies in Houston and in Mexico.

Their second child, Paul Applin, Jr. or "Bud," was born in September of 1927. As Esther and Paul continued to work, they always had household help. "Lola" was an important employee for the Applins in Ft. Worth taking care of both house and children. At some point during that time, Esther's Aunt Nettie, her father's twin brother's widow, came to live with them and stayed until Nettie's death in the later 1930s. Not long after that, Paul's widowed mother came to live with them. Paul, Jr.'s daughter, Patty Kellogg, of Gloucester, Virginia, remembers her father complaining that both mom and dad (Esther and Paul) were rarely home. It is true that Esther loved to join Paul in the field, to go to meetings and to collect samples. Patty remembers her grandmother, Esther, as being very strict and formidable with children.

The Depression years were hard on everyone, often Esther's consulting income sustained them when Paul's pay was not always forthcoming, and frequently, he had to take property or interests for pay. That did not pay bills. Esther learned to pass children's clothes around, trading for the right sizes and doing the same with toys.

Once, she was down to her "last nickel" and pawned her jewelry. Sometimes Lola's pay was postponed, but because she lived and ate with the family, she managed, too. Freight trains, nearby, brought a constant stream of young men to the back door, which they fed, unfailingly. Elderly neighbors needed help with food, and the Applins would leave it on the doorstep to not embarrass them.

Esther said,

> ...both children often saw things they wanted me to buy for them and my repetitious reply was, "We'll have to wait dears, and see if daddy gets his oil well" ... Paul ... got no salary, however, only bits of acreage that would pay off only when a producing well was drilled on, or near it. That made our spending money pretty scarce of course, but almost everyone was in, more or less, the same situation ....[Esther took a bus trip with the children out to West Texas while Paul was drilling a well on one of their leases. The children were half-asleep and overheard men speaking.] ... some men got on and were standing in the aisle talking about some well that had just "come in". Bud opened one eye and murmured, "Daddy's oil well?"

That well did not come in and things got worse before they got better. Esther was hit by a car and hospitalized for a few weeks, mostly with a shoulder injury. She was doing therapy and in great pain in the hospital room when the phone rang:

> When I answered the phone the manager told me that he had concluded the deal and would give us so much in cash and so much in oil. A very substantial sum to our way of thinking, and I lost all interest in the pain my shoulder. We paid all our "depression" debts and as soon as they could take off my brace, we all went up to New England.

Esther and Paul were able to make living and financial arrangements for another aunt and move his mother to Texas. She continued, "All in all, it was so nice to have plenty of money, no bills to worry about, and to be able to do lots of nice things for those who were dear to us."

Esther's sister, Helen Richards, also moved in with them for several years during this time and enjoyed spending time with Wegi and Bud. Helen was with them when WWII broke out, but soon took a job in Washington, D.C. By then, Wegi was in college, but Bud was a teenager, still at home.

Esther was recruited to teach at UT while several professors went off to war. She commuted home to Ft Worth every weekend, taking the overnight bus on Friday night and returning to Austin on Sunday night. She went through a couple of trials with "maids" to take care of Bud during the week, which did not work out, but fortunately, a former Ft. Worth maid heard about her needs and took over for the duration. UT wanted to keep her on staff after the war (the professor she replaced was killed in the War), but she was anxious to return to Ft. Worth to prospect with Paul and continue her consulting work. She declined. She and Paul would join the U.S. Geological Survey in 1944 and continue to work on coastal geology until her retirement in 1972.

Figure 20. Esther Richards Applin, 1937, Fort Worth, Texas. Her gravestone with Paul reads "Pioneers in Science—Partners in Love." (Photo: Patty Kellogg.)

Jean M. Berdan, in the GSA Memorial for Esther said,

> Her descriptions of logging samples on oil rigs in the early days *when she was the only woman among the crew of drillers and roustabouts* [author's emphasis], were fascinating and some of her stories about hotel accommodations in small southern towns were enough to make one wonder about how good the "good old days" really were. Her tale of entering the lobby of the most magnificent hotel in Tuscaloosa with sample bags on her feet because her boots were wet and muddy was typical of her strong sense of practicality and ability to laugh at herself. (1972, GSA Bulletin, pp 14-18)

Esther English Richards Applin (Fig. 20) was a Fellow of GSA, a charter member and an Honorary Member of SEPM, and a member of the Mississippi Geological Society where she was also made an Honorary Member. Esther's AAPG membership was brief, though she was a great contributor to the Association. Not being "employed" and being married to a fellow petroleum geologist who retained his membership likely ended hers as it did for several other married women geologists (i.e., Helen Plummer, Isabel Wasson, and Helen Tappan Loeblich). In 1960, the GCAGS presented Esther Applin with a plaque to honor her accomplishments where the renowned petroleum stratigrapher E.H. Rainwater wrote, "It is no exaggeration ... she has contributed more to the knowledge of Gulf Coast stratigraphy than any other person."

Retirement from the USGS did not end Esther's career; she continued working until her death. Esther and Paul's gravestone in New Hampshire reads **Pioneers in science—Partners in Love.**

Hedwig Thusnelda Kniker (1891-1985)

How did a tiny, attractive, brilliant female geologist end up in a former penal colony at the "southern end of the earth" where temperatures seldom rose above 57° F and winds often got up to 130 mph? Punta Arenas (population 35,000) at the southern tip of South America (Fig. 21) was where Hedwig Thusnelda Kniker resided and worked as a consulting paleontologist and stratigrapher for nine years between 1940 and 1949. Hedwig's parents were German immigrants to Texas and she was raised in one of the many German communities, Cibolo, speaking German.

Figure 21. Hedwig Thusnelda Kniker, one of the first international female consulting geologists. (Photo: Janice Kniker Lee, Houston, Texas.)

While many things could have compelled Hedwig to leave her consulting business in San Antonio and move to the far ends of the earth, one can imagine living in the hostile climate that prevailed during WWII was probably the most compelling. From 1941 onwards, anti-German sentiment was rampant and country wide. There were three German internment camps in Texas, more than in any other state. With a high-profile career in the oil industry, Hedwig, at age 50, may well have thought living in South America was preferable for a while and would be absent the paranoia German ancestry. Single and fluent in Spanish and Portuguese as well as German, she moved herself to Punta Arenas, Chile to work for the United Geophysical Company, which later transitioned into the Chilean government Corporación de la Produción de Fomento.

Her work was essential to exploring the area south of the Strait of Magellan. Hedwig Kniker was one of the first American female geologists to work and consult internationally. Interestingly, her contract for the Corporación was under the consulting firm of Hoover, Curtice & Ruby, Inc. New York City. That was Herbert Hoover, Jr., son of President Hoover and, also, son of Lou Henry Hoover, the first woman to acquire a degree in geology from Stanford University. (Lou Henry met Herbert Hoover, Jr. in their geology lab).

C. R. Thomas wrote about the geology and petroleum exploration in Magallanes Province, Chile, where Punta Arenas was the major "city." "The climate, while not severe, definitely is not good ... any judgment of the climate based on these [average temperatures] will result in an erroneous conception. Very few warm days (shirt-sleeve type) occur during the summer, and very few calm days occur during the year. The most noticeable feature ... is the wind. While winds of 100 kilometers per hour are not frequent, practically any wind less than 40 kilometers per hour is regarded as a zephyr" (Thomas, 1949, p. 1556).

Thomas refers to Hedwig Kniker's technical work several times in his writings: "The understanding of the [stratigraphy] was cleared up by Glen M. Ruby and C. L. Mohr and was definitely settled by the foraminiferal studies of H. T. Kniker (Fig. 22)."

Hedwig left a few notes about her travel to and from South America recalling that travel "... used to be by ship, now planes also, [Washington] & to [Buenos Aires]. Dangerous through Canales, many ships sink, often old and

Figure 22. Hedwig with four colleagues in Valparaiso, Chile; she consulted there during and after WWII for several years. (Photo: Hedwig Thusnelda Kniker Family Papers, #10774, The Dolph Briscoe Center for American History, The University of Texas at Austin.)

overloaded. 1st [air] trip—New Orleans to Santiago, good pilots (better than U.S.) very few accidents."

Hedwig Kniker was ambitious even as a child, asserting early on her intention to attend college. Born into a strong German family and community of central Texas, she taught school after high school to earn enough money to start college in 1913 at the University of Texas in Austin. Completing her B.A. degree in three years, she had three majors—geology, German, and psychology. She was the second woman (Ellisor was the first) to be granted a geology degree at The University of Texas. (Fig. 23) The 1916 *Cactus* Yearbook describes her as a student assistant in Geology, "If you ever want her, look on the third floor, for there she lives, studiously buried in her 'ologies' ...." In 1917, she finished her M.A. degree, writing a thesis on the Comanchean and Cretaceous Pectinidae of Texas.

Figure 23. Hedwig collecting samples for her graduate work at The University of Texas at Austin. Her field attire would substantially change in the future. (Photo: Hedwig Thusnelda Kniker Family Papers, #10775, The Dolph Briscoe Center for American History, The University of Texas at Austin.)

Marion Whitney, daughter of Hedwig's major professor, Francis T. Whitney (Fig. 24), who inspired a generation of micropaleontologists, shared her memories:

> Hedwig had a desk in my father's laboratory where I spent many hours as a very small girl. I was fascinated by her remarkable names that fitted together in a rhythm that I loved to reel off like the names of the fossils that they studied: Hedwig Amanda Thusnelda Christina Sofia Kniker! She dropped four of the seven names when she went into the business world. (Whitney, 1994, p. 90)

Hedwig spent time at Cornell and at the University of Chicago doing more work on paleontology between 1917 and 1920 (Fig. 25). Then she returned to Texas to work with J. A. Udden at the Bureau of Economic Geology where she and fellow geologist, Edmund Bell Stiles (brother of Bess Stiles, the geophysicist), compiled volumes on Paleozoic fossils to be used for identifying Paleozoic fossils in well cuttings. (Fig. 26) Hedwig is credited with identifying and naming the Cretaceous McKnight Formation, a common subsurface marker, which she identified in 1938 from wildcat well cuttings in Dimmit County (*Lexicon of Geologic Names of the United States* for 1961-1967, USGS Bull. 1356, Grace C. Keroher, p. 454).

Figure 24. Francis T. Whitney, The University of Texas paleontology professor, offered the first university course on the subject. He inspired a generation of micropaleontologists. (The University of Texas at Austin, Jackson School of Geosciences.)

Figure 25. Hedwig, second from right, on what was probably her first oil rig, circa 1920, when she was studying in Chicago. (Photo: Hedwig Thusnelda Kniker Family Papers, #10776, The Dolph Briscoe Center for American History, The University of Texas at Austin.)

Figure 26. Hedwig in the field wearing more "modern" field attire. (Photo: Hedwig Thusnelda Kniker Family Papers, #10777, The Dolph Briscoe Center for American History, The University of Texas at Austin.)

In the fall of 1921, she was offered the opportunity to set up a paleontological lab for The Texas Company in Houston. As mentioned in the previous section, she roomed with Alva Ellisor and Esther Richards, her "competitors" in other companies. They were encouraged to collaborate and that led to their publishing their Gulf Coast research results (Fig. 27). Enticed away from the Gulf Coast by the drilling activity in West Texas in 1927, she left the Texas Company and took a job in San Angelo with Phillips and later with Ricker and Dodson.

Figure 27. Typical laboratory attire for the 1920s era per Shell Oil retiree, Ed Picou. From left to right: Hedwig Knicker, Esther Applin, and Alva Ellisor. (Photo: Applin Family, Patty Kellogg.)

By 1930, she moved to San Antonio and set up her own consulting business. She always went by her initials as a consultant, H. T. Kniker, so that prejudice against her as a female might be avoided. It worked. Many times, clients were surprised to learn their consultant was a female.

"Though she was a geologist, Hedwig was heavily involved in the business side of oil and gas. She conversed often with CEOs from oil and gas companies ... most surprised when they heard her voice and found she was a woman" (personal communication with her niece, Janice Kniker Lee related in 2015).

Janice Kniker Lee shared other memories of her adored aunt:

> She decided I should study rocks and my sister should study fossils, so she continually sent specimens to us. But she also believed in people having a passion for what they did, so she was supportive when we chose other careers. She loved to spend time with her family, especially for holidays. She was a joy to be around, very fun loving and loved to talk sports, business and oil

and gas. She loved to tell jokes! And had a great sense of humor. When all the women were gathered in the kitchen, she would be in the living room talking "guy stuff" with the men.

Figure 28. The Tower at The University of Texas at Austin where Hedwig Knicker's carillon bells were installed, and the Kniker Carillon a tribute to her generosity. (Photo: Larry D. Moore, ca 1980, CC BY-SA 3.0, accessed 12/3/2016.)

Janice Kniker Lee remembers that Hedwig never did anything half way but what she did, she did it 150%. When she bought a home in Seguin and wanted to put in a garden, she researched gardening, seeds, plants, etc., and became an expert. Her backyard was more than sufficient for a magazine feature. When Janice told her aunt Hedwig she was engaged to someone from Seguin, Hedwig went to the high school teachers there and then to professors at UT in Austin and checked out the fiancé's worthiness and abilities!

Hedwig retired in 1950 and moved back to Seguin, Texas, where she continued to consult and publish her work. Her philanthropy includes setting up the Hedwig T. Kniker scholarship in San Antonio for high school students in science and providing carillon bells for "The Tower" at UT (Fig. 28). The Kniker Carillon is a tribute to her name. Hedwig was also a generous contributor to the Geology Department Foundation at UT.

Figure 29. Hedwig in her late retirement years, still joking and laughing at life. (Photo: Janice Kniker Lee.)

In 2008, Hedwig (Fig. 29) was inducted into the UT Jackson School of Geosciences Hall of Distinction. She was elected to Honorary Membership with the South Texas Geological Society, was an Honorary Member of the Gulf Coast Section of SEPM and was a member of AAPG for 59 years.

Chapter 7: Sources and References

Applin, Esther Richards, Alva E. Ellisor, and Hedwig T. Kniker. 1925. "Subsurface Stratigraphy of the Coastal Plain of Texas and Louisiana." *AAPG Bulletin*, vol. 9, no. 1, pp. 79-122.

Barrow, Thomas (Tom) D. 1962. "Alva C. Ellisor, Distinguished Geology Alumna." *University of Texas Bulletin*, July, p. 2.

Berdan, Jean M. 1972. "Esther English Richards Applin Memorial." *GSA Bulletin*, vol. 84, pp. 14-18.

Devastation of the Galveston Hurricane. 1900. Photograph. Library of Congress, Prints and Photographs Division. Washington, D.C. #LC-USZ62-120389. http://hdl.loc.gov/loc.pnp/cph.3c20389. Accessed 01/19/2017.

Ellisor, Alva. 1947. *Rockhounds of Houston: An Informal History of the Houston Geological Society.* Houston Geological Society. Houston, Texas, 99 pp.

Kellogg, Patty, Gloucester Virginia, granddaughter of Esther and Paul Applin. Personal communication, June 2016 through December 2016; source of photographs as cited in figure captions.

Keroher, Grace C. 1970. "Lexicon of Geologic Names of the United States for 1961-1967." *USGS Bulletin 1350*, 848 pp.

Kniker, Hedwig Thusnelda. Family Papers, 1887-1987. Dolph Briscoe Center for American History. The University of Texas at Austin, Austin, Texas.

Lee, Janice Knicker. Houston, Texas, niece of Hedwig Knicker. Interview with Amanda Haddad (04/2015), source of stories and photographs of Hedwig Knicker as cited in figure captions.

Martini, John. *Alcatraz Island – San Francisco Bay.* n.d. Annotated photograph. Alcatraz historian, Fairfax, California. Public domain.

Moore, Larry D. *The Tower at The University of Texas at Austin.* ca. 1980. Photograph. CC BY-SA 3.0. https://en.wikipedia.org/wiki/Main_Building_(University_of_Texas_at_Austin)#/media/File:The_Tower,_University_of_Texas_at_Austin_(ca_1980).jpg. Accessed 12/3/2016.

Pratt, Wallace. 1927. Photograph. American Association of Petroleum Geologists Archives, Tulsa, Oklahoma.

Reed, R. D. 1931. "Microscopic subsurface work in oil fields of United States." *AAPG Bulletin*, vol. 15, no. 7, pp. 731-756.

Rolshausen, F. W. and R. D. Woods. 1946. "The Search for Oil." *The Humble Way*, vol. 1, no. 5 Jan-Feb, pp. 17-22. Archived ExxonMobil files, Dolph Briscoe Center for American History, The University of Texas at Austin, Austin, Texas.

Teas, L. P. 1965. "Alva Christine Ellisor, (1892-1964) Memorial." *AAPG Bulletin*, vol. 49, no. 4, pp. 467-471.

Thomas, C. R. 1949. "Geology and Petroleum Exploration in Magallanes Province, Chile." *AAPG Bulletin*, vol. 33, no. 9, pp. 1553-1578.

The University of Texas at Austin. *Tom Barrow.* 1991. Photograph. College of Natural Sciences, Hall of Honor. Austin, Texas. https://cns.utexas.edu/about/hall-of-honor/past-recipients. Accessed 01/23/2017.

The University of Texas at Austin. *Edwin T. Dumble.* ca. 1890-1894. Photograph. The Jackson School Museum of Earth History. http://www.jsg.utexas.edu/vpl/history/. Accessed 08/2/2016.

The University of Texas at Austin. *Alva Ellisor.* 1915. Photograph. *The Cactus* yearbook. Austin, Texas. p. 221.

The University of Texas at Austin. *Francis L. Whitney (1878-1962).* n.d. Photograph. Faculty Through Time, In Memoriam. Jackson School of Geosciences. Austin, Texas. http://www.jsg.utexas.edu/about/history/faculty-through-time-in-memoriam/francis-l-whitney/. Accessed 01/19/2017.

University of Houston. *600 block of Main Street facing south at Texas Avenue.* 1923. Photograph. Special Collections, University of Houston Libraries, University of Houston Digital Library. Houston, Texas. Web. http://digital.lib.uh.edu/collection/p15195coll2/item/185. Accessed 01/18/2017.

University of Houston. *Houston downtown composite panorama.* ca. 1928. Special Collections, University of Houston Libraries, University of Houston Digital Library. Houston, Texas. Web. http://digital.lib.uh.edu/collection/p1519coll2/item/197. Accessed 01/18/2017.

Whitney, Marion. 1994. "Marion Whitney Replies…" *The University of Texas at Austin, Department of Geological Sciences Newsletter,* no. 44, p. 90.

The University of Texas, a fossil-collecting trip with Professor Francis Whitney. Hedwig Kniker is the second from the left. About 1916, and a woman's field attire was less than suitable for the task. (Photo: Hedwig Thusnelda Kniker Family Papers, #10778, The Dolph Briscoe Center for American History, The University of Texas at Austin.)

Chapter 8

Earliest Women Geologists to Enter Geophysics

Reflection Seismic, the first Discovery

Predicting where to find oil and gas buried deep below the surface of the earth was very difficult for early geologists. They took their clues from mapping rocks on the surface, seeing how rocks are folded or faulted and making sub-surface speculations. Sites for drilling were based on these speculations, and dubbed "prospects." But, this resulted in many wells being drilled that were "dry holes"—no commercial oil or gas. In these early years, Wallace Pratt estimated that 1000 wells were drilled before a large discovery was found (Pratt, 1937). That was expensive, even then, because the buried rocks were often more complicated than could be imagined. Paleontology was greatly assisting the search for oil and gas by enabling geologists to correlate—to match one strata or layer of rock with another and make better predictions. But, this technology had its limitations, especially in areas where the rocks were folded and faulted and greatly modified through the burial time.

Measuring sound waves that are created at or near the ground/surface was discovered as a useful tool for subsurface oil and gas exploration in the 1920s. The first exploration work (done in Mexico and on the Texas Gulf Coast) was with refracted sounded waves—meaning waves that bent as they traveled through rocks of different types. But the "*most powerful tool in exploration*" (Owen, 1975, p. 508) was when physicists and geologists worked together to look at reflected sound waves. Reflected sound waves bounce off a rock layer and return to the surface. Measuring the time it takes to send a sound wave into the earth and record its return gives a geophysicist (the person who combines physics and geology) an idea of how deep the rock layer is in that spot. The birth of geophysics!

This application to oil and gas exploration with reflection waves was born in Oklahoma when John C. Karcher and Burton McCollum began experimenting with it and applying for patents. Everette DeGolyer's company, Geophysical Research Corporation (GRC), was formed with the purpose of furthering this experimentation and bought out Karcher and McCollum's patent. For many months, the process was under development—creating better ways to make a sound wave at the surface from "thumping" with a hard object, to setting off dynamite on the surface, to putting dynamite in shallow holes drilled at the surface. They also developed better listening devices which gathered the sound waves and better ways for collecting and recording this data (see Owen, 1975, pp. 508-511 for more on reflection development).

Finally, it was time to test the technology with the drill bit.

Dollie Radler Hall

(See also Chapter 3, Earliest Managers)

Dollie Radler Hall (Fig. 1) played a key role in the advancement of reflection seismology for exploration.

It's Oil in Day's Work

DOLLIE RADLER, geologist, attending Petroleum Convention here, and the magnetometer, which locates oil structures.

Figure 1. Dollie Radler was instrumental to the reflection seismic program of 1927-28; the first discovery made using the data was in 1928. Newspaper photo of Dollie Radler with a magnetometer at the 13th Annual AAPG Convention. (Photo: San Francisco newspaper, late March or April, archived by Dollie's family, Bethan Read, Jackson, Mississippi.)

The first well drilled on a reflection seismic anomaly that was on Amerada's leases was a failure. But, in September, 1928, when Amerada's second well was drilled it became the **first successful oil discovery using reflection seismic.** Dollie and Sidney Powers used the records supplied by GRC to pick locations. The discovery opened the door for extensive use of reflection technology. It was later written, "She was a pioneer in the introduction of the reflection seismograph in oil finding in Oklahoma oil fields in the late 1920s" (*Broken Arrow Sco*ut, June 2, 1993, p. 6A).

The interesting untold story behind this was that during the time the data was being collected and analyzed, Sidney was critically ill and hospitalized on January 20, 1928 and was in and out of the hospital through June 10. In July, he was still ill, though frequently back in the office, and he remained difficult to work with and very pessimistic until he finally underwent spleen surgery in 1929 (correspondence between Dollie Radler Hall and Rodger Denison 1927/28). In fact, Dollie wrote to Rodger in July, 1928 that Sidney wanted to get rid of the whole geological department! Dollie related this memory to Tim Denison, Rodger's son, that Sidney did not recover his positive attitude and health until his operation (from Dollie correspondence Oct 21, 1974). While "Dollie and Sidney" were picking locations using the new seismic data, Dollie must have been carrying the bulk of the work load and responsibility for decisions.

Dollie was very involved with the experimental reflection seismic surveys of 1927-1929 as the manager in charge of all Oklahoma and Kansas exploration and sometimes branching to north Texas and areas in the Rocky Mountain region. Per her later words (Tulsa World, Dec. 24, 1978, page 8, Section G), she was also in charge of the crew supplies. Because the surveys were secret, the dynamite for the operations was never bought under the name of Amerada. Friends teased Dollie later about how many boxes of dynamite they saw with *her* name on them! In January 1928, she even had to deal with a GRC crew member suffering a "complete nervous breakdown" and his hospitalization [possibly reacting to the charge explosions]. She thought it was due to his WWI war experiences—it would be called Post Traumatic Stress Disorder (PTSD) today. She said, in her letter to Rodger Denison, "This trouble probably accounts for many of his peculiar 'tantrums' last summer." That was the summer of 1927, when GRC started their reflection seismic program in Oklahoma. February 3, 1928, she wrote to Rodger, "Finally got the G.R.C. settled yesterday. Surely have quite a program laid out. Wonder how long it will stand as outlined? Maybe until DeG's [DeGolyer's] next visit."

She mused additionally, "Guess you heard about the car DeG and Karcher burned up in Texas? Am sure very little was said about it here."

The secrecy of their reflection seismic operations is further revealed in her correspondence to Rodger January 30th, 1928 when she writes, "Received your telegram this PM about G.R.C. If your advice is asked wish you would point out the fact that we are being scouted by both Pure and Gypsy that the Pure scout is a graduate geologist and all men on the parties must be very careful in statements made and datum figures being used. Also, should follow a regular plan and not double back and retest shots as in past. We sometimes forget that other companies are not as dumb as we would like for them to be."

In June, she said to Rodger, "If you have any grievances to report against the G.R.C. I wish you would plan on being present here when the famous conference is held. If we don't say what we have to say now we will have another year of grief thrust upon us."

Reflection seismology proved to have such great prospective value that Amerada decided to restrict GRC's employment of the method to exploratory projects in which it was a sole or part-interest owner. The company maintained an imposing record for many years thereafter (1975, Owen, p. 511).

Early Female Geologists in Geophysics

Three other female geologists had careers in geophysics in the earliest days of that new technology. Bess Stiles was a founder of the Society of Exploration Geophysics (SEG), Grace Hower was the first to work on a seismic crew, and Anne Frank was the first female geophysical crew chief and could share her stories as a crew member during WWII and afterwards. Also, we can point to Fanny Carter Edson (see Chapter 4) as an early geophysical pioneer when she used magnetic data for mapping in the earliest part of the 20th century in Minnesota.

M. Elisabeth Stiles (1889-1965)

Figure 2. Bess Stiles, circa 1950. The only founding female member (1930), of the Society of Exploration Geophysicists. (Photo: Kathy Leadford, Austin, Texas.)

Margaret Elisabeth "Bess" Stiles chose to study geology at The University of Texas at Austin around the year 1910 (Fig. 2). She studied geology for two to three years and also worked as a secretary and assistant to J. A. Udden, the Director of the Bureau of Economic Geology (BEG). Udden was an early proponent of using seismic for oil and gas exploration (1965, Owen, pp. 509-510) and may have instilled Bess's early interest in geophysics. Bess is listed on the BEG staff in the records of 1905 through 1915 (she prepared the Annual Report for the year, 1915). Owen (1965, p. 523) mentions that she was the curator of collections at the BEG in 1917. Early BEG records of staff members are not very complete so it is difficult to piece together the working staff and their responsibilities in these early years.

The Stiles and Bell families were apparently early residents of Austin and/or Hamilton, Texas. Bess and her brother, Edmund Bell Stiles, remained in the area for some years as there are tax reports in 1919 showing that she and her brother owned a home together in Austin. Bess's brother also worked for the Bureau as a geologist and published several papers for the Bureau, one with Hedwig Kniker (see Chapter 7). He later married and had one daughter, Emily Bess Cathey. Emily Bess held oil and gas leases which were passed on to her children when she died in 1998. A great niece, Kathy Leadford of Austin, Texas, owns a share of these royalties and attributes them to "Aunt Bess."

Two very interesting Stiles' items are archived in the BEG files at the Briscoe Library in Austin. One is a manuscript, unpublished, that Bess wrote about a BEG Director prior to Udden entitled "Life and Reminiscences of E. F. Cummins" (by M. E. Stiles, 1922, Briscoe Library). Another item was a letter she wrote to a person who had inquired about oil potential of the Ellenburger Formation on her land and did not like the response she received from Director Udden. Bess wrote to the woman:

Dear Madam:

I regret to say that we have no publication on the Ellenburger other than the one listed at $5.00. This would be of no value to you at any price. It consists of microscopic views of the Ellenburger lime, made from thin sections of the stone prepared in our laboratory by trained workers and studied under powerful microscopes by trained men; and would be of value in determining the Ellenburger lime only by comparison with other such views, similarly prepared and similarly studied, of the material to be determined.

May I add to this a purely personal word, Mrs. Armstrong? You make the astounding statement in your letter to me that Dr. Udden was once geologist to the Kaiser. Let me say for your information that Dr. Udden is of Swedish extraction, not German; and that he is not only himself an American citizen of some fifty-seven years' standing, but that his father before him fought as an American citizen in the Civil War. In view of these facts, it is difficult to see how a rational person could make such a dangerously careless statement as you have made. Before you repeat such a statement, either orally or in writing, I would strongly advise you to look up the Revised Statute of this state regarding libel. I have no intention of letting your present remark go any further, as it may be due purely to ignorance on your part; but a repetition of the offense in some other quarter might not meet with such consideration, as Dr. Udden is widely known, and has many friends.

Very truly yours,
M. E. Stiles (Letter from M. E. Stiles archives, Dolph Briscoe Center, The University of Texas at Austin)

In the early 1920s, Bess left Austin to work in Houston where she was hired by L. P. Garrett, Gulf Oil's Chief Geologist, and a pioneer himself in geophysics. He was also an alum of The University of Texas and hired several geologists from the University during his career. His hiring of Bess coincided with his increased involvement in seismic exploration and the formation of Gulf's geophysical department. Although she was hired as a geologist, it appears she was hired for the new geophysical department and became the first female pioneer in geophysics. Esther Richards Applin (Chapter 7) noted that "Bess Stiles" also shared the famous living quarters in Houston that all the micropaleontologists of the 1920s shared.

Bess described herself as "office manager" for Gulf Oil Production's Geophysical Department when she joined AAPG in 1927. Gulf was the first company to use refraction seismic in North America and subsequently made the first discovery, a salt dome, in June 1924. Several other Gulf Coast salt dome discoveries quickly followed.

Figure 3. E. B. Stiles, sitting, brother of Bess Stiles; the woman behind him who has a family resemblance, is likely Bess. 1922 Southwest Geological Society meeting in Dallas, Texas. (Photo: Newsletter, University of Texas at Austin, Department of Geological Sciences, no. 13, 1964 p. 40.)

The first seismic crew for Gulf's earliest discovery was from Germany, Seismos Gesellschaft. They had developed a very slow profiling method and their technique was limited to finding only shallow salt plugs. Although it was a very slow operation, their early discoveries inspired many to immediately try seismic (Owen, 1975, p. 504-505). Roxana used a second Seismos crew and found at least six more salt dome discoveries between 1926 and 1930.

Amerada Petroleum's Everett DeGolyer and others embraced the seismic exploration concept and wanted to improve both speed and cost. The German company, however, was not keen on making the suggested changes prompting DeGolyer to form the Geophysical Research Corporation (GRC) as an affiliate of Amerada Petroleum Corporation in 1925. He had a team design new equipment, and in less than a year put its first two crews in the field in March and April 1926 under contract to Gulf Oil. E. E. Rosaire was the party chief and had immediate success for Gulf finding two new salt dome fields by June. Moss Bluff Dome was the first salt dome discovery using an American seismic company. There were ten more by 1928. Humble Oil under Pratt's direction and eventually Gulf developed their own seismic methods (Owen, 1975, pp 504-514).

Rosaire left GRC to form his own company, Independent Exploration Co, and hired Bess away from Gulf to work with him on incorporating the company in 1932. Bess Stiles and Rosaire were the co-authors of "Exploration on the Gulf Coast to 1936" (*GEOPHYSICS*, v. 1, p. 141-148. Bess was coauthor, with E. E. Rosaire, on two additional papers (Rosaire, E.E. and M. E. Stiles, 1932a 1932b).

Bess Stiles was one of nine women founders of the Houston Geological Society (HGS) in 1923 which was formed at Wallace Pratt's behest to host the

1924 AAPG Annual Meeting. Alva Ellisor was the first vice president of HGS (1924) and Elisabeth Stiles was vice president in 1925 and 1926. She served on several non-technical committees for the 1924 AAPG Convention and continued to be active as noted in reports from the 1941 Annual Meeting in Houston. (Fig. 3)

Bess was also a Founding member of SEG in 1930, the only woman among 29 men. She was active in the society and served on the Executive Committee as Secretary/Treasurer in 1937-38. Bess was one of the first two associate editors of *GEOPHYSICS*, the other being her colleague E. E. Rosaire. When SEG needed a business manager in 1938-39, she became "acting manager" until a manager could be hired permanently. In the mid-1940s, SEG again lost their Director and Bess stepped in and served in that role until a new Director was hired. Former SEG President, Sally Zinke, comments that, "Stiles 'saved SEG' during WWII as most geophysicists had been called to military service." Her colleagues felt Bess Stiles "set the standard" for volunteer efforts. She was the third person, and first woman, to receive SEG Life Membership in 1961 for her meritorious service.

Bess Stiles never married. Her great niece, Kathleen Leadford of Austin, Texas, relates that the family still has producing oil and gas royalties that she believes came from Aunt Bess's exploration efforts. Bess retired to her Circle S Ranch, in Hamilton County, Texas and died in 1964 at age 78.

Sara Grace Hower (1912-1993)

Sara Grace Hower may be the first woman to have worked on a seismograph field party, as she apparently did this before WWII. Grace, a native of Mifflintown, Pennsylvania, received her bachelor's degree at Barnard College, New York in 1933. She continued her education as a graduate student and teacher at Columbia University and Bryn Mawr College (Fig. 4). Toward the end of the Great Depression Grace left the east coast to work as a geological mapper for Aero Exploration Company in Oklahoma (Tulsa World July 24, 1993).

Figure 4. Grace Hower, Barnard and Bryn Mawr graduate. She struggled to find work in geology, so she taught and did geophysical work until WW II when she became employed at Amerada—going back to her "true love" –geology. Amerada was a company that enthusiastically combined geology and geophysics. (Photo: Mortar Board *yearbook, Barnard College, 1933, p. 68.)*

Dollie Radler Hall (Hall, 1965, p. 297) wrote of her:

> "[Grace] also taught for a short while at the depth of the depression and worked for a time in geological interpretation of areal maps without salary in order to prove that she could do the job [with Aero Exploration Company]. Later with S.S.C. [Seismograph Service Crew] she conducted magnetometer surveys [in the Arbuckle Mountains] and worked as a computer on a seismograph party."

In 1945 Grace Hower began work with Amerada Petroleum Company as a geophysical coordinator for exploration and exploitation (Tulsa World Jul 24, 1993). "When geologists were at a premium during the Second World War she returned to her first love, geology. She is now employed by Amerada. Her experience in both geology and geophysics makes her a valuable employee, especially in the coordination of geology and geophysics. Her hobby is adding to her rare collection of rocks and minerals, especially fresh water pearls" (Hall, 1965, p. 297). Grace was working for Dollie Radler Hall at Amerada as did many women geologists during Amerada's early years.

Figure 5. Grace when she was working at AAPG headquarters, after her retirement from Amerada. She is with her colleague, Robert Dott. (Photo: Pam Howell, Tulsa, Oklahoma.)

After Grace Hower retired, she worked her "third career" at AAPG as Bulletin Editor. She had a reputation of being eccentric and flashy and a "crusty type" with a full head of curly white hair and a penchant for bright- colored clothes. She was extremely professional, relates Ron Hart, AAPG staff who worked with Grace. She also volunteered at the government document department of the Tulsa Central Library (*Tulsa World*, Jul 24, 1993).

Grace's neighbor, Pam Howell, recalled that Grace had an amazing garden that she shared with friends and neighbors, and though tiny—about five feet tall—she was strong and physically hard-working. Grace Hower was a member of both the Geological and Geophysical Societies of Tulsa and was a member of AAPG for 50 years (Fig. 5).

Anne Robins Frank (1919-)

When Anne Robins told her family she wanted to study geology most of them discouraged her and said that it wasn't a fitting career for a lady. Her father, however, stood by her decision and said, "If that is what she wants, that is what she can do!"

Anne has forever cherished his support as she would the men who respected and supported her throughout her "unlady-like" career.

Anne Robins grew up in Canton, New York where her father was a college professor at St. Lawrence University. Her mother came from Massachusetts where she and all her sisters had attended Bryn Mawr College in Pennsylvania and where two had graduated. Anne recalls her aunts convincing her mother she wasn't mature enough to go to Bryn Mawr out of high school in 1936 (age 16) so she went for a year to Abbot Academy in Andover, Massachusetts. She said, "...the guardian Victorian ladies who watched over the girls at Abbot, Andover were over the moon. You need to know how Abbot treated the other half of the human race. Friday evening was date night at Abbot. There was a large room with several sets of upholstered furniture, a radio, no TV (hey – this is 1936!) and at least one chaperone. Each Abbot girl had a list of eligible young men who would be allowed to call on her on Friday only. The list had to be signed by her parents. My list had zero young men on it. My parents wouldn't approve–sight unseen. Abbot girls were expected to get their exercise in walks around Andover. There were several walks but they all followed prescribed paths. The young ladies had to wear low-heeled shoes, cotton stockings, gloves (pulled up to the elbow) and hats. The walks could be taken any day but Saturday (Andover boys had Saturday off). In fact, the only time our guardians admitted the existence of Andover boys was in preparation for our Senior Ball for which we were provided with blind dates from Andover (and we never saw them again)."

After a year at Abbot Academy, Anne enrolled in Bryn Mawr where she had intended to study French (Fig. 6). Required to take a couple of science classes, she signed up for geology and within two weeks she was sure that geology was what she wanted to do!

Figure 6. Anne Moring Robins, her senior year at Bryn Mawr College, 1939, (Photo: Bryn Mawr College yearbook, 1940, p. 76, with permission from Bryn Mawr College Special Collections.)

In 1938, during the summer after sophomore year in college, I went to the University of Michigan to take their Geology Field Camp (Fig. 7). We drove in station wagons (or what passed for SUVs in 1938) from Ann Arbor through Chicago, Madison, and then west to the Black Hills where we checked out Rapid City and then drove to Cheyenne and then down the front range to Rocky Mountain National Park and then to State Bridge, Colorado where we stayed for a month before doing a similar trip through Salt Lake City and then north to Idaho. From there we drove east into Jackson, WY from the back side of the Tetons. The University of Michigan had a camp about 20 miles south of Jackson. It was still there about 15 years ago when I made a second trip. The entire trip from Ann Arbor to Jackson was really something special for a student like me who had been across the Mississippi River only once and that was to Keokuk, Iowa. Dreams don't come true from things any better than that trip. And the best part of it is that I still feel that way [at age 96]! We spent the second half of our summer school in Jackson and then returned to Ann Arbor in the same convoy.

Figure 7. Anne in the field as a geology student at Bryn Mawr, 1939. (Photo Bryn Mawr yearbook, 1940, p. 76, with permission from Bryn Mawr College Special Collections.)

Anne went to work after graduating in 1940 for the Ohio Oil Company (later Marathon) in Marshall, Illinois and joined AAPG in 1942. She says, "The position consisted of taking dictation (I took no shorthand, just fast notes), typing (mediocre), and drafting (no idea). Yes, I was a secretary" (From *The Leading Edge*, Feb 1991, p. 47).

Ohio Oil Company "oozed" her into more geological tasks, running well samples and correlating well logs. She did not like living in Marshall and working in the Illinois area. She found it too "*flat, flat, flat!*" But Anne had promised Ohio Oil she would stay two years and did. When her two years were over, she went back to New Hampshire, where her parents had a summer place, and on the way made a stop in New York City to job hunt.

Making the rounds of all the oil companies while she stayed with Bryn Mawr classmates, Anne only had one nibble that she vaguely remembers was from Gulf Oil. However, soon after she arrived in New Hampshire she was contacted by the General Geophysical Company, which had been working for Ohio Oil acquiring surveys in Illinois. During her two years at Ohio Oil, Anne had become acquainted and socialized with the crew members and they had recommended her to their corporate office when the company was looking for replacements for crew members going off to WWII. They thought a "girl" could handle some of the crew work. General Geophysical offered Anne a job in Indiana, but she said she would go anywhere but Illinois and Indiana as she had been there and didn't want to go back. They said they had an opening in Oklahoma and Anne said, yes, sight unseen!

Anne Robins arrived with two suitcases of belongings in Pauls Valley, Oklahoma and became a "computer" on a field crew. A "computer" did all the math calculations with seismic recordings, adjusting for elevations, time deviations, velocity corrections, and converting time to depth, Anne recalled. Records were displayed with photographic techniques, one shot point at a time. The things done in Nano seconds today by a "black-box" computer were, of course, done by humans in the early seismic years. This was also true of "computers" for jet and rocket trajectories as well as for the code "computers" in WWII; behind the scenes were many women doing the math!

Anne commented further, "Neither two years at the Ohio offices nor, much less, an education in New England academia had prepared me for such a culture shock. The values and manners I had grown up with were of no use, and even a hindrance, amid that breed of men collectively known as a field crew. They worked hard, played hard, talked hard, and drank hard. Through the years, I met many of their kind and nobody could ask for a stauncher group of associates" (*The Leading Edge*, Feb, 1991, p. 47).

Anne continues, "It must have been awkward for those men to make room for a woman in the 'manly' world of doodle bugging [slang for working on a seismic crew]. But the anomaly was supposed to be only temporary, given that the shortage of young men left no other options."

Anne spent eleven years on field crews, first with General Geophysical, then Tidelands Exploration. She was the "mobile office" with the crews unless, on occasion, the surveyor needed her help in the field and then she would lend assistance. She became the first female party chief on a seismic crew. She collected the seismic records, prepared them for interpretations, did calculations for map making, made and drafted maps. She also developed subsurface maps with prospects, especially for the smaller independent companies that hired their services, because they did not have geophysicists on staff (Fig. 8).

Figure 8. Anne "computing" and interpreting on the road during her early career. (Photo: Frank, The Leading Edge, February 1991, p. 47.)

Anne loved the job and the work. During those early eleven years, she lived in 60-70 different towns along the Texas coast from Corpus Christi across the Louisiana coast, as well as northern Louisiana near Stamps and El Dorado, Arkansas, three Mississippi towns, and two in Oklahoma. She had to pack most of her belongings into empty "powder boxes" from the shoots for each move.

Being on a seismic crew, Anne recalls,

> ... was really a sort of community. Our town locations were often very small (like Grand Chenier, Louisiana) or very large (like Beaumont, Texas) so we had to be flexible. Our first step in a new town was to locate a spot to use as an office (for phone, storage, supplies and a headquarters) (Fig. 9). Then each of us found a place to live. We stayed in rooms in private homes, trailers, motels, boarding houses, whatever was available, even campers. Crew members had their families with them. Sometimes we had no running water or heat! Most of us found a local restaurant for food and coffee break, and when I opened a temporary bank account we were at home. We had a lot of community meals, such as fish fries or oyster stew. And we spent every evening getting ready for tomorrow by carrying out repairs to equipment or trucks. When we moved it seldom took longer than a day. Our personal vehicles and company trucks provided packing room for everything. The group traveled in a caravan on the highway to be sure nobody broke down or needed some kind of help. It was a long convoy, so they would spread out so that other traffic could pass between them.
>
> Our crews were made of almost anybody we could find. The only requirements were "good physical shape" and "speak English." The basic crew was composed of 13 people, one car and 6 trucks (we insisted on Ford F150s!) We picked up local personnel when needed and were always surprised to find illiterates wanting jobs. The shooter on one of our crews signed his name with an "X" but he could keep track of our inventory of supplies as though he'd been doing it all his life and he could repair machinery like trucks just like he knew what he was doing...and he did!

Figure 9. One of the crew's many accommodations while on the road—a quarterboat anchored in Marsh Island. (Photo: Anne Frank, Louisville, Kentucky.)

Once, one of our jug-hustlers [the title for the observer's helper who hand-carried the seismometers down the line to attach them to the recording cable at pre-specified spots] was given the job of counting the number of jugs [geo phones] down the line. When he returned, he gave the observer a handful of small sticks. He couldn't count, so he picked up one stick for every jug he found and brought the correct answer back!

Flooded with great memories, one of Anne's favorite laughs occurred when one of the crew members was stealing food out of the lunch sacks of other crew members. Apparently, his wife would not bother making a lunch for him and neither would he. Fed up with him doing this, one of the other wives made a "chocolate cake" full of Ex-Lax® and put some into her husband's lunch sack. It disappeared. But, the young fellow soon had to be hauled to the nearest hospital, and he never stole from the lunches again.

She enjoyed being along for the efforts to acquire data offshore and recorded many photos (Figs. 10-14), but only rarely got to see a well being drilled on her interpretations. She remembers one field discovery in Mississippi that was a result of her mapping but usually, after the project left her office, she did not know the results. Once Anne was in a grocery store in Houston and she ran into one of the men who had contracted her work. He said, "You found a pretty good little field out there [in Southern Louisiana]!" Otherwise she would have never known.

When asked about living almost all her adult life on the "flat, flat, flat" Gulf Coast, and how did she reconcile that with her dislike of Illinois and Indiana, Anne laughed and said, "The love bug bit!"

Figure 10. Crossing the intercoastal canal at Grand Chenier. (Photo: Anne Frank.)

In 1943, the love bug struck with the surveyor, W. R. Frank (Fig. 15). Their wedding was not what a New England bred girl might have dreamed of; W.R.'s sister and one of the crew members were witnesses for a brief ceremony in Woodville, Texas north of Beaumont. Eventually Anne and W. R. bought a small trailer to be able to move it along with the crew to various locations and for the next 10-12 years they always worked on the same crew.

Figure 11. Anne's crew working on the Gulf Coast, setting up a dynamite shot point. (Photo: Anne Frank.)

Figure 12. Drilling by hand, Laguna Madre, Texas. (Photo: Anne Frank.)

Figure 13. Photo of Anne's seismic crew off-shore, Gulf of Mexico. (Photo: Anne Frank.)

Figure 14. Moving the seismic crew around Marsh Island, Louisiana. (Photo: Anne Frank.)

Anne's son, John A. Frank of Louisville, Kentucky, said, "My dad was a Texas boy with only a high school education and may have always felt somewhat 'inferior' to the educated Robins' family in New England. When we visited them he would just go off fishing and would not socialize much. When my mother was the Crew Chief, I think he must have had a difficult time."

In 1948, several of the men from General Geophysical (Raymond St Germaine, Skeeter Jones, John Bible, and Jack Ferguson) decided to form their own company, Tidelands Exploration, and hired Anne and W. R. away from General Geophysical. She recalled, "We did little else but work to build a good professional reputation for our new company. And although we lived in a bigger and better house trailer, we still traveled the backroads up and down the Gulf Coast for the next five years."

In 1953, Anne Frank became pregnant with her only child and asked to be transferred to the main office to work in Hous-

Figure 15. Anne and her husband, W.R. Frank, 1948, in Bellville, Texas. (Photo: Anne Frank.)

ton so she would not have to travel with a baby. Tidelands was very accommodating and her job evolved to review the field maps, write final reports, and draft final maps. Anne was back at work a few weeks after having her baby.

In 1964 Teledyne wanted Anne to move to their accounting department, as she had been doing the crew accounting along with mapping, and the third phase of her career began! She found that she enjoyed the accounting as with accounting calculations she "*knew when she right!*" When doing geophysics, it was not always certain, and sometimes, because she was not privy to the end results, she did not know if she was "right!"

After being in Houston for five or six years, son John, remembers, "My Mom bought W.R. a gift of polishing and faceting equipment for gemstones. He became so consumed with the hobby he soon quit Tidelands and took it up as a profession. He made many trips to Brazil for raw material. One of his most amazing acquisitions came with a shipment of Brazilian topaz. When he cleaned up the largest in the bunch, he knew he had something special. He could have sold the pure but rough gem for a few thousand dollars."

That seemed incredible then, but today the faceted and polished stone is the Chalmer's Topaz (5,899.5 carats) on display at the Field Museum of Natural History in Chicago. Named for a former museum trustee, William J. Chalmers, it is one of the largest cut topaz gems in the world. Anne only remembers that every penny W. R. made was put back into buying more materials so they learned right away to live off Anne's salary. This allocation of resources proved providential as W. R. died in 1966, leaving Anne with a 13-year-old son to raise alone.

By 1972, Tidelands had morphed into Teledyne and Anne's friends, the founders, were no longer there. A new CFO came aboard and the two of them did not get along. One morning, over a rather petty issue he just fired her. He said, "*When you go to lunch, don't come back!*"

Devastated, never having lost a job in her life, and with a son in college, Anne had tearful goodbyes with her co-workers and friends, packed up her office, and went home. The phone was ringing as she walked in the door. Other [geophysical] companies had already heard the news and wanted Anne to come to work for them. She was only out of a job one afternoon.

Anne went to work for GeoData, mostly with administrative responsibilities and stayed there until retirement in 1986. But no, she couldn't stand total retirement. She worked part time with GeoData, a seismic brokerage firm, for another 15 years, and finally fully retired in 2001 at age 82. When interviewed, she was 96 and living in Louisville, Kentucky near where her son, an architect and construction manager for Hines, resides and manages construction projects all over North America.

Anne Robins Frank joined AAPG in 1942 and has been a member for 73 years. She has also been a long-time member of the Society of Exploration Geophysics (SEG) and is a life member of the Houston Gem and Mineral Society where she was on the Board of Directors for 20 years. (Fig. 16)

Figure 16. Anne Robins Frank, 97, in Louisville, Kentucky, telling her stories to Robbie Gries. (Photo: Matt Randolph, 2016, Tulsa, Oklahoma.)

Chapter 8. Sources and References

Frank, Anne Robins. 1991. "The Bryn Mawr Connection…" *Geophysics: The Leading Edge of Exploration*, Feb, 1991, pp. 47-48.

Frank, Anne Robins, Louisville, Kentucky. Personal communication, September 2015 through December 2016; source of photographs as cited in figure captions; video interview, April 30, 2016, archived at AAPG, Tulsa, Oklahoma.

Frank, John, Louisville, Kentucky. Personlal communication, September 2016.

Hall, Dollie Radler. Correspondence with Tim Denison, October 21, 1974. [Copies provided to Robbie Gries by Tim Denison, September 2014.

Hall, Dollie Radler. Correspondence with A. Rodger Denison, 1927-1928. [Copies provided to Robbie Gries by Tim Denison, September 2014.

Hall, Dollie Radler. 1965. "Women in Exploration: Abstract." *Tulsa Geological Society Digest*, v. 33, pp. 295-298.

Hart, Ronald, Tulsa, Oklahoma. Personal communication regarding Grace Hower, February, 2016.

Owen, Edgar Wesley. *Trek of the Oil Finders: A History of Exploration for Petroleum.* Memoir 6. Tulsa, Okla.: American Association of Petroleum Geologists, 1975. 1647 pp.

Parker, Roberta. "Happy Birthday, Dollie." *Broken Arrow Scout*, Wednesday, June 2, 1993, p. 6A.

Pratt, Wallace E. 1937. "Discovery Rates in Oil Finding." *AAPG Bulletin*, vol. 21, no. 6, pp. 697-705.

Read, Bethan, Jackson, Mississippi, great niece of Dollie Radler Hall. Personal communication September 2016 to January 2017; source of archived 1927 San Francisco newspaper photograph of Dollie Radler.

Rosaire, E. E. and M. E. Stiles. 1932, "Distribution of Salt Domes in Depth (abstract)." *PanAmerican Geologist*, vol. 57, no.4, p.316.

Rosaire, E. E. and M. E. Stiles. 1932. "The Effect of Geophysics on the Development Hazard in Gulf Coast Oil Fields." *Economic Geology*, vol. 27, No. 6, 1932, pp. 523532.

Rosaire, E. E. and M. E. Stiles. 1936. "Exploration on the Gulf Coast to 1936." *GEOPHYSICS*, vol. 1, pp. 141-148.

Stiles, M. E. n.d. Letter to Mrs. N. P. Armstrong. M. E. Stiles Archives. Dolph Briscoe Center for American History, The University of Texas at Austin, Austin, Texas.

Stiles, M. E. 1922. "Life and Reminiscences of E. F. Cummins." William Flecher papers, 1892-1933. Dolph Briscoe Center for American History, The University of Texas at Austin, Austin, Texas.

Tulsa World. "Four Here Recall First Reflection Seismograph Find 50 Years Ago: Amerada-GRC Opened Era at Oklahoma Wildcat." Dec. 24, 1978. p. G8.

Winfrey, Betty, Broken Arrow, Oklahoma, cousin of Dollie Radler Hall. Personal communication, October 2016.

Chapter 9

Post WWI: Notable Early Pioneering Women

An additional group of notable women complete the earliest pioneering era of female petroleum geologists. Some came into petroleum geology from non-science backgrounds, many overcame great odds, but all had long and productive careers in geology at a time when it was a non-traditional and highly unusual career for women.

Membership records from the American Association of Petroleum Geologists, which began in 1917 when the organization was founded, have provided the database to identify the earliest pioneering women in petroleum geology. However, there were also women in the profession who were not able to become members of AAPG for political or fiscal reasons. Though a thorough study has not been conducted to identify women in this category, several were gleaned from *The Biographical Dictionary of Women in Science* (Ogilvie and Harvey, 2000).

Agnes M. Farrell (1884-1989)

A "day job" as a copyist in the U S Patent Office in 1905 introduced Agnes M. Farrell, an accomplished concert pianist, to earth science (Fig. 1). Agnes transferred to the U.S. Geological Survey (USGS) in 1914 and after years of working with and around geologists, was inspired in her 40s to pursue a geology degree. She graduated from George Washington University in 1929 and was soon promoted from clerk to "geologist" at the USGS. She loved to travel and enjoyed many trips to the western United States to study geology (Fig. 2).

Figure 1. Agnes M. Farrell, about 1900, a concert pianist turned geologist working with resources for the Department of the Interior. (Photo: Farrell family, Jane Nelson, wife of Gregory Farrell Nelson, Agnes' great nephew, Fairfax, Virginia.)

When Agnes Farrell retired in 1953, Douglas Murray, Secretary of the Interior, cited her for Meritorious Service stating, "Miss Farrell, while working there as a clerk, undertook university training in geology, and on July 1, 1929, was appointed to the position of geologist, the capacity in which she was serving when she retired on February 28, 1953. During her long period of Government service, Miss Farrell constantly sought to increase her knowledge to be more valuable to the organization. She was outstanding in her dealings with other Federal agencies and the general public. Her appointment as Chief of the Correspondence, Records, and Reports Unit in the Oil and Gas Resources Section of the Fuels Branch was testimony of her fitness to assume responsibility."

Figure 2. Agnes loved her trips to the western US looking at the geology. (Photo: undated, from Jane Nelson.)

Agnes, an enthusiastic traveler all her life, sent post cards to her family on each of her trips. Her family relates that a memorable card was sent from Paris in July 1914 just a few weeks before Germany invaded France at the start of WWI. They forever chided her that she had to rush home early from that trip "after she started a World War!" (personal communication, Jane and Gregory Nelson). She was an avid golfer, playing until she was 88 years old. She continued her AAPG membership until 1984 and lived to the extraordinary age of 105.

Eva Endurance Hirdler Greene (1884-1982)

In 1911, Eva Endurance Hirdler was the first woman to graduate from the Missouri School of Mines and Metallurgy (Fig. 3). Although she completed all the mining engineering course work, the school, in a perceived attempt to discourage her from entering a male profession, only awarded Eva a general science degree.

Figure 3. Eva Endurance Hirdler at the Missouri School of Mines and Metallurgy, which quotes, "She needs no eulogy, she speaks for herself" and said that she aspired to operate a gold mine in California." (Photo:, Missouri School of Mines and Metallurgy [MSM] 1911 Yearbook, Rollamo, *p. 32.)*

In 1914, she married geologist Frank Greene who became one of the founders of the AAPG in 1917. The Missouri School of Mines and Metallurgy newsletter poorly anticipated Eva's future when they announced her plans to wed and said she would then "quit her profession." She did not quit and, years later in 1936 when Eva joined AAPG, she described herself as an independent geologist and oil operator.

In recognition of her full engineering career, the Missouri School of Mines and Metallurgy granted Eva Endurance Hirdler Greene a B.A. in Mining Engineering.

Helen Mandeville Martin (1889-1973)

A North Dakota native, Helen Mandeville Martin traveled east to attend the University of Michigan with the intention of becoming a writer. Instead, she changed her major, and in 1908, graduated with an A.B. in chemistry and geology. Helen taught high school geology and physiography in Michigan for eight years before returning to the University of Michigan in 1916 to obtain a master's degree in geology and chemistry. Upon graduation in 1917, she began her career as a geologist and editor for the Michigan Geological Survey (Fig. 4).

Figure 4. Helen Martin, Natural Resource geologist for the Michigan Geologic Survey after spending 11 years in the oil business in the 1920s. (Photo: Archives of Michigan: MS Number 93-71, Series 93-71-3.)

Helen joined AAPG in 1925 when she was employed by the Carter Oil Company in Tulsa, OK. Her application for AAPG membership indicated that prior to 1925, she had worked with the Michigan Geologic Survey and as a consultant for the Roxana Petroleum Company. Her work in the oil industry extended to 1934. Like many women with geology degrees after WWI who found that men were favored for positions in oil companies, Helen went back to work at one of the state geological surveys.

Helen Martin was well known as a geologist, a lecturer, and a prolific researcher. In addition to her geologic work at the Michigan Geologic Survey, she documented the emergence of female educators in the 1930s and made significant contributions to conservation education. She received awards from the U.S. Department of Health, Education and Welfare, the Public Health Service, the U.S. Forestry Service, and the American Forestry Association (Helen Martin materials 1820-1971, State Archive of Michigan).

R. Thomas Segall (1980, p. 5) wrote, "Helen was with the Michigan Geological Survey for nearly 30 years between the years 1917 and 1958 [except for the 11-year break in the oil industry], was one of our most productive colleagues. Geologist, geologic researcher, compiler of geologic maps, historian, writer, editor, lecturer, conservationist, and teacher. She authored five books, was responsible for the compilation of six geologic maps, and published numerous papers and short articles. Well informed on Michigan's natural resources, and greatly interested in conservation, Ms. Martin often included these subjects in her lectures and writings. One of the few women geologists of her time, she helped to pave the way for those women geologists who have followed. Her work has been an inspiration to many, and her lifelong devotion to geology and conservation has contributed greatly to the Survey and to the people of Michigan."

Helen Mandeville Martin was an AAPG member for 43 years until her death in 1973. She was inducted into the Michigan Women's Hall of Fame in 1988, fifteen years after her death.

Margaret Cameron Cobb (1892-1974)

With a strong academic background in geology, Margaret C. Cobb went to work for Amerada Petroleum Corporation in New York City after completing her PhD at Bryn Mawr in 1924 (Fig. 5). Margaret initially attended the University of North Carolina, but completed her A.B. at Barnard College. She was a graduate student at Columbia University (1915-16), a Fellow in Geology at Bryn Mawr College (1916-17), and an instructor in geology at Mount Holyoke College (1917-19). She worked part-time with Amerada doing research while finishing her PhD and before going to work for them full-time.

Figure 5. Margaret Cameron Cobb worked her entire career with Amerada Petroleum in New York City, (Photo: University of North Carolina yearbook, Pine Needles, *p. 185.)*

In Dollie Radler Hall's correspondence files (provided to the author by Bethan Read) a firm note from Sidney Powers in the Tulsa office to A. Rodger Denison reads as follows.

> June 6 '28
>
> Miss Margaret Cobb, NYC, has to keep loc. [locations on] all WTex wildcats for EDG [DeGolyer] & has not scout reports. Please send her complete E&W Tex scout report about every 2 weeks or even every week including Ferguson's. Also, white print map of Tex. Panhandle-NM joining Skelly-Kelly map on N. & preferable showing our leasehold. H. F. Bruns is making set W Texas mile to inch maps and wants to put on all wells so he will send them to you for their location! Must recommend broad area for Fry sand play. We can never make money buying 2 ac. ahead of plays. Must buy 2 counties ahead. Work out which way plays and sands are going and have some recommendations. DeG is in Tulsa next Thurs or Fri wants these recommendations & wants to see Karcher [geophysicist]. Shall we play San Saba River high to W or N?, etc? Get some broad scale ideas. We will show profit $4 a share for 1927, paid ½ of it in dividends. Must have some wild wildcat areas to lease. No one else will be canned except for inefficiency, but hold the axe over their heads (Fig. 6).

Not much is known about Margaret Cobb's geologic career except that she was with Amerada until she retired. It was thought she had become the "company librarian" and we located a remembrance on *Sweet Rocket blog*

Figure 6. Cartoon drawing of key players at Amerada, left to right: Margaret Cobb, geologist and executive assistant in NYC; Everette DeGolyer- President; Sidney Powers, Chief Geologist-Tulsa; Dollie Radler Hall- Acting Chief Geologist-Tulsa; Rodger Denison, Division Geologist-Texas. Cartoon by Joe Peter Campbell, 1969, of Key Amerada Employees for the 50th birthday celebration of Amerada, 1919-1969. (Cartoon: Dollie Radler Hall archives provided by Dollie's niece, Bethan Read, Jackson, Mississippi.)

about Margaret in the Amerada offices that reads, "The special woman's name was Margaret Cobb, and she was a geologist long before women were geologists. My dad worked for an oil company [Amerada], and after my mother died when I was nine he took me to work with him on occasion. I realize now that those were probably the days he didn't have someone to watch me at home, but at the time I thought he just liked to take me along. He was that kind of father. I usually spent a good part of each day with Miss Cobb. She oversaw the corporate library. She was a soft-spoken southern woman, to all appearances rather fragile, but she knew a ton about a lot of things, and the rocks and minerals in her office could keep me fascinated for hours. She took me for a walk in downtown New York and told me how garnets could still be found in the streets. My memories of Miss Cobb are among the most vivid and the most comforting from a terribly difficult time. I found her much later—when I was 30—but I don't remember how. She was quite elderly by that time, and living in Norfolk, Virginia. We exchanged some letters, and she still had the marvelous spidery handwriting I remembered from my childhood. Her brother notified me when she died" (*Sweet Rocket Blog*, 2011).

Margaret Cobb was a member of AAPG for 48 years.

Vita Lee Waters Chase (1896-1983)

Vita Lee Waters finished her education at the University of Oklahoma in 1919-20 and likely joined the workforce because of the skilled-labor shortage associated with WWI. Her parents had moved to Norman, Oklahoma specifically for their daughters to attend college. They purchased a boarding house near campus and boarded students for years (personal communication, Bob Wynn, Oklahoma City, great nephew). Vita Lee had an active campus life and was a charter member of Chi Upsilon, the Women's Honorary Geological Fraternity, along with petroleum geology pioneer Dollie Radler and five other women. Upon graduation, she was hired by an ExxonMobil predecessor, Carter Oil Company, in Tulsa, Oklahoma and joined AAPG in March 1920.

In November, 1920, Vita Lee Waters married Edmund Chase, a WWI veteran who had become an oil company accountant. The couple moved to Shreveport, Louisiana, likely for Chase's job, and with the move Vita Lee was fortunate to be hired by Louisiana Oil Refining Corporation (LORC). At that time, it was an unusual company or a company in an unusual situation that was willing to hire a married woman. It is open to speculation that she was hired by J. P. D. Hull, a geologic manager at LORC who was an admirer of a USGS field geologist Julia Gardner (see Chapter 6) and influential enough within the company to break with tradition. (Hull would later become Executive Director of AAPG in Tulsa.)

Figure 7. Vita Lee Waters Chase approximately 1929 in Tulsa, Oklahoma, where she worked for Amerada. (Photo: Bob Wynn, Oklahoma City, great nephew of Vita Lee.)

Around 1923, Vita Lee and Edmund Chase moved back to Oklahoma where Vita Lee took a job with Amerada Petroleum Company in Tulsa (Fig. 7). Her husband, Edmund, died tragically in 1936 when he was hit by a bus in front of their home in Tulsa. She, herself, had suffered several miscarriages and never had children but formed close relationships with her nieces and nephews.

Vita Lee worked for Amerada for the rest of her career. Interestingly, she would have worked for and reported to her Oklahoma University classmate, Dollie Radler Hall (see Chapter 3). They became good friends and Vita Lee's great nephew, Bob Wynn, remembers frequent visits to Dollie and Charles Hall's property in Broken Arrow where they kept horses and enjoyed watching the children play freely around the mini-ranch. Bob also remembers visiting Vita Lee in her Amerada office, which was spacious and equipped

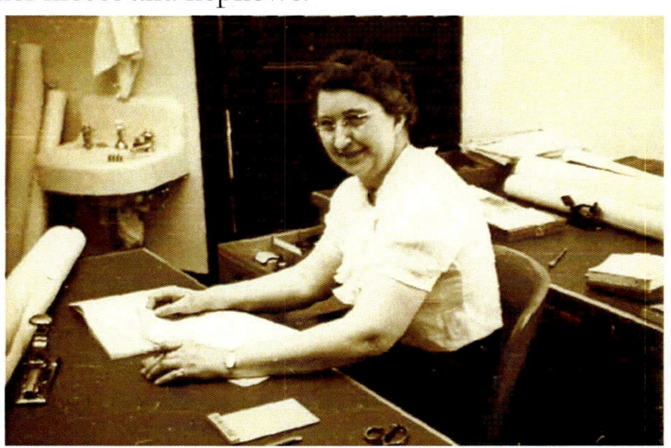

Figure 8. Vita Lee in about 1921, likely when she was with Louisiana Oil Refining Corporation. Her nephew, Bob Wynn, remembers visiting her Amerada office in Tulsa where it was spacious. This office was obviously not. (Photo: Bob Wynn.)

with a drafting table and desk. However, the spacious office was not enough to stop Vita Lee from grumbling about not being able to go into the field because she was a woman (Fig. 8).

Figure 9. Vita Lee enjoyed photography and took many photos like this one on an Amerada field trip in about 1932. (Photo: Bob Wynn.)

She retired from Amerada Hess in 1955. Bob Wynn lived with her during his senior year in high school (1957) to help her after she was treated for arthritis with shock treatments, a failed medical experiment of the late 50s. The treatments were debilitating but she did recover. In retirement, Vita Lee, a consummate photographer, enjoyed driving to locations throughout the United States in her always-new Ford, courtesy of her brothers' local Ford dealership (Fig. 9). It was also her ritual in late retirement to have frequent lunches with Dollie, by then widowed too, with another ex-Amerada employee.

Vita Lee Waters Chase died in 1983. Her membership in AAPG may have only extended for a short period from 1920-1923, but she had a long career as a woman in the oil business.

Isabel Basset Wasson (1897-1994)

Isabel Basset made history by becoming the first female United States National Park Ranger (Fig. 10). She set up a template for geologic and nature talks to be given by rangers and suggested the Parks hire college students on summer break to give informational talks rather than training bellhops which she had found an exercise in futility. Her idea of hiring students for the summer would become a tradition at many National Parks. When recounting the Birth of the National Park Services, Horace M. Albright told Robert Cahn, "I hired two seasonal rangers...the other was Isobel [*sic*] Bassett Wasson, who I had discovered the previous year with Kaltenborn's Brooklyn Eagle party. The Eagle tour group from New York was visiting the park and I was walking through the lobby of Mammoth Hotel one evening after dinner just in time to overhear a young member of the party giving a talk on Yellowstone. She was doing an outstanding job of it. So, I returned the next evening to hear her talk on the geysers and geological features of the park. She really knew her subject, and even included comparisons with geysers in New Zealand and Iceland. Complimenting her afterwards, I learned that her name was Isobel [*sic*] Bassett, she was a geology major just out of college, and she was on the Eagle Tour with her parents...I told her that if she would come back next year I would be glad to hire her as a seasonal ranger. She was married in the meantime, but still came to work for us in the summer of 1920 as Yellowstone's first woman ranger, one of the first in the National Park Service" (Albright, 1985, p. 120).

Figure 10. Isabel Basset Wasson, about 1920, in Yellowstone National Park, where she was the first female ranger and set the standard and procedures for giving geologic talks to the public. (Photo: Ed Wasson, Denver, Colorado, son of Isabel Wasson.)

Isabel was a Phi Beta graduate from Wellesley (1918) with a major in history that allowed her to take a wide range of science courses. She taught geology at Wellesley the year after she graduated and took additional geology courses at the Massachusetts Institute of Technology.

Isabel enrolled in the graduate program at Colombia University and met Theron Wasson, a petroleum geology student and her future husband. They married in 1920 and that summer she fulfilled an obligation she had with Yellowstone National Park to work as a park ranger. Marriage and career took her away from her degree efforts until 1934, when she would finally complete her Masters at Colombia University with a specialty in petroleum.

Figure 11. Isabel spent time doing field work for Oil in Venezuela in the early 1920s with her husband. The natives thought she was the boss. (Photo: from Ed Wasson.)

Isabel and Theron Wasson both went to work for Pure Oil Company (later Union Oil of California) in Chicago. He was tasked with setting up Pure's geology and exploration department; she worked and took classes at the University of Chicago.

In 1923 the Wassons traveled to Venezuela and traipsed through the jungle together near Lake Maricaibo on an exploratory venture for oil (Fig. 11). Isabel had suffered polio when she was three, but that never set her back from physical activity. At first, the natives mistook Isabel and another woman in the party for the "bosses" because both were clad in knickerbockers and puttees and the men were differential to them! Isabel's other stories about their adventures included exotic foods like armadillo, iguanas and iguana eggs, and yucca and the myriad of insects they encountered (*Brooklyn Dailey Eagle*, 1923, p. 4).

Isabel worked for Pure for six years (1922-1928) during which time she and Theron published a paper on Cabin Creek field in Wyoming about finding oil in a syncline (Wasson and Wasson, 1927, pp 705-719). They had three children, and their son, Edward Wasson, would become a petroleum geologist who lived and worked most of his career in Denver, Colorado. She eventually left the petroleum industry to raise her family and began a long career of teaching, lecturing, and public service.

Isabel and Theron Wasson divorced in 1953. She continued teaching and lecturing and focused more time on mentoring young naturalists, becoming an accomplished ornithologist, and archeologist as well as being dedicated to public service in River Forest, Illinois. Isabel Basset lived to a hearty age of 97 years.

Ninetta Alia Davis (1899-1986)

Aspiring for something better than an ordinary woman's life with career choices limited to stenography or bookkeeping, Ninetta Alia Davis set her goal to earn an unheard of annual salary for a woman in 1916 of $100,000 ($2.3MM in 2016 dollars). Having focus and commitment to her goal, she selected the profession of geological engineering and set her sights on a future in the oil business (Fig. 12). The Great Depression, family care, and, likely, some prejudice against women would offer many challenges to her dream of becoming a millionaire.

Figure 12. Ninetta Alia Davis, 2nd woman to graduate in engineering (geological) at the Colorado School of Mines, 1920. (Photo: Altman,et al, 1999, p.13).

Ninetta Davis entered the Colorado School of Mines (CSM) at age 16 and was awarded her degree in petroleum engineering in 1920. This was the second time in CSM's history that they granted a petroleum engineering degree to a woman. Ninetta recalled (Gries, 1984) that her school days were somewhat difficult: she was the only woman in the school at the time and the men either hated her or loved her. Harry Thomsen, who would later be her boss at Shell Oil in Denver, was at CSM at the same time and he remembered fondly that, "Everyone called Ninetta 'our co-ed'" (personal communication, 1984).

After her graduation, no other woman graduated from the CSM geology department until 1961. A prohibition of women attending Mines insinuated itself into the school even though its charter stated, *"The School of Mines shall be open to any inhabitant of the Territory of Colorado without regard to sex or color."* That charter was quietly set aside and forgotten for decades.

Immediately after graduation, Ninetta was offered employment by Midwest Refining Company in Casper, Wyoming in 1920. Midwest was, at that time, the fourth largest manufacturer of gasoline in the United States. Ed Owen recounts with admiration that Midwest "...were among the first in the United States to place implicit confidence in the judgment of a geologist" (Owen, 1975, p. 354).

Ninetta became a sensation in the oil business when she was interviewed in December of 1920 by the industry rag, *Petroleum Age*, where the headline rang out:

Meet a Lady Oil Engineer

*"Miss Davis, of Denver, Sets Her Mark at Getting $100,000 a year—
Stenography Too Slow, She Hopes to Head a Big Oil Company Some Day"*

by Staff Correspondent

Denver, Co.—Not content with being a common ordinary girl with ambitions for stenography and bookkeeping, Miss Ninetta A. Davis has acquired the honor of being the only lady oil engineer in the United States. [CSM did not have a geology degree, they granted a petroleum engineering degree with many geology courses. Though several women geologists were hired between 1918 and 1920, Ninetta was likely the first "engineer" hired in the business.]

Miss Davis has completed the mining engineering course in the Colorado School of Mines, one of the best institutions of its kind in the country. She has already started on her chosen career by getting a position with the Midwest Refining Co. at Casper, Wyo. [Artist's rendering of the photo in Article: Fig. 13]

Figure 13. Ninetta Davis, aspiring to be a millionaire at age 20. (Photo: Colby, 1920, p. 58.)

While at college Miss Davis took her course with a large class of young men, doing exactly the same preparation with the exception of the pick and shovel work. She says she believes she could have done that part as well as the boys. When asked why she chose the oil industry as a life work Miss Davis said: "There is no industry that has commanded the attention of the public more than the oil industry. It is the biggest money-making proposition that can be considered at the present time."

Hitches Ambition to a Star.

While at school the young women who were associated with Miss Davis, expecting to be self-supporting, were planning on being stenographers, bookkeepers and school teachers. Miss Davis was determined to prepare herself for something better, and set her mark at $100,000 a year. In putting her aim at $100,000 a year she was compelled to look around a little for a vocation that would pay that amount. Selecting engineering work, she entered the Colorado School of Mines. As the petroleum industry was more interesting than mining, she took the work in oil. On graduating from college, she got out and got busy among the oil companies and landed the position that suited her.

While attending college one of the boys sarcastically asked Miss Davis what she was doing in a mining school. He thought she ought to be in a young ladies' seminary, he said, learning how to be polite. She quickly answered him by saying that she did not want to take in washing to make a living; that she wanted to be able to support a husband in a first-class condition. That is the proper spirit, isn't it?

Miss Davis' work with the Midwest Refining Co. is concerned with the production of oil, beginning with geological investigation, then taking up the cost of drilling, cost of production, investigation of casing records, and making suggestions for the control of water in oil sands. She will have an opportunity to study the best methods of drilling wells and increasing production. It is her intention to take up the refining and marketing branch of the oil industry later.

Wants Business of her Own

Miss Davis is a remarkable young woman and has chosen a wonderful field for a life work. Equipped with her technical and scientific knowledge and with her natural ambition to succeed in the oil industry she should make a record for herself. The day has come for expert and technical knowledge for the solution of our petroleum problems. People with brains and scientific knowledge are the ones in demand. She hopes to supply both.

This young lady petroleum engineer has ambitions. She plans on having a business of her own someday. Her hope is to be president of a big oil company and perhaps horn John D. out of first place. Miss Davis has a lot of time to realize these high ambitions, as she is only 21 years old. She is a native of the rugged state of Colorado. Her parents are living at the present time in Denver. (Petroleum Age, Dec. 1920)

Ninetta's first job was as an assistant to the petroleum engineer with Midwest Refining Company in Casper, Wyoming. She remembers Casper as being a pretty rough boom town in those early days. Her salary was $150 a month and included stenographic duties. Four years later, she moved to Fort Collins to become an "office geologist" with Union Oil of California which had recently made two significant Denver Basin discoveries along the Front Range. However, Union closed the office, circa 1929, leaving her jobless at the very onset of the Great Depression. Undaunted, Ninetta, resilient and resourceful as ever, took a job in Denver as a bookkeeper in the back office of a department store for $15/week just to get by, and was thankful to have the position (Gries, 1984). She lived with her widowed mother and eventually nursed her throughout a long illness.

In 1934, she joined the U.S. Geological Survey (USGS) where she worked for C. E. (Cy) Dobbin as a specialist in sub-surface geology of oil fields in the U.S. western states. During her years with the USGS she became active in the Rocky Mountain Association of Petroleum Geologists (RMAPG—the original name of the Rocky Mountain Association of Geologists). Ninetta served as Secretary-Treasurer of RMAPG for two years from 1938-1939, as First Vice-President in 1940, and, in 1941, became the first woman to be President of RMAPG as well as being the first woman to hold her previous elected executive committee offices. When she was interviewed in 1983, RMAG had completely lost sight of having had a woman as president. That interview re-introduced Ninetta Davis to the Association and eight years later in 1991 Susan Landon would become the second female President of RMAG—a 60-year gap!

As RMAPG President, Ninetta faced a busy year, starting with the formation of a committee to study "*Possible Future Oil Producing Areas in the Rocky Mountain Region.*" This report was published in the AAPG *Bulletin* in August of that year. In addition, RMAPG committed to host the 1942 AAPG national convention, and much of 1941 was spent in preparation for this event. Ninetta served on the finance committee for the convention. Average attendance at the bimonthly meetings she chaired was about 25. Harry Thomsen remarked, "Ninetta conducted meetings efficiently; was a good administrator and got along well with everyone." She attended several AAPG Annual meetings, one as far away as El Paso, Texas.

In 1944, Ninetta left the USGS to become a junior geologist with Shell Oil at their new office in the Rockies. Her boss, Guy (Doc) Miller, also a Colorado School of Mines graduate, was frequently out in the field with the three other geologists leaving Ninetta in charge of the office where she combined the posts of geologist, oil scout, researcher, technician, and clerical staff. In 1948, Harry Thomsen came to Denver as manager of Shell's Rocky Mountain office and recalled, "Ninetta's contributions to projects were essential. She would take on a project and produce a complete regional study including all published material, cross sections, isopachs, current drilling activity, penetration charts and much more."

Ninetta was unhappy when, by (age) policy, she had to retire from Shell in 1959; it was from a job she loved and would sincerely miss (personal communication, 1983).

Swimming, previously an avocation, became her vocation after retirement and by 1962 she had helped establish synchronized swimming in the Rockies. Ninetta taught classes for the YWCA, the University of Denver, conducted clinics in Europe, and in her late 70s coached the Dutch national team. In 1976 she was named to the Citizens Savings Hall of Fame, an international sports shrine in Los Angeles, for her work in synchronized swimming. At 82 an accident impaired her eyesight and her activities were significantly reduced. A small woman, about

5'2", when interviewed in 1983, she was still in excellent physical condition, had a pleasant smile and said, "I just don't get mad about many things."

Ninetta Alia Davis may not have become a millionaire, but she had a richly rewarding professional and volunteer career that would pay dividends to future generations of women in geology.

Helen King Hodson (1902-1964)

Helen King Hodson, a member of AAPG for nine years from 1927-1936, was working in Venezuela at the time she joined the Association (Fig. 14). On her AAPG membership card, she indicated she was a geologist and paleontologist with field experience in Venezuela. She also belonged to the Société Géologique de France (SGF). Helen's future husband was Floyd Hodson, nine years her senior and a PhD geologist. Floyd apparently took a position with Standard Oil in Venezuela in 1922 a year before he and Helen married. After acquiring her bachelor's degree from Cornell University in 1924, Helen joined Floyd and did fieldwork with him. Their gastropod collections became the basis of Floyd Hodson's doctoral thesis which he completed in 1926. Floyd and Helen Hodson jointly published on their collections in the Bulletins of American Paleontology. One of the unfortunate aspects of several of these publications is almost no locality data for the fossils that they described and discussed were included because Standard Oil refused to allow the information to be made public. The Hudson's lived and worked in Venezuela until 1934.

Figure 14. Helen King Hodson worked in Venezuela with her husband, developed a substantial paleontologic collection and donated it to PRI in Ithaca. (Photo: courtesy of the Paleontological Research Institution, Ithaca NY.)

In May 1931, they made a brief visit to the U.S. for the birth of their daughter, Katherine Hodson, but soon returned to Venezuela with the baby in tow to continue their work. Around this time, changes began to take place in the scientific management of Standard Oil in Venezuela that became a source of problems for the Hodsons. Based on surviving correspondence, it seems new geologists employed by the company had begun to criticize some of Floyd Hodson's bio-stratigraphic correlations and geological conclusions. He took offense and tensions reached a critical point when in June 1934 the Hodson family abruptly left Venezuela. That their departure from Venezuela was not on good terms is suggested by the fact that they apparently did not have sufficient funds to pay for passage. The Hodson family had to work their way home as crew members of the steamship "Flagler," with Floyd as purser, Helen as stewardess, and three-year-old Katherine listed as "assistant stewardess."

They returned to Ithaca, New York, where Floyd and Helen joined the Paleontological Research Institution (PRI) established in 1932 by Gilbert Harris, professor of geology at Cornell University, and to which they had sent the large fossil collections from their decade in Venezuela as well as their large paleontological library. They evidently spent additional time working on the collections, as Floyd purchased a new microscope that was delivered to PRI. He served on the PRI Board of Trustees for three years starting in 1938, and in 1940 Floyd and Helen formally donated their library to the Institution.

Later, they departed Ithaca, curtailed their work in paleontology and moved to Broward County, Florida, north of Miami, where Floyd worked as a geologist and farmer. Helen Hodson died in Florida in 1964 and Floyd in 1971. In his will, Floyd bequeathed $129,000 to PRI, part of which was used to help pay off the mortgage of the present Paleontological Research Institution building.

The Hodson collection remained almost completely untouched at PRI for decades. When the task of unpacking was completed in 2010 it became clear just how large and valuable the collection is. It includes approximately 15,000 "lots" from approximately 2,000 localities across northern Venezuela, making it among the largest collections of Venezuelan fossils anywhere. Much of this collection consists of fossil mollusks from the Miocene to Pleistocene, including many undescribed forms and extensions of geographic or stratigraphic ranges. It will be a resource for research for many years to come.

This information about the Hodsons comes from a combination of sources, including materials in the Paleontological Research Institute (Ithaca, NY) Archives, and Visher, 1950.

Katherine Woodley Carman (1906-2008)

Katherine Woodley Carmen stands out as a young woman determined to achieve her degrees in geology despite the lack of requisite science, math, and engineering, despite having the requirement of reading competence in French and German, and despite the Great Depression (Fig. 15). Overcoming these hurdles, she proceeded to have a long and successful career as a micropaleontologist and stratigrapher. Katherine's perseverance resulted in her being the first female PhD in geology from the Massachusetts Institute of Technology (MIT). From the *MIT Alumni Association Newsletter* in April 1973, she wrote, "What got me interested in geology? - Perhaps the Lord: When I was so little—an only child—Dad and I would go walking on the then unspoiled beaches of Lake Michigan and around Colorado. I'd say: "tones Daddy, 'tones'- I couldn't say the word 'stones', and I'd load down his overcoat pockets with my treasures."

The *MIT Newsletter* recorded,

At Wellesley College, which Katherine entered in 1923, she took all the geology courses offered, then had to complete her schedule with a course in geography given by the Head of the Department on Saturday morning at 8:30 am—a horrible hour for a lively girl who liked to stay late at dances in Boston on Friday night! However, she was greatly impressed by the quiet 'but sure way" that Prof. Hervey W. Shimer from MIT gave lectures twice a week at Wellesley. Consequently, when she was awarded a Bachelor of Arts degree in geology in June 1927, she decided to apply for admission to MIT to carry on graduate work. Apply she did, and in the fall of 1927 she was accepted as a Special 4th - year student because she had to make up deficiencies in a number of science subjects before she could qualify for graduate work. This arrangement did not affect her determination but did make her wary.

Figure 15. Katherine Woodley Carman, 1927, she earned her bachelor's at Wellesley and her master's and Doctorate at MIT then joined the oil business, much of her prospecting in oil and gas was as a consultant. (Photo: courtesy of Wellesley College yearbook, Legenda, *p. 35, 1927.)*

In April 1973, Katherine wrote to MIT,

When I entered the door at MIT I was sure scared: But the Dean was cordial, Shimer was more than pleasant and old Waldy Lindgren was quite cordial ...."

After two years as a Special Student, attended by some difficulties with these deficiencies, she remained as determined as ever. On 8 June 1929, before leaving for summer work, she wrote Lindgren, 'On further consideration, I have decided to come back to Technology next year and take all the mathematics, physics, and chemistry if it takes ten years,' to which Lindgren responded on 26 June 1929: 'In reply to your letter of June 8th: I am glad that you have decided to take your medicine and go through with your degree at this Institute.'

Requirements were somewhat tougher then than now, forty years later. She had to meet the basic science requirements in mathematics, physics, chemistry and biology; the departmental requirements in geology, her major; minor requirements in petroleum engineering (4 subjects), her minor; and demonstrate a satisfactory reading competence in French and German. It is little wonder that it took her from 1927 to 1933 to get her degree; but she was a tenacious young lady and was not about to be intimidated by all those demanding requirements, and she retains that same spirit and tenacity to this day. Furthermore, it took much determination to continue her education as the Great Depression of the late 1920s and early 1930s swept across America, even with the scholarship aid she received from MIT for Years 1928-29 and 1929-30.

With her doctorate behind her, and with excellent training in invertebrate paleontology and micropaleontology, she quickly found employment in the petroleum industry, and spent the next forty years in professional work, at first employed by several petroleum companies, then more recently, until retirement, as a self-employed consulting geologist in Lakewood, Colorado. In a recent telephone conversation with her, I found that characteristic spirit of independence and tenacity of purpose as strong as ever, even in retirement (Shrock, 1982).

Though she struggled to meet requirements at MIT, in 1929 she became the first woman and indeed the first student to get a doctorate in geology at MIT studying with J. A. Cushman.

Katherine's early career is not known. Dollie Radler Hall (1965, p. 296) wrote of her, "She is an outstanding example of one of the few who mastered surface mapping."

Katherine lived and worked in Denver, Colorado for several years as a consultant and was a member of the Rocky Mountain Association of Geologists. She retired to Hayden, Colorado where she died in 2008. Katherine Woodley Carmen was an AAPG member for 72 years.

Mildred V. Armor Frizzell (1906-2007)

Figure 16. Mildred with her father, John Armor, and her younger brother in about 1913-16 in Cleveland, OK. (Photo: Frizzell family and AAPG Explorer, Special Issue, A Century, January, 2000, p. 26.)

Mildred V. Armor was the second woman to earn a master's degree in geology from the University of Oklahoma (OU, 1928) seven years after Dollie Radler Hall (1921). She was called "Old Timer" by her family and friends, a nickname she loved and promoted.

Ron Krakowski (2008) wrote this excerpt about Mildred, "As a young girl, while Mildred was visiting family in West Virginia, she was walking along a creek bed and picked up a piece of black shale and observed the fossil imprint of a fern, just as the present-day ferns that grew on the shale outcrop. It was then that Mildred [Armor] Frizzell became hooked on geology."

Figure 17. Mildred Armor Frizzell wrote on this Photograph, "John Armor's first Company Car. They worked on its engine so much they left the hood off. Daddy was field Supt. [Superintendent] for Gypsy Oil. Co. He let me play like I was driving. What a thrill! About 1913-16. Cleveland, Oklahoma." (Photo: Frizzell family, Michelle Bingham, granddaughter to Mildred, Lubbock, Texas.)

Because of her father's work in the oil patch during Mildred's early years, she lived in an oil field camp home and moved from oil pool to oil pool including Glenpool, Cleveland, Cushing, and many others (Figs. 16 and 17). A story Mildred told her children (personal communication Michelle Bingham) was how much she enjoyed going to the oil camps with her daddy. But one day, when at home with her mother, she asked, "Where's the goddamn milk!" That put an end to her excursions into the field, at least until adulthood.

Figure 18. Mildred Armor (left) at geology field camp, University of Colorado, 1927, with friend, Helen Fields. (Photo: Michelle Bingham.)

Michelle Bingham found photos of Mildred at a University of Colorado field camp in 1927 and remembered her stories of that special summer in Colorado (Fig. 18). She told her children about the boys in the field making fun of her and the other females, so, one night she and a friend stole over to their cabin and nailed their boots to the porch! Another story she wrote down for her children on her 88th birthday, describing:

The most exciting moment (or 60 seconds) of my life

The summer of 1927 Daddy was very busy as he was Spt. of Drilling in the Healton-Fox area. He decided Mother, Pat and I should spend the summer in Colorado. I could study Geology at Colorado University & Pat would attend a Boy Scout Camp near Boulder. Mother rented a house for the summer & I enrolled in the University. Near the end of the summer Field Course taught by a young man named Hoffmaster, he took a large group up to the top of the Arapahoe Glacier. We climbed the West side – no problem- no snow & little oxygen - but we stopped frequently.

As always in the Mts. I carried my rain coat; pick; Brunton compass; tin cup & consume cubes. Hoffmaster's young (& very athletic) brother guided & pushed up to the top. We were shocked when we looked down on the glacier that extended several blocks and were told we would have to return to basecamp by sliding down this glacier.

After eating the crushed sandwiches our teacher called us to the "brink" & told us his brother would show us the easy way to go down – He and his brother had grown up in the Mts & they were expert skiers! The glacier had carved out a cirque...on the east side of the Mt and there was a drop of 3 feet to the surface of the ice. The young Hoffmaster walked up to the edge (overhanging the glacier) & jumped off & skied down the glacier with grace and beauty (with only boots!) Most were like me – never even saw anyone ski before as we were from the plains of Kansas & Okla!

Our teacher explained we would use our rain coats as sleds and slide down. He picked an athletic boy to demonstrate how to do it. First, he put the rain coat between his legs & the teacher held him as he jumped down to the ice & seated himself on the coat, pulling it up in the front as a steering wheel. – "There", he said "Only one thing to remember!!! Hold your feet up in the air!!!" "If you touch the ice, you will start spinning!"

I was the third (first girl) to go. I did perfect until I almost reached the level area – became overconfident – let one boot hit the ice – That was it! I rolled for the last block – after I finally stopped, I got up (This was on the level area) walked back and collected my pick, cup, rain coat & waved, "OK!" to those waiting to start. This was a truly incredible experience. It was an emergency exit caused by an unexpected crevasse that had opened up across the planned descent on the edge of the glacier.

What made this so incredible was one woman in the group was very *large* & perhaps in her 30's (she looked very old to me) she was a grade school teacher from Kansas and terrified about our situation – Our teacher was terrific! He worked out a plan! He took his heavy raincoat & lowered one strong boy to the surface & held him till he pulled the coat up between his legs – then he lowered the woman and she straddled the coat as a sled & then another boy behind her to hold her on the coat. They made it to the bottom before they too - hit the snow and started rolling.

After the last student reached safety, our teacher jumped off the mountain top and skied down – Beautifully! Then another great Thrill – our teacher collected us & guided us to the ground & let us walk up under the glacier beside the powerful stream of melted snow that was flowing out. I remember I counted over 100 layers (annual deposits) each only a fraction of an inch in thickness! Then it started the afternoon rain & we had to hike several miles down the rocky slopes to the Colorado University Geology Field Camp – where we spent the night.

Ron Krakowski's article also describes the difficulties Mildred and her fellow female students faced at OU,

Mildred pursued a degree in science at Oklahoma City University (OCU) and received her B.S. in 1928. One of Mildred's instructors, who taught geology at the university, knew of Mildred's dream to teach geology and convinced her to get her master's which opened the door and allowed her to teach geology at OCU. Mildred worked her way through graduate school at OU by teaching in the morning at OCU and traveling to Norman for her graduate work in the afternoon. It required four years to complete.

Mildred and the other ladies did encounter some difficulties regarding the battle of the sexes in those early years at the university. It was a man's world during those times, as you know. Although Mildred and the other ladies wanted to attend summer field camp, the ladies were told that they could not. Not giving in to the decision, Mildred approached Dr. Decker who taught paleontology, and appealed to him to be

Figure 19. Dr. Charles Decker, who allowed the first women to attend the OU field camp and encouraged many toward their geology careers. He was a founder of AAPG in 1917. (Photo: Monnett, V. E., 1959, p. 264.)

allowed to do fieldwork (Fig. 19). Dr. Decker finally agreed to let the three women attend field camp provided that they find a place to stay near the camp and their own means to get to camp. The three ladies were assigned to map the Hunton formation in the Arbuckle Mountains. Mildred and the other two ladies headed for field camp by car with Brunton compass, notebook, and a pup tent in hand. They approached the Boy Scout leader at Falls Creek Boy Scout Camp who allowed them to camp with the Scouts and establish their basecamp among them.

Soon after Mildred and the other ladies completed field camp, Dr. Victor Monnet of the OU Geology Department was no longer opposed women pursuing a geology degree. Female interest in geology soon began to prosper including Dr. Gould's wife and daughter developing an interest in geology as well. There were many pictures of girls in long skirts going on field trips to study geology. The department would take group trips by train to the Arbuckle's [mountains] to study Oklahoma geology. Because of Mildred's persistence and passion, no one complained about women earning their degrees in geology. [Charles Decker, professor at OU and Dr. Charles Gould, Department Founder and Oklahoma State geologist were both founding members of AAPG in 1917.]

Ron Krakowski continues, "Mildred taught at OCU for years, spending weeks during the summer doing field mapping around Turner Falls. She caused the geology department to be substantially enlarged while she was there. She met her husband, John Frizzell, when he enrolled in an OCU geology class and they married in 1933."

Though she quit teaching in 1939 when she started her family, she, and her husband, who was talented at working county records and reading maps, continued to be associated with the oil business. John Frizzell went to work with Mildred's father in 1933 to learn the petroleum drilling business. In 1950 they bought rigs from Kerr-McGee; Dean McGee, a family friend, worked a deal with John Frizzell to give him enough drilling work to cover the purchase of the rigs.

Mildred was a Founder of the Oklahoma City Geological Society (OCGS) newsletter, *The Shale Shaker*, which gained an excellent reputation for publishing oil business news. Much of that success can be traced to Mildred's years as Editor of the publication. Mildred was an Honorary Life Member of the OCGS and a member of AAPG for 73 years. Never one-dimensional, Mildred was active in the arts, music, and museums of Oklahoma City.

In 1958, she and her husband joined the Butterfield Overland Mail Centennial re-run from Tipton, Missouri to San Francisco. One hundred years after the first transcontinental U.S. mail overland delivery in 1858 covering 2,795 miles, the Frizzells retraced the route with their own beautifully restored old Concord stagecoach (Frizzell, 1960).

Margaret Stearns Bishop (1906-2005)

Margaret Stearns was the first woman to earn a PhD in geology from the University of Michigan (1933) (Fig. 20). Unlike many women in that period, she was a stratigrapher and not a micropaleontologist. She began her career with Pure Oil Company immediately after receiving her A.B. in 1929. She returned to school to earn her PhD and in 1933 and thereafter rejoined 'the Pure' in Saginaw, Michigan. In 1935, Margaret was transferred to Chicago as Assistant to the Chief Geologist where she met the somewhat shy and serious but always cheerful geophysicist, Barton Bishop. They married in 1937 and a year later she and Barton moved back to his hometown in Michigan to establish Bishop and Bishop Consulting. The following years included supporting the war effort, the addition of three children to the family, and Margaret becoming the first female to be president of the local school board.

Figure 20. Margaret Stearns Bishop, about 1920, first female PhD from the University of Michigan, worked for Pure Oil Co. Later, established the geophysical program at the University of Houston, where she was Chair of the Geology Department. Authored the book, Subsurface Mapping. (Photo: Richard Bishop, Houston, Texas, Margaret's son.)

During this time, the petroleum industry in the Permian Basin was booming, and the Bishop's consulting jobs were increasingly in Texas. Consequently, in 1953, they moved to Houston, Texas. Dr. Margaret Stearns Bishop changed her career focus again, becoming a professor at the University of Houston where she remained until retiring in 1971.

Her devotion to petroleum never wavered. As a noted subsurface specialist, in 1960, she authored the widely quoted and utilized textbook, *Subsurface Mapping* (Bishop,1960). At the University of Houston, in an early effort to popularize geology, she invoked the National Teacher Education Act and established one of the early programs to teach non-geologist science teachers how to teach geology.

In 1967, Margaret became the Geology Department Chair and as such, established the University of Houston geophysical program in 1969. From its inception to today, the program has attracted professors with international reputations and students who have become international leaders. It is now the largest geophysical program of its kind in the United States. The program had been discussed for many years but she got the job done! The petroleum industry played a significant role in starting the geophysical program because of their technical (not commercial) input. Her success stemmed in part from being an early practitioner of teambuilding, skills that she extracted from her close relationships with others in the University, Exxon Production Research Company, and Shell Development, USA.

Post retirement, she and her sister, Phyllis Lewis, and a former student, Dr. Barry Sutherland, authored five editions of *Focus on Earth Science*, the most widely used geology textbook for secondary schools in the United States (Bishop et al., 1976). The book was also translated into Spanish and Chinese. In an unusual move, but characteristic of her standards, she successfully sued the publisher to remove her name from the book when the publisher's edits inserted incorrect science. She had her principles and could be prickly.

Looking back, what do we learn from Margaret's biography? From a technical perspective, she was born with great intellectual ability but perhaps more importantly; it was how she approached her career. First, Margaret enjoyed practicing geology – whether as a teacher, researcher, an explorer or interacting with other professionals. From the perspective of working day to day, she experienced and acknowledged the limitations society commonly places on individuals – but she focused on the opportunities. While she experienced salary discrimination, she always said she had never experienced professional discrimination. In other words, she chose to ignore it. In short, she loved her profession, recognized that the world was not always fair but refused to limit herself by temporal attitudes.

Her geologist son, Richard Bishop, related these words, "Mom took great pride and pleasure in the accomplishments of her students as they went beyond the University and became leaders in the oil industry. Nothing gave her more pride than to be at an AAPG or HGS meeting and point to the accomplishments of one of her students. She took great pride in her membership in the American Association of Petroleum Geologists because these were people of great character."

This observation about Margaret's character was typified in a letter from John Ireland in response to seeing her obituary; he recounted to the Bishop family her role in his career:

> It's with a heavy heart that I read your bio-essay in Sunday's *Chronicle* concerning your Mom's passing. She was an important influence on my life also. Years ago, she believed in me and gave me a break by awarding me with a scholarship, forever putting me on a course into geology. I then had some of life's temporary bad luck. Feeling uncomfortable with the scholarship – I went into her office and voluntarily gave it up, but told her that I'd one day see her down the road. Well, it was a winding road thru many more of life's adventures and another University. I did see her again – 12 years after our first meeting...at an AAPG convention - in Denver ('80). While browsing the AAPG bookstore I looked up and there she was along with your Dad. It was instant recognition and elation. Among other things, I was able to tell her that I achieved my master's degree and was working for a major company. She told me that she had always believed in me and that some people are just winners. It was a proud moment for me – one that I'll treasure forever. Just to see the satisfaction in her eyes! Anyway, as I said – she was a special influence on me.

Margaret Stearns Bishop was a member of AAPG for 68 years. Her son, petroleum geologist, Dick Bishop, provided the majority of the biographical information for this story.

Dorothy Jung Echols (1916-1997)

Dorothy Jung was a geologist determined to be employed in petroleum or contributing to the petroleum industry by overcoming any obstacles that might challenge her—whether it was hiring attitudes, marriage and moving with her husband's jobs—or having four children while continuing to work (Fig. 21).

After acquiring her bachelor's degree at New York University and her master's at Columbia University, Dorothy headed to Houston for a job in the petroleum industry she knew she would love. In her memorial, L. Greer Price commented on Dorothy's determination to work as a geologist, "... a Houston geologist advised her to get a job working in the Humble Coffee Shop, where she would likely meet a husband. But she was not deterred" (Price, 1997).

Dorothy found work with the Republic Production Company (Sinclair Oil) as a geologist and micropaleontologist. After three years, she married Leonard S. Echols who was with Shell Oil and had to quit her position to move with him to New York. There she quickly found a job with the Texas Company as assistant to the chief geologist in their Foreign Division.

Figure 21. Dorothy Jung Echols, in St. Louis at Washington University, about 1960. She started in the oil business in Houston, became a professor at Washington University, and consulted for decades in partnership with Doris Curtis. (Photo: L. Greer Price, Socorro, New Mexico.)

In 1942, Leonard's career with Shell Oil once again compelled Dorothy to resign, this time to go with him to St. Louis. She again quickly found work in the oil business, this time consulting for the Pond Fork Oil and Gas Company of Charleston, West Virginia. In 1948, she also started teaching classes at nearby Washington University, though she had never intended to be a teacher.

When Leonard died in 1963, Dorothy was teaching full-time and raising their four children. In 1979, a friend from her Columbia University days, Doris Curtis (see Chapter 10), retired from Shell Oil in Houston and they formed a consulting business together. Doris not only worked with Dorothy, she became part of her family; Dorothy's children knew Doris as Aunt Dodo. Dorothy and Doris traveled throughout the world together and attended many geologic conferences. Their consultancy continued until Doris Curtis' death in 1991 and Dorothy persisted until her own death in 1997.

L. Greer Price, in his Memorial to Dorothy, says, "... her greatest legacy was as a teacher...her ability to instill her students with a basic understanding of field geology ... was remarkable. Her brand of teaching was unique ... and extended well beyond the classroom. Her house...was a second home for many ... her annual swimming pool parties and the late-night bouts of poker [were fond memories for all her students. She] instilled in her students a desire to be responsible members of the geologic profession and to look at all research with a critical eye. Attendance at professional meetings was de rigueur—both for Dorothy and her students—not only to keep up with 'the latest poop,' but also to know the people involved...."

Dorothy Jung Echols may never have intended to be a teacher, but she was recognized for being an extraordinary educator when she won the prestigious Neil Miner Award from the National Association of Geology Teachers in 1982. She was a member of AAPG for 56 years.

Margaret H. Hawn Mirabile (1915-1982)

Margaret Hawn was greeted by drilling crews on rigs in 1939 and into the 1940s with the comment, "This is not the sort of job I'd like my daughter to have!" She started work with Roland and Wilson of Centralia, Illinois after graduating from the University of Chicago (1938) and one year of graduate study. But, she could not afford to finish and went to work in the oil patch, a career that she enjoyed for over 40 years.

She worked for many small oil companies exploring in the Illinois Basin; Allied Oil Production Company, W. C. McBride, Inc., William E. Brubeck, R. K. Petroleum, Spartan Petroleum, Robert Dayson, and the T. W. George Estate. In 1960, with her landman husband, Andrew E. Hawn, Margaret consulted and prospected. After Andrew died, she worked for Richard Beeson, in Evansville, Indiana and was responsible for a number of Illinois basin discoveries. Her last discovery before her death was in the Renault Sand in southern Indiana where the initial well came in for 560 BOPD.

Figure 22. Margaret Hawn Mirabile, Illinois Basin oil finder, she started her career fielding remarks from rig crews who thought women were not supposed to be out on a well. (Photo: Kaveny and Berven, 1983, p. 881.)

Margaret was President of the Illinois Geological Society, and the Indiana-Kentucky Geological Society, and President of the Eastern Section of AAPG. She shared her knowledge through numerous publications. She moved to Denver near the end of her life but continued to prospect in Illinois, Indiana, and Kentucky with the Prospect Petroleum Corporation of Denver.

Margaret Hawn Mirabile (Fig. 22) was remembered for her zest for living, her avid mineral and fossil collecting, and being very athletic and involved with her English setters and her horses. She, with her smiling countenance and vivacious spirit, married Charles Mirabile shortly before her death (Kaveny and Berven, 1983).

Louise Houssiere Herrington (1918-2002)

Figure 23. Louise Houssiere at the University of Oklahoma, 1940. (Photo: University of Oklahoma Sooner *yearbook, p. 319; Western History Collections, University of Oklahoma Libraries, Norman, Oklahoma.)*

The oil business was in the blood of Louise Houssiere long before her birth. Her grandfather, Eugene Houssiere, and her father were Jennings, Louisiana businessmen who owned the Houssiere-Latreille Oil Company. Louise was the middle child of seven and after earning a B.A. degree in Chemistry from Incarnate Word College in San Antonio (Fig. 23), she followed her two brothers to the University of Oklahoma where she enjoyed taunting her younger brother about her superior grades in geology and other classes. Louise attended the Massachusetts Institute of Technology (MIT) where her older brother had also attended, and earned her master's degree in geochemistry in 1941. Louise may have been one of the first women oil company summer interns, having worked for seven summers in high school and college (1934-1940) with an independent oil operator.

With the onset of WWII, Louise's geochemistry degrees helped her secure a job with the Baroid Division of the National Lead Company in Houston both as a mud engineer and to run their laboratory. After about a year, Louise found a position as Chief Micropaleontologist with Texaco where she was put in charge of the paleontology laboratory for south Texas.

During this time, she met and married James T. Herrington, who was in the service working on "anti-American activities" with the Counterintelligence Corps (CIC) and the Office of Strategic Service (OSS), the precursors to the Central Intelligence Agency (CIA). In mid-1943, he was transferred to the Manhattan Project in Cleveland, Ohio. Louise landed on her feet in Ohio, finding a job with the Sohio Petroleum Company and worked on the geology of south Louisiana. Professional jobs for women were easier to find during the war but the pay, based on Louise's experience, was usually 25-30% less than her male counterparts.

In 1945-46 the military asked James to move to Los Alamos. He and Louise contemplated the career move and decided to leave military life and return to Texas. James resumed his job with an insurance company in Freeport, Texas but the transition was not as simple for Louise who was not able to find a job in the area and after two years, they moved to Houston. With the war over, Louise was unable to find a job with an oil company but was hired by the University of Houston where she would teach for three years. Like several of the war-time women hires, teaching was one of the few post-WWII job options.

In Houston, Louise was again close to her Louisiana home and started working on family oil properties, bringing her prospecting skills learned at Sohio to the Houssiere leases in Louisiana. When her father became very ill in 1953, she and James moved back to Jennings, Louisiana where she worked tirelessly on managing the mineral interests, prospecting and leasing, unitizing production, and developing fields. She was a meticulous worker, a trait required for an area where royalty interests had four and five decimal points and in an era before computer calculators, that necessitated great time-consuming ardor. She had an extraordinary memory and was very successful in this final chapter of her career. James eventually left the insurance business and joined the Houssiere family oil business to help work on lease acquisitions.

It is easy to see how her daughter, Dawn Herrington, would become attracted to the oil business and follow a path to Texaco in her career. Dawn is a geologist and Gulf of Mexico Exploration Manager for Ecopetrol in Houston. Louise Houssiere Herrington joined AAPG in 1944 and was a member until her death in 2002, 58 years.

Warda Bleser-Bircher (1905 – 2006)

First female petroleum geologist from Switzerland

Figure 24. Warda Bleser-Bircher, first Swiss female geologist, with geologist A.W. Bally (left) and Paul Bleser's assistant, Ben Olsen, on Muncho Lake. (Photo: Warda's personal photo collection, archived ETH Zürich, Archiv für Zeitgeschichte. Appreciation to Monika Gisler for the use of her story and photo.)

In 1949, Iran contracted a group of Swiss geologists to develop geologic maps and prospects to allow the country to become independent of the British Anglo-Persian Oil Company (Anglo-Iranian Oil Company). But before the pioneer, Arnold Heim, and his co-workers traveled to Iran, Switzerland already had a female geologist in residence in Iran, Warda Bleser-Bircher. Warda Bircher, born in Cairo in 1905, studied Natural Science (1928-1934) with a specialty in geology under Rudolf Staub in Zurich. She received her doctorate in 1935. Her family, originally from Kuettingen AG (Switzerland), had been doing business in Egypt since 1862. Having dual citizenship, she completed her school and university education in Switzerland and returned to Egypt two years following her education. (Fig. 24)

Warda found it very difficult to find a position as a geologist, but in 1937 she was hired in Turkey. From 1937 to 1938 she worked as a paleontologist in Ankara, where she helped with the development of oil deposits of that country. (This was a period when Mehlika Ribnikar [nee Tasman] was becoming interested in paleontology, and was perhaps influenced by Warda to study for her degree—see WWII Chapter 10.) Warda had developed a friendship with Paul Bleser during her studies in Zurich and he, too, had a difficult time finding a job, but eventually went to work for Royal Dutch Shell in 1937 in their Columbian office. Later, they would reunite and get married.

At the beginning of WWII, Warda Bircher found a position as a paleontologist with Shell of Egypt, her country of birth. The situation in Egypt was not stable and she continued the job until, in March 1941, she took a position in Teheran with the State Mining Department. This was when the Shah was initiating his strategy to increase oil independence. Warda Bircher was restricted from fieldwork and focused on the identification of fossils in the laboratory. "Patience, method and critical judgment are the cornerstones of all scientific work," she wrote to her parents. A philosophy she adhered to throughout her life.

As difficult as it was to find a position as a single woman, it became impossible after she married her longtime boyfriend, Paul Bleser, in 1946. From then on, she accompanied her husband wherever Shell sent him. They moved to New Guinea, then Java, Nigeria, Canada and eventually, Cambodia. Warda Bleser-Bircher was relegated, like so many female partners of men in the oil business, to the role of supporter. She, however, insinuated herself into his work, refusing to end her career. It was not easy, because corporate rules, certainly for Shell at the time, demanded that data and results were kept secret, even from wives. But she pressured the company and finally gained a half-time position as a laboratory paleontologist.

In Owerri, Nigeria, she joined her husband in his fieldwork and produced an independent report, which Shell management rejected by return of post because of their policy of confidentiality—interpreting her work as compromising this confidentiality. Warda Bircher-Bleser was not content to remain in the camp when her husband was in the field—she described the camp community as uninteresting and lacking in intellectual stimulation. Therefore, she accompanied her husband into the field whenever possible.

Eventually, she occupied herself with the botanical garden at her parents' home in El Saff (Egypt). Her father had begun a systematic effort to describe the plants in his garden. After Paul retired from Shell, they took over her father's botanical garden and took residence in El Saff. Warder continued this botanical project and, in 1960, she published an encyclopedia of the plants. In 1964 she successfully fought the state attempt to take over the botanical garden. In 2006, Warda Bleser-Bircher died at the proud age of 101 at her final residence in Tessin, Switzerland (Gisler, 2014).

Yvonne Wahl Gubler (1903 to 2002)

The first female petroleum geologist in France

Yvonne Wahl was born in Lyon, France. She received her B.S. in science from the Sorbonne in 1925 and in 1927 was married to Jean Gubler, a Swiss geologist she met in university. By 1928 she had been awarded her PhD, also from the Paris-Sorbonne University. As a student at the Sorbonne, she surveyed the Ubaye Nappe in the French Alps with attention to syntectonic sedimentation. From 1928 to 1933 she and her husband lived in Indochine, then a French colony, and in Cambodia. She published her thesis work and began her family, giving birth to two sons. (Fig. 25)

Figure 25. Yvonne Wahl Gubler, 1929, in Hanoi, Indochine (today North Vietnam), where she worked with her husband, Jean Gubler, and started her family. (Photo: Dominique Gubler, Paris, France, Yvonne's son.)

In 1934 Yvonne and Jean moved to Morocco where he was the Chief Geologist for the Geological Survey of Morocco and she continued to assist in his work and publish with him. They had two more children during this time. Jean Gubler tragically died at a young age in 1940, leaving her widowed at age 37 with four sons to raise. Remarkably, Yvonne succeeded him at the Moroccan survey as Chief Geologist and explored the Western Rif Range and the Paleozoic from the Ougnat to the Tafilalt (Burollet, 1979, and personal communication with Dominique Gubler, Yvonne's son).

In 1941, during WWII, Yvonne returned to France and became the Director of the Sedimentology Division of the Société Nationale des Pétroles d'Aquitaine (SNPA). She also created the sedimentology laboratory for the SNPA, whose offices had been relocated to Toulouse outside the Nazi occupied zones during these war years. The state oil company was active in the Aquitaine basin in southwest France, and discovered the Lacq oilfield, a 6 TCF gas-field.

In 1946, Yvonne joined the Institut Français du Pétrole (IFP) as Director of the Sedimentology Department and she worked for the IFP for 23 years, both as a researcher for basin studies (environment of deposition, sedimentology, log interpretation related to depositional environment, and seismic stratigraphy), and as a professor specializing in petroleum. One of her many credits at the IFP is being responsible for the discovery of the natural gas field of Hassi-Messaoud in Algeria. An assignment of note was the time she spent in Brazil and Equador creating offshore research facilities. She was very enthusiastic about sharing her deep knowledge of geology, with a naturalist's approach. As a careful observer of the different types of sedimentation, in both clastics and carbonates she loved working in the field, primarily in the Alps. (Fig. 26)

Figure 26. Yvonne Wahl Gubler, 1947, a proven oil finder in Morocco, she moved back to France in 1946 as Director of the Sedimentology Division of the SNPA in Toulouse and opened the sedimentology laboratory. (Photo: Dominique Gubler.)

French geologists credit Yvonne Gubler as one of the founders of modern French stratigraphy—combining facies determinations with paleontology. She insisted that geologists combine stratigraphic correlations with paleontological data for more accuracy and determine depositional environments using foraminifera as well as other tools.

Max Bordenave of Paris, France, wrote of Yvonne,

> She had a strong and determined personality. She always tried to understand geological processes and to help people to understand, and she liked to share her knowledge. Students who were trained at IFP are indebted to her for her very thorough and interesting courses. She published many papers, [75 or more] based both on specific examples from her fieldwork in the Alps and Pyrenees, and on sedimentological problems worldwide.

After her retirement in 1975, she founded and promoted higher education on "Methods and Recognitions of Sedimentary Basins" at the University of Orsay (currently University Paris Sud) and enabled university graduates to be prepared for work in petroleum and mining. An indefatigable volunteer and organization creator, Yvonne was a founder the Association of French Sedimentologists and was president from 1964 to 1975. She was also president of the International Association of Sedimentologists (IAS) at a time when publishing in French was done for both the Bulletin de la Société Géologique de France and Sedimentology.

H. Reading (2003), said of Yvonne's service,

> Without her the IAS would have never evolved as fully as it has. It enables easy access to information, membership fees accessible to young colleagues, thematic volumes at affordable cost. Her term ended with the International Congress of Sedimentology in Nice (1975) but her legacy continued as this Congress is now essential for the professional development of geoscientists. Her forte has always been to work hard toward the dispersal of knowledge and optimizing communication. Those who knew her also knew her capacity for welcoming and stimulating new, non-conformist ideas, calling into question "dogmas."

Max (personal communication) reminisced:

> Madame Gubler was one of my most respected professors at the IFP school in 1956. (Fig. 27) At the time, she was teaching sedimentology and was very enthusiastic and knew her subject thoroughly. Her very interesting classes at Rueil-Malmaison were followed by a two-week fieldwork training session in the Alps. Every day the team of some twenty students, averaging 25 years old, took walks along difficult paths with an abundance of vertiginous slopes and cliffs to investigate the tidal influences, estuarine or fluvial sedimentary features. She was strong and fit, and, though 62 years old at that time, could walk long hours. We students tired well before she did. She used to allow short rests every two hours, with a thirty-minute stop for lunch.
>
> So, we plotted amongst ourselves how to make the lunch rest period longer. We knew she particularly liked chestnut cream, a delicacy from the Ardèche region where I now live. We decided unanimously to buy a can of chestnut cream and offer [it] to her at the next lunch stop.
>
> "Madame Gubler, please have some chestnut cream, please have some more..." The students, myself included, smiled to ourselves while she was enjoying eating the whole can of chestnut cream! Then she said "I think I have had too much chestnut cream and if I rest, I will rest too long, therefore let's start our afternoon session without any rest."
>
> We could only admire her more...and, indeed, all of my life I have felt indebted to her for excellent training.

Figure 27. Yvonne, 1957, relished leading field trips when she was at the Institut Français du Pétrole (IFP) and director of the Sedimentology Department in Paris. (Photo: Dominique Gubler.)

Her son, Michel Gubler, recalled a field trip that he had joined as she led 25 students up the Ubaye valley. At 1800 meters (5900 feet) they suddenly were caught up in a dense fog and it was near the end of the day. They could not see well enough to find their way back to camp, but she told them, "I have mapped the nummulite beds in this area and if we find them, we can follow them along the outcrop back to our awaiting dinner!" Soon the students found one nummulite, then a couple more and, finally, the outcrop, which they followed safely down the valley. That night I took a lot of pride in the students remarks about how astonished and impressed they were with my mother's expertise. She was affectionately known by all her students as "Tante Yvonne."

With retirement, she moved to Savoy, located in the northern part of the French Alps, where she remained active in promoting the "Aiguilles Rouges Natural Park" west of the Chamonix valley. Yvonne Gubler died in 2002, at the age of 98.

She was a recipient of the French Legion d'Honneur and in 1978, a book was published by the French Society of Sedimentology, *Dynamics and Methods of Study of Sedimentary Basins*, and dedicated to Dr. Yvonne Gubler. It covered the topics she loved and studied during her career, such as basin analyses, log analysis (electro-facies), and seismic stratigraphy. In the "Tribute to Madame Gubler" (Majithia, p. 1), C. Sallé writes,

> The strong personality of Madame Gubler has marked her epoch in the evolution of technics [sic] but more so in the moulding of men. Her lesson of courage, tenacity and enthusiasm have helped a good number of her old students to overcome the difficulties of the journey and enabled each according to his capacity, to participate in the adventure of the great geologic discoveries of the last decades.

Every two years, in recognition of her work in the field of sedimentology, the Yvonne Gubler Prize is awarded to a research scientist by the French Society of Sedimentology which is based at Bordeaux University, a gesture of continuing respect for this pioneering French woman scientist. Dr. Yvonne Wahl Gubler was an AAPG member for 24 years.

Frances Charlton de Rivero (1904-1974)

Frances Charlton worked in Venezuela for Pure Oil Company's subsidiary, Orinoco Oil Company and lost her heart to that country. After sixteen years in the oil business and working toward a PhD, she moved to Venezuela permanently and became the first female geology professor in Venezuela in 1943 and later the first Department Chair (Fig. 28). She was possibly the first female chair of a geology department in a co-educational school in all the Americas, North and South. She taught, did research, published, and established an excellent reputation in stratigraphy and paleontology. She married Manuel de Rivero in 1935 and became a Venezuelan citizen.

Figure 28. Frances Charlton de Rivero, first female chair of a coeducational geology department in the Americas, possibly in the world. She worked for Pure Oil in Venezuela in the 1930s. (Photo: O. Mendez and O. Rey, Caracas, Venezuela.)

Frances Charlton was born in Brooklyn, New York May 25, 1904, and graduated Summa Cum Laude in Arts with majors in Geology and Latin at the Vassar College in 1924. In 1926, she obtained her Master of Arts from Columbia University and the following year started working as a micropaleontologist for Pure Oil Company in Arkansas. In 1929, Frances transferred to Maracaibo for Orinoco and worked there until 1931 as a staff micropaleontologist. She attempted to pursue her PhD in geology at the University of California Berkeley, but for economic reasons, did not finish her thesis concerning the micropaleontology of the Miocene Bowden Formation, Jamaica.

Frances went back to work for Pure Oil with the Gulf Coast Division in Louisiana from 1933 to 1935 as Chief of Staff of the Micropaleontologic laboratory. In the late 1930's she took postgraduate courses in Spanish, and Hispano-American Literature at Columbia University and worked with Dr. Marshall Kay, keeping herself up-to-date in stratigraphy.

In October 1943, Frances became a full professor at the Geology Institute in Caracas, (later it became the Geology Department, and Engineering Faculty of the Universidad Central de Venezuela--UCV) and conducted research in paleontology and stratigraphy. She taught for 28 years, educating many generations of Venezuelan petroleum geologists, and retired in 1971. Frances held many academic and administrative positions and represented the University and the country on several National and International Committees. She was a key author of the first Venezuela Stratigraphic Lexicon.

Frances Charlton de Rivero was the recipient of many awards during her career including Vassar´s Women of the Century in 1961. In 1965, because of her "first" as Chair of the Geology Department, the Venezuela Ministry of

Education awarded Frances the Orden 27 de Junio en Segunda Clase for her contribution to Venezuela. She was a member of AAPG in the 1930s.

The source of information for this short biography is a chapter about Frances Charlton de Rivero by Professor O. Rey. Maria Antonieta Lorente contributed to the English translation for this book and takes responsibility for any inaccuracies, as does Robbie Gries in her paraphrasing. Photo from O. Mendez for use in Professor Rey's chapter regarding Frances Charlton de Rivero.

Female geologists in the former Soviet Union

Four early female geologists in the former Soviet Union appear to have been focused on petroleum exploration in their paleontologic careers (*The Biographical Dictionary of Women in Science*, Ogilvie and Harvey).

Sofia Viktorovna (Karpova) Semikhatova (1889-1973)

Sofia Viktorovna (Karpova) Semikhatova was possibly the first Soviet woman in petroleum geology, beginning her career in 1924. Sofia used macrofossils (largely brachiopods) for her biostratigraphic work to sort out the stratigraphy of the Carboniferous, mainly in the Volga-Ural province; work which was extremely important to understanding the geology of this petroleum-bearing region of Russia then, the Union of Soviet Socialist Republics (USSR). She worked early in her career at the Moscow Geological Oil Institute (1924-1942).

In 1942, Sofia, her husband, and three children evacuated to Tashkent and she went to work in the Uzbek Geological Administration until they returned to Moscow in 1944. At that time, she returned to the Oil Institute and was involved with establishing gas development. In 1953, Sofia Viktorovna Smikhatova became employed by the All-Union Scientific Research Geological Oil Institute, where she worked until the end of her life in 1973 (Ogilvie and Harvey, pp. 1175-1176).

Dagmara Maksimilianovna Rauzer-Chernousova (1895-1996)

Dagmara Rauzer-Chernousova may have been the second Soviet woman in petroleum geology. (Fig. 29) She began her career in 1918 but did not work in petroleum until 1931. Her key work before and during WWII in micropaleontology in "Ural Oil" and the Research Geological Oil Institute was to sort out the stratigraphy of the Paleozoic using micropaleontology. It was important for drilling not only for oil and gas exploration, but it was also used for coal and salt exploitation. She convinced exploration groups of the value of micropaleontology and the need for specialists and proceeded to train many geologists for the task. Dagmara was awarded the Lenin Prize, the highest scientific award of the Soviet Union and was bestowed with the title of Honored Science Worker of Science and Technology of the USSR.

Figure 29. Dagmara Rauzer-Chernousova, Russian bio stratigrapher, credited with the discovery of the extensive and highly productive Ishimbay group of oilfields in a late Paleozoic carbonate pinnacle reef trend along the southern pre-Ural region in Bashkiria. (Photo: Cushman Foundation, Journal Foraminiferal Research, *v. 30, no. 2, p. 81, April 2000.)*

After her Moscow University bachelor's degree in 1918 and after her marriage, Dagmara, her small daughter, and her husband moved to the Crimea for his health (tuberculosis). She volunteered as a research worker in a Sevastopol Biological Station of the Academy of Sciences and combined her work with teaching. Starting in 1931 Dagmara became involved in micropaleontology and worked in that area until her death in 1996. She received her PhD in 1945 in Moscow from the Geology Institute.

During her career, Dagmara attacked the important and difficult questions of classification and stratigraphic subdivisions. She wrote extensively of the biostratigraphic borders of the Carboniferous and Permian, the Kasimovian stage, and the distribution of foraminifera in Sakmarian and Asselian seas. She also specialized in the evolution of foraminifera of the Upper Paleozoic and the classifying the paleoecology of foraminifera. Dagmara was especially interested in changes in foraminiferal walls, and the meaning of these changes for classification (Ogilvie and Harvey, 2000, pp. 1078-79).

Charles Ross and Paul Brenkle said of her work, "During World War II, the Soviet Union was increasingly concerned about the possible loss of the Caspian and Baku oil fields which were the country's mainstay for petroleum. As a result, oil exploration was intensified in other areas, and Dr. Rauzer-Chernousova was selected to be part of this effort. She is credited with the discovery of the extensive and highly productive Ishimbay group of oilfields in a late Paleozoic carbonate pinnacle reef trend along the southern pre-Ural region in Bashkiria. After World War II, she formed the Micropaleontology Laboratory at the Geological Institute which became world-renowned in the study of late Paleozoic foraminifera" (Ross and Brenkle, 2000).

Valentina Galaktionovna Morozova (1910-1989)

Valentina Galaktionovna Morozova credits Soviet Union politics for playing a large role in her decision to become a geologist, "...life was difficult for...talented people of her generation." She drew beautifully, sang professionally, played the piano, and spoke four European languages fluently. But, accused of "subversive activities," she and a group of her school friends were arrested. She was convicted but was released on probation and prohibited from living in seven cities. Valentina became a paleontologist because her college options were limited due to her conviction even though her scores were exceptional. She graduated from Leningrad University in 1933 and was employed by the All-Union Research Institute of Geological Prospecting. She took post graduate courses at Moscow University, and in 1937 defended her thesis on the changes in foraminifera at the Cretaceous/Tertiary boundary. Valentina was awarded a medal "for Courageous Work during the Great Patriotic War," for her work in studying the stratigraphy of oil-bearing Paleozoic sediments in the Bashkirian Cisurals.

She was employed as a geologist at the Mineralovodskaya Expedition of Scientific Research of the Moscow Institute of Geological Exploration and studied the stratigraphy of oil-bearing Paleozoic deposits of the Bashkirian Pre-Urals. This involved extensive fieldwork on the Soviet-Iran border and the Lenkoran Lowland, where she contracted malaria. In 1949, Valentina went to work "studying the Mesozoic and Cenozoic stratigraphy in the southern part of the USSR and on the Russian Platform. Politics again intervened in 1950, when the ministry of state security brought up the old charges against her. [The Stalin years ran from 1929 to 1953]. She was summoned to the KGB, which demanded that she inform on her colleagues. She refused, but this experience, which occurred at the same time she lost her father to starvation during the siege of Leningrad and her twenty-year-old brother on the Leningrad front was too much for her to bear and she became gravely ill, never to completely recover."

"She was one of the first to speak of the influence of cosmic factors on foraminiferal evolution, including the catastrophic disappearance of Mesozoic plankton at the Cretaceous/Tertiary boundary. Although much of her work was theoretical, it was also valuable for oil prospecting and geological surveys. She published over fifty scientific works, including four monographs and ten reports" (Ogilvie and Harvey, pp. 915-916).

Yelena Nikolayevna Polenova (1915-1987)

World War II and the need for petroleum moved Yelena from academia to the application of micropaleontology for finding oil in the Devonian of the Russian Platform. She had been introduced to geology when her father died and she moved to live with geology professor, Dr. B. K. Polenoy. Yelena acquired her bachelor's degree at the University of Leningrad in 1937. She worked on the Jurassic foraminifera from the Emba oil-bearing region of the Soviet Union and took graduate courses. She did fieldwork in Western China, middle Asia, and Kazakhstan.

Polenova used ostracods (a diverse group of small aquatic crustaceans) to unravel the stratigraphy of the Devonian and it appears this was the first time that ostracods were used for this purpose. Over a 17-year period, a Soviet school of ostracodologists was developed for the entire country. In 1962, she returned to studying the Jurassic of Siberia and the Arctic and part of Middle Asia. A series of monographs provided Yelena Nikolayevna Plenova with worldwide acclaim (Ogilvie and Harvey, *The Biographical Dictionary of Women in Science*, Ogilvie and Harvey, 2000).

Chapter 9 Sources and References

Albright, Horace M., and Robert Cahn. *The Birth of the National Park Service: The Founding Years, 1913-33.* Institute of the American West books, Vol. 2. Salt Lake City: Howe Brothers, 1985. 120 pp.

Altman, Kathleen, Susan Riebe, Tiffany Abbink, Mary Beth Beach, Judy Bolis, Sandy Kramer, Cathy Mencin, Tara Schenk, and Pamela Tittes. 1999. A Century of Women at Mines. Florence Caldwell Centennial Celebration Commitee and the Women in Science Engineering and Mathematics Program. Colorado School of Mines, Golden, Colorado. 86 pp.

Bingham, Michelle, Lubbock, Texas, granddaughter of Mildred Armor Frizzell. Personal communication, July 2016 through January 2017; source of photographs of Mildred Armor Frizzell as cited in figure captions.

Bishop, M. S. *Subsurface Mapping*. New York: John Wiley & Sons Inc. 1960. 198 pp.

Bishop, Margaret S., Berry Sutherland, and Phyllis G. Lewis. *Focus on Earth Science.* Columbus, Ohio: Charles E. Merrill Publishing Co., 1976. 536 pp.

Bishop, Richard, Houston, Texas, son of Margaret Bishop. Personal communication, May 2014 through October 2016; source of photograph of Margaret Bishop as cited in figure captions.

Brooklyn Daily Eagle. "Brooklyn Woman Braves Jungle to Explore Vast Venezuelan Oil Fields." 20 May, 1923, p. 4.

Bordenave, Max, Paris, France, colleague of Dr. Yvonne Gubler. Personal communication, January 2017.

Burollet, P. F. 1978. "Award of Honorary Membership to Mme Yvonne Gubler." *Sedimentology*, vol. 16, pp. 164-165.

Colby, Lester B., ed. "Meet a Lady Oil Engineer." *Petroleum Age.* January, 1920, vol. 7, no. 12, p. 58. https://books.google.com, Accessed 08/2016.

Frizzell, John, Tulsa, Oklahoma, son of Mildred Frizzell. Personal communication, July 2016 to September 2016.

Frizzell, Mildred Armor. 1959. "Editor's Note, page 126." *In* Gould, Charles Newton. ed. *The Chronicles of Oklahoma*. Norman: University of Oklahoma Press, 1959. 282 pp.

Gisler, Monika. *'Swiss Gang'–Pioniere der Erdölexploration: Schweizer Pioniere der Wirtschaft und Technik.* Zürich: Verein für wirtschaftshistorische Studien. Schweizer, 2014. 120 pp.

Gries, Robbie. 1984. "Profile: Ninetta Davis." *The Outcrop.* Rocky Mountain Association of Geologists, January, p. 7

Gubler, Dominique, Paris, France, son of Yvonne Gubler. Personal communication, January 2017; source of photographs of Yvonne Gubler as cited in figure captions.

Gubler, Michel, Paris, France, son of Yvonne Gubler. Personal communication, January 2017.

Hall, Dollie Radler. 1965. "Women in Exploration." *Tulsa Geological Society Digest*, vol. 33, pp. 295-298.

Kaveny, Bridget, and Robert J. Berven. 1983. "Margaret Hawn Mirabile Memorial." *AAPG Bulletin*, vol. 66, no. 5, p. 881.

Krakowski, Ron. 2008, "Mildred Frizzell." *The Shale Shaker.* Tulsa, Oklahoma, May-June, p. 225.

Michigan Geological Survey. *Martin, Helen Mandeville.* n.d. Photograph. State Archives of Michigan: M.S. Number 93-71, Series 93-71-3.

Monnett, V. E. 1959. "Charles Elijah Decker Memorial." *AAPG Bulletin*, vol. 43, no. 1, pp. 263-266.

Ogilvie, Marilyn and Joy Harvey, eds. *The Biographical Dictionary of Women in Science,* Ogilvie and Harvey, 2000. Volumes 1 and 2. London; New York: Routledge, 2000. 1499 pp.

Owen, Edgar Wesley. *Trek of the Oil Finders: A History of Exploration for Petroleum.* Memoir 6. Tulsa, Okla.: American Association of Petroleum Geologists, 1975. 1647 pp.

Price, L. Greer. 1997. "Dorothy Echols." *GSA Memorials.* Dec., vol. 28, pp. 69-72.

Rey, O. "Geología: Frances de Rivero." *In* Lopez, L. and M. A. Renaudo (eds.), *Mujeres en Ciencia: Venezuela sus historias inspiradoras.* Caracas, Venezuela: Academia de Ciencias Físicas, Matemáticas y Naturales, in press. 216 pp.

Ross, Charles A., and Paul L. Brenkle. 2000. "Dagmara Maksimilianovna Rauzer-Chernousova." With permission from the Cushman Foundation, *Journal of Foraminiferal Research*, vol. 30, i. 2, pp. 81-82.

Sallé, C. "Tribute to Madame Gubler." 1998. page 1. In Majithia, Margaret. General Editor. *Dynamics and Methods of Study of Sedimentary Basins.* New Delhi: Oxford & IBH Publishing Company Pvt. Ltd., 392 pp.

Segall, R. Thomas. 1980s. "A Brief History of the Michigan Geological Survey." p. 5. http://www.michigan.gov/documents/deq/GIMDL-GGGSDH_302337_7.pdf. Accessed 12/2016.

Shrock, Robert Rakes. *Geology at M.I.T 1865-1965: A History of the First Hundred Years of Geology at Massachusetts Institute of Technology, Vol. II.* Cambridge, Mass.: The MIT Press, 1982. pp. 406-408.

Susan's Sweet Rocket blog. Aug 17, 2011, sweetrocket.blogspot.com/2011/08/missmargaretcobb.html. Accessed 02/2015.

University of North Carolina. *Margaret Cameron Cobb.* 1909. Photograph. "*Pine Needles* yearbook." Chapel Hill, North Carolina, p. 185.

University of Oklahoma. *Louise Houssiere Herrington.* 1940. Photograph. "*Sooner* yearbook." Western History Collection. Norman, Oklahoma. p. 319.

Visher, Stephen Sargent. *Indiana Scientists: A Biographical Directory and an Analysis.* Indianapolis, Indiana: The Indiana Academy of Science, 1951. 286 pp.

Wasson, Theron, and Isabel Wasson. 1927. "Cabin Creek Field, West Virginia." *AAPG Bulletin* vol. 11, no. 7, pp. 705-719.

Wellesley College. *Katherine Woodley Carman.* 1927. *Legenda* yearbook. Wellesley, Massachusetts, p. 35, with permission from Wellesley College.

Chapter 10

WWII: Women Who Joined the Industry

By the late 1930s, the hiring of women into the oil and gas business had slowed down. The market for micropaleontologists was saturated and industry had begun to adopt a philosophy of not hiring women into exploration departments. A general estimate of this impact can be surmised from the AAPG membership records by the number of women who joined the Association before, during, and after World War II. For the five years prior to the War, about 1-2 women joined AAPG per year. During the War, from late 1941 through 1944, an average of 17 women joined AAPG per year. This included many women who were underemployed in the late 1930s and who were finally able to find geology jobs with oil companies. AAPG records, personal documents, and career memorials are available for the women who entered the petroleum workforce during that time (Graph 1).

Although women were being hired, the distressing fact was that once employed, women often were required, by corporate policy, to resign when they got married. The only two married women from this book's research who kept their industry jobs when WWII was over were Anne Frank, who was working for a geophysical company and was considered invaluable as a crew chief (her husband worked as a surveyor on the same crew) and Ruth Lebow, who worked in her husband's family-owned business and which she later ran (see Chapter 8).

Based on the available records, approximately 60 women joined AAPG during WWII, and fourteen of the women who joined and remained single retained their jobs and had long careers. Two women, Marie Gramann and Hazel Peterson, lost their jobs in a downturn in the 1960s and changed to underpaid positions teaching college. Two women, who were single, left the petroleum industry by choice: Beverly McMahon became disgruntled with the industry's glass ceiling and started a second career teaching and Leola Bunch left industry for a career in law. One woman, Doris Curtis, who did not marry until 1950, was required to quit Shell Oil, also began university teaching. Only after divorce was she able to resume her career as a geologist at Shell. Unfortunately, the records indicate that most of the women, 28 of the 60, got married and left the industry for good. The remaining nine married women stayed employed as geologists by consulting, teaching, or joining a State or Federal Geologic Survey. This was a tremendous loss of expertise, talent, and diversity for the petroleum industry. Sociological surveys during this time asked women if they wanted to continue to work after the War and were overwhelmingly met with the positive answer that about 80% wanted to maintain their careers (Renzetti & Curran, 2002, p. 215). Women were not "happy to quit and take care of hearth and home."

Doris Sarah Malkin Curtis (1914-1991)

Figure 1. Doris Malkin at the microscope during her early career at Shell Oil Co. (Photo: Doris' niece, Lucy Suchman, Saltspring Island, British Columbia, Canada.)

Doris Curtis was the "can-do" pioneering woman in geology whose nieces affectionately called her "Aunt Dodo." Doris gave of her talents unstintingly. She tended each task and each project with focused attention and unflagging energy, and as a result was successful (Fig. 1).

Her lifelong friend and professional colleague, Dorothy Echols, wrote about her,

> During her undergraduate years at Brooklyn College, she decided on her major field, geology. She received her B.A. from there in 1933 and entered the graduate program at Columbia University in New York. She received her M.A. in 1934 and stayed on for her PhD.
>
> This is when and where I met my friend Doris. She had just survived her PhD oral examination when I walked into Schermerhorn's hallowed halls. In not too many weeks, we were great pals, double dating, cutting Journal Club, and starting our weekends early. By 1938, when I left with M.A. in hand for Houston to seek a job, we were dearest friends. (Echols, 1991)

In 1939, when Doris had completed all the required course work, examinations, and most of her fieldwork for her PhD she, too, went to Houston to find a job (Fig. 2). Doris had some difficulty locating a suitable job with her credentials, but within a few weeks was working for an independent.

In 1941, as the War effort intensified, Doris landed a job as a micropaleontologist for Shell Oil Company in Houston. Her niece, Susan Suchman Simon, recalls Doris telling about her day of onsite interviews. She was shown around the Shell facilities by a gentleman geologist and, at lunchtime, he took her upstairs to the Executive lunchroom where they were refused entry because it was for "men only." The gentleman was totally chagrined and took her someplace else, apologizing profusely. He seemed worried that she might refuse to take the job with Shell because of this incident, but she simply smiled and said, "Don't worry. I'll fix that after I get the job!" A sign of the times, however, was that Doris, with her PhD near completion, was hired as a micropaleontologist/secretary (Fig. 3). Secretary. Think about it.

Figure 2. Doris Malkin in Houston with her dream job at last, paleontologist with Shell Oil. Her title, however, included "stenographer." Her first paycheck was for $87.50 for the month in 1941. (Photo: Doris' niece, Susan Suchman Simon, Chapel Hill, North Carolina.)

Now hired, Doris immediately volunteered to help with hosting activities for the AAPG convention in Houston, making her presence known to the established authority in micropaleontology, Alva Ellisor.

Dorothy Echols, in her Memorial, said,

> From 1942 to 1950, as exploration emphasis shifted, Shell Oil relocated Doris to offices in Baltimore, and Tallahassee, as stratigrapher and geologist (Fig. 4). During this phase of her career, she also dusted off her thesis

Figure 3. Doris with her first car purchase, 1941, Houston. (Photo: Susan Suchman Simon.

Figure 4. Doris at work in Tallahassee. (Photo: Lucy Suchman.)

notes and finished her fieldwork in Maryland, with her mother as field assistant. From then on, Doris assumed responsibility for her mother's care. "Momma Malkin," as we called her, lived with Doris or in an attached house or apartment until 1979 when nursing-home care was required. Columbia University awarded Doris her PhD in 1949, and her dissertation was published in 1953. (Echols, 1991)

Doris' niece, Susan, recalls that Doris' social life was challenging while her mother was alive and living with her because "Momma Malkin" would scrutinize any dates or company that visited Doris and make her judgments about them. This was when Doris was in her 50s! Finally, Doris bought a duplex and put her mother into one side where she could not be involved in Doris' socializing.

After nine years of employment, in 1950, the first phase of her Shell career ended when Doris married a Shell engineer from Houston, Mark Issacs (Fig. 5). At that time, nepotism policies precluded her continuing in the company, and thus she moved into academia, joining the earth science faculty of the University of Houston (Echols, 1991). When she taught, as she did a couple of times in her career, she always became a role model and mentor to young women, whether they were in geology or any other field.

Figure 5. Doris with first husband, Mark Issacs. She had to quit her job with Shell Oil when she married. She turned to teaching at the University of Houston, research at Scripps Institute, and to teaching at the University of Oklahoma. (Photo: Lucy Suchman.)

Doris was a life-long learner and loved the challenge of absorbing entirely new aspects of the geological sciences. In 1953, Doris participated in the famous Francis Shepard-directed *API Project 51* sponsored by Scripps Institution of Oceanography. The discomforts and hardships of cruising for days on end were ignored. True scientists scoff at such "minor" inconveniences, intent as they are in observing, measuring, gathering data, and inevitably being rewarded for their persistence by many "aha!" moments. From that adventure, Doris completed a detailed study on ostracods of the northwest Gulf of Mexico.

Echols continues writing of Doris,

> In 1954, when her work at Scripps was completed, she and her husband moved to Norman, Oklahoma, Doris to teach at the university and her husband to continue his research. From 1954 to 1959, as instructor, assistant professor, and associate professor (tenured), Doris taught sedimentary geology. Her courses were so popular that enrollment had to be restricted. Her infectious enthusiasm and wide-ranging grasp of the earth sciences inspired many of her students to pursue professional careers.
>
> After five years of teaching [a second marriage, Figure 6], and divorce, Doris returned to her first love, the petroleum industry. She was re-hired by Shell and assigned to a special studies group at Shell's Baton Rouge Exploration office. In 1960, this group was relocated to New Orleans, where Doris initiated regional studies of time-synchronous sandstone deltas in the petroleum-rich Miocene of coastal Louisiana. In 1970, a synthesis of this seminal research was published in SEPM Special Publication No. 15. In 1975, Shell transferred Doris to Houston, her original petroleum turf, as staff geologist in their International Venture Group. Later, she moved to a research assignment at Shell Development Company. Doris retired from this position in 1979, and she and I formed a geology consulting partnership. When she died, Doris was engaged in this partnership, Curtis and Echols, and was also an active adjunct professor of geology at Rice University.

Figure 6. Doris' second marriage with Neville Curtis did not last and after her divorce she was able to return to Shell Oil as a stratigrapher. (Photo: Lucy Suchman.)

A tireless publisher, she wrote over thirty papers on paleoecology, biostratigraphy, ostracods, transgressive-regressive sedimentation, deltas, and the source and migration of hydrocarbons in the Cenozoic of the Gulf of Mexico basin. Doris' papers teach the basic principles of stratigraphy and exploration, that advanced computer technology and software packages are excellent exploration tools, but they are only as good as the geological interpretations they are based on. Reading her publications, one can see these basics:

1) not to jump to conclusions,
2) not to correlate sands mechanically,
3) to first understand the depositional environments,
4) to fit prospects into a play, and
5) to tie the play into the trend.
6) Nothing stands alone; everything is connected and part of the big picture.

Doris held many prestigious "first" positions:

First female president of the Geological Society of America (1991).
First female president of the American Geological Institute (1980-81).
First Female president of the Society of Economic Paleontologists and Mineralogists (SEPM) (1978-79).
First Honorary Member and first female president of the SEPM Foundation (1989-91).
First female Distinguished Lecturer for AAPG (1983-84).
Second female Honorary Member of AAPG– 20 years after Dollie Radler Hall.

Doris also co-wrote the book on *How to try to Find an Oil Field* (Curtis, 1981). When she was President of SEPM, she made tremendous efforts and progress towards bringing the emphasis back on "Economic Paleontology" in the society (Fig. 7). She said, "By combining all of our—publications, public relations, meetings, committees, plus a bit of 'jaw-boning', I think we have begun to turn the tide more toward an economic micropaleontology emphasis, while not in any way sacrificing the excellence and prestige that had been built up on all other fronts" (*Quest*, 1979). Doris' SEPM Presidential Address was memorable as she attempted to marry the Gulf Coast Tertiary geology with geochemistry to produce a realistic workable model for predicting the distribution of undiscovered oil and gas, and provide an analogue in unexplored offshore basins with similar histories.

Figure 7. Doris when she was President of SEPM. (Photo: Quest, publication of Shell Development Co, Houston, Texas. p. 9.)

Edward B. Picou, Jr, her friend and colleague from Shell, in a moving tribute to her wrote,

> Her positive outlook and "can-do" attitude towards life and her science never allowed for pessimism or gloom...One thing for sure, Doris was a most unique lady...we had many, many conversations in the office with topics ranging from her early days at Shell to her taste in classical music. She often told me that on a typical weekday evening she would write as many as two dozen letters or notes to friends and associates...she believed in communicating with everyone. In addition to the letters, it wasn't uncommon for her to make many long-distance calls in between writing letters. However, if she was working on a technical paper, either on her own or with Dorothy Echols, she would often stay up until the wee hours of the morning if she was close to developing a new concept.
>
> I'll never forget those weekends when we exchanged home visits when we were working on our "epic" 1976 paper. She kept us fortified, if at her place, by fixing dinner and while doing so, poured us some of her special vodka which she kept in the freezer of her refrigerator. Literally, the vodka poured like viscous honey. But, she said you never needed ice cubes which diluted the vodka. She could out-drink me, for sure."

Writes another colleague of Doris' many talents,

> Doris Curtis was a remarkable lady, with many talents and many accomplishments. In her profession as a petroleum geologist, she was the noted authority in Gulf Coast biostratigraphy. She had the ability to analyze faunal and facies data from existing well samples and interpreting these data for us to use in oil

and gas exploration. Doris was a helpful counselor for scientists involved in exploration investigations. She was a good listener and a good advisor. Her business expertise and executive skills were used to manage scientific organizations like SEPM and GSA. Doris had a knack for inspiring staff and volunteers to do their best. Doris was an outstanding lecturer. She had a talent for weaving science and art into communication that was meaningful, comprehensible, and effective. What fun to be with Doris on social occasions. At any function—professional dinners—student organizations— committee meetings— picnics— field trips— she would enrich the occasion with her wit, her widespread knowledge, her genuine interest in any subject. (Echols, 1992)

Another colleague recalled,

Doris and I did not always agree, although I do not recall ever having a quarrel with her. She had firm convictions and did not hesitate to articulate them. However, she was able to alter her course in the face of a convincing argument without rancor. I never experienced any activity on her part that was self-serving. (Echols, 1992)

One colleague remembered Doris articulating her convictions on a wellsite by rising to her full five-foot stature to "straighten out" a burly, six-foot-five-inch roughneck who was poorly collecting samples. She could be formidable, but she was "witty, sociable, intellectually stimulating and just plain fun to be around."

While in New Orleans, Doris was active in the League of Women Voters. She was later president of the Oklahoma Chapter and a leader in the League's Environmental Quality Committee. Geologists love the earth and are true environmentalists. She understood the industry's role in conservation and pollution prevention. Due to her civic and professional leadership roles, in 1967 she was one of four delegates selected to participate in an exchange visit to Russia (then the USSR). She received the Matrix Award in Houston for Women in Community Service, was a Distinguished Alumna of Brooklyn College, and was a Fellow of the American Association for the Advancement of Science (Fig. 8).

Her niece, Susan Simone, recalls that it did irk Doris, at cocktail parties or gatherings, when spouses of the men she worked with would ask her how many children she had. When she answered that she had none, they invariably would get very sad-eyed and lament to her how terrible that was. She would "grin and bear it" but always wanted to say, "Well, have you ever been in a submarine? Or hiked in Tunisia?!"

She felt it was too bad they could only think of a woman's success in terms of having had children. That said, she did have her "chosen children" —nieces, nephews, surrogate children, students and protégés—who added to her fully lived life.

Even after being diagnosed with acute leukemia in April 1991, Doris continued to work and travel until the last two months before her final hospitalization. Susan was not surprised as she watched Doris take charge of her fight against cancer. She recalled that Doris organized family and friends with tasks and responsibilities from paying bills to donating platelets, and many other maintenance chores—then relaxed and counted on them to do their best, which, of course, they did. At one point during her chemo, Simone brought her greeting cards and watched as she opened those from the geology "Good Ole Girls" in Denver (Robbie Gries, Anny Coury, Susan Landon, Jeanne Harris, Cindy Stewart, Mary Beth Cooper, Nancy Darnell, Penny Frush, Randi Martinsen). The cards were on the risqué side and she commented to her aunt, "Wow, you have some rude friends!"

Doris smiled her famous big smile and said, "Isn't it wonderful!"

Her character was as open and accepting as it was eclectic. She had friends of all ethnicities, financial status, educational backgrounds, religious and political views and she treated them all with kindness and respect. Her interests were so diverse, from the science she immersed herself in to the

Figure 8. Doris Malkin Curtis, indefatigable contributor to science, associations, and society. (Photo: Echols, 1992, p. 175.)

soap operas she would watch for diversion. She swam every day, played classical piano every day, attended ballets, concerts and symphonies. And she absolutely delighted at geological meetings; enjoying old friends and making new ones. She was an indefatigable contributor to science, associations, and society.

Doris Curtis passed away on May 26, 1991. In 2007, the Gulf Coast Section SEPM established the Doris Malkin Curtis Medal to honor her as a pioneer and an expert in the paleontology and stratigraphy of the Gulf Basin where she worked for more than 50 years. Doris was a member of AAPG for 53 years.

Marie Gramann (1913-2016)

When Marie Gramann was taking her geology classes at The University of Texas at Austin (UT) in the mid-1930s, she was irate to find she could not be granted a bachelor of science degree unless she attended geology field camp—except women were not allowed to attend the UT field camp. Without field camp, women could only earn a Bachelor of Arts degree. Women in other universities applied for and took camp at more progressive schools like the universities of Michigan, Wisconsin, Chicago, and Oklahoma. Marie raised a ruckus about field camp at UT until the department finally took action; they found two other women, Mildred Winans and Katherine Archer, to join her and made the necessary arrangement for sleeping and toilets, and let all three into the camp (Figs. 9a, 9b). Marie Gramann won a difficult battle for a bachelor of science degree with honors in 1936. Marie was so proud she had broken that barrier—what she did not know was that the barrier was immediately put back into place as soon as she left, and it was years before the UT field camp permanently opened up to women, again.

After Marie graduated, she had a hard time finding a job even with her B.S. Marie wanted to work in the petroleum industry but she was not a micropaleontologist—one of the few "acceptable" jobs for women in industry. The only job Marie could find was drafting at the Texas Rail Road Commission, a government agency that regulated the oil and gas industry

In 1941, when WWII made it easier for women to be hired in the petroleum industry as geologists, Marie went to Houston. She pounded the pavement and knocked on the doors of Humble and Gulf and finally got a job with Stanolind in their San Antonio office (Fig. 10). It was a city where, due to the war and presence of military bases, it was as difficult to find lodging as it was to find a job.

Figure 9a. The three first women in The University of Texas Geology Field Camp in 1935, but also the last ones for a long while. Marie Gramann on the right, Mildred Winans on the left and Katherine Archer center. (Photo: Milliken, 1994, p. 86.)

Marie loved the geologic work and covered the activity of South Texas. She got along well with both the geologists and the engineers and knew she had finally "made it" with them when they invited her to join them for a beer at "Ella's Bar" on the first floor of the building. Marie remembered, "Ella was the worst-looking old hag you ever saw, but I didn't care—I had made it!" She wasn't a beer drinker so she rarely went back, but she was satisfied to have broken another barrier.

Subsurface electric log correlation was one of her prime responsibilities. Marie most enjoyed correlating when she had micropaleontology reports from drill samples to integrate with the log records, otherwise she knew the subsurface cross section was extremely hard to construct with confidence.

Figure 9b. Marie Gramann insisted on being allowed in field camp to enable her to earn a Bachelor of Science degree. (Photo: enlarged from previous photo.)

Fig. 10. Marie Gramann at work in San Antonio during WW II for Stanolind Oil. (Photo: Chadney, 2013, p. 54.)

Marie recalled,

The only well I ever sat on [wellsite geology] was in Duval County. I called that "the Wilds of Duval County." Thank heavens there was another geologist along with me. The two of us went down about two in the morning and there were at least six gates to open. [Gates had barbed wire strung between posts. The post had to be lifted out of a wrap of barbed wire at the base and at the top and placed back in the loops after the car went through. It often took two people to manage to get the post back in the loop. Marie was a small woman, about 5 foot 2 inches and did not think she had the strength to close a barbed wire gate without assistance.]

When we got there, well there was a lot of "waiting", but it was worth it. They would bring up samples that we would smell, or taste which isn't exactly gourmet food, but it was wonderful because I had never been on a well. We had to wait a long time for the logs. I did things that I would never have expected to do and really gained an insight into how wells are drilled and the testing that must take place.

There was a micropaleontologist in the Houston office that did an awful lot of fine work and he sent little notes to another geologist [a man] in our office that were a lot of fun because he always signed them "with love and kisses." Then that geologist left and so I got the paleo reports from him and I wondered if I would get the "love and kisses." I didn't at first, but finally, after several months, I got "With love and kisses." I had graduated!

These early years, during the War, Marie would occasionally go to Saturday and Sunday afternoon teas or dances held by the Red Cross to help entertain the San Antonio cadets. Sometimes she, like other single girls during the War, would volunteer to make sandwiches and to visit the wounded in the local hospitals.

In 1947-48, Stanolind transferred Marie to Corpus Christi where she worked with two male geologists and the office engineers. The office geologists did not like working with a woman, perhaps, Marie thought, because she had seniority over them. One of the geologists refused to speak to her; he would not even say hello. Marie got along well with the engineers having worked closely with engineers in San Antonio, and this made the male geologists even more upset as "geologists were not supposed to talk to engineers."

The in-office affronts were bad, but worse was the time she was out of the office on vacation, and a couple of the men wrote a report on the geologic area she was assigned. Marie considered it poorly written and felt it undermined her job because they wrote it when she was out of the office. Finally, Marie felt she had to move on as it was too uncomfortable working with those men. She found a job in Austin with Heep Oil Corporation and enjoyed work as a petroleum geologist for 6-7 more years.

Being a female geologist did have its advantages. Once, while driving back to Austin from Brownwood where her parents lived, Marie saw a Shell Oil rig drilling not too far from the highway. She knew the well was a deep test and was curious whether they had reached the Precambrian. Marie stopped and went up on the rig floor; because she was a woman, they did not suspect she was a geologist in the oil industry; they talked freely with her.

Working as a geologist for Heep provided many opportunities for travel around south Texas. The company had a twin-engine plane and she often flew on it to gather information, pick up drill samples, or visit other companies with Mr. Heep.

Marie laughs about a geophysicist trying to take her to the San Antonio Petroleum Club while she worked at Heep. She warned him that women were not allowed, but he was sure she was mistaken. They went, and the Club refused to admit Marie because she was a woman. He declared, "But, she's a geologist!" It made no difference and he ended up terribly embarrassed. It was 25-30 years before Petroleum Clubs would accept female members and professionals.

Fig. 11. Marie teaching geology at Howard Payne University. In 1974, the yearbook was dedicated to her "Because of the inspiration she has given us in friendship, in professionalism, in scholarship and in personal conduct … ." (Photo: The Lasso *yearbook, 1974, Howard Payne University, p. 4.)*

In about 1955, Heep Oil Corporation was sold and Marie was laid off. She went to Brownwood to stay with her family while she looked for another job. Coincidentally, her parents began to need living assistance. To occupy her time, she started doing volunteer work at Howard Payne (Baptist) University and, to her surprise, they asked her to teach geology (Fig. 11). Within days she signed the contract. It was on a Saturday, and she was supposed to start on Monday without text books or any preparation. Marie had only one rock sample, a geode she had purchased in Creede, Colorado on a family vacation.

As soon as she had a chance, she drove down to her alma mater, UT, to get teaching materials. They were not much help and only gave her book titles to order. However, they did refer her to Baylor University in Waco, Texas for materials. Baylor was most generous with samples and supplies and developed a friendly relationship with Marie, soon inviting her to join them on field trips.

She recalls taking a geology class out on a field trip and it included several huge, bulky football players. When she got back and was ready to turn in the University vehicle, she found a big sign the fellows had put on the back of the van saying, "Help! Help! We've been abducted by a mad geologist!" She laughed so hard about her tiny frame being able to abduct anyone, let alone football players! She kept the sign for years as it always made her laugh.

While teaching at Howard Payne, a Baptist University, Marie was very cautious about teaching or saying what she called the "E" word (evolution) in her classes. No one told her not to, she just did not want to rattle that cage. When Marie taught, she would say various things "changed through time." Marie was paid only $100 a month for that first year—a nervous year because the college president's daughter was in her inaugural class. Marie's "temporary" job ended up rounding out her career for 20 more years. Marie loved teaching and stayed at Howard Payne until she retired.

Marie continued her geology education throughout her teaching years by taking short courses not only in Texas but also in places like New Mexico and Colorado. She recalls a geomorphology course at Colorado State University where the professor was hostile and rude to her and the other woman in the class, calling them, "You poor souls!" Marie chose to laugh it off and, thereafter, often referred to herself as a "poor soul." Marie later found he was turned down for a job at her Alma Mater (UT, Austin) and she decided maybe HE was the poor soul!

Marie was born in 1913 in Cuero, Texas and has always been fond of her Texas life. She stayed single and enjoyed treating herself to a trip to Neiman Marcus in Dallas occasionally, adding to her very sophisticated wardrobe (Fig. 12). When Marie was 100, she fell in her house on a Saturday evening and lay there without food or water and unable to get up or call until Monday. About noon, when Meals on Wheels came to leave her meal at the door per their arrangement, she called out to them for help and they rushed her to a hospital. She recovered from the fall but, true to her life of independence, was disappointed to never to return to live in her home.

Figure 12. Marie Gramann, age 102, during an interview with Robbie Gries, October, 2015, Brownwood, Texas. (Photo: Robbie Gries, Denver, Colorado.)

Marie was active in the Abilene Geological Society and loved the field trips. She was the only woman most of the time. She retired in 1990 but continued to follow the profession and loved reading her AAPG Explorer—especially about the Barnett unconventional shale gas play. Marie Gramann was an AAPG member for 73 years. Marie Gramann died in late 2016 at the age of 103.

Hazel A. Peterson (1916-1996)

Hazel Peterson was hired during World War II by Shell Oil Company in Houston immediately after graduating from The University of Texas with her master's degree in 1942 (Fig. 13). Within the year, she changed jobs to work for the The Texas Company, continuing her work as a subsurface petroleum geologist in Tulsa and then Houston. In 1944, she began working for Sun Oil Company in Dallas and was later moved to Corpus Christi where she continued as a prospect and subsurface geologist. Single, she was geographically mobile and lapped up experience wherever she went. She soon acquired international experience in Canada, South America, and other places with her fourth employer, Seaboard Oil and Gas. Hazel worked as a geologist until the downturn in the petroleum industry in the 1950s, when even Hazel's broad experience and mobility could not help her keep or find a position with an oil company.

Figure 13. Hazel A. Peterson, about 1949, when employed with an oil company. (Photo: James Peterson, Denver, her nephew.)

Resilient and determined, Hazel spent four years working as a petroleum independent and consultant. She continued to generate prospects and partnered with her father, Howard L. Peterson, who in his later years became a landman to acquire leases and get them drilled. Hazel's prospects would be farmed out or farmed in and turned to an operating partner for drilling. The Petersons would keep either a working interest or a royalty interest in each project. Hazel's personal files, archived by her nephew, James Peterson, in Denver, Colorado, include oil and gas prospects in Stephens, Rusk, Liberty, Wood, Callahan, Pecos, and Crocket counties in Texas, as well as projects in Louisiana and Mississippi. Many were successful enough to give her some degree of financial independence. In 1958, Hazel started a third phase in her career—teaching at East Texas State University in Commerce, Texas, where she would retire in 1978. Hazel continued her oil and gas prospecting during her teaching years and, also, consulted in and published on water resources, hydrology, and groundwater.

When Hazel was introduced as a geologist, she detested the common remark, "You don't look like a geologist!" (Fig. 14).

She discussed this phrase with a group of women and they all agreed it was rude and annoying. Hazel shared with the group that once she was with a fellow geologist when he introduced her to a gray-haired genial geologist. The gentleman asked about a pair of sisters who had been geologists for a local company.

"Oh, they both got married," her friend replied.

"Well, I'm not surprised," the gentleman laughed, "I knew those girls were too pretty to be geologists for very long!"

Then suddenly remembering Hazel's presence, he blushed and, turned to her and stammered, "Oh! Nothing personal meant by that remark—that is, I mean—."

Hazel smiled politely and just said, "I understand."

She was aggravated, not only by the remark, but also by the lack of his awareness that women geologists usually were forced to give up their jobs when they marry because company policy still frowned on married women working! (from Hazel's correspondence and writings, provided by nephew James Peterson).

Figure 14. Hazel hated the persistent statement, "You don't look like a geologist!" She always challenged the question, "What SHOULD a geologist look like?" Hazel on the beach, about 1945. (Photo: James Peterson.)

Wage and job discrimination in academia

became an issue and a focus of Hazel Peterson's teaching career. She became a fighter for equity, though unfortunately, she never found it for herself. In correspondence to her department Chair before she retired, Hazel related her frustrations with never having adequate office facilities. This was also true for the one woman newer than Hazel on the faculty. The men consistently had better office quarters, laboratories, and, of course, better pay. Hazel acquired her "own" office only after 18 years of sharing a limited space with others. Male professors, whom she helped to recruit and hire, and who had less seniority than her, were awarded offices and lab facilities long before she was. Their pay and their raises always left her compensation lagging considerably behind theirs. One of the placating excuses was that she did not have a PhD, even though she had been told when she was hired that her substantial experience in the oil business made up for the degree. In addition, she could point to the same inequities between her and her male colleagues who did not have PhD's—they were paid more.

Hazel developed undergraduate and graduate courses which were utilized by the higher-paid and, in her opinion, less-competent, instructors. She complained, her students complained, but, to no avail. She found she was paid even less than the average salary within the "lower rank" of assistant male professors. There was always an excuse, usually the budget, yet there always seemed to be adequate funds for raises among her [male] colleagues. (From her personal correspondence, provided by nephew, James Peterson of Denver, Colorado.)

Hazel detailed this discrimination in a letter to the AGI Committee of Women Geoscientists in 1974,

> ...repeatedly [we are] told "there is no discrimination." Where the only faculty required to share offices and teaching-research classrooms are women, where a young man without a doctor's degree is hired at a higher rank than a woman with tenure who is denied that rank for lack of that doctor's degree, where a male counterpart is given two years of full twelve months of contracts and the female is told a budget shortage restricts her to 10½ months one year and 9¾ months the second year, where all male orders for facilities and equipment are commonly approved and females are often denied a large portion of similar teaching or research requisitions—these cannot be called anything but prejudicial treatment.

Hazel continued, documenting the long-term cost of salary discrimination to retirement benefits,

> The restrictions on university salaries and total university income, however, is of more importance than a short-term affair; under our current retirement plan which has to supplement social security, the total benefits due on retirement are dependent on the total income and both personal and university deductions. This means, I found recently, that for every summer I was asked to find employment or NSF participation elsewhere so that my male colleagues could have contracts—as was openly stated on more than one occasion—I will have lost anywhere from 12 to 25% of my normal benefits, in addition to the lesser salary paid me, like my female office mate, in comparison to male counterparts, most of whom I helped screen and recruit for their positions over the past 15-16 years. There is, moreover, no way for me to retrieve the loss in salary nor the loss in future retirement income, since the state is involved. In the event of any suits involving me, I could also find my state salary completely cut off—through one means or another. (Correspondence of Hazel Peterson, provided by nephew, James Peterson, Denver, Colorado.)

In correspondence to her faculty chair when she retired in 1978, she asked that no parties or celebrations of her retirement take place as she was too disappointed in the many years of sub-par treatment she had endured to enjoy what to her would be a hypocritical ceremony.

She said,

> I, therefore, do not intend to be the doddering little lady with the over-sized orchid—tearfully listening to the magnanimous resolution on her retirement. I am dead serious, therefore, when I say I want no eulogies, farewell dinners, "gifts", honors, etc. In every course, my students have expressed their appreciation for my efforts to give them what I felt they needed for future careers and a better cultural background. They have, moreover, expressed their opinions to other students who, in turn, enrolled in my classes with a feeling of confidence and the knowledge I will treat all comers with the same fairness I expect from others. (Perhaps it was for this reason that the black students—both in my classes and...in work studies...worked harder and more enthusiastically for me than for many faculty). Students returning to campus, moreover, have verified my judgement by detailing the benefits of my instruction and counseling which they further

recognized in the positions they acquired upon graduation or in graduate instruction at "name" schools elsewhere.

Figure 15. Hazel, second from left, in a field camp, during her college days with female colleagues. (Photo: James Peterson.)

Hazel had a generous spirit which began early in her career with her family. In 1949, while she was still working with Sun Oil, her father, before he became an oil landman, was trying to save the family farm and wrote to Hazel for assistance with a $450 bank payment that was due. Hazel supplied the help from her salary which, at the time, was not much more than $200 per month (from her personal files and personal communication with James Peterson). Hazel was a philanthropist to many causes from victims of child molestation to victims of hurricanes. She usually initiated a charitable fund by stating, "I'll start the fund with X number of dollars," which was always quite generous, remarked Hazel's memorialist, Natalie Massengale in 1996.

Hazel was a member of AAPG for 52 years. (Fig. 15).

Grace Hower (1912 – 1993)

Grace Hower was underemployed with a geophysical company between college and World War II (see Chapter 8, Geophysicists). Amerada Petroleum Company provided a friendly environment for female professionals for decades (Refer to Dollie Radler Hall Chapter 3) and Grace secured a job with Amerada in Tulsa when the War began.

Mary Louise Rhodes (1916-1987)

Mary Louise Rhodes was able to find employment in the oil business with the Standard Oil Company of Texas in Houston because of, and only during WWII. (See Chapter 5, Wellsite Women.)

Eleanor Thompson Caldwell (1918-2009)

Eleanor Caldwell told her nieces and nephew that, "she could not love a man more than she loved geology" and, therefore, never married. They saw that demonstrated year after year as they visited her in New Orleans. They loved, respected and especially enjoyed Aunt Eleanor's eccentric and wonderful personality.

Her love of career was illustrated very aptly when she fled inland to Birmingham, Alabama ahead of Hurricane Katrina in 2005. Eleanor was uncomfortable flying, so her niece and nephew, Judy Carriveau and John Rhoades, drove to pick her up in Birmingham and take her back to her home state of Massachusetts where they lived. Eleanor was 87 years old and yet insisted that they pull over, outcrop after outcrop, the entire way to Massachusetts, so she could collect rocks along the way.

Figure 16. Eleanor Caldwell, 1938, found work with Shell Oil and later Humble Refining once WW II began. (Photo: Kaleidoscope *yearbook, with permission from Middlebury College.)*

Once Eleanor had her niece and nephew drive to Hattiesburg, Mississippi, where, 40 years earlier, she had lived and still had a bank safe deposit box. She asked them to go to her bank and retrieve the contents and close the account. They had no idea what they would find, but were amazed to discover it was full of rock and mineral samples when they opened it! Nothing else. Eleanor had paid rent on that safety deposit box for 40 years to keep some of her rocks and minerals. When they delivered them to her she was delighted to have her treasures again and exclaimed, "Oh, that is why I haven't seen those samples in a while!" Eleanor proceeded to name every specimen and tell them when and where she collected it. That was no surprise to them; they remembered her house in New Orleans had dozens of bookcases, all full of geologic specimens.

Eleanor told them what a struggle it was for her to find a job when she got out of College, in 1941, and before Pearl Harbor was bombed. She had her master's from Smith College and her bachelor's from Middlebury College in 1939. (Fig. 16). Despite her degrees, companies flatly told her that they did not hire women. The more companies tried to discourage her, the more determined she became. Eleanor eventually found a job in early 1942 in Washington, D.C. as a cartographer for the Office of Strategic Services (OSS, the precursor to the Central Intelligence Agency, CIA) and later at the Geophysical Laboratory of the Carnegie Institute, investigating the lining of 50-calibre machine guns—she said, "This did nothing to further my career!"

Finally, in 1944, during the war, Shell Oil, Inc. offered Eleanor a job in Houston as a Junior Paleontologist and, a year later, transferred her to Tallahassee. Humble Oil and Refining hired her away from Shell in 1947 and she moved back to New Orleans where she spent 39 years in their employment. She retired in 1986 as a senior professional geologist. She spent her career working on the subsurface stratigraphy of Mississippi, South Alabama, South Georgia, and Florida. Her geologic archives were donated to Tulane University after her death.

Figure 17. Eleanor Caldwell at Middlebury College where she was discouraged from taking geology—a man's field. (Photo: her niece, Judy Carriveau, Easthampton, Massachusetts.)

Eleanor's graduate work covered the foraminifera of Puerto Rico which she published in 1962. She also published on saline deposits and on the stratigraphy of southeast Mississippi from her work with Humble. She was active in the Southeastern Geological Society and a member of AAPG for 65 years.

Eleanor Caldwell wrote to Middlebury College that she became interested in geology when she was eight years old when her father showed her dinosaur tracks in the Triassic shale of the Connecticut River near Holyoke, Massachusetts and when they explored caves along the eastern scarp of the river valley. Years later, when she arrived at Middlebury and wanted to study geology, she was discouraged from doing so, as this was a "man's field" (Fig. 17). She prevailed. After her death, her devoted nephew, John Rhoades, and his sister, Judy Carriveau, took Eleanor's ashes and sprinkled them into those Triassic dinosaur tracks (personal communication, John Rhoades).

A bequest to Middlebury College now supports the sciences Eleanor loved, including the R/V David Folger (Research Vessel) on Lake Champlain. A lab in McCardell Bicentennial Hall bears Eleanor Thompson Caldwell's name in recognition of her legacy at Middlebury.

Louise Anna Fillman (1898-1983)

Louise Anna Fillman was the first woman geologist employed by Shell Oil in the Permian Basin (Fig. 18). What was more unique, Louise was 43 years old when she left her professorship at Simpson College, Iowa, to take a job in the oil business in Midland, Texas during WWII. Louise, unlike many women who left academia to work in the oil industry during the War, did not return to teaching afterwards.

Louise attended the University of Iowa during WWI and was an Undergraduate Assistant in Geology (1919-1920) and a Graduate Assistant in that department from 1921-1924 (Fig. 18). Her geology field camp, in 1921, was unique in having six women in the class of twelve. She completed her PhD with a thesis on the Cenozoic history of the Black Hills of South Dakota and Wyoming.

Louise was no doubt a top student because in 1925, a year after her graduation, she was chosen to temporarily fill the vacancy in the geology department at the University of Iowa when Professor Trowbridge went on sabbatical leave. Many years later in 1945, Louise Fillman travelled to her alma mater from Midland, Texas, and presented an oil portrait of Professor A.C. Trowbridge to the University of Iowa to commemorate his outstanding work in geology.

Before the War, Louise taught geology at Simpson College in Indianola, Iowa for 16 years and assisted Lowell Robert Laudon (1928) on "The Stratigraphy of the Kinderhook Series of Iowa" by providing him with her extensive collections of fossils from the Wassonville Cherts. When she left academia for the oil business, her excellence in stratigraphy, and, perhaps her overall experience, led her to become the senior member of a four-woman geological staff by 1955. A local newspaper article (*The Odessa American*, June 5, 1955) shows a photo of her examining a core taken from a West Texas well. The newspaper article provides a snapshot of the dawning of a new era of a cautious, perhaps a bit tongue-in-cheek, acceptance of women geologists. It states,

Figure 18. Louise Fillman was the first woman hired by Shell Oil in the Permian Basin. (Photo: Hawkeye *yearbook, 1920, with permission from the University of Iowa, Iowa City, Iowa, p. 42.)*

> Women geologists are no longer an oddity in the never-ending search for petroleum. And West Texas has its share of feminine rock hounds. Midland which claims the title of Oil Capital of the Permian Basin, has about 10 now working for oil companies. Others can be found in Abilene or San Angelo, and it's not surprising to find one now and then "sitting on a well" at some desolate spot away from the office or laboratory.

The *Odessa American* article continued,

> All of her time with the company is in stratigraphy work. "For the first 11 years with the company," she says, "all I did was run samples. That's enough to kill most people, but I really like it. It's no handicap to sit behind a microscope. Actually, it's more like an avocation than work. The more you can remember about a previous well; then the more interesting the next one is." As a stratigrapher on the area, her main duties are to examine cuttings or cores from wells, and to call pay zones and pick formation tops. She doesn't believe a woman's place is at the wellsite.
>
> "I only stayed at wells (exploratory wells where a geologist is needed) in emergency instances during the war. I don't believe a woman belongs at the well. However, I will say this: The few times I did have to sit on a well, I was never treated more like a queen than I was by workers at the rig."
>
> "Being a woman has been a handicap in her work in some ways," she admits. "A woman in her field of work actually had to do a better job."

The only times she has ever really been resented by her male co-workers, she says, was in a few instances from newly-hired geologists. "They were in a training program under me, and I'd say five of about 50 balked—they refused to take training under a woman, who they said shouldn't be here. Anyway," she said, "we got them straightened around. They took the training and even liked it. Now we're good friends." But. Dr. Fillman's favorite work is not teaching — despite having spent 16 years at it. "I'd just as soon run samples from wells as to play golf. And I used to like to play golf," she said.

Louise Fillman remained in Midland and became Head of Discovery for the Western World, Shell Oil Company and published many papers throughout her career. While working for Shell, she was the chairman of a Lexicon Committee that, in 1958, published a "Lexicon of Pre-Pennsylvanian Stratigraphic Names of West Texas and Southeastern New Mexico," (*West Texas Geological Society*, 153 pp.) an oft-referenced work. She retired from Shell in 1958 and remained in Midland until her death in 1982.

Louise Anna Fillman was Vice President of the West Texas Geological Society in 1958 and was an Honorary Life Member of the Society. She was a member of AAPG for 41 years.

Beverly Edith McMahon (1922-2013)

Figure 19. Beverly McMahon, 1943, who joined Shell Oil as a field geologist and thought she hit the "glass ceiling." (Photo: The Coloradan *year-book, with permission from CU Heritage Center, University of Colorado, Boulder, Colorado, p. 86.)*

Beverly McMahon graduated from the University of Colorado (CU) with a B.S. in geology (with honors) in 1944 (Fig. 19). She worked for Shell Oil Company as a field geologist and opened two oil fields in Texas that were still producing at the time of her death in 2013. Her obituary mentions that she felt she had hit the "glass ceiling" in Shell and returned to CU and earned a PhD in 1966. Her work on paleo-magnetism was a precursor to the "plate tectonics theory" of the time. She taught at several universities and retired to Ontario, Oregon in the late 1970s. She was an ardent outdoorswoman and horse enthusiast (*Eureka Times-Standard*, Oct. 4, 2013). Beverly McMahon was a member of AAPG for 72 years.

Virginia Marcelle Mousley (1917-1987)

Figure 20. Virginia Mousley joined Atlantic Refining in Shawnee, Oklahoma. (Photo: Sooner *yearbook, Western History Collections, University of Oklahoma Libraries, University of Oklahoma, 1941, Norman, Oklahoma.)*

Virginia Marcelle Mousley, graduated from the University of Oklahoma at the onset of WWII and went to work for Atlantic Refining in Shawnee, Oklahoma (Fig. 20). Details of her work history are not known. She was a member of AAPG for 43 years.

Diane Loranger (1920-2004)

Diana May Lally Loranger went to work for Imperial Oil in Canada during WWII (Fig. 21). She was born in Edmonton, Alberta, but grew up in Red Lake, Ontario, Canada where she was the first high school graduate out of Red Lake High School. She studied geology at the University of Manitoba and in 1943, despite locking horns with the Dean when she insisted on majoring in geology, was the University's first woman to graduate with a bachelor's in Science.

Figure 21. Canadian Diane Loranger in the Rocky Mountains of Alberta, circa 1947 approx. (Photo: Imperial Oil Review, *p. 48; provided with permission from Glenbow Museum, Glenbow Archives, IP-14a-1828, Glenbow Museum, Calgary, Alberta.)*

She preferred to be called Diane and is possibly the first Canadian woman to enter the oil and gas business. She rose to a senior supervisory position by the time she retired. Interviews, in 1954, with the *Calgary Herald* quoted, "she had to prove her strength, endurance, and knowledge to her male colleagues but, before long, she was pioneering new techniques in locating oil." One incident Diane described was on a field excursion with a group of men when they covered a rugged 14 miles. She was determined to keep going though she felt like crying "uncle." The following morning, several men were absent when they readied for the day; apparently, they had been trying to wear her out, and instead, wore themselves out (Wood, 1954). (Fig. 22)

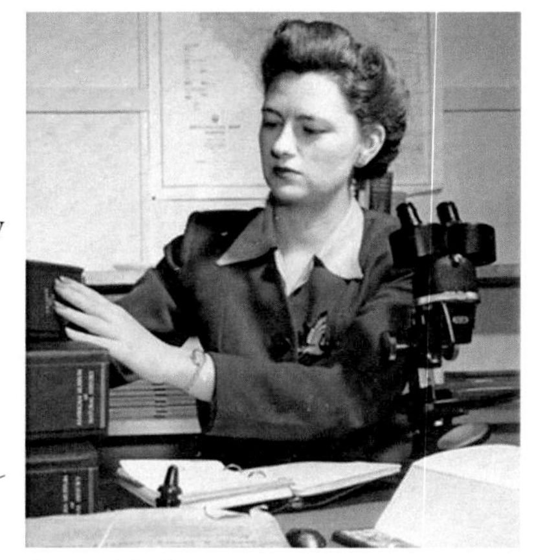

Figure 22. Diane examining samples in Royalite Oil company office, Turner Valley, Alberta, 1946-47. (Photo: with permission from Glenbow Archives, IP-14a-1471, Glenbow Museum, Calgary, Alberta.)

Diane Loranger earned her PhD while employed, published numerous papers, and lectured across North America and Europe. She was athletic, independent, and adventurous. Diane repaired her own cars and flew her own plane to job sites, where she was often the wellsite geologist. She built her own log cabin in the Canadian Rockies over the course of five years. Diane was an active member of the Alberta Association of Petroleum Geologists and a member of AAPG.

Women who Married and Stayed in Industry After the War

Ruth Young Lebow (1919-2007)

Ruth Young Lebow left Atlantic Richfield in California when she married, and took on all the geology for the family-owned company, Lebow-McNee Oil Co during WWII (later Lebow Oil Company). Her work included the necessary wellsite duties and she often brought her young son and daughter to the field while she ran samples (see Chapter 5, Wellsite Women in Geology).

Anne Robins Frank (1919-)

Anne Frank joined the General Geophysical Company during WWII. Seismic crews were desperate for field personnel and when they hired this female geologist to work on a crew, with her attention to detail, she soon became Crew Chief. Anne was likely the first female crew chief on a seismic party. After the War, Anne continued with the company for several years and joined a new company started by several principals of the old company (see Chapter 8, Geophysicists).

Mehlika Tasman Ribnikar (1912-2007)

Figure 23. Mehlika Ribnikar in the 1940's, enjoying one of her many past times, horseback riding in Turkey. (Photo: Hasan Sarikaya.)

Mehlika Ribnikar went back to work during WWII after completing her graduate studies at The University of Texas in Austin. She worked most of her career at the Geological Survey of Turkey (MTA). (Fig. 23)

Mehlika was born in 1912 in Istanbul and graduated from Arnavutkoy American College for Girls in 1932. Her work at the Turkish Survey translating English geological reports into Turkish got her interested in geology. In 1938, Mehlika was sent by the MTA to the United States to study geology. She returned to Turkey during World War II passing through Pearl Harbor the day before it was bombed by the Japanese in December 1941.

That year, Mehlika married Cevat Eyup Tasman, a well-known mining and petroleum engineer with a degree from Columbia University, and went back to work for MTA (Fig. 24).

Figure 24. Mehlika Ribnikar in the 1940's analyzing samples on a wellsite in Turkey. (Photo: Hasan Sarikaya, Ankara, Turkey.)

Unlike many organizations during those times, Mehlika was not required to quit from the Survey when she married, but could continue her work. Turkey's government (1919-1938) under Mustafa Kemal Atatürk, was committed to education and equality for women

Figure 25. Mehlika Ribnikar on a drilling rig in Turkey in the 1940s. (Photo: Hasan Sarikaya, Ankara, Turkey.)

and completely reformed the educational and professional environment.

In 1956, following the death of her husband, Mehlika left MTA and started a private consultancy, assisting many petroleum companies including ESSO. Mehlika was one of the founding members and first woman president (1966-1968) of the Association of Turkish Petroleum Geologists (TPJD). She published a book, *Tatbili Mikropaleontoloji (Applied Micropaleontology)*, in 1975. Mehlika Tasman Ribnikar was a generous contributor to her alma maters and to the AAPG where she was a member for 57 years. (Fig. 25)

Marie Joanna Clark Hill (1919-2005)

Marie Clark went to work during the War but did not marry until much later; she worked throughout WWII and well beyond, until retirement. She graduated from the University of Southern California in 1943 and joined Richfield Oil Corporation that same year (Fig. 26). Marie was part of the team that discovered Cuyama Field and oil in Prudhoe Bay.

Figure 26. Marie Clark at the University of Southern California, 1943, before joining Richfield Oil Corporation. (Photo: El Rodeo yearbook, 1943, USC Libraries. With permission from the University of Southern California History Collection, p. 172.)

Don Clarke of Long Beach, California, recalled his friendship with Marie and several of the stories she told as he ferried her to geology meetings in the years before her death,

> It is a bit more Hollywood-like than most stories. She was a young beautiful geologist at Richfield who fell in love with her famous geologist boss, Mason Hill [AAPG President, 1962]. Mason was not only famous for his work at Richfield, but also was married to one of the highest socially placed women in southern California and with whom he had a big beautiful house and children. Once Mace fell for Marie he had her transferred overseas (Asia). When she came back stateside, Mason was divorced. They married and built a beautiful custom house with a fantastic view high up in Whittier, traveled the world together and had a long life together (Fig. 27).
>
> Prior to meeting Mason, Marie had dated the legendary California geologist, Tom Dibblee, who also fell for her and gave her his first painted stone. (He was famous for these painted stones and made many for his eventual wife, Mason Hill's secretary. Small world.) Marie saved the stone her whole life. Marie truly loved her geology and stayed active all her life. She was elegant, intelligent, and very protective of Mason. She was also his sounding board for geological ideas. They made a great team.

Figure 27. Marie Clark Hill in 1980 looking at an outcrop in Ecuador. (Photo: Don Clarke, Long Beach, California.)

Mary Jane Cole Robinson (1923-2015)

Mara Marie (Robinson) Brachman, daughter of Mary Jane Robinson, writes of her mother:

One of the most important things to remember about Mary Jane Robinson was that her pursuit of geology was inspired by her natural curiosity for the world around her. She was a self-proclaimed "rock-hound." She did not view herself as a trail blazer or role model. She did not set out on her career path to prove herself to the world or strike a blow for her gender. She merely pursued topics that interested her, be it owning a custom jewelry business, engaging in creative investing, or discussing politics. My mother was a very free-thinker.

One of my earliest memories was when Mary Jane took her mother (my grandmother) and me, as a little girl, to a well she was drilling near Nocona, Texas. My mother had generated several Caddo/Ellenberger prospects for OPUBCO (the oil and gas division of Oklahoma Publishing Company) and we drove to the wellsite so my mother could supervise a DST over an Ellenberger drilling break. Before arriving, my mother told me that some of the roughnecks on her wells had trouble taking instructions from a woman. To solve the problem on this occasion, we arrived at the well with a platter of warm, gooey, fresh-baked chocolate chip cookies! Not only did the roughnecks perform the DST and trip out of the hole in record time, they claimed it was the first successful test they had witnessed in years.

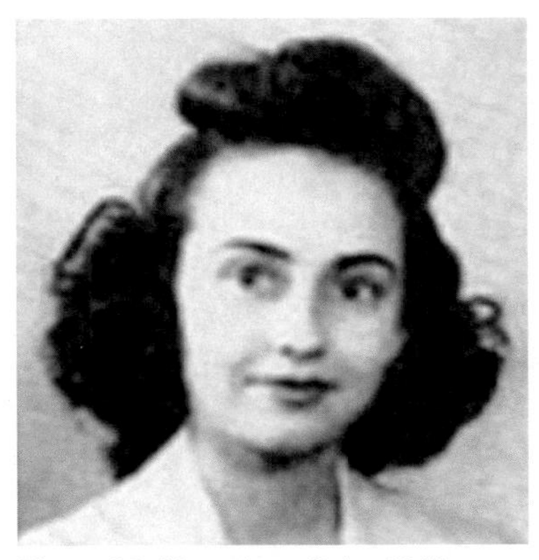

Figure 28. Mary Jane Cole, 1943, before she joined Magnolia Company in Oklahoma City. (Photo: The Horned Frog *yearbook, Texas Christian University, Fort Worth, Texas, p. 128.)*

Mary Jane started her career during WWII after finishing her degree with the old Magnolia Company (later Mobil Oil) in Oklahoma City (Fig. 28) in 1944. Back then, women were hired only as paleontologists. After two years of looking at fossils under a microscope, she had an offer from a small independent company for nearly double the pay. When she submitted her resignation, Mary Jane said that the Magnolia exploration manager was absolutely furious with her, told her she wasn't worth that much, but grudgingly offered her a fairly substantial raise. She did not accept.

Eventually, Mary Jane left Oklahoma City and accepted a teaching position at Hardin College (later, Midwestern State University) in Wichita Falls, to be closer to her family. Mary Jane was hired to teach speech, but also taught a couple of geology classes, almost as an afterthought. After two years, my mother was ready for new challenges and, turning down an offer from Hardin to start a Geology Department, she returned to Oklahoma City to work for another, small operator.

The best story from those years comes from my husband, Steve. In the late 1980s, Steve was Treasurer of the Houston Geological Society. An elderly geologist was leaving a sizeable donation to the HGS, and Steve went to the geologist's home to have him sign some papers. After signing, Steve said the geologist began to wax eloquently about the "good old days." He then told Steve a story about a young, female geologist who worked for him in Oklahoma City, during the War. Apparently, after a rather harrowing night of logging and looking at cuttings for a well he was drilling in North Texas, the young geologist took him to her parent's home in Electra for a warm dinner and a place to sleep, rather than trying to find a vacant motel. The story ended with a wistful,

"I wondered whatever happened to her?"

Steve told the geologist,

"I'll tell you exactly what happened.... She's my mother-in-law!"

Mary Jane was born in 1923 in Wichita Falls, and grew up in Electra, Texas. Back then, Electra didn't have a hospital. One thing that Electra did have, were pump jacks. In fact, a sign at the edge of town, today, declares Electra as the "Pump Jack Capitol of the World." Mary Jane grew up around oil field workers; her father owned a shoe repair store in Electra and fixed their work boots. My mother liked to go to the shoe repair shop after school and listen to stories of the oil field. Though she was interested in geology, after graduating high school, Mary Jane attended Texas Christian University and majored in speech. Eventually, her love of rocks won out, and Mary Jane changed her major to geology.

By the late 1940s, Mary Jane realized that she needed more education to progress as a geologist. She decided to return to school and enrolled at the University of Oklahoma for her Geology master's Degree. At OU, she taught labs and attended undergraduate and graduate classes. Most of the other geology students were returning GI's. Arriving late to an undergraduate class one day, my mother grabbed an open seat next to one of the veterans, Malcom, "Mike" Robinson, my Dad.

Mary Jane and Mike travelled throughout Oklahoma and Texas after they married. Even though Mary Jane had her master's Degree, and Mike his bachelor's in geology, jobs were scarce and Mike rough necked to support the couple. Soon, they settled in Fort Worth, and then moved to Oklahoma City. My father worked for Champlin, ERG, and other independent oil companies while my mother raised two children. In the early 1970s, Mary Jane returned to generating prospects in her old, familiar "stomping-grounds" in the Fort Worth Basin.

Mary Jane caused many, shallow Caddo and Strawn wells to be drilled, but strongly believed in untapped Ellenberger potential beneath the old, shallow structures. Some of these features had been producing oil since the early 1900s, and the challenges facing her involved both geology and obtaining leases. Nevertheless, with the backing of , she managed to drill several Ellenberger wells in and near old fields. Most of those prospects originally were generated by her in the 1940s.

Mary Jane had many of her own unique exploration methods (Fig. 29). She had a great deal of success twinning dry holes, drilled in the early 1940s, by one, particular operator. My husband once asked her how she was so confident that those wells she drilled would be successful, since they were right next to dry holes. My mother replied that everyone knew that operator had over-promoted his wells to investors, so he was forced to plug and abandon them regardless of actual results! Many conversations that Mary Jane had with my husband were about geologic ideas, but more concerned leasing. On one occasion, OPUBCO's landman was struggling to obtain a lease over a prospect my mother had generated. Many mineral owners, at that time, had a deep-rooted, long-standing mistrust of landmen. So, Mary Jane visited the mineral owner, accompanied by a mutual acquaintance, my grandmother! The mineral owner was an elderly widow who used to be their neighbor in Nocona. As they walked into the woman's house, Mary Jane noticed dozens of jars filled with pickles. As my mother relates,

" ...before that woman would sign the lease, your grandmother and I had to eat one pickle from every jar. For over two hours, we munched on pickles and had to pronounce each one both crunchy and tasty!"

Needless to say, they got the lease!

Mary Jane's association with OPUBCO had its ups and downs. One of her first deep wildcats was one of her most successful wells, the second time she drilled it. The first time it was drilled, the engineer hired by OPUBCO took matters into his own hands because he did not trust a female geologist, even though that female geologist generated the prospect, picked the location, successfully DST'd several potential zones, *and* picked pay zones and perforations on the well log. Armed with all that information, the engineer brought the well log to the one place in Electra where all of the local experts were available for consultation – the Dairy Queen. He and several farmers and roughnecks picked a completely different set of perforations and forwarded them to OPUBCO headquarters in Oklahoma City for approval. Mary Jane said that she was amazed, with so many holes shot in the casing, they still managed to miss all the oil-bearing zones. After many heated conversations, an offset well was drilled with a much more successful completion. That well is still producing, today.

Figure 29. Mary Jane Cole Robinson on one of her many wells she developed and drilled. (Photo: Mara Marie Brachman, Houston, Texas.)

Mary Jane continued to generate and sell prospects on her own, or as a partner with others, until she was 87 years old. In her later years, my mother contacted other, elderly geologists in Oklahoma City and formed a group that met periodically called "The Feisty Fossils."

Women Who Married Had To Quit; Some Became Consultants or Joined a Geologic Survey

Louise B. Freeman Clarkson (1908-2004)

Louise Freeman was the first woman to get a geology degree from the University of Kentucky in 1932 (Fig. 30). She immediately started work as Kentucky Assistant State Geologist and taught at the University of Kentucky before continuing for her master's in geology. Louise left Kentucky and completed her education obtaining a PhD from the University of Chicago in 1940.

Louise entered the oil business during WWII (circa 1941) and was employed in Corpus Christi, Texas. Sometime after the War she married Francis Clarkson; he was not a geologist but was involved in the oil business. Together, they forged a company, Casa Grande Oil. In 1955, they moved their company to Abilene, Texas, where she continued as a geologist putting together prospects for the company.

Louise and her husband enjoyed outdoor hobbies together—hunting, fishing, and photography. She was also a pilot and flew in Women's Air Races. Louise was a fellow in the Geological Society of America, the Petroleum Society, the American Geophysical Union, the Society of Economic Paleontologists and Mineralogists, the Gulf Coast Association of Geological Societies, the Corpus Christi Geological Society, and the Abilene Geological Society.

Figure 30. Louise Freeman Clarkson went into the oil business during WWII, later formed Casa Grande Oil with her husband. (Photo: University of Kentucky Libraries Special Collections Research Center, 1932. yearbook, p. 26.)

Louise retired to Corpus Christi and lived there before her death. Louise Freeman Clarkson was a member of the American Association of Petroleum Geologists for 56 years (Information from *The Abilene Reporter-News*, March 1, 1955).

Evelyn Wilie Moody (1918-2000)

Evelyn Wilie Moody took great pride in being the only female consulting geologist in Houston at one point in her life. She had a feisty spirit that surrounded everything she did. It was no surprise to those who knew her that the injury that ultimately brought Evelyn down, a broken hip, was sustained on the dance floor when she was 82 years old!

Evelyn Wilie initially attended Baylor University before she transferred to the University of Texas and graduated with a B.A. in geology (1938) and a master's in 1940, both with honors (Fig. 31). Evelyn's daughter, Jennifer Moody, wrote about her,

Figure 31. Evelyn Wilie graduated from The University of Texas with honors in geology and education in 1938. (Photo: daughter, Jennifer Moody, Austin, Texas.)

> Mom talked about her time at Baylor University as a time of testing her independence. Family stories include her "blowing up" the chemistry Lab and being carried out and dumped in the fountain to wash her off. She also said she was "expelled" because she refused to wear hose and wore white ankle socks instead—she loved white ankle socks and continued to enjoy wearing them until she died. It is not clear why, but Mom always gave the impression that she had been invited to leave Baylor.
>
> Her entire family moved to Austin in 1936 so Mom could attend The University of Texas. This was a super move by all accounts. All I ever heard were great stories about her life there as a sorority girl (Pi Beta Phi) and student. She especially loved studying geology, where she was usually the only female in the class. Mom was a great flirt and enjoyed this singularity throughout her life.

Figure 32. Evelyn Wilie when she was working at Arkansas Fuel Oil Company during WWII in Shreveport, Louisiana about 1944. (Photo: Jennifer Moody.)

She was advised by her Mother to get a degree in Education as well as Geology because Geology was a "Man's field" and it would probably be hard for her to find a job. Indeed, when she first graduated with her master's in Geology in 1940 she could not find a geology job and so took a teaching job in Chilton, Texas where I think she taught 6th grade. It was a miserable time for her. She talked about how hard it was to control the class—she thought because she looked not much older than some of the children. She told a story about the kids turning over their chairs and pretending to be lions in cages—the principal or coach had to come and get the class under control.

Mom wrote her master's thesis on "The cultural influences of the Balcones Fault", which combined geology and anthropology in a groundbreaking way. As I recall, she never talked about her M.A. until I was in college and becoming interested in archaeology. Apparently, as much as she admired her advisors, something happened about crediting her with this research in a publication and she forever had her nose out of joint about it. Mom had a bit of a passive-aggressive approach to working in a "Man's field": she refused to learn to type so she could never be forced into secretarial work. Her later published papers and books were all handwritten!

Soon after WWII started, Mom was able to find work as a geologist at the Arkansas Fuel Oil Company in Houston. As much fun as she had as an independent 24 to 27-year-old working woman geologist—first in Houston, then New Orleans, and, finally, Shreveport—she was disappointed to be stuck in the lab doing paleontology (Fig. 32).

Her dream was to be in the field, finding oil and gas, and sitting on the wells as they came in. But much to Mom's chagrin, in those days oil wells were considered rough and gritty and no place for a woman. In fact, it seems not to have been until 1946, after she married, that she finally got to sit on a well in Homer, Louisiana with our Dad (Fig. 33)

When Mom and Dad got married in February, 1945, Mom had had her M.A. in geology for five years. Dad only had a B.A. I think they both must have decided that it would be good for his career to get an M.A. so they moved to Golden, Colorado where Mom worked (I think as a Research Assistant, but I am not sure) to put Dad through the Colorado School of Mines. In 1947, he finished his master's in Geological Engineering and Petroleum Production Engineering and then went back to work for Gulf Oil where he had been employed before the War. They soon moved to Kuwait to help bring in the big Gulf oil field there. Mom was fearless in those

Figure 33. Evelyn Wilie and John Moody, Sr. sitting on a well in Homer, Louisiana, 1946. Evelyn wrote on the back of the photo "The first time we sat on a well...." (Photo: Jennifer Moody.)

days and traveled by herself from the U.S. through Europe and Egypt to Kuwait to join Dad. She also had her first child, John D. "Sandy" Moody, Jr., in the local Kuwait hospital in May 1949, where she was visited and given presents by the local Sheik.

From the time John Moody, Sr. went back to work for Gulf in 1947 until Mom and Dad divorced in the mid-1970s, she did not have a paying job in geology. That, however, did not mean she quit being a geologist. She was an enthusiastic researcher on many of Dad's publications, especially during the 1950s and 1960s, even though he apparently never acknowledged her contributions. This irritated her as I clearly remember her talking about it—but it was the 1960s and wives were wives.

Figure 34. Evelyn and Hollis Dow Hedberg, 1963, on an AAPG Field Trip to the Canadian shield. As was often the case, she was the only woman on the trip. (Photo: Jennifer Moody.)

Mom did an excellent job of promoting Dad in the oil business world and attended conferences with him throughout their marriage [John Moody was President of AAPG in 1970-71]. With her by his side his career took off—not that he was not brilliant on his own, but Mom was definitely an asset (a geologist and a beautiful, charming woman), which they used to his advantage (Fig. 34).

All the while, Mom was forging a strong network of friends and contacts in the petroleum industry, which eventually helped set her up as a geologic consultant when she struck out on her own in the mid-1970s after their divorce. Mom also championed the careers of her children. Sandy became an attorney for Exxon in Houston and I became an archaeologist.

I would be remiss if I did not write something about what it was like for me to be raised by these two geologists (not to mention my grandfather, C. L. Moody, also a geologist [AAPG President 1950-51]. Through the mists of time it seems like most of our family vacations in the 1950s and early 60s were centered on geology; looking for fossils and arrowheads in west and south Texas, driving along new roads to see fresh roadcuts. My sister, Misty Moody, and I would sit in the back seat of the car and have to tilt our arms to show the bedding plane of the bedrock in the scarps. I remember a particularly harrowing trip through the Alps when Mom and Dad had learned of a new road across a very high pass. The road was not paved and we got caught in a snow storm. At the time, I did not think all this geology stuff was much fun. In fact, I did not like it at all and would sit arms crossed in the car and refuse to get out.

My attitude did not change until late in my college years, as I slowly became interested in landscape and environmental archaeology. As my interest developed, it was a huge surprise to me how much geology I had actually absorbed by being raised in a geology family! Both Mom and Dad visited me on excavations in Greece in the early 70s where I was working as a graduate student and artist. Their fascination with Aegean geology was infectious and eventually helped define my doctoral thesis, "The Cultural and Environmental History of the Khania Region of West Crete, Neolithic to Late Bronze Age." Mom came over to Crete while I was doing my doctoral research and we had such fun pondering the relationship between the local geology and archaeology (Fig. 35). I particularly remember a later occasion when she met one of my mentors, A. T. "Dick" Gove, a geographer from Cambridge University. We had been in the field and came back to the house to prepare dinner. When Mom went to shower, Dick turned to me and said, "Jennifer, your mother is a formidable woman!"

And, so it was, that the interplay between geology, climate, and culture became my specialty—that little girl that used to sit pouting in the back of the car. Never say never!

It was a messy divorce, and in 1974 Mom moved from New York to Houston where she reconnected with old college friends, many of whom were in the oil business. By 1975, she was consulting for General Crude Oil. Friends and colleagues encouraged her to "hang out her shingle" as an independent geologic consultant, and so she did. In 1979, she was excited to open her office in The Main Building, a hub of independent activity at the time (Fig. 36). It was a close-knit community and Mom thrived. But, it was tricky. Dad was also an independent geologic consultant by then and some big guns in the oil patch felt they had to choose between them to work and continue friendships.

Mom tenaciously maintained her office for twenty years, into the 1990s. She landed big consulting contracts with General Crude Oil, Shell Oil, and others. She was the key in the discovery of several big gas fields in south Texas. Sandy thinks one was an Austin Chalk prospect in Lavaca or Gonzales County with General Crude. Both Sandy and Misty remember another discovery with Shell. We don't know what she was paid, but do know that she made a great deal of money in a short period. According to Sandy, she was never able to negotiate an overriding royalty in the prospects she developed, but, was paid some bonuses.

Figure 35. Evelyn, age 61, on the outcrop in Crete where Jennifer Moody's Cambridge colleague declared, "Your mother is a formidable woman!" (Photo: Jennifer Moody.)

Figure 36. Evelyn Wilie Moody, 1981, in her Houston consulting office where she made the most of a late career in the oil business. (Photo: Jennifer Moody.)

Evelyn Wilie Moody was active in the Houston Geological Society (HGS) and Society of Independent Earth Scientists (SIPES). For HGS she was head of the library committee finding homes for the plethora of logs the library archived. She was awarded the President's award in 1999. She served as an original SIPES Foundation board member and later as Treasurer and President, and was honored with the Outstanding Service Award from the SIPES Foundation in 1986 as well as Honorary Life Membership of the Houston Chapter in 1994. She co-authored two books: One with Doris Curtis, et al., 1981, *How to try to Find an Oil Field* and *Petroleum Developments in Africa*. And, edited two manuals for SIPES, *The Manual for Independents* and *Roadmap for the Self-Employed*. Evelyn Wilie Moody was an AAPG member for 32 years.

The Two Florences

Florence Robinson Weber (1921-) and Florence Rucker Collins (1921-2015)

Florence Robinson and Florence Rucker were paired together in geology field camp at the University of Chicago because of their names, and began a lifelong friendship. They both graduated with their bachelor's degrees in 1943 and went to work in Houston for Shell Oil.

"While there—inspired by an exhibit of U.S. warplanes 'intended to raise patriotic feelings' but which instead piqued their interest in learning to fly—they obtained their pilot licenses. Gas rationing meant no fuel for a car, but they could buy gas for a plane," wrote Collins' daughter, Julie Collins, in a 2011 tribute to her mother in the *Fairbanks Daily News-Miner*. "By the time the pair learned to drive [a car] in 1947, they had already flown from Texas to Florida."

After the war, they returned to Chicago for their master's degrees in 1948. While in graduate school, they took a summer road trip to Alaska over the newly opened Alaska Highway. They decided they liked it, and were able to secure positions in 1949 with the Naval Oil Unit of the USGS.

"Just being two women in this field – that was unusual enough," said Hank Schmoll, a scientist emeritus with the U.S. Geological Survey (USGS) in Denver, who recalled hearing about the Florences before beginning his career in Alaska in 1955. "Some of the guys would perhaps semi-snort at them," he said. "What are these gals doing? Nobody ever said that, but I'm reading between the lines, so to speak" (Saucier, 2014).

With their plane, the two friends could reach places their male counterparts could not. Prior to Weber landing her first field job, Robinson Weber and Rucker Collins often gave male geologists lifts to and from spike camps before they were able to get helicopter support. They battled Alaska's harsh weather conditions and their small aircraft's frequent need for refueling in areas where fuel was scant.

In 1949, both landed jobs with the USGS in Fairbanks performing microscopic rock-core analysis in an office. They envied the men who mapped outcrops in the "exotic far north," Julie Collins wrote. And if the USGS would not send them into the field, they decided they were going to send themselves. The Florences bought a new, two-place Cessna 140 for $3,800 for taking weekend trips to Nome, Kotzebue, Anaktuvuk Pass, and Canada. Starting in Kansas, where they bought their plane, they made their way back to Fairbanks via Texas – hardly a beeline, but a path that clearly revealed a spirit for adventure.

Smoll continued, "Weber and Collins spent the early part of their Alaskan careers studying the structure and stratigraphy of test wells in the Naval Petroleum Reserve No. 4 (NPR-4) on the North Slope," said Ric Wilson, a USGS research geologist and former assistant to Weber. "NPR-4 consisted of several petroleum and oil reserves and was established in 1923 by the federal government to secure fuel for both world wars. The Florences analyzed well cores, chips and logs for reservoir potential in formations."

Florence Collins later said, "We were annoyed. We were disgusted. Girls weren't supposed to be able to do fieldwork, but we thought we were capable of doing that."

While working in the NPR-4, Weber and Collins co-authored a paper suggesting that a large subsurface crater near Point Barrow where the Avak well was drilled was likely formed by the impact of a large meteor—a theory considered far-fetched in its day.

"I don't know this for certain, but I suspect that interpretations such as this were probably way too controversial for USGS editors at the time," said AAPG member Gil Mull, retired employee of the Alaska Division of Geological & Geophysical Surveys. "The Florences' interpretations were not included in the formal report on the exploratory wells drilled at Barrow and Avak. However, more recent studies of the area by geologists Arthur Banet, Tom Homza, and Robert Swenson, give substantial amount of support to these interpretations," Mull said. "The significant thing in my estimation is that the Florences – two women in the USGS, an organization that at the time was predominantly a man's world – did some really detailed work that revealed a lot of innovative thinking, some of which was way ahead of its time," he added (Saucier, 2014).

The Florences worked in Alaska until 1954 when the Survey moved the office to Washington, D.C.; they moved, also, and spent two years writing reports, which became the 12 chapters of USGS Professional Paper 305 (which discusses the subsurface and engineering geology aspects of the USGS exploration of NPRA between 1944 and 1953).

To get back into the field, they made use of their pilot licenses and offered the Survey a special service: access by seaplane into the interior of Alaska. "They [USGS] wouldn't hire women as fieldworkers otherwise," Florence Collins said. The float plane could go places the guys couldn't go. Moving together back to Alaska, the two Florences flew up from Washington, D.C., in a SuperCub with floats.

Weber produced several studies beginning in the late 1950s that explored various routes for numerous proposed roads across Alaska, including a road to Nome. "The road to Nome should be of particular interest to the state today," said Wilson, explaining the state is finally considering building it. Weber also added to the knowledge of the regional bedrock geology of interior Alaska – working with renowned geologists Troy L. Péwé and Clyde Wahrhaftig – and eventually published a map of the Fairbanks quadrangle in 1966. "To this day," Wilson said, "it's the only Fairbanks quadrangle map we have." Moving full steam ahead, Weber produced engineering geologic maps in 1971 for the TransAlaska Pipeline route from Prudhoe Bay to Valdez. "In 1986, she returned to the Livengood area as a project leader for the Alaska Mineral Resource Assessment Program and produced a much more detailed map," Wilson said. In a nod to her efforts, a Middle Devonian gastropod of the Livengood quadrangle was named after her by AAPG member Robert B. Blodgett, a consulting geologist and paleontologist in Alaska. He called it the "*Mastigospira weberae*" (Saucier, 2014).

In the mid-1980s, Weber shared what many considered eccentric insights regarding surficial deposits, namely gold, in the lower parts of rivers on the Alaska Peninsula. While it was commonly held that the deposits came from headwaters, Weber argued that the offshore, heavily mineralized Unga Island was actually the source of the deposits. "She believed they were carried by glaciers moving from the offshore island before their deposition in the lower reaches of the mainland rivers," Wilson said.

Her reasoning was based on her belief that glaciers from the Pacific Ocean flowed northward, pushing toward the mountains of Alaska. In her day, glacier movement was thought to be the opposite. Her theory later proved to be true (Saucier, 2014).

"Florence has had just incredible insights into such a broad range of geology that I just can't imagine anyone better," Wilson said. "She was my idol."

Further flooring her colleagues, Weber dared to suggest that the Tintina Fault System did not rotate around a bend in the subsurface of the Livengood quadrangle, as was commonly believed. Rather, Weber surmised that the fault originated in British Columbia and developed a series of overthrusts in Alaska's interior.

Wilson explained, "She concluded the Denali Fault system acted similarly, in part explaining the terrific height of Mount McKinley."

"Alaska is an incredibly mobile place," he said. "Everything is moving around. People who were knowledgeable of that part of Alaska probably got what she was saying, but people who approached things from a more general perspective probably didn't get it. She outlasted most of the people who didn't believe her."

Figure 37. Florence Rucker Collins and Florence Robinson Weber with their Cessna 140, Washington, March, 1957. (Photo: Ray Collins, son, Fairbanks, Alaska. website, http://sail2ak.com, accessed 1/3/2017.)

The plane that the two Florences bought in 1959 continues to be flown today by Florence Collins' daughters, Miki and Julie, out of Lake Minchumina," (personal communication, 2016). Florence Collins' son, Ray, followed their footsteps and became a geologist. (Fig. 37)

When Ric Wilson took Weber to the Fairbanks airport in the 1990s to catch a flight, he showed her a large display of Alaskan pioneering aviators that included a picture of her. "I'm no pioneer," she rebuffed. "I'm not that old." She was in her 70s at the time. Florence Robinson Weber was an AAPG member 60 years. Florence Collins died in 2015.

Lucille Evelyn Treybig Langford (1919-2008)

Lucille Treybig Langord's family remembers her as, "a witty, creative, enthusiastic, spontaneous, and feisty red head. She always had a giggle, an idea, a solution and never gave up!" (*Austin American Statesman*, 9/25/2008). Her daughter, Lauren Langford, when contacted, provided these early family memories of her mother,

> Lucille Evelyn Treybig was born in Yoakum, Texas, where her father was a banker, her mother a violinist, piano teacher, and homemaker. The family was well off until the Great Crash of 1929. Shortly thereafter they moved to Austin where Mr. Treybig worked in the State Comptroller's office in the capitol building.
>
> Education was important in the family. Living in Austin made going to college much easier for Lucille than for her brothers, Benny and James A. Treybig, who were at Rice University in Houston. When it came time for Lucille to choose a major, she wanted to be a petroleum geologist just like her brothers (both with the Texas Company by that time). She eagerly enrolled in geology at The University of Texas at Austin. She was an honor student every year, never made a grade lower than an A, was Phi Beta Kappa, and graduated in 1941 with a B.S. degree *summa cum laude* in geology and a minor in Spanish (Fig. 38). She wanted to continue on to get a master's degree, but needed money. A young professor in English, Harry Huntt Ransom, helped her get a scholarship for $300 and for additional money, she tutored students in Spanish. In 1942, she became engaged to a new student, Eldon Langford. He had just graduated with a B.S. in geology and petroleum engineering at the University of Houston. In 1942, both Eldon and Lucille graduated with master's degrees in geology.

Figure 38. Lucille Treybig, about 1941. After earning her BA and MA at The University of Texas at Austin she went to work for Amerada Petroleum in Houston. (Photo: Lauren Langford, Bellaire, Texas.)

> Armed with a superior education, Lucille was ready to get a job as a geologist, but was turned down because she was "unskilled." Along the way, Lucille had neglected to study Gregg shorthand, office dictation, coffee making, and filing. She was told point blank in job interviews that she would have to learn the skills of a secretary because that was where she belonged in the bustling petroleum business. After many rejections, she finally landed a job as a micropaleontologist with Amerada Petroleum Corporation in Houston. She was elated to get the job, but understood that fieldwork would never be "suitable" for women. Her job was essentially that of a technician scanning core samples. In the meantime, Eldon, waiting for finalization of a job offer, was working as an electrician in the freighter shipyards in Baytown. In early 1944, he went to work for Superior Oil and joined a [seismic] doodlebug crew in West Texas. In April 1944, Lucille quit her job, took the bus

Figure 39. Lucille and Eldon Langford were wed in 1944 in Seminole, Texas. (Photo: from Lauren Langford.)

to Seminole, and married Eldon on Texas Independence Day, April 21. The wedding was a simple civil affair. (Fig. 39)

In the years to follow, the couple moved from oil patch to oil patch - Levelland, Chickasha, Weatherford, Alice, and more. Eldon drew maps, put dynamite in holes, recorded the waves, and hoped it was a lucky day. Lucille cared for three children and baked lemon meringue pies. When the times got rough in the late 1950s and early 1960s, Lucille and Eldon decided that they needed stable incomes to support their three children. They moved to San Antonio and applied for teaching jobs. Eldon had no problem getting a job teaching geology in a local university, but it was more difficult for Lucille. She had been out of the business too long, was female, and could not be in the same department as her husband. She never blinked.

Lucille returned to UT, earned a PhD in bilingual education, and started teaching second grade in one of the poorest schools in San Antonio. Her classrooms always scored the highest in reading, math and science. Evenings, Lucille helped all the kids in the neighborhood with algebra, geometry, "Beowulf to Burns", and writing. In the summers, she taught geology and earth science at a local private university.

Lauren, speaking of her and her brother's childhood continues,

> At home, she emphasized academic achievement, curiosity, creativity, and independence. Geology talk always prevailed in the Langford home. Most road trips had a stop or two to examine fossils and formations. The three Langford children graduated from university: history, civil engineering, and medicine. She taught her children that men and women could do the same jobs.

Providing additional insight into how industry attitudes affected her mother, Lauren writes,

> The early-on career rejections made an obvious impact. The hurt feelings and resentment were never totally erased. She openly and justly steered her own daughter away from the traditional rituals of being a passive female in society. She encouraged her daughter to excel, travel, and study languages. And in turn the daughter, fluent in three languages, became a physician and professor... brother Benny stayed in the oil business and founded Louisiana Oil Exploration Co. (LOXCO, Inc.). James made his career at Texaco.

Lauren concludes with this perception of her mother.

> She was brilliant. Perhaps she was too intelligent for her times. She wrote poetry, prose, was an accomplished pipe organist, swimmer, member of the Daughters of the Republic of Texas, and a world traveler.

A poem Lucille wrote that the family treasured:

Circle

A figure that never ends
And so it is with friends
They never have
To make amends.
It is with a strong bond
That they are steadfast and true.
If you look in a mirror
I'm talking about you.

Lucille Treybig Langford continued her membership in AAPG for 15 years. (Most of Lucille's story was written by Lauren A. Langford, MD, Professor, Anatomic and Neuropathology, Neuroanatomy, Julius-Maximilians-Universität Würzburg, Germany.)

Women Who Returned to Teaching After the War

Katherine F. Greacen Nelson (1913-1982)

Fig. 40. Katherine Greacen Nelson took off from teaching during WWII to work for Shell Oil and Hunt Oil. After the war, she returned to the University of Wisconsin at Milwaukee. (Photo: University of Wisconsin)

Katherine was the first woman to earn a doctorate at Rutgers University; her bachelor's degree was from Vassar (1934). She taught at Milwaukee-Downer College and curated for the museum. During the War, Katherine Greacen worked for Shell Oil and Hunt Oil in Midland, Texas (Fig. 40). In 1946, Katherine returned to teaching at the University of Wisconsin where she made significant contributions to education, the University, and the geologic community. In 1950, she married attorney, Frank Nelson.

Katherine established the Department of Geological and Geophysical Sciences at the University of Wisconsin, Milwaukee, and was its first Chair. She had no limits on her "educational ambitions" which ranged from congressmen to school children and from television to newspapers. Katherine facilitated the purchase of the Green Museum from Milwaukee-Downer and initiated a public education program. She was an esteemed member of many professional associations and was the first woman president of the Wisconsin Academy of Sciences, Arts, and Letters as well as president of the Wisconsin Geological Society. Katherine was the first woman recipient of the Neil Miner Award with the National Association of Geology Teachers.

"She was a tranquil and energetic person with a kind word and helping hand to all, and always with a beautiful smile. To her the Earth was a remarkable place to be understood, appreciated, and enjoyed. She was the perfect model of what a college professor should be ... colleagues in her department hosted a paleontological symposium to honor her life." These papers were subsequently published in a special memorial volume (Kluessendorf, et al, 1984).

Katherine Greacean Nelson was an AAPG member for 39 years.

Caroline Ella Heminway Kierstead (1904-1985)

Caroline Heminway (Fig. 41) was a professor in geology at Smith College from 1928 to her retirement in 1969. She took a leave from the university to work for Shell International during WWII, from 1943 through 1945. After the War, Caroline returned to Smith and continued to teach. She was a micropaleontologist and lectured on all aspects of geology. She married Friend Hans Kierstead in 1947.

Caroline Heminway Kierstead was an AAPG member for 30 years.

Figure 41. Caroline Heminway Kierstead took a leave from teaching at Smith College to work for Shell International during WW II. (Photo: 1925, Llamarada yearbook, Mt Holyoke, south Hadley, Massachusetts, p. 93.)

World War II Losses and Gains

Helen Fowler Tuttle (1912-2008) was one of the early female geology graduates of the University of California at Berkeley (1933). She initially worked for the U.S. Coast and Geodetic Survey doing fieldwork to map uncharted lands in Northeast Arizona. She married Edward Tuttle in 1936 and honeymooned in the back country of the California Sierras.

During WWII, she was hired by Union Oil of California, but her son, Professor Ed Tuttle, UCLA, recalled that she was forced out of her job to make room for returning vets. He recalled that the prevailing attitude was often that married women did not *need* the job and therefore were expendable. She chose to start a family and throw herself into many civic and charitable activities. Her travels and photography were displayed and presented to several clubs in Southern California.

Helen remained an AAPG member for 60 years and often incorporated geology field trips into her international travels (personal communication, Dr. Edward Tuttle, 2014).

Peggy Frances Parthenia Cantrell Devonshire (1921-1986) received her undergraduate geology degree at the University of Oklahoma (OU) in 1944 and joined Humble Oil Company in Mobile, Alabama. When the War was over, Peggy left industry and went back to OU for her master's degree. She never worked in the oil industry again, but became a technical librarian for Dow Chemical Company in Tulsa, Oklahoma. Peggy married a University of Tulsa professor, Leonard Devonshire, circa 1953. Peggy Cantrell Devonshire was an AAPG member for 29 years.

Joyce Waters McCann (1917-1980) worked for Klaus Exploration in Lubbock, Texas, and Schlumberger in Houston, Texas, during WWII after receiving her B.A. in geology from the University of Colorado in 1940. She married in 1946 and did not return to the industry. Joyce Waters McCann was an AAPG member for 16 years.

Ethel Margaret Davis Tripp Roberts (1917-1998), a graduate with a B.A. and M.A. from the University of Rochester, New York, was teaching at Bryn Mawr in Pennsylvania when WWII started. She went to work for the Texas Company in New York and they posted her to Wichita Falls, Texas. Ethel left after the War and never returned to the industry. Ethel Davis Tripp Roberts was an AAPG member for 24 years.

Margaret A. Tribble Cross (1919-2000) went to work for Phillips in Bartlesville, Oklahoma, in 1941 after acquiring her B.A. in geology at the University of Oklahoma. She married in 1942 and did not return to work in industry again. Margaret Tribble Cross was an AAPG member for 18 years.

Ruth Ream Smith (1918-1994) was assistant to the Chief Geologist at the Texas Company in Los Angeles after brief work with Tide Water Associates Oil and Honolulu Oil Corporation. She resigned at the end of the War in 1946. Ruth Ream received her B.A. in geology from the University of California, Berkeley in 1933. Ruth Ream Smith was an AAPG member for five years.

Millicent A. Renfro Rhodes (1918-1993) joined the Texas Company in 1941 in their Fort Worth office. She had a B.A. and M.A. in geology from Texas Christian University. Millicent Renfro Rhodes was an AAPG member for 16 years.

Ruth E. Wilson Montgomery (1918-?) joined Atlantic Refining in 1942 with a B.A. and an M.S. in geology from the University of Minnesota. She apparently quit when she married. Ruth Wilson Montgomery was an AAPG member for 18 years.

Frances Tuttle Wilkinson (1920-1999), with her B.A. in geology from Cornell University in New York and an M.A. from Smith College in Pennsylvania, went to work for Shell Oil Company in Shreveport, Louisiana, in

1943. There is no indication she worked in industry again after she married in 1947. Frances Tuttle Wilkinson was an AAPG member for 17 years.

Eleanor Young Bright (1920-2008) went to work for Standard Oil of California during WWII (1942) after earning her geology degree at the University of California. Eleanor changed jobs to work for Rio Bravo Oil before she married in 1946. There are no records of continued work after her marriage. Eleanor Young Bright was an AAPG member for nine years.

Dorothy Baumeister Speziale (1911-1996) earned her B.A. and M.A. degrees from Hunter College, 1940, and Oklahoma University, 1942. She went to work for Skelly Oil in Wichita, Kansas, during WWII as a paleontologist. Dorothy married in 1943 and did not continue her geology career. Dorothy Baumeister Speziale was an AAPG member for nine years.

Elsie B. Chalupnik Schiermenz (1921-) received her bachelor's degree at The University of Texas at Austin (1943) and went to work for Barnsdall Oil Company in Houston during WWII. Elsie did not continue her geology career after her marriage in 1948. Elsie Chalupnik Schiermenz was an AAPG member for an unknown number of years.

Mary Louise Treadwell Lawton (1921-2003) received her degree from Cornell in 1944 and went to work for Adkins Oil in Tulsa, Oklahoma, during WWII. Mary Louise married in 1944 and did not continue her geology career. Mary Treadwell Lawton was an AAPG member for an unknown number of years.

Ruth M. Dudley Crump (1916-) worked for Shell Oil as a stratigrapher in Tulsa, Oklahoma, in 1944. Prior to the War, she worked with R. C. Moore at the Kansas Geological Survey. Both her bachelor's and master's degrees (1938, 1939) were from the University of Wisconsin. Ruth apparently left industry after marriage in 1947. Ruth Dudley Crump was an AAPG member for three years.

Janet Hoover Sewell (1918-1975) worked during the War for the Ohio Company in Illinois, and at the end of the War for Cities Service in Wichita, Kansas. She received a bachelor's degree (1940) and did graduate work at the University of Illinois. After marrying in 1946, Janet did not continue her geologic career. Janet Hoover Sewell was an AAPG member for three years.

Lois J. Schulz (1920-?) went to work for Stanolind in Midland, Texas, in 1944 with a geology degree from the University of Illinois. Lois Schulz was an AAPG member for six years.

Holly E. Smith Anderson (1921-) graduated from Smith College in 1944 and joined Superior Oil in Midland, Texas. She ended her geologic career when she married Ken Anderson. Holly Smith Anderson was an AAPG member for four years.

Elizabeth (Libby) Herald Alexander (1922-2001) after receiving her bachelor's degree from The University of Texas, went to work for Humble Oil and Refining in San Angelo, Texas, then later worked for American Republic Oil Company. Libby married Eugene Alexander in 1951 and did not stay active in industry. Elizabeth Herald Alexander was an AAPG member for seven years.

Mary Elizabeth Sheldon Weir (1922-2012) was hired by Sun Oil in San Antonio, Texas, in 1943 after completing her requirements for her geology degree at The University of Texas at Austin (1944). Her son, Max H. Weir III, wrote of her,

> She became Sun Oil Co.'s first female geologist, working out of the Milam building in downtown San Antonio. After getting her degree, she went door-to-door to oil companies to ask for interviews without a résumé in hand. Her efforts eventually landed her a job. Mary Weir worked there for several years and loved it, but her mother didn't approve and gave her an 11 pm curfew on the weekends. She did not go into

the field, but worked with maps and drilling logs to find oil. Her boss paid her more than men in comparable positions because she was so efficient. (*University of Texas Geology Department Newsletter*, 2012)

He added, "She couldn't tell anybody how much she made because he didn't want to get them all mad."

As more men returned from World War II, she left her profession and eventually taught at John J. Pershing Elementary School. She married widower, Max H. Weir, who had three children and, stepson, Max, says, "She was the only mother we ever knew." Max accompanied her on golf trips to North and South America, Europe and Asia (*The University of Texas at Austin, Geology Department Newsletter*, 2012, pp. 92-93.)

Mary Sheldon Weir was an AAPG member for eight years.

Mia Suverkrop Rasaur Alexander (1923-2015)

Mia Suverkrop was typical of the female geologists who went to work in industry during WWII and were forced to quit when they married. But atypical for that time was Mia's return to the industry on two occasions before finally giving up her career. What is also special about Mia's experience is that she wrote about her war-time work experience in expressive detail before her death in 2015.

Mia was the daughter of a geologist, Lew Suverkrop, and grew up in and around the oil patch in California. He wanted Mia to see what geologists do and arranged a job for her with an acquaintance when she was undecided about a major in college. The job turned into an unpleasant experience; however, she was still convinced geology was the career for her.

> Thanks to my dad, I got a job as a draughtsman/steno for The Texas Company at $100 a month. I took a short course in short hand so that I could take dictation. I liked the work, especially the drafting. I didn't like the geologist. This geologist was a friend of my dad's. After about five months, I decided I wanted to go back to school, partly because I had finally made up my mind that I wanted to be a geologist, and not a geologist's flunky. Most of all, I was tired of being subjected to what would be called nowadays, "verbal sexual harassment." At age 19, I did not know how to handle the maudlin talk of love from a plump, unattractive man with a wife and two children who happened to be my boss and "horror of horrors" a friend of my father's! This was the only experience of this nature that I ever encountered during my working career. I quit the job and told my dad I wanted to study geology and enrolled at the University of California at Berkeley. I figured not all geologists would be lecherous creeps.

After getting her geology degree at UC Berkeley in 1944 (Fig. 42), her father set her up with an interview in San Francisco with SoCal. She wrote,

> When I went to work for SoCal I prepared to make it my career. I loved everything about it - the people, the work, the atmosphere, the seriousness, the friendships. I particularly liked doing something few women did at that time. My four-month stint in the San Francisco (SF) office was a great way to begin my career as a geologist. Some of the reports and letters I read dated from the twenties and thirties and earlier. I learned a lot of California oil geology and Standard Oil Co. oil exploration history. John Connelly, told me stories about the depression and the fact that no employees were let go during that time. The company just cut their work period down to 3 days a week. Bud McGurty had lived at the Standard Oil 11-C camp in Taft for some years and knew some of my dad's friends and had many funny tales to tell. He was like a quirky little old comedian playing Santa Claus in the movies. Or maybe one of his elves. When he had nothing else to do, he would read the SoCal policy manual, a giant size loose leaf volume, and turn the pages and hum.

Figure 42. Mia Suverkrop, 1942, at UC Berkeley field camp, prior to joining SOCal during WW II. (Photo: Mia S. Alexander, Seattle, Washington, provided in 2014.)

I spent a lot of time in the drafting room...a long narrow room with windows overlooking Bush St. From the windows, you could look down and see the tobacco shop just across the street. Because of the war, it was sometimes hard to get cigarettes, so the drafting room kept an eye on the shop and if they spotted a cigarette delivery truck, they would pass the word and everyone would race down the elevator and across the street and maybe luck into a carton.

After four months in the SF office, I was transferred to Bakersfield, California to be on a GSI crew. I left San Francisco behind with mixed feelings. I would be sorry to say goodbye to my new SoCal friends. Still, it was exciting to think about working on a seismic crew. My major at Cal had been geology, with the emphasis on seismology. Perhaps I could actually use some of that knowledge. My dad was overjoyed at the prospect of having me around home for a while. My brother, Bard, was in the Air Corps in England, in a bomber squadron. My little brother, Donny, aged 19, was in the Army, fighting in the Philippines. My mother, at age 44 had joined the WAC and was doing her basic training at Hunter College in New York.

I showed up my first day of work in Bakersfield at the Standard Oil building near the center of town and met my boss, Mr. Borys... [who] told me that I would be working up the street in the office of the GSI crew. GSI was the Geophysical company contracted by Standard to do the actual fieldwork. "Your job will mainly be drawing cross sections from seismic data, like this." He said, as he opened a map tube and showed me a cross section showing the dips. "Bob Weideman, the other SoCal geologist on the crew will get you started. Dick Peck, our head surveyor happens to be here and I'll get him to show you to the office. It's over Wickersham's Jewelers."

...Dick Peck was a loyal Standard Oiler, around 40 with a fatherly manner. I felt comfortable with him right off the bat. He walked me over to Wickersham's and up the stairs to the second floor. There I met the geologist, Bob Weideman, who was about my age, the GSI Party Chief, Francis Hale, and his assistant, Bob Dundan. The office consisted of two rather small rooms. In a corner of the main room was Mr. Hale's desk facing the wall. Behind it was a long heavy table about the size of three card tables put together. Between the desk and the table was Mr. Hale's swivel chair. In the opposite corner of the room by the window, were the drafting table and stool that were assigned to me. The second room was where the two Bobs worked.

Francis Hale was out with the field crew part of the time, dealing with the shooting, where and how deep to shoot plus tending to any kind of personnel problems there might be. Dick Peck didn't even have a desk in the GSI office...He was in charge of the surveyors and the positioning of the recorders...The seismic records were strips of photographic paper, about eight inches wide and as much as 12 feet long. This is the reason for the long table behind Francis' desk. He spent most of his time in the office sitting in his swivel chair, scooting up and down picking the dips from the records on the table and swiveling around to work at his desk. When he was finished with some records, Bob Dundan would come in and get them and take them in to the other room where he and Bob Weideman would put the information together with the locations and depths of the shootings. This is the information that came back to me that I would then depict graphically in a cross section. The working with numbers and maps was just the kind of thing I loved doing. I liked the people and the casual atmosphere. Another plus was the location of my drafting table. It was right next to a window and sitting on my stool I could look down at the alley behind the building. I had a good view of the entrance of "The Alley Cat," a low life bar.

Amazing things happened down there every day. One day I saw a woman repeatedly hitting a man over the head with her handbag and then taking a ring off her finger and throwing it at him. Another day there was a fight between a couple of men that started in the alley and moved on down to the street where one of the men got the better of the other and bashed his head against the bumper of a parked car. The police finally showed up. I have often wondered if seeing life in the raw in that alley affected my own behavior. I had a running, more or less friendly, argument with Bob Dundan about whether or not he made an occasional mistake in the dip information he was giving me. At some point, I bet him a nickel that I would find a mistake again. He took the bet. A few days later I found a mistake (I thought.) He said it wasn't a mistake. We argued. Me loudly. "I want my nickel!" I felt the way I did when I had last had a fist fight with my little brother when I was fourteen. I said, "Let's go down in the alley and settle this." Bob disappeared into the other room. I looked over at Francis. He was hunched over his desk, pretending to ignore the hullabaloo. I retreated to my drafting table. I was ashamed.

In the spring of 1945 the crew had finished their work in the Bakersfield area and were going to be working on locations in Ventura County, and an office would be set up in Santa Paula, California. I was informed that I would be staying in Bakersfield, working on old records under Mr. Borys' supervision. I was momentarily crushed by this development. I had been happy with my chummy group and the close quarters over the jewelry store...When Dick Peck went on a three-week vacation, Mr. Borys told me that I would be joining the crew in Santa Paula and would stay in Dick's boarding house there during the week. I enjoyed every minute. The crew had lunch together every day at [the] local cafe and then played a game of pool in the parlor next door. I still love playing pool. Soon after I returned to the Bakersfield office, the crew was moved to a new location, Whittier, Calif. This time I would go with them. I guess my three weeks in Santa Paula was a kind of test and I passed...Our office was very like the Bakersfield and Santa Paula ones. But no Alley Cat Cafe outside my window. My weekday home was the William Penn Hotel, a small, comfortable, sedate place. Not a hotel I needed to dress up for. Whittier was a much bigger town than Santa Paula with a bigger selection of places to eat. But no pool hall at lunch. Nevertheless, I continued to enjoy the camaraderie of the office crew.

By now I knew my job well and felt I was contributing to the seismic efforts of the GSI crew with my cross sections. Working directly on records while in the Bakersfield office helped me to better understand the end results of the shooting. It was exciting to think that I might chance to come across an anomaly of importance. Dick Peck was with us. He continued looking out for me in his fatherly way...One wonderful day, Dick came into the office and said he was going out into the country where the GSI field crew was shooting and would I like to go along. Hot diggety! Going out in the field was an unexpected surprise. We got to the shooting site about ten am. I was able to wander around on my own watching the shooting and recording. No one paid much attention to me. At lunch time, all the men took a break and someone gave me a sandwich and a coke. The coke must have done it. I needed a rest stop. I had not noticed one in the area we drove through. About one o'clock I was getting desperate. I caught Dick by himself and asked him, "Is there a Standard Station around here?" He said, "Yes. About a half mile down that road. Here, take the survey truck." and handed me the keys. I had never driven a truck of any kind. At that moment, I was too anxious to turn it down. I figured it couldn't be too different from driving a large car. I climbed in and put the key in the lock and discovered my short legs could barely reach the pedals. The gear shift was so long I could not push it all the way forward. Sitting on the edge of the seat I finally got the motor started and shifted into the lowest gear. I was afraid to try to put it into a higher gear and maybe stall. I turned on to the road and headed for the Standard Station. I found it! Dick congratulated me when I returned to the site. He didn't say anything about my driving.

When I married in 1946, most married women did not work. They took care of the home and the children. I don't remember even thinking about it. I quit my job when I married my first husband. He was a Marine Corps flier, back from the war and recovering from leg wounds. Because he could no longer pass the Marine Corps physical but liked the military life, he went to a Police Academy and worked briefly as a policeman. Then he went the U.S. Army and applied for a regular commission as an Officer. This required him to attend various courses at various schools around the country. By this time, we had a child and had bought a house in California. We decided that it didn't make sense for me and Ginny to follow him around. We stayed behind. I decided to see if I could get a job with Chevron in the LA office. Child care was the only problem. Ginny was one and a half now. The lady who lived next door to our house in West Covina had no children of her own and was crazy about Ginny. She offered to take care of her while I looked for permanent daycare. [Eventually] I found Chular and she was a gem. Ginny called her "CaCa." Chular stayed overnight at our house on weekdays.

When I walked into Mr. Winham's [SoCal] LA office...I felt I had come home. He...spent very little time interrogating me before offering me a job. He said that I would be in a large office with the people I would be working with... Someone said, "Welcome to the "Snake Pit." The room had about six desks and four drafting tables and one light table. I was assigned a desk. They showed me the mirrored closet where I could hang my coat. There was a window blind on the mirror so that when the sun shone through the windows in the late afternoon the reflection in the mirror wouldn't blind us all. The drafting tables were available to everyone. For a while I was doing all kinds of little jobs somewhat similar to what I had done on the geophysical crew.

Things got more interesting when I started doing work for Dr. Ed Lammers, whose desk was in the Snake Pit. He had taught at Washington and Lee in Virginia. Ed's youngest child was a little girl the same age as my child, Ginny. He was a warm friendly person and a brilliant teacher. I felt as if I had a geology class whenever I worked on something for him. He was doing a job with another geologist, Hal Bemis, about deepening a well to find a particular oil-bearing formation. Ed was trying to prove that, because of a thrust fault, the formation should appear twice in the well log. I could use what I learned in a civil engineering class at Cal to make a three-dimensional drawing of the area of the well. I felt I was contributing.

Another female geologist, Ida Dobler, was assisting Hal, who had his own office. Ida and I sometimes got to go into Hal's office with Ed and listen to them argue. We denizens of the Snake Pit became good friends. We all went down to the coffee room together and talked about our families. Some of the male geologists were out in the field most of the time and we would hear about their exploits and adventures.

...In October, my husband had finished his tour at the JAG school and would be going to the CID school in Baltimore. It would be a longer tour and we needed to be together. So, this time Ginny and I would go with him. I was sad when it was time to say goodbye to my Snake Pit friends. I had enjoyed them as much as those on the GSI crew and knew I probably would not see them again. In April 1950, my husband, Dink Rasaur, got the orders for his next assignment. He was to join the 1st Cavalry Division in Japan. We drove to California where Ginny and I would wait until he found housing for us there. In June 1950, the Korean war began.

I received my last letter from Dink about three weeks after the war started. He had written it on the dock in Korea. The division had just landed there. In August 1950, the Army "Missing in Action" telegram arrived. The U.S. Army was retreating down the Korean peninsula at the time. News reports were grim. By the end of the year, things were getting worse. I was beginning to plan for the ultimate bad news. I went into the LA office of Chevron and saw Mr. Winham, asking if there could be a place for me in the Exploration Dept. again. He said "Yes. Whenever you're ready." I was grateful to him and SoCal for their understanding of my situation. I sold my West Covina house and found a convenient compact apartment in Arcadia with a view in the distance of the Santa Anita Race Track.

In January 1951, I got the final word that Dink had been killed in action in Korea. I went back to work at SoCal assisting one of the senior geologists. I always took my time leaving Ginny each morning at the school and then racing into LA to work so as not to be late. Then after work I raced to Pasadena to pick up Ginny. Her face was usually dirty sometimes streaked with tears. She apparently wouldn't let them wash her face. I got several speeding tickets during this time.

My work was the most tranquil part of my day. My work with John Ruth was different from that in the Snake Pit. For one thing, John was a stratigrapher. I learned a lot more about sediments and how the strata were deformed. The *one time* I was slighted (for being a woman) was while working for John Ruth. A new hire, Roger Alexander, was being shown around the office by a Senior Geologist. They came into the office I shared with John Ruth. Roger was introduced to John, but not to me. I met Roger later in the day when I went down to coffee with the guys. Roger made a good impression on everyone. Having grown up at West Point and Princeton, his manners were impeccable. He loved all sports, field geology and birding. His blue and white cotton cord suit pockets were bulging with binoculars, camera, note books and bird books. By the end of that coffee break, he knew everyone's name. If I had not met Roger, [who became] my second husband, I would have happily worked for the Standard forever. Like most large Oil Companies, SoCal did not allow husbands and wives to work in the same office. I loved my work, but have no regrets about leaving. Our family spent the next twenty years like gypsies, moving every two to four years. We lived happily in Salt Lake City, Marin County, Houston, Texas, Perth, Australia and finally, Saudi Arabia."

Mia Alexander never returned to geology, but continued to love the oil business life and the travels associated with it. Mia was an AAPG Member for an unknown number of years.

Yang Yi (1920-living)
China's First Woman Petroleum Geologist

This biographical writeup is primarily from Ma Zhen, 2014, April 18, China Petroleum Newspaper, *translated to English by Guonong Hu, geologist, Denver, Colorado. Guonong studied under Li Desheng, who was with Yang Yi in the first field party in the Yumen Oil field, 1945. Photos from Ma Zhen and the family of Yang Yi. A version of this was published in the* AAPG Explorer, *2015, September.*

Yang Yi was the first deputy Chair of the Department of Geology, China University of Petroleum. Like her husband, a legendary petroleum geologist, Zhang Jiahuan, she enjoys a peaceful and quiet life, but despite her quietness, history long remembers her legacy as the first Chinese woman in petroleum geology. Her life herald's the intellectual woman's struggle after the May Fourth Movement (1919) for women's liberation and women's desire to shoulder social responsibilities like their male counterparts.

Yang Yi was born in 1920 in Anxin, Hebei Province. After the Xinhai Revolution (1911), a wave of new industry and commerce emerged. Her father took advantage of this opportunity and established a textile business, "Gao Yang Homespun," during the Republic Era (1911-1949). Yang was born into a wealthy family and she has always had a tenacious and rebellious spirit. When Yang was a teenager, the family moved to South Street in Beijing. She went to Siming Martial Arts School and learned skills and athleticism that served her all her life. As a youth, Yang resented her older brothers and sisters for relying on shares in the family business and lacking ambition to better themselves. She was determined to leave the security of the family behind and establish an independent life. After the Japanese occupation of Beijing in 1937, Yang's desire for independence made her even more determined to leave Beijing (Fig. 43).

During the summer recess of her senior year in high school, Yang was excited to hear that Beijing University, Qinghua University, and others fled the Japanese occupation and formed the National Southwestern Associated University in Kunming, Yunnan Province. Yang lied to her mother about her intentions and got money for her journey to Kunming. She and several friends went to the French Embassy and asked for help buying tickets to Vietnam. Their plan was to go to Kunming by routing through Vietnam. However, their plan was foiled when they were caught by Japanese military police and imprisoned. Yang was whipped and tortured and her family was forced to pay a bribe for her release. Additionally, Yang's family feared persecution because her oldest brother was associated with an anti-Japanese organization so they decided to split up and move to Shanghai. Knowing that she needed her high school diploma to apply to the Southwestern Associated, Yang waited until she received her high school transcript and then boarded a ship from Tianjin to Shanghai.

Figure 43. Yang Yi collecting fossils near Beijing, China. (Photo: Yang Yi's daughter, Zhang Min, Beijing, China.)

In 1940, Shanghai, too, fell into Japanese occupation. Yang Yi was extremely distraught and disobeyed her parents' wish to go to Shanghai University. She tried to apply to the Southwestern Associated, but because she received the application materials too late, she could only apply to an agriculture college in Yunnan. After passing the entrance exam, she was told to wait in Kunming for assignment.

Yang Yi boarded a ship from Shanghai to Haiphong, Vietnam, and then traveled from Haiphong to Hanoi, and from Hanoi to Kunming via Hekou. Arriving in Kunming, Yang was in tears because she was finally out of the shadow of Japanese occupation and rule. Yang, however, did not report to the agriculture college. In September 1940, she applied to Yunnan University. After the exam, Yang found out that Southwestern Associated was also recruiting. She applied again and was admitted to the Department of Physics.

Yang's longtime dream had finally been realized and she was extremely happy. Her joy was only diminished by the sad realization that she might never see her mother again. And she did not.

Yang's outgoing and independent nature and rebel spirit led her to pursue geology where she could work outdoors in the field. A year later after starting her studies at Southwestern Associated, she transferred to the Department of Geology. A young man, Zhang Jiahuan, was following a similar path. He transferred at the same time from the Civil Engineering Department to the Geology Department. In the spring of 1945, Yang Yi and Zhang Jiahuan were partnered to go to a village, Kebocun, for fieldwork on their senior theses. Tall and handsome, Zhang took good care of Yang Yi and with shared ideals, they fell deeply in love.

The Yumen Oilfield in northwest China's Gobi Desert was in its early stage of development and there was a desperate shortage of geologists due to the war. Few women were in the field of geology and even fewer would chose to do fieldwork in the middle of a wasteland, but Yang Yi chose this work after graduation. Zhang's father had planned and saved money for Zhang to study overseas, but Zhang chose to marry Yang and go with her to Yumen. They both wanted to contribute to the China's war against Japan by exploring for oil.

On July 21, 1945, Zhang and Yang held a simple wedding at their school. Three days later, Zhang put Yang Yi on a plane to fly to Chongqing, the war-time capital, while he stayed with their luggage and hitchhiked to Chongqing. It took him a month and half to reach Chongqing.

After reporting to Gansu Oilfield Bureau in Chongqing, the young couple started their journey to Yumen in the back of a truck in late September. Roads were very poor and rough and it took them a month to travel 2,500 kilometers. Winter was approaching and it was turning cold, and they were not prepared. At Lanzhou, the couple bought old sheep skin coats. As the truck slowly moved to their destination, the landscape became increasingly inhospitable and the weather worse. But with love in their hearts and common goals kept they kept optimistic and persevered.

That year, eight geologists arrived at the Yumen Oilfield, joining their leader, Sun Jianchu (1897-1952), who discovered Yumen Oilfield in 1938. He had recently returned to China from working in Louisiana, Texas, Oklahoma, and Southern California for two years. Sun Jianchu is still regarded as the earliest pioneer for Chinese petroleum geology. This was the first petroleum geological exploration team in China; Yang Yi was the only woman (Fig. 44).

Yang and Zhang studied field geology, reviewed geological literature, and wrote trainee reports. Sun paid special care to Yang, not only because she was the only woman, but also because she was intelligent and diligent. Yang had a natural love for geology and Sun afforded her extra guidance both with work and tutoring and could be very strict. One example was that Yang Yi loved to sing Beijing opera and encouraged by her colleagues, she stepped onto a stage and sang a piece. When Sun heard about it he scolded her, "As a learned person, you should be reading books instead of singing opera." She never sang opera again.

Early in 1946, the Exploration Department of the Gansu Oilfield Bureau was formed and Sun Jianchu was named its director. In June, the department moved to Lanzhou and in April, Sun led the team to conduct detailed fieldwork and structural mapping in the areas around the Laojunmiao oilfield. This was the first-time Yang Yi could do fieldwork and realized her dream to become an exploration geologist (Fig. 45). As she travelled through the Gobi wilderness on horseback, Yang Yi was making history – she became the first Chinese woman in

Figure 44. Director Sun Jianchu on the left and Yang Yi to the right of him, having breakfast outside their yurt at Damalianquan, 1946. (Photo: Zhang Min.)

petroleum geology (Fig. 46). She tied her hair into a pair of thick braids and worked in the hot sun and through sand storms, enduring everything her male colleagues endured. Yang felt that her martial arts training gave her a strong body full of energy. Her endurance even surpassed some of her male colleagues. At night, in the darkness around their tents, there were often wolves with blinking green eyes, but Yang had no fear. Shouldering a shotgun, she went to hunt them with the men (Fig. 47). The only special consideration she received was that the team set up a separate tent for her and her husband.

Figure 45. Yang Yi, with her hair in braids, and her husband, Zhang Jiahuan, comparing field notes in a Mongolian yurt, Summer 1946. (Photo: Zhang Min.)

Figure 46. Yang Yi, second from left, making history on horseback in the Gobi Desert, in 1946. (Photo: Zhang Min.)

The exploration team spent the day working in the field. In the evening, they organized their data and discussed geological problems. Yang felt she was the happiest woman in the world. After two months of fieldwork, she and her colleagues authored "Geological Report on Qingcaowan Structure" with 1: 10,000 geologic map and structural maps. Soon after, Yang participated in the detailed geological investigation along the northern mount front of Qilian Mountain, including Qingcaowan in the west, east to Dahongquan, Laojunmiao, and ShiyouGou. This investigation yielded a wealth of data for the later development of Yumen Oilfield (Fig. 48).

In August 1947, the Director of the Paleontology Department of the National Geological Survey, Dr. Yin Zanxun (founding father of Chinese paleontology, PhD Université de Lyon) came to collaborate with Yang's team and conducted a paleontological study to discern the biostratigraphy of the Qilian Mountain and surrounding areas. Director Sun sent Zhang Jiahuan and Yang Yi and one other geologist to work with Dr. Yin's team. The survey area was vast and extended deep into the mountains. It was particularly hard work because down in the valleys the weather was dry and hot, but up in the mountain tops, the weather was windy and cold to the bone. Despite the cold, they once climbed to the main peak of the Qilian Mountain, the Devil's Mountain, to observe ice bridges.

Figure 47. Yang Yi doing her part in the hunting party in Qingcaowan. From left to right, Zhang Chuangan, Situ Yuwang, Zhang Weiya and Yang Yi. (Photo: Zhang Min.)

Dr. Yin Zanxun's project re-directed Yang Yi's fate, as often happens when one works with a legendary expert. Under the guidance of Dr. Yin, Yang Yi developed a strong interest in paleontology.

Figure 48. Summer 1946, fieldwork at Hanxia, Qilian Mountains. From left to right: Zhang Chuangan, Situ Yuwang, Zhang Jiahuan and Yang Yi. (Photo: Zhang Min.)

Her ability to identify fossils was recognized and she began her career in stratigraphy and paleontology (Fig. 49).

In January 1948, Yang Yi was sent to Nanjing to identify the tremendous number of fossil specimens gathered over the years. Yang officially became a protégé of Dr. Yin's and her academic credentials increased rapidly.

In the spring of 1949, artillery attacks of the Chinese Civil War (1946-1949) temporarily ended Yang's research. Dr. Yin sent her to Lanzhou to avoid the war. She returned to Director Sun with data and property of the exploration department that required protection. They continued their work as they embraced the arrival of the People's Liberation Army.

In March 1950, Yang Yi was assigned to Qinghua University to teach paleontology and in September 1951, Yang's old Exploration Department was moved to Beijing from Lanzhou and was placed under the Petroleum Administration Bureau, reporting directly to the State Council. Yang's husband, Zhang Jiahuan, chose not to transfer to Beijing with Director Sun, but remained in northwest China because there was still significant geology and exploration work to do. He wanted to be on the front line of exploration. Yang was supportive of Zhang's choice and worked in Beijing, raising their young child by herself.

Figure 49. Summer 1947, Yang Yi on the left, at Maoshila fossil site in the Qilian Mountains. (Photo: Zhang Min.)

Universities in old China before 1949 did not have petroleum-related majors, but to meet the nation's need for petroleum, a petroleum engineering department was formed in Qinghua University. A year later, under the direction from Premier Zhou Enlai, the Beijing Petroleum Institute was founded. Zhang Geng was appointed to be the Chair of the Geology Department and Yang Yi was appointed Deputy Chair of the department. This appointment was nothing less than groundbreaking, as few women achieved these higher academic appointments even after the Xinhai Revolution (1911). In the male-dominated field of geology this was particularly exceptional.

In 1955, Yang's husband, Zhang Jiahuan, joined the new Petroleum Institute and became a lecturer of physical geology. The couple had been married for ten years. They had experienced life in a tent in the wilderness and were now in their new home in the nation's capital. And they continued their pursuit of geology. Yang Yi developed a reputation for her tireless, machine-like work ethic. She was busy with the startup of the geology department construction, compilation of teaching materials, conducting scientific research, and taking care of her husband and child. She was busy but content.

Unfortunately, as Yang Yi was about to embrace a bright future, she became a victim of China's many episodes of political turmoil. In 1957, like 300,000 other Chinese intellectuals, she was convicted as a rightist and prosecuted in Mao's Anti-Rightist Movement. Her scientific career was cut short.

Figure 50. Yang Yi, a proud grandmother, in 2014. (Photo: Zhang Min.)

Twenty-two years later, in 1979, her conviction was finally revoked and the wrong done to her redressed. Retired by then, she again approached her beloved field of geology with a passion and compiled and co-authored an "English-Chinese Geology Dictionary" and "English-Chinese Petroleum Dictionary."

Yang Yi, in 2014, was 93 years old and had lost much of her memory to Alzheimer's disease (Fig. 50). Her home was raided so many times during the Cultural Revolution that her scholarly articles were lost or destroyed. Her husband Zhang died in April 2014. Friends of hers stumbled upon some old photos in a confiscated goods warehouse after the end of the Cultural Revolution, which we were encouraged to include herein.

Marie Tharp (1920 to 2006)

In 1942 during WWII, Marie Tharp was a student at Ohio University where she "found geology, not friends." Her senior year, Marie saw a notice on the bulletin board advertising the "Petroleum Girls" program at the University of Michigan (also see Chapter 11, Helen Foster). Not satisfied with the program at Ohio University, Marie pulled up her roots mid-semester and headed to Michigan where she completed the heavy-duty petroleum curriculum with its intensified field course, by summer 1944.

She was easily placed into a job in the oil business with Stanolind in Tulsa, Oklahoma, but like many women of her generation, quit when she married, and followed her husband to New York. Marie sought out work in academia and made an enormous mark for oceanography and science, creating the first global sea floor maps. From Columbia University website, we learn,

> In 1948, at age twenty-eight, Marie walked into the newly formed geophysical lab at Columbia University and practically demanded a job. The scientists at the lab were all male; the women who worked there were relegated to secretary or assistant. Through sheer willpower and obstinacy, Marie was given the job of interpreting the soundings (records of sonar pings measuring the ocean's depths) brought back from the oceangoing expeditions of her male colleagues. The marriage of artistry and science behind her analysis of these dry data gave birth to a major work: the first comprehensive map of the ocean floor, which laid the groundwork for proving the then controversial theory of continental drift (Felt, 2012, cover jacket).
>
> A pioneer of modern oceanography, Tharp was the first to map details of the ocean floor on a global scale. Her observations became crucial to the eventual acceptance of the theories of plate tectonics and continental drift in the earth sciences. Working with pens, ink and rulers, Tharp drew the underwater cartography, longitude degree by latitude degree, based on data from sonar readings taken by pioneering earth scientist Maurice Ewing and his team. Piecing maps together in the late 1940s and early 1950s, she and colleague Bruce Heezen discovered a 40,000-mile underwater ridge girdling the globe. By this finding, they laid the foundation for the conclusion from geophysical data that the sea floor spreads from central ridges and that the continents are in motion with respect to one another—a revolutionary geological theory at the time. Years later, satellite images proved Tharp's maps to be accurate (2016).

Figure 51. Marie Tharp, who was a U. Michigan "Petroleum Girl" and then worked with Stanolind before her career in oceanography. Here with one of her Ocean Floor maps. (Photo: Creative Commons website -- http://alchetron.com/Marie-Tharp-794903-W.)

Marie Tharp did not enjoy recognition for the scope of her contribution during her life, but instead appeared content to have her long-time partner, Bruce Heezen, accrue most of the accolades (Felt, 2012). However, in 2001, she was recognized for her pioneering work in oceanography and awarded the first annual Lamont-Doherty Heritage Award (Fig. 51).

Chapter 10. Sources and References

Alexander, Mia Suverkrop Rausaur, Seattle, Washington. Personal autobiographical writings and personal communication, August 25, 2014 and November 11, 2015; photo from MIa Alexander as cited in figure caption..

Austin American Statesman. "Lucille Evelyn Treybig Langford Obituary." September 25, 2008. Copy provided by Lauren Langford, daughter of Lucille Treybig.

Brachman, Mara Marie (Robinson), Houston, Texas, daughter of Mary Jane Robinson. Written communication and source of photograph as cited in figure caption.

Carriveau, Judy, Easthampton, Massachusetts, niece of Eleanor Caldwell. Personal communication; source of photograph as cited in figure caption.

Chadney, Courtney. "Her Brilliant Career: Marie Still Loves Geology." *AAPG Explorer*, December 2013, vol. 34, no. 12. pp. 54-55. Source of Marie Gramann photograph as cited in figure caption.

Clarke, Don, Long Beach, California, colleague of Marie Clark. Personal communication October 2014 to December 2015; source of photograph as cited in figure caption.

Collins, Julie. 2011. "Recollections of Mom at 90 and Her Pioneering Spirit." *Fairbanks Daily News Miner,* May 29, 2011. http://www.newsminer.com/recollections-of-mom-at-and-her-pioneering-spirit/article_7397012b-66bf-5641-b27a-34f635f8adea.html. Accessed 9/2017.

Collins, Julie, Lake Minchumina, Alaska, daughter of Florence Rucker Collins. Personal communication, December 2016.

Collins, Ray, Fairbanks, Alaska, son of Florence Rucker Collins. *Florence Rucker Collins and Florence Robinson Weber with their Cessna 140.* n.d. Photograph, http://sail2ak.com. Accessed 01/03/2017.

Columbia University. "C250 Celebrates Columbians ahead of their time, Marie Tharp." Columbia 250. Created between June 2003 and December 2004. http://www.c250.columbia.edu/c250_celebrates/remarkable_columbians/marie_tharp.html. Accessed 01/22/2017.

Curtis, Doris M., Patricia Wood Dickerson, Donald M. Gray, Helen M. Klein, and Evelyn W. Moody. *How to Try to Find an Oil Field.* Tulsa, Oklahoma: Pennwell Books, 1981. 94 pp.

Echols, Dorothy Jung. 1991. "Memorial to Doris M. Curtis 1914-1991." *GSA Memorials*, pp. 175-183.

Eureka Times-Standard. 2013. "Beverly E. McMahon Obituary." October 4, 2013. http://www.legacy.com/obituaries/times-standard/obituary-print.aspx?n+beverly-e-mcmahon. Accessed 09/17/2017.

Felt, Hali, *Soundings: The Story of the Remarkable Woman Who Mapped the Ocean Floor.* New York, New York: Henry Holt & Company, 2012. 340 pp.

Gramann, Marie, Brownwood, Texas. Personal communication 2014 through 2016; video interview, 7/24/2015, archived at AAPG, Tulsa, Oklahoma.

Hobgood, Martha. 1955. "Mrs. Louise Clarkson is Abilene's Woman Geologist." *The Abilene Reporter-News*, March 1, 1955, p. 28.

Kluessendorf, Joanne, Donald G. Mikulic, Rachel and Richard Paull. 1984. "Katherine Greacean Nelson Memorial." *AAPG Bulletin*, vol. 68, no.6, pp. 786-87.

Langford, Lauren, Bellaire, Texas, daughter of Lucille Treybig Langford. Personal communication, January 2017; source of photographs as cited in figure captions.

Lexicon Committee, Louise Fillman, Chairman. "Lexicon of Pre-Pennsylvanian Stratigraphic Names of West Texas and Southeastern New Mexico." Midland, Texas: West Texas Geological Society, 1958. 153 pp.

Loranger, Diane. *Geologist Diane Loranger using microscope to examine samples in Royalite Oil Company office, Turner Valley, Alberta.* 1946-47. Photograph. Glenbow Archives, IP-14a-1471, Glenbow Museum, Calgary, Alberta.

Loranger, Diane, *Diane Loranger, a geologist for Imperial Oil Limited, at work testing formations in the Rocky Mountains, Alberta.* 1947. Photograph. Glenbow Archives, IP-14a-1828, Glenbow Museum, Calgary, Alberta.

Middlebury College. *Eleanor Thompson Caldwell.* 1938. *Kaleidoscope* yearbook. Middlebury, Vermont, p. 26.

Milliken, Kitty. 1994. "Participation of Women in the Graduate Program of the Department." *The University of Texas Geology Department Newsletter*, no. 44, pp. 86-88. [Photograph of Marie Gramann at the University of Texas Geology Field Camp.]

Min, Zhang, daughter of Yang Yi, source of photographs provided to Ma Zhen, Beijing, China, and to Guonong Hu, Denver, Colorado.

Moody, Jennifer, Austin, Texas, daughter of Evelyn Wilie Moody. Written communication, August 28, 2017 through December 15, 2017; source of photographs as cited in figure captions.

Mount Holyoke College. *Caroline Ella Heminway (Kierstead).* 1925. Photograph. *Llamarada* yearbook. South Hadley, Massachusetts. p. 93.

Peterson, James, Denver, Colorado, nephew of Hazel Peterson. Personal communication, correspondence, writings, and photographs, April 2016; photographs as cited in figure captions.

Renzetti, Claire M. and Daniel J. Curran. *Women, Men, and Society.* Boston: Allyn and Bacon, fifth edition, 2002. 497 pp.

Rhoades, John, Northampton, Massachusetts, nephew of Eleanor Caldwell. Personal communication, October 2016.

Sarikaya, Hasan. Ankara, Turkey. Personal communication, October 2017 to December 2017, additional biographical information for Mehlika Tasman Ribnikar; source of photographs as cited in figure captions.

Saucier, Heather. "Pioneer Geologists: Soaring Beyond the Glass Ceiling." *AAPG Explorer*, November 2014, vol. 35, no. 11. http://www.aapg.org/publications/news/explorer/details/articleid/13209/pioneer-geologists-soaring-beyond-the-glass-ceiling. Accessed 10/2016.

———, "PROWESS Honors China's First Female Geologist", *AAPG Explorer,* September 2015, vol. 36, no. 9. http://www.aapg.org/publications/news/explorer/emphasis/Articleid/22543/prowess-honors-china's-first-female-geologist. Accessed 01/2017.

Shell Development Company Houston. *Quest*, Quarterly Publication, April 1979. p. 9. Source of photograph of *Doris M. Curtis, President of SEPM* as cited in figure caption.

Simon, Susan Suchman, Chapel Hill, North Carolina, niece of Doris Malkin Curtis. Personal communication, 2014-2016; source of photographs as cited in figure captions.

Suchman, Lucy, Saltspring Island, British Columbia, niece of Doris Malkin Curtis. Personal communication, 2014-2016; source of photographs as cited in figure captions.

Takken, Suzanne. n.d. Photograph. Suzanne Takken Papers, M.S. 523, Archives of Women in Science and Engineering, Special Collections and University Archives, Iowa State University Library.

Texas Christian University. *Mary Jane Cole* (Robinson). 1943. Photograph. *The Horned Frog* yearbook. Fort Worth, Texas, p. 128.

Tharp, Marie. Tharp with Ocean Floor map. n.d. Photograph. With permission from Marie Tharp estate; Creative Commons. http://alchetron.com/Marie-Tharp-794903-W.

University of Colorado. *Beverly Edith McMahon.* 1943. Photograph. *The Coloradan* yearbook. CU Heritage Center, Boulder, Colorado, p. 86.

University of Iowa. *Louise Anna Fillman.* 1920. Photograph. *Hawkeye* yearbook. Iowa City, Iowa, p. 42.

University of Kentucky. *Louise Freeman Clarkson.* 1932. Photograph. *The Kentuckian* yearbook. Lexington, Kentucky, p. 26.

University of Oklahoma. *Virginia Marcelle Mousley.* 1941. Photograph, *Sooner* yearbook. Western History Collections, University of Oklahoma Libraries, Norman, Oklahoma, p.82.

University of Southern California, *Marie Clark.* 1943. Photograph. *El Rodeo* yearbook. USC Libraries, History Collection. Los Angeles, California, p. 172.

University of Wisconsin. *Katherine F. Greacen Nelson.* 1982. Photograph. Milwaukee Wisconsin. http://nagt-jge.org/doi/pdf/10.5408/0022-1368-27.1.15?code=gete-site. Accessed 01/26/2017.

Whittier Daily News. " Hill Obituary." August 13, 2005. http://www.legacy.com/obituaries/times-standard/obituary-print.aspx?n+marie-joanna-clark-hill. Accessed 09/17/17.

Weir, Max H., III, [stepson of Mary Elizabeth Sheldon Weir]. "Mary Elizabeth Sheldon Weir-1943." *The University of Texas at Austin, Geology Department Newsletter,* 2012, pp. 92-93.

Wilson, Ric. 2009. "Florence Robinson Weber Honorary Membership and Distinguished Service Award." *The Alaska Geological Society Newsletter*, May 2009, pp. 4-5.

Wood, Rosemary. "Attractive Young Woman Who Studies Fossils Does Not Conform to Usual Picture of a Geologist." *The Calgary Herald*, November 6, 1954. p. 6.

Zhen, Ma. "Yang Yi, Pioneer Geologist." *China Petroleum Newspaper*, April 18, 2014. Translated to English by Guonong Hu, geologist, Denver, Colorado, 2014.

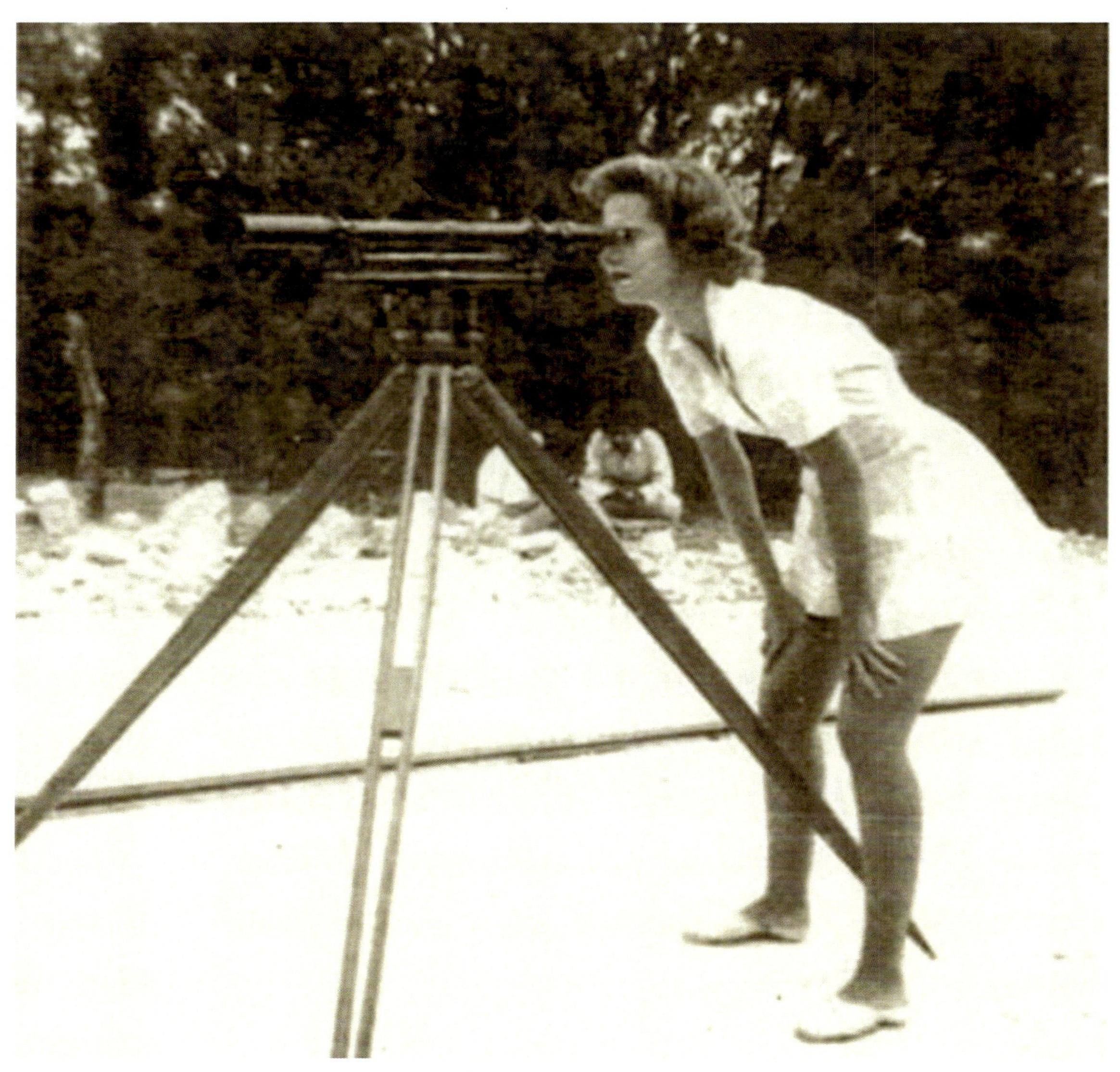

Jackie Covo, geology student, 1943, The University of Texas at Austin. (Photo: Kitty Milliken. 1994. "Participation of Women in the Graduate Program of the Department." The University of Texas Geology Department Newsletter, no. 44, pp. 86-88.

Chapter 11

WWII: Women Who Served Their Country in the Military

Countless female geologists served their country during WWII in notable defense activities. These activities included military service and work related to their geologic expertise or expertise in math and science. These women contributed tirelessly to the war effort and sometimes at great personal risk. We have captured the stories of only a few.

Julia Gardner (1882-1960)

Julia Gardner (see Chapter 6) joined the "Military Geology Unit" of the Geological Survey during WWII (Fig. 1). She described terrain conditions and geologic factors involved in planning, establishing, and maintaining beachheads in many parts of the world. She brought to the task knowledge obtained in her travels overseas and the ability to read fluently in several languages. Although nearing retirement, she worked as hard as any, putting in long hours, sometimes around the clock. Incredibly, Julia used her paleontological skills and pinpointed specific beaches in Japan that were the launch location of balloon-borne incendiary bombs targeting the Pacific Northwest forests of the U.S. She did this by identifying the origin of the shells [fossils] in the sand ballast of the balloons.

Figure 1. Julia Gardner, not only went to France in WWI to nurse, but was in the Military Geology Unit of the USGS during WWII working on beachheads and identifying sediment origins in Japanese incendiary bombs. She went to Japan after the war to help in the mapping project. (Photo: J. P. D. Hull, Denver, Colorado.)

After the war, Julia signed on for a tour of duty in Japan working with Japanese geologists and the mapping unit of the Supreme Allied Command.

Linda Green Miller (1892-1986)

Figure 2. Linda Green Miller served on the Petroleum Administration for War board in Washington, D. C. during WWII. (Photo: The Bernard L. Majewski papers, University of Wyoming, American Heritage History Center.)

Linda Green Miller (see Chapter 2) was appointed to the Petroleum Administration for War (PAW) (Fig. 2). The PAW was established in 1942 to provide the oil needed for the Allied war effort and was abolished in 1945 when the war was over. The U. S. enlisted the aid of American oil companies, all of which responded without hesitation to the challenge of meeting the incredible new demands for fuel and other petroleum-based products.

Linda moved to Washington, D.C. to thoroughly apply herself to the demands of the PAW. Women were rare on this important council: Linda Miller, Virginia Kline (geologist), and Ruth Sheldon Knowles (oil and gas journalist) were the only ones identified in this research.

Ellen Nora Posey Bitgood Roblin (1905-1982)

Figure 3. Ellen Posey Bitgood worked as a chemist in Las Vegas, likely looking for magnesium for airplane parts and bombs. (Photo: Sue Tappeiner, Fanny Carter Edson's granddaughter.)

Ellen Posey Bitgood (see Chapter 5) worked as a chemist in a war plant in Las Vegas during the war (Fig. 3). A likely place where she would have worked was the Chemical Division of the Chlorine Branch of Basic Magnesium Inc. (Sholl Rostine, 2013). This facility was very rapidly built to meet the high demand for magnesium, a lightweight metal used in incendiary bombs and airplane parts.

Virginia Harriett Kline (1910-1959)

Virginia Kline served, with Linda Green Miller, on the Petroleum Administration for War as an Analyst in Chicago (Fig. 4). She had worked with Michigan Oil Exploration Company, Chapman Minerals Company, and Sohio Producing Company as well as consulted and taught. After the war, she signed on with the Illinois Geological Survey in their Oil and Gas Section where she remained working until her death. Virginia Kline was a respected stratigrapher and published extensively during her career.

Figure 4. Virginia Kline served on the Petroleum Administration for War as an Analyst. (Photo: AAPG Bulletin, *v. 44, no. 1, p. 113.*

Margaret Olava Erikson Oros (1912-2007)

Margaret Olava Erickson was the first woman to receive a Bachelor of Arts in geology from University of North Dakota (UND) in Grand Forks in 1939. She did graduate work at UND until 1940. During WWII, she worked for Bendix Aviation in Hollywood, California; the Aluminum Company of America as a spectrographer; and, in 1948, as a chemical engineer (Fig. 5).

Margaret had modest roots and rode a horse to her one-room school house near Sheyenne, North Dakota. One of her relatives tells the story that she picked up a rock when just a child and asked her father about it. He sent it off to the geology department at UND for identification and her love of rocks was born.

After the war, in 1950, Margaret married Peter Oros and they had one son. In that same year, Margaret joined the Illinois Geological Survey in Urbana, Illinois, where she became a petroleum geologist and assistant professor. In 1962, she would change her career one last time to work at the Kansas Geological Survey in Lawrence. Her husband died in 1974 and Margaret continued working until 1978 when she retired from her role as head of the oil and gas division. In her retirement, she revised and published the invaluable book *Oil and Gas in Eastern Kansas.* She was an associate scientist emeritus at Kansas University. In 1990, Margaret Olava Erikson Oros was presented the Sioux Award, the UND Alumni Association's highest honor.

Figure 5. Margaret Olava Oros worked at Bendix Aviation during WW II and the Aluminum Co. of America as a spectrographer. (Photo: Nyle Jordre, RioVista, California, Margaret's nephew.)

Margaret was a member of AAPG for 50 years. She enjoyed traveling the world, and possibly a holdover from her war years, she was an avid ham radio operator.

Helen Reynolds Belyea Bassett, (1913-1986)

Helen Belyea served in WWII from 1943 to 1945 as a Lieutenant in the Women's Royal Canadian Naval Service (WRCNS) tasked to look for submarines offshore Canada (Fig. 6). She trained at HMCS Conestoga in Galt, Ontario, and was later stationed at the special wireless station at HMCS Coverdale in Moncton, New Brunswick. The primary purpose of this station was taking bearings on German U-boats and assisting with search and rescue operations of aircraft in distress. Later, Helen was assigned to Ottawa where she possibly was with the Mercantile Plotting Section of the Trade Division tasked with tracking and recording the movement of every known ship around the world (McLaren, 1987, p. 198-201). Though the women in the WRCNS were paid less than men, they did not complain and they earned a "reputation for conscientious efficiency which can scarcely be exaggerated" (Milner, 2012).

After the War, in 1945, Helen began her career with the Geological Survey of Canada (GSC) in Ottawa as a subsurface stratigrapher. She worked principally on mapping and studying the stratigraphy and resources in the Devonian of the Western Plains and the Northwest Territories. Helen was frustrated at first with the limitations given to women doing fieldwork, but worked to change the system and developed into a formidable field geologist. The GSC was discriminatory in paying women less than men with the same responsibilities but none-the less in 1950, she helped establish the GSC office in Calgary. Helen enjoyed the great number of young geoscientists in the Calgary office, relishing the intellectual stimulation that technical meetings generated.

Figure 6. Helen Belyea served as a Lieutenant in the Woman's Royal Canadian Naval Service during WW II. (Photo: Glenbow Archives pa-2166-132, Glenbow Museum, Calgary, Alberta, Canada.

She became adept at working well samples and doing seismic interpretations to further the understanding of her basin research. A rough day in the field often ended in what she called "crummy" cabins, dressed with a little bottle of scotch that was available for a quick nip to aid in preparation of the day's notes. Helen's fieldwork extended beyond Canada and she traveled worldwide to find other Devonian carbonate models to help unravel the stratigraphy she was investigating.

Helen's B.S. in geology was from the University of New Brunswick (1934), her M.A. from Dalhousie University (1936), and her PhD was from Northwestern (1939). She was also the recipient of numerous scientific awards and honorary degrees.

Helen Belyea was an AAPG member for 19 years. She enjoyed the outdoors, horsemanship, skiing, and driving her little red sports car to her cottage on Lake Windermere as often as possible. (O'Donnell, 2000, pp. 166-169.)

Elizabeth "Betty" Anne Baker Elliott (1918-2001)

Betty Anne Baker volunteered for service and was employed in Seattle by the Corps of Engineers, Alaska Defense command, as a civil engineer (Fig. 7). This position directly related to finding water supplies for troops, testing gun emplacement sites, and assessing airport runway stabilization. She also trained Army engineers to utilize native terrain to establish temporary runways in forward positions. The Alaska Defense command had thirty-nine projects in three areas: Aleutian-12, coastal-15 and interior-11 (Bush, 1976).

Figure 7. Betty Anne Elliott volunteered during WW II and served in the Alaska Defense command. (Photo: Sooner *yearbook, 1940, p. 150, Western History Collections, University of Oklahoma Libraries, Norman, Oklahoma.)*

Betty was born in 1918 in the small town of Clinton, Oklahoma; the daughter of a prominent physician. She excelled in sports and academics and was valedictorian of her high school class. At the University of Oklahoma, Betty initially enrolled in a pre-med curriculum. However, through her friendship with Dr. Charles Decker, one of the founders of AAPG, she was encouraged to pursue the science of geology. Dr. Decker was an inspiration to many women in geology. Betty participated in the first presentations of electric logging and aerial photography ever made in a university setting. She received her B.S. in geology in 1940; one of two women in a class of forty.

After graduation, Betty moved to the University of Colorado (CU) to pursue a graduate teaching fellowship in micropaleontology. She reached back to her college friends in Oklahoma to acquire micropaleontology samples for her new micropaleontologic library at CU, enabling her Colorado colleagues and future generations to teach and conduct research.

World War II and Betty's volunteer service interrupted her quest for a master's degree. During the war, in 1941, while in Washington State, she married Guy Lee Elliott, a budding physician. After her service, they returned to Colorado where Betty worked in Denver for the U.S. Geological Survey (USGS) as a micropaleontologist and stratigrapher. She was assigned to White River Plateau and "Maroon" problems, where her war service photo interpretation skills were used once again.

When Guy took a position in New York City, Betty moved, too, and started looking for a job. Finding a job was not easy in the Post WWII years, but Betty had one contact, Gail Molten, Senior Vice President of Chase Manhattan Bank. Molten had met Betty at the USGS and was impressed back then, and he offered her a position in the New York office as a financial analyst. When Molten learned Betty missed her work in geology, he recommended her to Fred Wilcox at Socony-Vacuum headquarters. Wilcox was the exploration manager for the Western Hemisphere and Betty quickly became Regional Geologist for Southern Europe.

After her husband died prematurely, Betty asked to be relocated back to Oklahoma where she still had family. Resettling in Oklahoma in 1960-with Socony-Vacuum, now Mobil Oil, she worked on the stratigraphy of the Permian-Pennsylvanian boundary, Springer sandstones, and the Arkoma Basin. She excelled at sample identification and, more unusually for those days, did wellsite work (sat wells). She later recalled to younger geologists that she never had a problem working in the field, she thought, because hard work and competence were respected. Occasionally a tool pusher would even "spruce up" the mud logging trailer when she was scheduled to arrive on the wellsite.

In 1976, Betty was transferred to Dallas to help Mobil evaluate offshore Atlantic, East Coast Triassic Basins, and Central America. Mobil was establishing a training program for young geologists and Betty was again instrumental in guiding and training young geologic minds. She was affectionately nicknamed "Aunt Betty" and found the experience to be one of the most satisfying assignments of her career; those under her tutelage had tremendous respect for her.

Betty retired from Mobil in the mid-1980s and opened a consulting office in Dallas where she remained active professionally. Her nephew, Ken Houck, described her as somewhat of a "serious, tough woman, romantic, well-appointed, polite, completely honest, but tough as they come" (personal communication with Valary Schulz). She was a delightful fixture at industry events with her easy, pealing laughter, and flaming red hair, captivating both young and old.

Betty worked extensively with her professional societies and was recognized as the first female AAPG Pioneer Award Recipient in 1999, Honorary Member of the Dallas Geological Society, and Fellow in the GSA. Her outreach extended to high schools where she introduced classes to geology and the use of a microscope. She also conducted field trips for Girl Scouts and other groups. Betty was an AAPG member for 47 years and described geology as "a treasure hunt for life." (Betty's biographical information was provided by Valary Schulz, who wrote her citation in 1999 for the AAPG Pioneer Award.)

Elizabeth (Liz) Anne Watson (1915 – 2000)

Figure 8. Liz Watson, first woman hired at Union Oil, loved her field geology. (Photo source: Courtesy of The WASP Archive, Texas Woman's University, Denton, Texas.)

In 1939, Elizabeth "Liz" Watson was the first woman to be hired by Union Oil in California after she received her bachelor's and master's degrees from Stanford University (1938, 1939) (Figs. 8 and 9). She was also a trail blazer in WWII. Already a pilot when the war broke out, Liz took a leave from Union Oil and joined the Women's Airforce Service Pilots (WASPs) as part of the 2536th Army Air Forces Base Units (AAFBU) class 44 W-5 (Fig. 10). Liz was stationed in Aloe Army Field in Victoria, Texas, and Laredo Army Air Base in Laredo, Texas, where she towed targets with the AT-6 TT and B-26 and also flew the P-40 and P-63 (http://twudigital.cdmhost.com/cdm/).

Figure 9. Fieldwork in California for Liz's master's thesis. (Photo: Courtesy of The WASP Archive, Texas Woman's University, Denton, Texas.)

It is not commonly known that 38 women died in the process of ferrying planes during the war. "... they flew whatever they were asked to fly, and dealt with balky aircraft, malfunctioning equipment and occasionally deadly crashes" (Rickman, 2016). When they died, the military took no responsibility for them. Their friends and families had to pay for transporting their bodies home and for burial and with no recognition. They only were given veteran status in 1977 and, in 2002, they were affirmed as eligible for interment at Arlington—but the Army immediately overturned that decision. On the WASP website (http://wingsacrossamerica.us/wasp/stats.htm) is a comparison of the costs for flight training between men and women. Women paid all their own transportation costs, paid for their own uniforms, were charged for their room and board, and had no insurance (compared to $10,000 for each man). This was truly a dedicated group of women.

Another female geologist, Virginia Clair, of Wichita Falls, Texas, was also a WASP (43-4), though less is known about her career in geology. She was an AAPG member from 1954 to 1981. The North Texas Geological Society mentions her briefly, "After the war she worked for a time as a geologist for Reno Oil Company (Gee, 1976)."

After Liz was deactivated and returned to her job with Union Oil, she continued her military service when she obtained a civilian instrument rating and took Civil Air Patrol training. Liz remained in touch with her WASP cohorts at least until 1968 when she attended that year's reunion (1968 June WASP Newsletter, 44-5).

Figure 10. Elizabeth A. "Liz" Watson. In the WASP during WW II, she ferried planes across the continent for the war effort. (Photo: Courtesy of The WASP Archive, Texas Woman's University, Denton, Texas.)

Liz retired from Union Oil in the late 1970s but continued to mentor young women on careers in the oil and gas industry. She graciously volunteered to send photos and encouragement to young women considering majors in geology. In a letter to one young woman, Liz says, "When I first went to work for Union Oil Co. of California in 1941, nobody had heard of 'women's lib.' For years, I was the Company's only female geologist. Now there are dozens of women geologists, geophysicists, etc. on the Company payroll and their opportunities are unlimited." (Fig. 11) Liz goes on to give the young woman advice on which groups to contact, among the list was AAPG. She always ended her letters with "Good luck!"

Figure 11. Liz Watson in the University of Wisconsin field camp, circa 1938 near Lander, Wyoming. Liz and several other female students sun bathed on the outcrop, her joie de vivre always apparent. (Watson archives, American Heritage Center, University of Wyoming.)

Elizabeth Anne Watson was an outdoors person all the way. She played tennis, skied, and was also an avid photographer (1968 June WASP Newsletter). She was a member of AAPG for 40 years.

Helen Nina Tappan (1917-2004)

Helen Tappan Loeblich, world renowned micropaleontologist (B. S. 1937, M.S. 1939, University of Oklahoma; PhD, 1942, University of Chicago), answered the call to fill academic and government positions when needed during WWII (Fig. 12). Her first effort for the war in 1942-43 occurred when her husband, Alfred Loeblich, joined the army. Helen took over his teaching responsibilities at Tulane University, becoming the first female geology instructor there, and she juggled that with the care of their first child. 1942 was also the year she joined AAPG.

Figure 12. Helen Tappan Loeblich was in the Fuels Division of the Navy Oil Unit, USGS, during WWII. (Photo: Sooner *yearbook, 1939, p.25. Western History Collections, University of Oklahoma Libraries, Norman, Oklahoma.)*

Helen's second war effort came in 1943-44 when she joined the Fuels Division of the Navy Oil Unit, U.S. Geological Survey (USGS) contributing and working in that Division until her second child was born in 1944. From 1947 to 1956 she worked in the Alaskan Branch of the USGS.

When Alfred took a position in California with Chevron, Helen joined the geology faculty at the University of California, Los Angeles (UCLA). The University catalogue ironically stated that women were not allowed to have geology as a major. Her memorial states,

> Helen graciously dealt with prejudice against women in geology for years... at the USGS she was told she would not have a secretary because she could type for herself! ... [At UCLA] she obtained numerous scientific grants, in fact, more than any other professor in the department at the time. However, she was the only Lecturer in the department from 1958–66, hired on an annual basis, at lower salary, without benefits, a practice that continues with academic women today. As a proponent for women's rights and the Equal Rights Amendment, Helen finally decided that she had had enough of this discrimination. She wrote to the Chancellor and resigned. Fearing the loss of thousands of dollars of her grant monies, the UCLA Regents, within days, held a special meeting and immediately made her a Full Professor in 1968 (Loeblich, 2004, p. 86-89).

Helen's memorial aptly described her quiet but formidable nature and her renaissance abilities. She was fluent in many languages and for her micropaleontology research she often learned the basics of many Eastern European languages. That, coupled with her ability with Russian (she had the Cyrillic alphabet on her typewriter), placed both Alfred and her on the CIA "watch list." Consequently, they were subject to annual CIA investigations for several years during the Cold War. (Loeblich, 2004, p. 86-89)

Helen Laura Foster (1919-present)

On May 2, 2016, a large, white SUV pulled into the hotel parking lot in Carson City, Nevada, and we waited for Helen Foster to alight for our first meeting. When the door opened, a tiny little woman, no more than four feet ten inches tall, climbed out of the cab (Fig. 13). Her face as smooth as a teenager's except for a few smile wrinkles on either side of her mouth. With an abundance of energy and twinkling eyes, Helen still exuded her fearless and competent nature. She walks at least two miles a day and lives in her own home. Helen is 97 this year and has recently successfully rehabilitated from a broken hip. Helen was interviewed for five and a half hours and wasn't near fatigue. Articulate, she spoke with enthusiasm and amazing recall of her full and adventurous life.

Figure 13. Helen Foster, May 2, 2016 shows Robbie Gries some of her photos from Japan in the late 1940s and 1950s. (Photo: Matt Randolph.)

Figure 14. Helen sitting on the board in front of her family's homemade "camp car" with her parents, baby sister and a friend in 1924. Her father (middle) built the "RV" long before they were invented for the public and they camped for the summer in the northern peninsula of Michigan north of Seney. Note their Ford, purchased from Henry himself. (Photo: Helen Foster.)

Born in 1919 in Adian, Michigan, Helen has memories of her mom and dad telling stories about driving to Detroit every year or so to buy a new Ford from their friend, Henry—that would be Henry Ford (Fig. 14). While she was in high school, Helen's life changed quickly when her father died, and the family was left with few resources during the Great Depression.

Helen earned a scholarship to the University of Michigan and supplemented her living with odd jobs. She roomed each year in a facility with other girls who had to work and needed inexpensive rooms. They all found ways and means to garner the least expensive meals. The job that earned Helen the main meal of the day was helping to serve lunch to a grade school class and watch over them while they napped, if they napped. Another job was part of Roosevelt's National Youth Administration (NYA) program. Helen said she failed dismally on yet another job when she tried waiting tables.

Helen's decision to major in geology started when she studied the college course catalog to choose a required science class. She and her mother were ardent readers of books and articles on exploration and travel, especially those by Roy Chapman Andrews; adventure was in their blood. Her mother suggested geology and, after two weeks in class, Helen was totally hooked. But, because jobs were scarce for women, Helen thought the practical path was to get an education degree, too, so she could get a job teaching.

Combining geology and education caused some difficulties, notably that she was pushed to the biology field camp instead of the geology field camp in the spring of 1939. Helen really wanted to attend geology camp in Wyoming, so she found a professor in the geology department who she thought she could persuade to sign a paper authorizing her enrollment. After considerable cajoling, he signed the paper and Helen slipped into camp. No one questioned the authorization, even though the professor was not the proper person to give permission. Geology field camp was all Helen expected it to be, and though she did not realize it at the time, it was the beginning of her life-long career as a field geologist (Fig. 15).

Figure 15. Helen followed by students trying to ford the upper Hoback River, Wyoming, 1943. (Photo: Helen Foster.)

After receiving her bachelor's degree, Helen taught for a year to earn money for graduate school. Helen returned to the University of Michigan in 1942 where she worked for Dr. K. K. Landis, Chairman of the Geology Department. She recalled,

> One day he came into the office and said that he had an idea and that he'd like to know what I thought about it. He did this often, but this time he was especially enthusiastic. It was war time. Pearl Harbor had been bombed less than a year before. Men were disappearing daily from the University, either being drafted or enlisting. Students in all departments were becoming scarce. Food, gasoline and tires were being rationed. It was doubtful as to whether the University could carry on many of the normal activities, including field trips and field camps. The U. S. needed everything that the petroleum companies could provide, but their men were being drafted. Questions arose as to how long the Department of Geology could continue to function with so few students. How could they justify and run a summer field camp?
>
> Landes told me that he had an idea which would help the department, encourage women students in geology, and benefit the country while it helped the petroleum industry. "How about a concentrated program in petroleum geology, primarily for women, that would provide adequately trained personnel for the petroleum companies and would do it quickly?" he postulated (personal communication).

The brainstorm soon became a reality. The women who participated were commonly referred to as "*The Petroleum Girls*" (Fig. 16). Foster continued,

Figure 16. "The Petroleum Girls" of the University of Michigan, 1943, were featured in the LSA Magazine in Spring 2002, p. 47-48. Helen Foster is 5th from the right in the front row. Marie Tharp (Chapter 10) is 3rd from the right in the second row. (Photo: Helen Foster.)

> ...Nine women began Landes' program in the spring of 1943 and all nine finished and received certificates in February 1944. The participants had an extra-long session at Camp Davis [Wyoming], taking the regular 8-weeks field course and then adding an additional 4 weeks of fieldwork. Michigan could keep its summer camp going in 1943 because of this program. We received extra gasoline rations and could buy some tires for the station wagons. At least three graduates of the program went directly to work for oil companies, and one for the USGS Others worked later in their careers for oil companies; some went into other fields of geology after the war or continued their education in geology or other fields.

Figure 17. Helen's overnight field camp while doing PhD field work in Wyoming, 1945. The 1937 Ford she purchased from Henry Ford's nephew under wartime restrictions. (Photo: Helen Foster.)

Helen used Camp Davis as headquarters for her graduate fieldwork in Wyoming's Gros Ventre range. Following family tradition, Helen bought herself a very used 1937 Ford for her fieldwork, this time from Henry Ford's nephew (Fig. 17).

Oil companies were interested in Helen's work, and she enjoyed going to AAPG meetings so she joined the association as a student. She completed her master's and PhD by 1946 when the war was over; however, many employment options for women were also eliminated with the end of the war. Helen took a job as instructor in geology at Wellesley College. She had taught for a year and a half when a friend in the USGS wrote to Helen and pleaded with her to come to Japan and take over her job with the Military Geology Branch of the USGS. It appears Helen's friend wanted to return to the States to get married and her USGS boss would not let her go unless she found a replacement!

Helen still had another semester to teach on her Wellesley contract and set the request aside. However, when she mentioned the opportunity in passing to her Wellesley colleagues they encouraged her to accept. They promised to cover her spring classes and she was persuaded to go. The employment process was cumbersome and took months to get through the government vetting process, but finally, in April of 1948, she was flying over the Pacific Ocean. The Military Air Transport (MATS) DC4, originated in Fairfield-Suisan Army Air Base (now Travis Air Force Base) in California, and island hopped to Hawaii, Johnston Island (an atoll), Kwajaein, Guam, and finally, Tokyo. Inside, the DC4 was configured for military transport, not comfort; Helen and the other mostly GI passengers had to sit on a canvas bench along the side of the fuselage for the entire trip.

Except for work on the disastrous Fukui Earthquake, which struck the Hokuriku region June 28, 1948 shortly after her arrival in Japan, Helen's first year was spent gathering and compiling scientific literature and data on the geology of the former Japanese Mandated Islands. She visited universities throughout the country and worked with Japanese professors and experts. An annotated bibliography of geologic and soils literature of the western North Pacific islands published later in English embodied much of this work.

While in Tokyo, Helen recalled that every morning at 11:00 am, General MacArthur would arrive at his headquarters in his impressive military limousine and, every day, a huge crowd of Japanese would be there to have a chance to see him. Helen remembered that he was very respected and admired and she, too, occasionally joined the crowds to watch his morning appearance.

Figure 18. Helen wearing a yukata *provided by the Inn where she was staying. The tradition was to change into the robe once settled in your room and use it for trips to the bath. (Photo: Helen Foster.)*

Helen's commitment to the Japan assignment was for one year, but after a year, the USGS wanted her to extend her stay (Fig. 18). Not knowing her fate, Helen had been trying to find a teaching position back in the U.S. during the year she was in Tokyo. As luck would have it, an offer from Northern Michigan University at Houghton came the day after she had signed with the USGS to continue work in Japan. Unknown to Helen, her life course had now been set, and the rest of her geologic career would be with the USGS. When Helen returned to Japan, she had insisted to the Branch Chief that it was on the condition she could have some time to get into the field on a geologic project of her own choosing. She officially chose mapping ash deposits from Mt. Fuji; however, on weekends she took up the "hobby" of climbing and observing volcanoes all over Japan.

An important "hobby" volcano was Mihara Yama on the island of O Shima, south of Japan. Commonly on Friday nights she would board a small ship, along with many Japanese sightseers and sometimes a fellow geologist or friend, and sail to O Shima. Helen would spend the weekend observing and photographing the volcano; she was intrigued and excited when the volcano was erupting and pouring hot, glowing lava over the sides of the crater and super-hot lava (bombs) were being hurled at her.

Figure 19. Helen sitting on recently cooled basalt, at Mihara Yama, 1951, after one of many explosive eruptions. (Photo: Helen Foster.)

In September, 1952, a military plane reported seeing a large area of discolored water south of Tokyo near the Izu Islands. The USGS office staff became excited because they realized that the pilots might have seen a submarine volcano that was erupting or starting to erupt. Because any such activities are always of concern to the Military, as consultants to the Army Engineers, the USGS staff suggested flying there to investigate.

In time, they were informed that a plane would be made available and Sherman Neuschel, USGS-Branch Chief, and Helen headed for the airport (Fig. 19). Helen and her Branch Chief were greatly surprised when, instead of some ordinary military plane, they saw a very spiffy-looking plane with large, individual, plush, swivel chairs—each by a clean window. They later learned that it was one of General MacArthur's special planes. (Fig. 20)

Along with some military personnel, Helen and Neuschel flew to the site and observed and photographed the large area of discolored water. They were well aware from pumice floating on the ocean surface that it was an erupting submarine volcano. Later it became known as Myojin-sho. For their photography, the pilot was instructed to fly around the margin of the disturbance not over it. At first, he did so, but then to their horror, he flew directly over the area for what seemed to Helen like a very long time. Fortunately, the plane escaped without harm. Later that same day, the Kaiyo Maru, a ship belonging to the Japanese Hydrographic Department with scientists aboard, was destroyed when it sailed over the area. The submarine volcano delivered a massive eruption, destroying the ship and all the passengers. Helen knew she had been very lucky on the plane.

Figure 20. Helen descending from one of General Douglas McArthur's planes after a trip to see Myojin-sho, a submarine volcano that erupted in 1952. Behind her is Sherman Neuschel, USGS branch chief. (Photo: Helen Foster.)

Another volcanic project she worked on was Mt. Asama, an active volcano where the Japanese had special scientific activities in process. The U.S. wanted to do military mountain training there and it resulted in some serious conflicts of interest. Another time, there was an unexplained explosion on Iwo Jima and Helen flew there with fellow geologist Gilbert Corbin to investigate. Apparently, the explosion resulted from the sudden release of an underground accumulation of steam that was under high pressure beneath artificial fill.

Figure 21. Helen with adopted friend, Oscar, 1955, on Ishigaki-shima, the army compound where USGS mappers lived on the sandy beach of a lagoon. Oscar was a war dog left behind by the Japanese. (Photo: Helen Foster.)

When more islands in the Ryukyu chain were chosen for further mapping, Helen became Chief of the Ishigaki field party (Fig. 21). For a year and a half, she lived and worked on the island. She had a small bungalow, which contained her office and bedroom, on the beach of a lagoon and, for companionship, she inherited an abandoned Japanese war dog, Oscar. She hired a 16-year-old girl, who learned English from missionaries, to be her field assistant.

Figure 22. Helen in the center of the back seat with office friends on a lunch hour ride in Tokyo in an antique Franklin. (Photo: Helen Foster.)

Some of the dangers on the island were the poisonous habu, a snake that was largely nocturnal and for which there was no antivenin; also, the fist-sized Yamangi, a gray moth larva that camouflaged with tree bark and was dreaded by the natives because of the painful reaction it caused when touched. Sea snakes were poisonous but rarely bit, and Helen only brushed up against one once while swimming there. Aware of the dangers, Helen also relished the adventure. One time while mapping in the jungle on the western part of the island, she and her young assistant got lost and did not make it back to their car before dark. Some of the local people noticed they were still out and formed a search group with lighted torches. They found the two women and led them back to the village. Helen said she had not been frightened, only excited that she had fulfilled another dream—that of seeing the jungle at night with its many phosphorescent insects and other phosphorescent inhabitants.

On one occasion, Helen was requisitioned to cover the Military Geology on Okinawa while the geologists there took a brief leave. A notable difference in Okinawa was being issued a gun and told to carry it every time she left her quarters as there were dangerous, renegade Philippine soldiers on the island. Helen thought it amusing to check in her gun at the Officer's club before each meal, and reclaim it to walk back to her Quonset. In all her time in Japan, it was the only place where there was some danger. In Tokyo and everywhere else she went, she felt safe and free to move about anywhere, anytime, day or night (Fig. 22).

Helen was not, by far, the only woman geologist to serve in the Military Geology Branch in Tokyo. Among the earliest geologists was another of pioneer AAPG member, Julia Gardner (see Chapter 6). Helen recalled hearing of Julia with considerable humor, describing her as very independent and strong-willed. In Julia's eagerness to help Japanese geologists. she sometimes broke the military regulations; her unforgivable crime seems to have been buying her "allotment" of cigarettes from the PX and giving them to a Japanese geologist she knew well. Julia was very pointedly asked to stop more than once but kept on; as a result, the Branch was forced to arrange for her return to the U.S.

Helen laughs at her travels with Japanese geologists, "About my experiences in Japan—I used to say that I had 'slept with every notable Japanese geologist'. When I went on field trips with Japanese geologists we would spend nights in local Japanese inns. Usually there was one very large room and quilted mats would be laid out in rows on the tatami floor. We would all sleep together in this room, many men and one woman, me."

Figure 23. The Annual Meeting of the Geological Society of Japan in the early 1950s. Helen is in the "honored" seat front row middle. The highest-ranking geologists always sat in the front rows and the students were relegated to the back rows. (Photo: Helen Foster.)

Figure 24. Helen at a conference with Japanese colleagues. (Photo: Helen Foster.)

Helen attended many field trips and Geological Society of Japan meetings. She was always treated as an honored guest, which meant when the photos were taken she had to sit "front and center" (Fig. 23). The culture of Japanese intelligentsia demanded that geologic gurus, sages and experts be in the front rows and students the rear. The Japanese had no female geologists; however, because she worked for years with the professors in many of the universities, she thinks the schools were somewhat influenced to accept women into the profession. Two women acquired their PhDs in geology while Helen was in Japan (Fig. 24).

On one field trip, their group of geologists stopped at a hot springs resort which bragged about having separate men and women's bathing facilities. This was very unusual, as bathing facilities were mostly together. So, being dirty and grimy from the day in the field, she was very eager to take advantage of the baths. Helen got into her robe and went to the door marked in English "Women," right beside the door marked for "Men." She opened the door and saw the women's long, empty, steaming-hot pool and, with it, a huge, long glass window separating the women's and men's pools, and she was looking right at all the naked men. She quickly backed out and did not get her steaming bath that night.

Another funny adventure that could have ended badly occurred when she and fellow geologist, Arnold Mason, decided to have a look at Mt. Fuji over a weekend. They drove up to about 7000 feet and parked at a meteorological station where they could access the main trail. It was off-season for climbing so they had the mountain to themselves. The weather began to worsen, getting cloudier and misty, but Arnold wanted to get to the top, and she wanted to go around to the side and look at a cinder cone. As they only had one map, they decided that Arnold would take it, thinking she might have better visibility at the lower elevation. She took a good look at the map before he left and headed toward the cinder cone.

Helen recalled,

> The weather was miserable. I got to the cinder cone and looked around for a while and decided I should head back. I didn't think that I had to hurry because I figured that Arnold had the longer hike. I was chilly, wet and miserable and I had lost a lot of elevation going to the cinder cone. The only trail going back to the main trail was very much lower in elevation and thus much longer in distance as the mountain spreads out rapidly as you approach the base. I had hoped that there was possibly another cross trail in between, but that was not the case. I wished that I had the map so that I could see just what the distances were.
>
> It got later and later and no cross trail showed up. I had picked up a trail heading down, but as I went down I knew I was getting farther and farther from the car. It got later and was getting dark. I began to come to fields and other signs of civilization. At about dark I came to a building and peaked in the window. A group of men only in loin clothes were making merry around a roaring fire after a hard day's work in the fields. I wanted to ask them about the trail, but figured that I would probably just mess things up as I wouldn't be able make them understand. Thus, I left that wonderful warm fire behind and went on, figuring there would be more civilization soon.
>
> The trail went on and on through fields and across gullies, but no cross trail. Finally, I came to a small village. I remembered from the map that this was where a cross trail that I knew about passed through to a point near the Meteorological Station. But I realized that I needed to be sure that I got the correct trail. Now there were many small trails showing up leading to unknown points. I picked out a well-lighted building in which I could see several grown men and surprised them when I knocked on the door. After a great deal trying with my meager Japanese mixed with their almost complete lack of English I got them to understand that I wanted them to show me the correct trail to the Meteorological Station. It was finally decided that

one of the villagers would show me the way because there were many trails and they understood that in the dark I might get lost. One unlucky villager was chosen to accompany me, but I had to wait awhile as he got ready.

Finally, the villager was ready with his foul weather gear, his knapsack, gun, and umbrella and silently we headed off on the trail. He led forth with his umbrella giving him good protection from the light rain. After several miles of silent steady walking through mostly lightly wooded country he stopped and said to me "*Choto matte, kudasai*" ("Wait a minute, please"). He handed me the umbrella and motioned for me to hold it over him. I dutifully held the umbrella over him and to my surprise, he proceeded to unbutton his pants. Then he leisurely relieved himself, buttoned up his pants, took the umbrella back, and off we went for many more silent miles. I thought, "It was a pleasure to have been of service!"

We finally reached the end of the trail and were met by Arnold and numerous others that he had pressed into service to find me. We still had a long drive to find warm food and dry clothes.

Hirohito's Marine Laboratory

Helen remembered,

It was common for the Tokyo Office of the USGS (Pacific Geological Surveys—the name of the USGS office in Tokyo changed several times while I was there) to have distinguished visitors and short time workers, advisors, etc. I believe that it was in the mid 1950's when Dr. K. O. Emery from the University of Southern California paid us a visit bringing with him his recently completed first underwater scientific marine movie film. It was widely acclaimed in the scientific field and the first of its kind. We all enjoyed and appreciated the opportunity to view the film, and, knowing that the Emperor of Japan, Hirohito, was himself a marine biologist, it was boldly suggested that he might like to see the film.

Figure 25. Helen and others standing in front of the Emperor's Laboratory, 1953. K. O. Emery is in the light suit. (Photo: Helen Foster.)

Through proper military channels it was arranged to ask the Emperor if he would like to see the film. We received a very definite "Yes" reply and the film was delivered and viewed by the Emperor. He was so interested and pleased he asked if the film could be retained long enough for his son, Akihito, to see it. This was done, and soon we received word that the Emperor would like to show his appreciation by inviting us to visit the palace grounds. Any one visiting Tokyo can't miss seeing the large moat encircled area with its impressive stone walls. However, we knew that inside, there was no fancy castle or palace because, contrary to all military orders, a wayward, undisciplined GI had bombed the Imperial grounds and many buildings had burned during the war.

Figure 26. Helen in Emperor Hirohito's private science laboratory. (Photo: Helen Foster.)

We eagerly accepted the invitation and our party consisted of Dr. Emery and Charles Johnson, myself, and Ted Sumida as translator, from our Tokyo office (Fig. 25). On arrival within the palace grounds, we were informed that the Emperor could not meet with us because of an unexpected meeting with an ambassador, but that we would be shown the Imperial grounds. There were two highlights for me. First, we were privileged to visit the Emperor's scientific laboratory (Fig. 26). We saw his beautiful huge Nikon microscope specially constructed for him. Then we viewed many of his personal laboratory notebooks (very impressive). The laboratory was complete in every way including white-coated assistants. Next, the stables interested me most. It was lunch time and the magnificent horses were being fed, so I have said ever since that I had lunch with the Emperor's horses.

Meeting the Emperor

The first time that I saw the Emperor was about 1949. It was the opening of Parliament. I had met a lady who was one of the few lady members of that august body and she invited me to come with her. The parliament building itself is impressive and (at that time and probably still is) one of the best engineered and constructed buildings for earthquake resistance in the world. The members of parliament, guests, etc., were gathered in a huge crowd in front of the building and much to my surprise ended up in an orderly procession into the building. Members of parliament were dressed in many different ways showing their affiliations and honors. My lady friend wore her PhD cap and gown. It was a huge noisy crowd inside and my friend tried to tell me what was going on but I only remember seeing the Emperor. He was seated high up and rather distant from where I was, but to me he looked sort of frail and scared.

Later, I had the opportunity to meet the Emperor in person. Professor Hisashi Kuno of Tokyo University became a very close friend. He was receiving an award which was presented to him by the Emperor and he invited me to the ceremony. After receiving the award, Kuno introduced me to the Emperor. He seemed very friendly, likeable and interested and understanding of Kuno's work and award. I was surprised as to how at ease Kuno was with him and how they both sort of acted as though they were on the same level.

Adventures

Helen worked in Japan from 1948 to 1957, with just occasional trips back to the states. Her flights to and from Japan and around the Japanese islands were always an adventure. Their DC3 was converted to a three-engine aircraft by mounting a third engine on the nose. Almost always on the long flights across the Pacific, they lost at least one engine, and occasionally two! Helen remembers once losing two engines between Iwojima and Guam and it was feared they would have to ditch the plane. Somehow, the crew kept the third engine going and they limped into Guam safely.

Figure 27. Bamboo raft on which the cooking was done while Helen was on a geologic field trip down the Mai Ping River in Thailand after the Pacific Science Congress in Bangkok, 1957. (Photo: Helen Foster.)

Another story Helen tells about her travels was about rafting the Mai Ping River in Thailand. She remembers,

> Following the successful conclusion of the Pacific Science Congress in Bangkok which I had just attended in 1957, I joined a field trip to see the geology along the Mai Ping River in Thailand (Fig. 27). It was the last opportunity to see this geology because a dam was soon to be constructed and the geology would be drowned.
>
> We flew north to Ching Mai and enjoyed a short

visit there while our bamboo rafts were being constructed. The plan was to harvest the bamboo here where it was cheap and plentiful. The rafts would be quickly put together with all native materials, we would float the river, and then the rafts would be disassembled and the bamboo sold. It would bring a good price to the south where we would end our journey. In Ching Mai, good drinking water was scarce so I learned about sipping cool refreshing coconut milk from a hole in a freshly picked green coconut. It was great!

Finally, our rafts were ready to go. Each raft carried four passengers plus two pole men. Two people sat on the front of the raft and two on the back, riding just barely above water level. There was a thatched roofed shelter between and once you were afloat there was no connection or communication between the front and rear passengers. There was a little patch on the side of the shelter halfway between the front and back which could be reached by carefully picking one's way along the side of the raft. This was where there was an enclosed hole which served as a toilet.

One raft was designed differently and was the cook raft. It carried the cooks and all the food supplies. The food supplies included live chickens which were killed as needed. Cooking went on while floating the river as well as when we were tied up at shore. The only communication between rafts was by the leaders who had a motor boat and flitted between rafts. When we needed to go to shore to look at outcrops we were ferried in the motor boat.

Elizabeth Shepherd (wife of oceanographer Fran Shepherd) and myself were the only women so we sat together on the front of one raft. We enjoyed each other's company and solved our rafting problems (which were numerous) together. We never so much as even washed our faces for the entire trip. The water of the Mai Ping was filthy, filthy, filthy. There were dead pigs and other decayed animals floating along in it. Even as far north on the river as we were, it was terrible, and it got worse as we went down stream. Elizabeth had some 3 inch pre-moistened squares that were made for removing make up and we used them for what little washing we could do of our faces. Some of the group, particularly the Australians, didn't seem to mind going into the water. Ugh!

During the day, we floated leisurely most of the time, but there were a couple of rapids which were exciting—the rafts were handled only by the two pole men, one at each end of the raft. Hence, the rafts were not very maneuverable. The chickens would squawk, the pans would rattle, and we would hold our breath as the cook raft careened past the rocks (Fig. 28).

Occasionally we would see natives along the shore. They would beg us for malaria medicine. Some would have live snakes for sale or trade. Many had belts and trinkets made from snake skins which they tried to sell us. It was very sad to see the very poor and sick villagers along the river. You sometimes wondered how anyone could live along such a filthy river and not be sick. However, often they were shouting, dancing, and eager for visitors.

At night, we would pull up along the shore and the cooks would put the finishing touches on the evening meal. One meal, prepared by our leaders, I especially liked. It was considered a hunter's fare. Green bamboo stalks were hollowed. Then a little coconut milk poured in the bottom of the shoot followed by a layer of uncooked rice. This procedure continued, one layer after another, until the shoot was filled. Then it was cooked over the camp fire. I would love to have some today.

Figure 28. Floating down the Mai Ping River, Thailand. (Photo: Helen Foster.)

At night, also, there would be monkeys in the trees. We were continually listening for wildlife, especially tigers. Theoretically guards were posted to watch for tigers, but I am not sure how effective this was. Although we saw and heard a little wildlife, the journey produced more rocks than animals, as was expected. One of the geologists once asked a leader if they had any problems with snakes and if they were afraid of them while doing fieldwork. The leader replied, "Only the human ones." This northern part of Thailand jungle was close to Thailand's unsecured borders and was a very dangerous area.

Our trip ended in a busy area where they were beginning dam construction. Our rafts were disassembled and the bamboo sold. We made our way back to Bangkok very happy and very dirty. I now remember almost nothing about the geology that I saw and learned on the trip, but I have many other great memories and made some lasting friendships with Thai geologists and Elizabeth Shepherd (personal communication).

Back in the U.S.

Upon returning to the United States in 1959, Helen spent some time writing up all her reports in Washington, D.C. She was also asked by AAPG to write a report on the Japanese petroleum situation for one of the annual reports in the Bulletin and gave several papers at AAPG meetings.

In 1960, Helen joined the Alaska Terrain and Permafrost Section of the Military Geology Branch, and began geologic work in Alaska (Fig. 29). This included fieldwork and map preparation for the Army Winter Maneuvers. When the USGS discontinued this work for the Army Engineers in 1965, Helen transferred to the Branch of Alaskan Geology in Menlo Park, California, where she spent the rest of her mapping career, and which she described as, "lots of fun."

The exciting part was flying into the field on helicopters that would drop her off and return to pick her up at the end of the day; however, sometimes they did not return that day. Helen and a field assistant would have to spend the night by a campfire hoping they would get picked up the next day; they did have radio contact most of the time.

One time, the helicopter broke down before picking up Helen and a colleague. It was chilly and rainy and they spent the night sitting by their campfire. They had only a little emergency food in their packs that they rationed

Figure 29. Helen checking a typical high point in the Big Delta quadrangle, Alaska, 1978. (Photo: Helen Foster.)

based on a pickup early the next day. Morning came and went and no helicopter. Their scraps of food were almost gone. They radioed the pilot to find out when he was coming and to hurry. Helen said to the pilot, "We are eating our LAST meal." He radioed back "I certainly hope not!" They got picked up before nightfall.

The first five years Helen worked in Alaska, she was still in the Military Branch of the USGS and the military provided the helicopters for their fieldwork. The Military often used their flights as opportunities for pilot training as the co-pilot was commonly less experienced than the pilot. Long flights to and from the field offered good opportunities to practice blind flying and things could get a bit dicey when a blind-folded pilot was at the controls. Geologists would just be collateral damage (Fig. 30).

Figure 30. Florence Weber, Terry Keith, and Helen with a chartered helicopter, in 1978 at Cherokee Delta Junction. (Photo: Helen Foster.)

Helen recalled another time,

In the mid 1960s we were using Army H-21 helicopters (flying bananas) to assist us in our fieldwork in south central Alaska. My field assistant and I were checking some outcrops near the West Fork of the Fortymile River, making spot landings, mostly in bushy and somewhat marshy (muskey) terrain with occasional trees. Our crew consisted of a pilot, co-pilot and crew chief. Suitable landing spots near the outcrops were hard to find.

I indicated to the pilot the outcrop that I wished to visit and he chose a landing spot, started to land, and then immediately picked up saying that he could move us closer to the outcrop. Then all at once there were ear splitting noises, a very hard jolt as we hit the ground...then silence. The pilot shouts "What the hell happened?" And the crew chief meekly replied, "We hit a tree, sir." The H-21 had wooden rotor blades and they had shattered into flying projectiles, one of which came through the fuselage just above my assistant's head. We hadn't been very high and the relatively soft marshy ground softened our fall, so there was little damage to us or the copter except for the very essential rotor blades.

We were only a few miles from the Taylor Highway, a gravel road leading to Dawson across the border in Canada. It had very light traffic with an occasional tourist coming through. It was decided that because my assistant and I knew the area well, we would hike out to the bridge on the Taylor Highway and try to get a ride into Tok, the nearest town. Thus, we were getting our packs loaded and were just heading out when the pilot shouted to us to "wait!" The crew had talked things over and decided that "it would look bad" if two women walked out to get help while all the men waited at the plane. The pilot had to stay with the plane, so a very unenthusiastic co-pilot shouldered a pack and pushed his way with us through the brush.

We eventually reached the highway. After a very long wait a car of tourists came along. They were loaded, but agreed to squeeze in one person. We sent the co-pilot because he needed to contact his base (and my assistant and I were much better able to cope with a long wait at the bridge, despite ruthless mosquitos). Just before dark our second helicopter located us and we all spent the night at our headquarters. The grounded helicopter got new blades and eventually flew out.

Another near disaster occurred at the end of the 1969 Alaska field season,

... when Jo Laird, her first season as my field assistant (now professor of geology, University of New Hampshire), and I were dropped off on a gravel bar on the Middle Fork of the Fortymile River. I flew in first and Jo came later. We set up a tent and spent the night on the bar.

The next morning, we headed out and spent 6 rather miserable days trying to do geology in rain and snow. (It was early in the season for snow, but it came anyway). We had planned to reach the Kink, a historic place on the Fortymile River, the night of the 11th, but the weather had slowed us down. It was snowing hard the morning of August 12 and we hastened to reach the Kink because our pilot, Marvin Warbelow, was to meet us there and drop off supplies.

When we finally reached the Kink, we were dismayed to find that the gravel bar was in the middle of the river and we had to wade to get there. It was still snowing and we were soaking wet and shivering when the Supercub landed. Marvin had only intended to drop off our supplies, but the weather was such that we could not accomplish any more geology, so we talked him into taking us out. It was clear that if we didn't go now, there was no telling when we would get out. It was also clear that he would not be able to make a second trip that day or probably any day soon. Jo and I put on some dry clothes that Marvin had brought and we all got in the Supercub and watched the snow come down. Now, it was snowing too hard to take off. Finally, we had a lull in the storm and Marvin and I got out and cleared snow off the wings with Jo's rain pants, which she had kindly loaned us. Jo sat on my lap (a Supercub is only a 2 seater).

As we began the take-off it began to snow hard again. As we neared the end of the gravel bar Marvin was trying desperately to get us in the air. Twice we almost made it and then it snowed harder and we got a down draft as we passed by a cliff along the side of the river. Marvin made a final desperate attempt to get into the air, but instead we settled into the river at the end of the gravel bar. As water rushed into the plane, we sat for a few seconds in stunned silence. I thought that I ought to say something, but didn't know what, so I said, "Well, I guess we've had it." Silence. So, in a minute I said, "Well, I guess we've had it." and Marvin finally awakened from shock and said, "Yes, I guess we have." Now things were floating out of the plane. Jo was desperately trying to grab stuff, but she could only hang on to so much.

We determined that by hanging on to the wing of the plane we could wade to shore. The plane was now solidly on the bottom of the river. We unloaded the plane and carried everything ashore in the freezing cold water. Then Marvin built a roaring fire and we left Jo to warm up and Marvin and I went back out in the river to try to get the plane ashore. We worked for quite a while unsuccessfully trying to spill the water out and drag the plane. We would go into the river and work for a while, and then out and warm up by the fire and then try again. Marvin thought that perhaps Jo could provide the little extra strength that we needed. Marvin didn't want to ask her to come back out into that cold water. However, Jo was willing to give it a try and we finally did get the plane up on shore.

The only real damage to the plane was a bent propeller. We put all the gear under the plane, took a minimum of gear with us—and headed out. We figured that we could walk out to Chicken on the Taylor Highway in a couple of days. It was still snowing, we had a good fire going and only a little daylight left so I suggested that we spend the night by the fire and take off at daylight. I knew that the walking was going to be very difficult along the river. However, Marvin wanted to get started, so off we went. We made only 2 or 3 miles before it was too dark and wet to go farther. We ended up building a small fire in a gully and sitting by the fire all night. Water began to trickle down through the gully adding to our misery.

As soon as it was light we were off. We went downstream a few miles along the river and then headed up a tributary stream. I always like to avoid walking along mountain streams or in the stream bed, but pilots like to follow streams, so we followed the stream for several miles. Marvin slipped on some rocks and injured his knee. Finally, I said that we couldn't follow the stream any longer and had to head up the mountain. We followed partly snow covered caribou trails. Jo and I were leading the way and Marvin was painfully dragging along behind. Jo and I had been out all summer and were accustomed to the terrain, but poor Marvin wasn't used to climbing and his knee was very painful.

Jo and I reached the top of the ridge just below a small summit. The snow was 2 feet deep in places and ice elsewhere. We contoured around the highest point cutting our hands in the snow and falling continuously. The wind was fierce and Jo was trying to help me hold the map so that I could determine by which one of several ridges we should descend. By the time Marvin reached us, I had determined our route and we finally got out of the wind and into the shelter of small trees and brush. We were heading for a mining camp where I hoped that we could obtain shelter, even though I knew it was closed for the year.

Just about dark we reached Fortyfive pup (a pup is a small stream) and the mining camp! It was closed tighter than a drum. Nearby was a tiny cabin which was used as a place for guests to sleep which we got in to when Marvin skillfully removed a window pane. The cabin had a small bunk bed, a wood stove, and a chair. We squeezed in. Marvin built a fire in the stove and we found a can of Spam and one can of soup and shared that for supper. Marvin was the most tired and collapsed on the bunk and was soon asleep. Jo piled in on top of him. I sat in the chair all night and kept the fire going.

At daybreak, we crawled out the window, replaced the pane, and were on our way to Chicken. Now we had a trail to follow! In mid-morning two friends from Tok searching for us in a Stinson spotted us and dropped Marvin a note. Marvin was greatly cheered.

We had one short trek left —to the Chicken air strip. Two small planes came in to fly us to Tok. Then we had 30 more miles by car to Cathedral Bluffs on the Alaska Highway where we were making our headquarters. A few days later Marvin flew in to the Kink and brought out our gear, the bent propeller, and of course, the rocks that we had collected. A new propeller soon arrived via Alaska Airlines and Marvin flew to the Kink again and put it on the plane. He and his sons rigged up a raft and floated the plane back to the island. They took off from the gravel island with no problem and flew the plane back to Cathedral Bluffs.

But this is not the end of the story! Marvin Warbelow died a few months after our incident because of injuries incurred from an explosion while working on a plane. He had been a stalwart of the Alaskan community (from Nome to the Tetlin Indian Reservation) for many years. He taught in the Eskimo and Indian villages, he flew the sick and injured to hospitals, his advice was widely sought in many a community. He served in the Coast Guard during World War II. In his honor, the rugged mountain that we climbed in the snow storm was officially named Mt. Warbelow.

Marvin Warbelow's children had never been to Mt. Warbelow. Last summer (2015), his son, Arthur Warbelow, and daughter, Cyndie, organized an "expedition" to visit the mountain [Helen was 94 at this time!]. About a dozen of us rode a variety of ATVs (All Terrain Vehicles) from Chicken to Fortyfive pup. We camped at Fortyfive pup and used some of the old dilapidated cabins with the permission and help of an owner. The next day we went as far as possible up the mountain ridge on the ATV's (scary! —riskier than the plane incident) and then hiked the rest of the way to Mt. Warbelow in perfect weather. I stumbled over the same huge boulders that had been so difficult in the snow in 1969. A flag and some notes were planted on Mt. Warbelow and we all had a great time doing it.

Grin and Bear It

Helen had a great many animal experiences and she recalls the time she was in her tent and heard some unusual noises outside. She poked her head out the tent opening and realized she was peering between two moose legs!

A notable bear story was when Helen was traversing a ridge alone after the helicopter had dropped her off in a valley (Fig. 31). As she headed up toward the top of the ridge, she noticed that not only were the blueberries ripe, but there were also lots of bear sign. She got to the crest of the ridge and was trying to get to a higher point when she spotted a big, blonde grizzly coming toward her as he ate blueberries. She wanted to get away before he saw her, but he spotted her and every time she moved he came closer. She got on the radio to tell the helicopter to pick her up where she was and soon. But talking on the radio made the bear more curious and he came closer, finally within about 15 feet of her. She held her backpack in front and talked to him calmly—until finally the copter arrived and scared the bear away. She thought she was lucky because the bear seemed young and found blueberries more to his liking than her.

Figure 31. Helen ready for the field any given day in Alaska. (Photo: Helen Foster.)

A more dangerous situation arose when she was again alone and making her way to her campsite for the night. She was on an open, grassy, flat area with almost no bushes or trees when she spotted an interesting outcrop some distance away. She thought that, if she unloaded the rocks out of her pack, she could hurry over to the outcrop, see what it was, and still return in time to reach her campsite before dark.

As she was unloading things out of her pack, she glanced up and saw two black bear cub faces peeking up from the grass in front of her. She thought, "Uh-oh, there is going to be a mama bear around nearby," and looked around to see the mama bear bearing down on her. She quickly tried to find something in her backpack to throw at the bear; her rocks were too big and heavy; and food was a poor choice. Finally, she grabbed an almost empty tin of shoe polish and threw it. It hit the bear right in the nose and distracted her enough for Helen to move aside. When the bear looked up again, there was a clear path to the cubs and she went for them, not Helen, and led them away.

When asked if that had put an end to her day, Helen said, "Oh no, I was just upset that I was going to have to haul my fully-loaded backpack all the way to that outcrop. What a nuisance! But it was a good thing I went because it turned out to be a high-grade asbestos deposit. The USGS announced the discovery in a circular, as was customary for such finds, and there was a grand rush to stake it."

A tragic event that made the bear danger more poignant was when her former field assistant, Cynthia Dussel-Bacon (Fig. 32), was doing fieldwork alone and was mauled by a bear. Cynthia almost lost her life when the bear dragged her by her head and arms, mauling her arms. She managed to get to her radio and get rescued in time to save her life. Cynthia lost both arms, but continued her work on Alaskan geology with the USGS for a productive and dynamic career. She has become a role-model for people using prosthetic arms.

Helen retired in 1986 and moved to Carson City, Nevada, where she had invested in some real estate that was nearer to where her sister lived. She continues to love travel and adventure and has made it a point to visit geologists and other professional friends she had made throughout her international career.

Reflecting on her memories, Helen says, "… thinking of early days in Wyoming which led to me thinking about early associations with AAPG…the more that I realize the importance of it. I was much inspired and impressed with the outstanding geologists that I have met and a few that I got to know well. My first major publication in 1947 was in AAPG. I had the honor in 1962 to participate in the AAPG Circum-Pacific Basin's Symposium. Now AAPG associations have re-entered my life and are adding great new friends and experiences." Helen has been an AAPG member for 70 years.

Figure 32. Helen and Cynthia Dussel (later Dussel-Bacon) taking off on a back-pack trip in the Big Delta Quadrangle, Alaska, 1976. One of the few places where they could start on a real trail instead of a caribou trail. (Photo: Helen Foster.)

Chapter 11. Sources and References

Bow Valley field trip of the Alberta Society of Petroleum Geologists, Alberta. 1956. Helen Belyea, enlargement from Photograph. Glenbow Archives, PA-2166-132, Glenbow Museum, Calgary, Alberta.

Bush, Col. James D. JR. Eng. 1976. Narrative Report of Alaska Construction 1941-1944, U.S. Army r.: Written Nov-Dec, 1944: (http://apiai.org/wp-content/uploads/2016/03/1941-1944.-Narrative-Report-of-Alaska-Construction.-US-Army-r.pdf. Accessed 11/39/2016)

Foster, Helen. Carson City, Nevada. Personal Communication, 2014 through 2016; source of photographs as cited in figure captions; video interview, May 2, 2016, archived at AAPG, Tulsa, Oklahoma.

Gee, David E. 1976. "A Brief History of the North Texas Geological Society." *North Texas Geological Society*, Wichita Falls, Texas.

Hull, J. P. D., Jr., Denver, Colorado, son of J. P. D. Hull [colleague of Julia Gardner]. Source of photograph as cited in figure caption.

Jordre, Nyle, Rio Vista, California, nephew of Margaret Olava Oros. Source of photograph as cited in figure caption.

Lawrence Journal World. "Margaret Oros 1912-2007 New Rockford, N.D." November 7, 2007.

Linda Green Miller, Petroleum Administration for War board. ca 1940. Photograph. The Bernard L. Majewski papers. University of Wyoming, American Heritage History Center. Laramie, Wyoming.

Loeblich, Elizabeth. 2004. "In Memoriam: Dr. Helen Nina Tappan Loeblich, October 12, 1917-August 18, 2004." *The Journal of Foraminiferal Research,* vol. 35, no. 1, pp. 86-89.

McLaren, Digby. 1987. "Helen Reynolds Belyea, 1913-1986." *Transactions of the Royal Society of Canada*, Ser. 5, vol. 2, pp. 198-201.

Milner, Marc. 2012. "The Navy's Women—70th Anniversary of the Wrens: Navy, Part 54." *The Legion Magazine*, December 12, 2012. https://legionmagazine.com/en/2012/12/the-navy-e2-80-99s-women-e2-80-9470th-anniversary-of-the-wrens-navy-part-54/. Accessed 6/15/2016.

O'Donnell, Cynthia Nelles. 2000. *Alberta Women in the Field: Geoscientists in the Resource Industry, Government Research, and Academia, 1914-1999.* PhD Education thesis, University of Toronto, Toronto, Canada. pp. 166-169.

Oros, Margaret O. 1960. "Memorial - Virginia Harriett Kline." *AAPG Bulletin,* vol. 44, no. 1, pp. 113-114. [Source of photograph of Virginia Kline.]

Randolph, Matt. *Helen Foster shows Robbie Greis photos from Japan, 1940 and 1950s.* 2016. Photograph. Tulsa, Oklahoma.

Rickman, Sarah Byrn. 2016. "The Female Pilots We Betrayed." *New York Times*, February 21, 2016, p. SR6.

Scholl Rostine, Irene B. "Our Turn: Working Women in The Las Vegas Valley, 1940-1980." (2013) UNLV Theses, Dissertations, Professional Papers, and Capstones. 1884.
http://digitalscholarship.unlv.edu/thesesdissertations/1884. Accessed 01/25/2017.

Tappeiner, Sue, Corvallis, Oregon, granddaughter of Fanny Carter Edson. Personal communication, March 20, 2016; source of photograph as cited in figure caption.

The University of Oklahoma. *Betty Anne Elliott.* 1940. Photograph. *Sooner* yearbook, p. 150. Western History Collections, University of Oklahoma Libraries, Norman, Oklahoma.

The University of Oklahoma. *Helen Tappan Loeblich. Sooner* yearbook. Photograph. 1939, p.25. Western History Collections, Libraries, Norman, Oklahoma.

Watson, Elizabeth A. Correspondence, news clippings, and regional records, 1915-2000. The WASP Archive, Texas Woman's University, Denton, Texas. Source of photographs as cited in figure captions.

Elizabeth Watson University of Wisconsin Field camp. ca 1938. Photograph. Watson archives, American Heritage Center, University of Wyoming, Laramie Wyoming.

A female geologist's duties in the 1950's often including filing, typing, shopping for bosses, other menial tasks around the office … and less pay. (Photos: Coury family files, 2nd photo - "ClasicStock / Alamy Stock Photo," and Susan Suchman Simon)

Chapter 12

Post WWII: Women in Petroleum Geology

Post WWII women, the women who entered or were in the industry between the end of WWII and Affirmative Action in the 1970s, fought some very distinct battles to have a career in the oil business.

They did not have the advantages of prior generations—namely:

- Women in WWI were not only needed to replace the men who had been called into military service, they enjoyed the support of early male geologists who themselves had fought discrimination and derision as geologists from management and were perhaps more empathetic.
- Many women between WWI and WWII enjoyed the popularity and respect that was created with critically needed micropaleontology skills.
- Women employed during WWII, again, had the advantage of oil companies needing to increase production for the war effort and hiring geologists to fill in for those who had gone to war.

The Post WWII women not only did not have these advantages but also were up against a not-so-subtle societal push to put women back into the home. This came with pervasive propaganda of the times extolling the "Ideal Woman"—the little lady, taking care of hearth and home, and taking advantage of new "domestic gadgets" to make her life easier. Magazine and television ads and stories encouraged a woman to pamper her husband, mind the children, always be cheerful and competent at housekeeping skills, and not to compete for jobs that men needed more than women. An example, which occurred in most if not all companies, is illustrated by *The Magnolia News*, in August 1957, the Magnolia Petroleum company magazine article entitled

"Are you a help or a handicap to your husband?"

The "Ideal Woman" is shown, in her fresh dress, pearls, and, no doubt, high heels, greeting her husband at the door with a big smile and two clean and happy children.

She starts his work day with well-balanced meals, on schedule; she has a sound knowledge of calories and vitamins. Their children get up and eat a big breakfast with Dad before he leaves for work.

During the day, if something goes wrong, like the oven malfunctioning, without bothering her husband at work, she calls the repairman. Minor decisions at home should be made by the wife.

A period of relaxation before supper is necessary for her husband, and he is shown in photos, relaxing with the newspaper while she prepares dinner.

On weekends, she guards his health, insisting he take a break from mowing the lawn to cool down and relax.

The article includes a full page test of twenty questions for women whose husbands are employed at Magnolia, as to whether they nag, have honey-do chores lined up, don't have meals prepared on schedule or properly, don't make it a priority to listen to his troubles, don't keep the house clean enough, don't believe keeping the house is worthy of their talents, and especially whether they bother their husbands at work, keep your husband up late, or lose your temper if your husband does not agree with you. If the wife scored poorly on this test, the article says: "This indicates an unhappy and negative attitude on her part which can and does jeopardize the entire family's home life. She is a HANDICAP!" (*Magnolia News*, 1957, p. 9.)

Some might argue that, after the war, women wanted to stay home; but, a survey at the time indicated that as many as 80% of the working women felt working outside the home led to a more satisfied life (Renzetti & Curran, 2002, p. 215). Popular culture sought to propagate the concept of the ideal role for women. Sociology studies have found that government propaganda, popular magazines, and films reinforced traditional concepts of femininity and instructed women to subordinate their interests to those of returning male veterans. But the media now included the powerful element of television which helped to create and instill four stereotypes (Holt, Jennifer, 2014):

- A woman's place is in the home.
- Women do not make the important decisions.
- Women are dependent and need a man's protection and acceptance.
- Men regard women primarily as sex objects and, thus, a lower status.

The last bullet point has probably been the hardest to dispel and continues to be a pervasive problem in society. The roles and compensation offered to women on TV and in movies today illustrate how women continue to be objectified by their looks (Berg, 2015) and (*Wikipedia*, 2017, "Exploitation of women in mass media"). Jennifer Holt (p. 2), who posted her work on "The Ideal Woman" of the 1950s on "Soundings" at California State University at Stanislaus, states,

> In the 1957 "Magnolia News" magazine, we see the evidence of this in their article which thanks women for their help in a refinery during the war, but says it is now time to go home. To quote: "During the war, many women left their homes patriotically to help meet the increasing demand for war workers. Now, that the war has ended, the Beaumont Refinery has reverted to its prewar policy of not hiring married women, and many of those hired during the emergency have returned to keeping house. However, those married women whose husbands are still in the armed forces will continue to work until their husbands become civilians again." The article proceeded to list the names of 23 women that had "left Magnolia's services" at the Beaumont refinery THAT month. Imagine the number for all of Magnolia!

The "seven sisters" of magazines (not the "seven sisters" of oil companies or accounting firms): *Better Homes and Gardens*, *Family Circle*, *Good Housekeeping*, *Ladies' Home Journal*, *McCall's*, *Redbook*, and *Woman's Day* advanced the stereotype of the "Ideal Women" in every issue.

The corporate attitude illustrated above was also an attitude embraced in the federal government at the same time. Secretary of Labor in 1957, James P. Mitchell, said, "The most fundamental job of American woman was 'being a good wife', a homemaker, a mother" (Hartmann, 1994, p. 90). This was during the Cold War when Vice President Richard Nixon and Undersecretary of Labor James O'Connel [*sic*] measured superiority over the Soviet Union in terms of its ability to keep women in the home (Hartmann, p. 91). O'Connel [sic] remarked, "The highest calling of a woman's sex is the home" (Hartmann, p. 86). When the National Manpower Council expressed concerns about America "losing out in a race [with the Soviet Union] for highly trained manpower," it contrasted the *thirteen thousand* [author's italics] female engineers graduating each year in the Soviet Union compared with fewer than one hundred women obtaining engineering degrees in the United States (p.91). The framework for this attitude within the government was strongly developed in the McCarthy era, a period sometimes called "the Red Scare," when "National leaders as well as popular culture proclaimed that women's role in the international crisis was to strengthen the family and raise new citizens emotionally and mentally fit to win the Cold War. Women and women's organizations that stood for equal rights underwent loyalty investigations and were labeled subversive" (Hartmann, 1994, p. 85).

As one would expect during this time, public schools followed suit. *The Home Economics High School Text Book of 1954* taught the same ideal female role as the *Magnolia News* magazine article: "have dinner ready, prepare yourself, prepare the children, minimize all noise, be happy to see him, listen to him, make the evening his." Women who bucked the trend, by either keeping their wartime jobs or who had found a job in the post-war era, had many hurdles. First, their pay was typically 30% less than men in the same job; sometimes 60% less. Second, they were almost always, if not always, required to do work men did not do, such as typing, filing, posting, drafting, and running errands for the boss.

In interviews for this book, women from this post-war era would often say, "Well, of course, I accepted lower salary; what else could I do?" "To complain could likely result in losing the job!" "I loved my job; I wanted to work; I did what I had to do to keep my job."

Marie Gramann, Susan Cage, Anny Coury (see Chapter 10 and this Chapter), and many others accepted this subjugated role because they loved geology, loved working outside the home, and loved the oil business. They felt that they had no recourse if they wanted to keep their jobs. Marie Gramann was unable to get a job in industry before the war and became a draftsman for the Texas Railroad Commission, but during the war, she went looking for work and found it in the petroleum industry which she loved so much that she remained an AAPG member to age 103. In the post war years, it became more difficult for Marie Gramann to keep a job in industry and like many women of that era, she took a teaching job at a small private university.

Susan Cage was engaged to a geologist when she went to work for Gulf in 1950. She was required to work her way up from file clerk to draftsman, until finally they promoted her to geologist after almost two years. Her husband, who was injured just out of college and unable to join the workforce for two and a half years, was hired by Gulf, too: an admirable gesture for an oil company as it was uncommon to have both husband and wife working for the same company. However, her husband not only did not have to "work his way up," he also started with a salary 60% higher than hers.

Anny Coury's boss said repeatedly when he gave her an evaluation or a raise, "Your work is as good as the guys. You are terrific, but I'm not allowed to pay you what they make."

She always smiled and said, "It's ok! I'm just happy to have the job!"

That was what one had to do in those days: accept being paid less and expect fewer opportunities for advancement.

Another point frequently made by these post WWII women was that they almost all HAD to "know somebody" to get a job in the industry. Susan Cage's father called a friend in the Dad's Club of the University of Texas, Austin. Jeanne Ferrin and her sister, Rosamond Haertlein, got in the door through their father's Gulf colleagues.

But, on the other side of that coin, many companies would not hire someone if they had related family there. Susan Longacre, the first woman to be editor for AAPG and the first woman Chair of an AAPG Committee (Publications), had difficulties when she was job hunting in 1969. Shell wouldn't hire her because her father worked for them. Other companies would not hire her because her father worked for a competitor. Finally, she found a positon with Getty who seemed to feel her position in research would not be compromised by her father's position as a chief geophysicist in offshore operations for Shell. She, too, started at a lower salary than the men in the same position, but within four years the Equal Employment directives motivated Getty to equalize her salary to that of her male colleagues. Had she ever complained? Absolutely not.

Anny Coury had no contacts to rely upon and just pounded the streets in Houston until she found a job with a very small independent. Carolyn Miracle Ross did not have contacts and took eight years to land a position as a geologist after college. After many menial jobs, she had worked her way up to librarian for Phillips when a manager "discovered" her and created a path for her to work as a geologist. Joan Mizer, MIT graduate, after many challenges to stay in the petroleum industry, finally gave up.

Hazel Peterson, who was readily hired during WWII, had a hard time keeping a job in the industry after the war (see Chapter 10). Eventually, like many other women in that situation, Hazel found a job teaching at a small regional college. Hazel recognized, too late, how detrimental the lower pay could be when it came to retirement. She saw that taking a lower salary meant her pension was going to be much lower. She fought hard for equity, but to no avail. She, also, was one to get her hackles up when guys would say something about the girls quitting when they got married because she knew that the "girls" were often required to quit when they married.

Doris Curtis, nine years into her career, was required to quit Shell due to nepotism rules when she married in 1950 (see Chapter 10). Later, after divorce, she returned to Shell for another 20 years. She, like other women of that era, accepted the salary inequities. When Doris retired after 29 years, her smaller pension afforded her little cushion. Her niece, in executing her estate, was surprised how little her aunt had to live on and realized that only her consistent lifelong frugality allowed her to live within her retirement means.

Canadian Helen Belyea (see Chapter 11), a true pioneer for women field geologists, was frustrated by having to accept lower pay and having to live with restrictions on her field travel due to her gender.

Gwenn Jensen, likewise, in 1967, was offered only a position as a receptionist or a draftsman. She chose receptionist and worked her way up to geologist within two years, doing the work but not getting the recognition. Mary Beth Cooper, who earned her MA in 1969, was discouraged in job interviews; "I was told that I could be hired as a secretary or a bug-picker, but not as geologist. It wasn't until after the civil rights legislation passed and companies had quotas that I could be hired as a geologist." She worked outside of geology until 1975 when she landed a job with Chevron because of their diversity requirements from the Equal Employment Opportunity Commission (EEOC).

The women who broke through entrenched rules in academia to earn their geology degrees before and during WWII, and fought to have and to keep their careers in the oil business after the war, were "ideal" petroleum geologists. They were technically proficient, resilient, and loved the industry.

Anny Buchstab Coury

Anny Buchstab graduated from high school in Fort Worth, Texas, at age 15. She earned her geology degree in 1949 at age 19 from The University of Texas at Austin (Fig. 1), and then, continuing to exceed expectations, she went to Houston and got a job in the oil business. This was quite a feat, at that time, for any woman, but especially for someone who "knew no one" and had no connections. Post WWII employment was directed toward male veterans so she went door to door, day after day, until she landed a job. This perseverance had become natural for a woman who, as a girl, had escaped the Nazi invasion of France.

Anny's parents, born in Ukraine and Poland, hastily left University in Ukraine and escaped to France when persecution of the Jews began in that country. Once settled in Lille, married and, with their first child, they still feared German Nazi aggression. Lille was only five miles from the Belgium border. Anny recalled, "My parents planned to have only one child, as they knew they needed to be able to flee. They geared their lives for an eventual escape from Hitler."

Figure 1. Anny Buchstab earned her geology degree at the tender age of 19 in 1949 at The University of Texas at Austin. (Photo: Coury family, Denver, Colorado.)

In grade school, Anny remembers going to school with her lunch in one hand and her gas mask in the other; she frequently had to take cover in bomb shelters. She still remembers the time she was halfway between school and home and was terrified when the alarms sounded. She was only five and didn't know which way to run. When the Nazis finally invaded, Anny and her mother caught the last train to Paris. Her father stayed behind for work, and later, barely escaped on a truck heading to Paris as the German tanks entered Lille.

The trek through Europe began—her father moved them several times to cities in France that were not occupied by Germans, but ultimately, after a couple of years, they had to flee France entirely. Her father paid a taxi driver to drive them to Spain, then across Spain to the Portuguese Embassy at the border. There, the wait for visas to cross the border was almost impossible; long lines; people turned away day after day. Finally, after once again being unsuccessful getting papers, her father hid in the Embassy restroom. Anny's voice quivers as she says, "I cry every time I tell this story. My father heard the cleaning crew arrive that evening and ventured out into the office and found the consul general still in his office. My father, he ... he got on his knees and begged for visas to save his family. My father was an educated man with a doctorate, a proud man, but, he went to his knees. And we got the visas."

They lived in Portugal, neutral during the war, for a couple of years and her father found work, though it was not legal. Finally, after applying for safe havens all over the world, they were accepted in the United States. Her father's PhD in chemistry no doubt helped. Anny was 11 years old and, out of necessity, she spoke four languages; English became the fifth. She was twelve when they arrived in Fort Worth, via New York and Louisiana.

Figure 2. Anny Buchstab. (Photo: Coury family.)

Anny attributes some of her success to early advice from her father. When she was in high school in Fort Worth, Anny asked him if she should take typing, and he said, "No, do NOT take typing! If you do, you won't be treated as a professional!"

He was forward-thinking about women in professions and it was great advice. Anny also remembered,

> I really wanted to go to medical school, but I could not get into medical school for several reasons—I was a woman, I was Jewish and there were quotas for Jews and, lastly, I was not a veteran!
>
> So, I was taking a geology course at The University of Texas in Austin and Professor Sam Ellison talked to me about majoring in geology (Fig. 2). I think, unconsciously, it attracted me to be in a field that was not normal for women. I wanted a challenge. So, I got my degree in geology and went to Houston and started looking for a job. The first thing they asked me was, 'Can you type?' (personal communication, 2014).

Anny's first job was with a small, independent geophysical company, Hoard Exploration Company, where she was correlating geophysical records. She says she learned a lot there but was terribly bored. Continuing her search, Anny soon had a job offer from a consultant, J. Brian Eby, who had an office in the Esperson Building near Hoard's office. He, too, asked if she could type and again she said, "no." He put Anny to work on geology where she helped with his reports and evaluations. He was a true prospector. It was good work, but after awhile she really wanted to work for a larger company where she could do more geology and less paper work. Anny inquired at Humble and all the larger companies and had no encouragement. At that time, there were only four women who she knew of working in petroleum in Houston; they included Doris Curtis, Joyce Jones, and Ann Leeds.

Figure 3. Anny Buchstab Coury, horsing around with colleagues at Western Natural Gas, Houston, Texas. About 1959. (Photo: Coury family.)

Eventually, Anny got a job with Western Natural Gas (Figs. 3 and 4), a subsidiary of El Paso Natural Gas, and had a sympathetic boss, Paul Nelson, who told her when he hired her, "You know, I can only pay you $225 per month. My male geologists get $275 per month, but I am not allowed to do that for women."

Figure 4. Anny at an office party, Western Natural Gas, about 1960. She developed onshore and offshore prospects. (Photo: Coury family.)

Anny had an assigned area and oversaw the drilling of mostly development wells in Matagorda, Aransas, and Hidalgo counties, occasionally offshore Gulf of Mexico, and West Texas. She was gradually able to work up wildcat prospects for drilling, too.

Every year Anny would go in for evaluation and Paul would say, "You are doing great, your projects are great, your well oversight work is great, your attitude is great. If you were a man you would be getting a much better raise, but it is out of my control!"

He seemed to hate that he had to pay her less. She would just say, "It's fine, Paul."

Figure 5. Anny with colleagues on the offshore platform drilling her first offshore discovery well, Block 608, in the Gulf of Mexico. Possibly the first woman to visit an offshore rig. (Photo: Coury family.)

Anny worked for Western Natural Gas for 12 years. At that time in the late 1950s, she was making more money than husband, Glen Coury, a chemical engineer for Shell Oil whom she married in 1957. Anny wasn't unhappy and loved her work. And says now, "What could anyone do about it in those days?"

For Anny, it was fun making maps and overseeing the drilling in her area. She loved going offshore to visit a well on her prospect in Block 608 in the Gulf of Mexico (Fig. 5). In 1956, she was possibly one of the first, if not the first woman, to visit an offshore rig. It was a physical challenge because she got very seasick and after the helicopter dropped her off, she had to climb a ladder up to the rig floor with the other visitors, which scared her to death.

When Anny had her first child in 1958, she worked until the day before her son, Clifford, was born. Then, she came back to work almost immediately, working one to two days a week for a year. Management wanted her back full-time, but acquiesced to part-time. Eventually, Anny, wanting a stronger commitment to part-time work, went to work for Union Texas (see Chapter 13, Affirmative Action women, where "part-time" was often full-time with half-pay). Her new boss, Frank Sonnenberg, was great as a mentor to a woman and put Anny to work on stratigraphic traps around salt domes. Some of her work during this time evolved to looking for sulfur around salt domes using very old well data that was hand-written on yellowed-paper reports.

After her second child, Rina, was born in 1961, Anny took leave from geology and during her one day a week when she had a babysitter, took up a long-desired hobby of carving rock. Anny apprenticed herself to a stone carver in Houston who assigned her to help on small projects. Once when her mentor ran out of little jobs for her, he gave her a huge piece of Indiana Limestone and told her to just do whatever she wanted. The rock, under Anny's creative vision, began to become a large white owl (Fig. 6).

Figure 6. The Rice University owl, carved by Anny Coury, 1965. She took the family to France "on the wings of an owl" to live for several years and learn to speak French. (Photo: Coury Family.)

One day, several Rice University architects were touring through the stone yard looking for facing on new buildings and saw the owl Anny was creating. They asked when it would be done. Working only one day a week, she knew it would not be soon, but, husband Glen was due to complete his PhD in 18 months and Anny knew she had to be done by then.

She told them, "A year and a half!"

They asked how much she might sell it for, and Anny had, fortuitously, just looked at the cost to move the family to France, which was $1500 by boat.

She said, "$1500!" They immediately agreed to buy it. Later, she thought, "If only I had looked at flight prices and said $4000, they might have agreed to that, and we could have flown.""

Regardless, in 1967, she took the family to Grenoble, France, "on the wings of her owl." There everyone would learn French, her birth language. She took a three-year break from geology, except for doing translations and interpretations for ENG, the French Center for Nuclear energy where Glen worked as a chemical engineer.

Anny and her family returned to the U.S. in 1971 when Glen accepted a job in Washington, D.C. She worried that there would be no jobs for a geologist. Anny didn't consider the U.S. Geological Survey (USGS) because she thought they were only interested in PhD's. and instead she applied to work at a petroleum magazine office (possibly *World Oil*). When she interviewed with them, the editor thought she was overqualified for their job. He was a friend to the Chief Geologist at the USGS and called to tell him about Anny's extensive experience in the oil industry. This coincided with the 1970s oil crisis when the USGS was in the process of forming and deploying the Petroleum Division. Dick Sheldon hired Anny within three days (usually jobs with the USGS took months to finalize) and, it was with equal pay and equal opportunity, as government jobs had all aligned with the new EEOC policies.

Anny did not have a master's or PhD, but she was put in charge of a group of a dozen people (all with advanced degrees) to complete a huge project, "Offshore Mineral Potential of the U.S. and the World," for a Law of the Sea Conference in Geneva to be held within a few months. Anny accomplished the job in three months, keeping her "old fuddy, duddy PhDers" on track and on schedule. She was aghast when the Assistant Chief Geologist—who contributed almost nothing to the effort—succeeded in putting his name first on the report because alphabetically, his name beginning with "A" came before her "C" in Coury. In fact, because it was "alphabetical," she became the fourth of five authors (*Professional Paper 817*).

About this time, Dr. Peter Rose was hired away from Shell Oil to open an Oil and Gas Division in Denver, a city where ardent skiers, Anny and Glen, dreamed of living, and because of her substantial oil and gas experience, she was offered a position. In 1974, the Courys moved to Denver. Her first major task was creating an equal area map "*Basins of the World*" with over 600 onshore and offshore basins—a task never before accomplished. She and colleague, Tom Hendricks, were to ride herd on the entire project. It was a project that she is the proudest of in her 25-year career at the USGS.

The "Basins of the World" project also led to Anny being asked to be the "volunteer" chief editor of AAPG's Basins of the World series (published between 1989 and 1994, *Divergent/Passive Margin Basins, Interior Cratonic Basins, Active Margin Basins, Foreland Basins and Fold Belts*, and *Interior Rift Basins* as Memoirs 48, 51, 52, 55, and 59, respectively), another very satisfying project.

Early during her time at the USGS, it was discovered that the Oil and Gas Branch geologists were denied raises on the same level as other geologists because there were publishing requirements in other Divisions that were not possible for the Oil and Gas Branch. Anny went to management and complained, providing ammunition as to why they could not be evaluated in the same way. She won the battle and changed the compensation structure for the Oil and Gas Branch. What a difference from her early days in industry when she felt she had no recourse with pay inequities. This was a far cry from her attitude in the 1950s: "It's ok, I'll work for less." She worked in oil and gas research before her final promotion to Assistant Chief Geologist, prior to retirement. It was a rare accomplishment for someone with only a bachelor's degree.

She recalls with great humor when one of her bosses, a woman with a PhD, would be so petty as to take the time and make the effort to go through all the division mail, and if something was addressed to "Dr." Anny Coury, she would take out her pen and mark through "Dr."

Anny Coury retired from the USGS in 1995 and has dedicated her most recent 20 years to her stone sculpting career. Her pieces have been on consignment at various galleries in Denver. She and Glen traveled to the Ukraine recently and visited the villages where her parents were born, though most evidence of the Jewish communities that existed there previously has been eliminated. Anny is 87 now. For her 85th birthday, she and her family backpacked into the Colorado Rockies and carried their own loads. She stays young teaching yoga (Fig. 7).

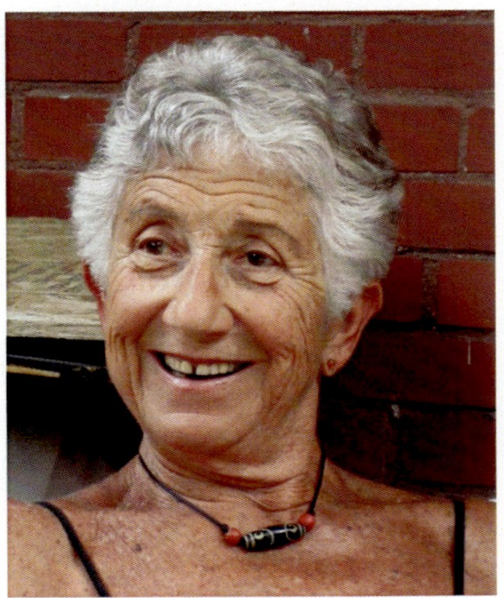

Figure 7. Anny Buchstab Coury, oil geologist, resource geologist, map maker, world basins contributor, and yoga teacher. (Photo: Coury family.)

Anny Buchstab Coury was born in Lille, France in 1929. She earned her bachelor's degree at The University of Texas at Austin in 1949. She and Glen Coury married in 1957 and live in Denver, Colorado. She was an AAPG member for 40 years.

Susan Kiefner Cage

Figure 8. Susan Kiefner, 1951, finds a job with Gulf Oil, beginning with secretarial duties before advancing to geologist. (Photo: Susan Cage, Georgetown, Texas.)

Susan Kiefner attended Stephens College, an all-girls school in Colombia, Missouri, from 1945 to 1947 and enjoyed general science and chemistry (Fig. 8). She transferred her junior year to The University of Texas at Austin (UT) in the fall of 1947. It was an interesting time in the UT geology department. Many of the male students were veterans of WWII, entering college on the GI Bill (a law passed in 1944 that provided educational and other benefits for people who had served in the armed forces in WWII), and were a formidable group to deal with. This was at a time when Sigma Gamma Epsilon, the geology honors club, did not allow females, and would not for several more decades. Susan joined an "informal" girl's geology group that called themselves "Smilodons" (Sabertooths) and enjoyed the camaraderie and support of this group of five to ten young women.

Susan contracted polio during the summer of 1949 before entering her senior year. Fortunately, her case was mild and she was able to return and graduate with her class. When she graduated in 1950, it was difficult for a woman to find a job in the petroleum industry; this was rarely accomplished without knowing someone in the company's employ. Susan's father was active in the local Dad's Club, where he met Howard Hough, a geological manager with Gulf Oil. Mr. Hough encouraged him to send his daughter around so they could meet. When Susan arrived, he stated up front that Gulf was not hiring females, but he could offer her a job as a file clerk and then "see what happens." Susan went to work for $250 a month and was filing electric logs.

In 1951, Susan became engaged to Jack Cage (Fig. 9), a geology classmate at UT. He was in a serious automobile accident a few months later and in and out of hospitals in San Antonio for over two years. Susan would leave work Friday afternoon, take a bus to San Antonio from Houston to visit Jack, and then return late Sunday night almost every weekend for two years. While he was recovering, she had a chance to advance from filing clerk to draftsman and finally, after being assigned a 23-county area of south Texas for the construction of regional maps, she was promoted to geologist. Without formal celebration or recognition, a little blue handwritten note was slipped onto her desk announcing her new status. She had met the "see what happens" challenge.

After a few years at Gulf, Susan shared an office for a short time with another female UT graduate, recently transferred from the Amarillo office, Jeanne Allen. They both recall being sent out by their boss one cold, blustery day to Christmas shop for the secretaries. They recognized they were doing something that would never have been asked of their male colleagues, but they would not have dreamed of complaining.

Figure 9. Susan with fiancé, Jack Cage, who was injured in an automobile accident prior to their marriage. (Photo: Susan Cage.)

Susan and Jack got married when he came out of the hospital. After a year of him trying to find full-time work as he continued to regain his health, Susan asked Gulf if they would interview him. In 1952, Gulf, with an admirably advanced attitude toward married couples, hired Jack. He was immediately given the position of geologist, and his starting salary was 60% higher than hers, even though she had been there almost three years. Again, she never considered complaining.

In 1958, she and Jack were asked to move to Corpus Christi and start a new district office for Gulf. They loaded all the necessary company maps into a car and headed south. Her office was the size of a broom closet and she jokingly recalls that she was careful to always eat a light lunch so she could fit back into her space after lunch. Eleven years later, when Gulf Coast drilling had slowed, most of the office work became preparing well data for the new life of "the computer." In 1969, the small Corpus Christi group was scattered to other Gulf offices and the Cages were transferred to Bakersfield, California.

In Bakersfield, Susan was assigned to Alaska exploration focused primarily in the Gulf of Alaska. This was in preparation for a Federal Offshore Lease Sale to be held in the early 1970s. Owing to a serious oil spill in the California Santa Barbara Channel in 1968, the sale had been postponed indefinitely. Susan embraced the challenge to learn not only the Alaskan geologic section, but, she also gave herself a crash course in West Coast geology. No layer cake stratigraphy there.

Alaska provided a steep and difficult learning curve. Little was known of the surface geology and with only one well drilled in the Gulf of Alaska, even less was known about the subsurface. Susan needed to find sections to measure in the nearby mountains, but Gulf would not let her go to Alaska for fieldwork. Being resourceful, she put together a sampling program for some of the geologists that worked for Gulf's partners. She learned enough about the stratigraphy to worry that since the onshore sediments were mostly glacial till, the offshore sedimentary section would likely not have enough porosity or permeability for a commercial reservoir. Eventually, with the acquisition of abundant seismic data, a structure was identified and the need to fulfill a drilling obligation overrode her caution to management about the potential absence of reservoir quality. Sure enough, the large anticline identified on seismic was drilled but had no reservoir rock quality.

Her years in Bakersfield were hardworking but otherwise fruitful and were thoroughly enjoyed. Susan shared a glimpse of those years when she, as the lone female member of the San Joaquin Geological Society, had the "distinction" of always being asked to draw the winning raffle ticket for a bottle of whiskey at their evening meetings.

Figure10. The 1980s brought "dress for success" to women in the oil and gas business. Susan was back in Gulf's Houston office after years in Bakersfield, CA. (Photo: Susan Cage.)

After 10 years, the office in California was closed in 1978, and the Cages were transferred back to Houston. Susan was promoted to her first managerial job with a staff of six men and one woman in her group (Fig. 10). They were looking for "elephants" (giant oil fields that, by some company definitions, were expected to produce at least 500 million barrels) in East Texas—not an easy task. Susan recognized how clearly times had changed with Affirmative Action and the recruitment and hiring of more women and minorities. One day, she was asked to "pose" as an audience for a photography session with a female geologist, Marsha Green, who had two years' experience—in today's terms, a "young professional." Only the back of Susan's head and several other managers in the room would be shown in a tiny inset at the bottom of the magazine ad. The company was staging a presentation for a Gulf Oil advertisement to go on the back cover of *Time* magazine (See Marsha Green, Chapter 16), as well as 5-6 other magazines. The ad would celebrate "women" in exploration and a "new gas field" discovered by the young woman. Susan looked at the maps on the wall and realized she had made a discovery in the same area twenty years prior, but no celebration or photo shoot was done with her discovery. Yes, these were different times.

In 1983, Susan retired after the Gulf merger with Chevron. One great advantage of Affirmative Action being implemented, for her personally, was that Gulf "equalized" her salary to the same level as the men with her experience and contributions and she retired with the pension she deserved. Looking back, Susan remained disappointed that she had never done wellsite work, but at Gulf, almost no exploration geologists, male or female, went out on wells. This was reserved for the Production Department.

Figure 11. Susan and Jack Cage, after retirement to Georgetown, Texas. (Photo: Susan Cage.)

Susan recalls that throughout her career, everywhere she went she had to "start from scratch" proving herself and her abilities. The hard work and challenges of her career, although tiresome at times, was recognized and appreciated by her colleagues, and, Gulf Oil honored Susan as a true "pioneer." One of her previous bosses sent her a warm congratulatory letter which was amusing to her, considering he had frequently slammed the door in her face and was downright rude in other ways. Her co-workers, while saying goodbye as she retired, kept referring to her as a "pioneer" and a "role model." These were new terms to Susan. She said, "I never felt like a pioneer!" (Fig. 11)

Susan Kiefner was born in 1928 in Houston, earned her bachelor's in geology at The University of Texas at Austin in 1950. She and Jack Cage were married in 1953. Susan Kiefner Cage joined AAPG in 1968 and has been a delegate to AAPG for the Houston Geological Society. She is currently widowed and living in Georgetown, Texas, and is still a member of AAPG.

Suzanne Takken (1925-1997)

Suzanne Takken (Fig. 12) did everything in life with gusto and enthusiasm. She was a charter member and leader of several geological organizations including the Oklahoma City Geological Society, American Institute of Professional Geologists (AIPG), and Association for Women Geoscientists (AWG). She was a member of AAPG over 50 years and established and endowed the Suzanne Takken Memorial Grant that is awarded annually to a deserving graduate student through the AAPG Grants-in-Aid Program. Her biography attached to the award states,

Figure 12. Suzanne Takken, 1950s looking at samples, working for Mobil Oil in Tulsa, Oklahoma. (Photo: With permission from Suzanne Takken Papers, MS 523, Archives of Women in Science and Engineering, Special Collections and University Archives, Iowa State University Library.

> Suzanne Takken, an only child, was born April 25, 1925, in Cleveland, Ohio. She graduated from the Rocky River High School there in 1943 and enrolled in her father's alma mater, the University of Michigan. [Her father died in 1947, one week before her graduation from the University of Michigan.]
>
> In the summers between school years she worked in war plants packing parts in cosmoline. To help support herself during college she took a job in the school cafeteria. After only two days she decided that was not her kind of work so she applied for another job. She was assigned to assist Professor George V. Cohee in his work with rock samples – chance happening that led her into a life-long career in geology.
>
> Susan had been offered a job with Magnolia Oil Company (Mobil Oil) in either Midland, Texas or Oklahoma City, and after consulting with her mother, Clara Elrich Takken, a very strong woman in her own right, they decided to quit Cleveland and both make a new start in Oklahoma City.

She retired from Mobil in 1970, continued to consult and became an adjunct professor in the Land Management School at the University of Oklahoma—where she also wrote the *Landman's Handbook on Petroleum Exploration* (1978).

Continuing from the AAPG Foundation website,

> Suzanne was active in professional geological organizations throughout her career. She joined AAPG in 1947...and the Oklahoma City Geological Society in the same year and was awarded Honorary Lifetime Membership in 1982 after serving in many offices, including president and editor of *The Shale Shaker*. [She published several papers on the petroleum geology of Oklahoma.]
>
> She and her mother were active in amateur theater in Oklahoma City for many years. She dabbled at oil painting and made jewelry. She was a leader in a Great Books discussion group. She played golf and started writing a novel. Her conversations at lunch would vary from oil prospects to national energy policy, to philosophical jaunts into education, lifestyles, and religion. She loved to travel, especially in her later years, and her favorite places were in the Orient and the Pacific Ocean. She asked that her ashes be spread in her favorite ocean, the Pacific.
>
> Suzanne was on her way home to Oklahoma City from California when she was stricken by a massive visceral hemorrhage in Santa Rosa, California, and died November 9, 1997. She had just spent two weeks at her vacation home in Sea Ranch, California, following her attendance at the Association for Women Geoscientists [AWG] meeting in Salt Lake City. Suzanne served as president of AWG in 1989-1990 and was completing a two-year term as director of the AWG Foundation. She was honored at the meeting by the naming of the Suzanne Takken Encourage Award in recognition of her work as a role model and mentor for younger women geoscientists. [Susan bequeathed an endowment to AWG for the "Susan Takken Student Research Presentation Award" to cover travel expenses to national or international conventions.]

Although widely traveled and vastly conversant, unfortunately, Suzanne's personal stories of her career were not recorded before she died. From a letter to Helen Foster (See Chapter 10) she said, regarding her WWII years at the University of Michigan, "...if there had once been a prejudice against women in geology, it evaporated during WWII. I certainly did not notice any."

She continued, "I have encountered some prejudice during my working career, but not a whole lot. And now I am regarded by some as a pioneer, which I certainly am not."

Jeanne Flavia Allen Ferrin

Jeanne Flavia Allen was born into the oil business. Her father, Bryant Allen, was a geologist in Mexico and Texas for 15 years and then in East Texas and Mississippi. Jeanne went to college in Jackson, Mississippi, first to Belhaven College, then to Millsaps College where she took her first geology course during her sophomore year. As WWII was winding down in 1946, Jeanne, following her older sister, Rosamond Allen Haertlein, transferred to The University of Texas at Austin (UT) (Fig. 13). Both sisters earned their degrees in geology. Soon after she arrived, the GI's landed at UT and swelled the geology classes beyond anything ever seen before and, maybe, since.

The veterans were difficult on the young women in the department; if the women made a good grade, the GIs would always say, "It's just because you're a girl!" (Personal communication.)

Jeanne remembers that there were about a dozen women at the time. Still, she says, being a girl was not all bad because the professors always remembered you. Dr. H. B. Stenzel especially took the girls under his wing and helped them out. Stenzel also knew Jeanne's dad and was happy to have a second generation of Allens at UT. The Chair of the department at that time was not as nice and seemed quite rough on the women, but Jeanne remembers other students saying he was grouchy to everyone, men and women alike.

The geology honor society, Sigma Gamma Epsilon, was "men only" at the time, and would be for several more decades. Consequently, the women in geology formed their own group called the Smilodons which included previously featured Susan Keifer. Jeanne graduated in 1948 with a B.A. degree in geology because the B.S. degree required the UT field course and women were not allowed on the course at that time. What Jeanne did not know was Marie Gramann (Chapter 10) had broken the UT field camp barrier ten years before only to have the door shut again after she graduated.

After graduation, Jeanne was taking a breather at home in Tyler, just having fun and playing golf when her father said, "Don't you think it's time to get a job!"

Figure 13. Jeanne and Rosamond Allen, 1948, two budding geologists. A Junior Faculty Fund was established at The University of Texas at Austin in their names by Albert Haertlein, Ros' son. (Photo: Deeny Haertlein, Fredericksburg, Texas.)

With a referral from her father's friends, Rusty Byers in the Fort Worth office of Gulf Oil, hired Jeanne. She was hired as a secretary, though, and because she did not know how to type, Jeanne just shuffled papers until she was finally transferred into geology. Jeanne echoed what Susan Kiefner Cage said: women who did find work in the petroleum industry during those years usually had some kind of contact in the business; otherwise, it was near impossible to get hired. Jeanne broadened her geologic network and became a member of AAPG in about 1949.

In Fort Worth, Virginia Cox, a geologist who was several years older than Jeanne, took her under her wing and trained her. Jeanne was mostly running (describing) samples at that time. Her boss valued her ability to run samples and would often have Jeanne redo work done by some of the men to catch formation tops they had missed. Though not allowed to sit wells, Jeanne visited a wellsite with Bob House from Wichita Falls. The motel where the three women geologists were staying was awful, dirty, and smelly. One of their colleagues said, "Well, get used to it! This is how we have to live out here!" At the wellsite, the well blew out and her jacket was covered with oil spots. Jeanne has kept that jacket, unwashed, all her life.

After training, Jeanne was transferred to Amarillo where she met another woman geologist, Louise Jordan, a PhD from the Massachusetts Institute of Technology (MIT), who worked for Sun Oil and was largely responsible for setting up Sun's entire office. When the job was completed, Jeanne remembers that Sun unceremoniously "let her go." That mistreatment of Louise made a lasting and disturbing impression on Jeanne. After Louise left Amarillo, Jeanne was the only female geologist in town and her most enjoyable experiences became helping with company field trips to Colorado.

In early 1953, after four years in Amarillo, Jeanne married Charlie Ferrin. Charlie had spent two years in the oil business before going to medical school in Galveston. When he started medical school, she took a transfer with Gulf to Houston. There, she briefly shared an office with her friend from UT, Susan Kiefner Cage (Fig. 14).

Figure 14. Jeanne Allen Ferrin, left, worked for Gulf in Houston where she shared an office with Susan Cage. (Photo: Susan Cage, Georgetown, Texas.)

In 1954, when Charlie accepted an internship in Denver, Jeanne asked for and got a transfer to Gulf's office located in the Brown Palace Hotel in Denver. At that time, no one in the office except Jeanne had experience running well samples, and Gulf was starting a large drilling program in eastern Colorado. Jeanne's sojourn in Denver was disappointing because she was not assigned a specific area and felt she was not given much to do. Ironically, the situation changed when the Denver office was shut down and she was asked to stay on for a year and a half while they completed the closure. This was Jeanne's only opportunity for management responsibilities, overseeing the wellsite geologists and the geophysicists.

By the time the Denver office closed in 1959, her husband, Charlie, had moved to Central Texas to complete his residency and she joined him in Austin. That relocation ended Jeanne's career in geology because there were no oil companies in Austin, and it became a convenient time to start a family. She cherished her great memories of the Gulf days all her life. Even though women were not paid as well as the men and were often not given a chance to fulfill their potential, Susan felt being in exploration was the highlight of her career. Jeanne did find it ironic that *oil companies hated to hire women and have them quit after a few years and have a family. While they seemed to think nothing of their men working for a few years and then quitting to take a higher paying job with an independent* [author's emphasis].

Jeanne's sister, Rosamond (Ros) Allen Haertlein, also went to work for Gulf Oil, also through family connections, but in Shreveport, Louisiana. "Ros" told Jeanne, "It doesn't matter how you get your job, it is what you do that counts!"

Ros was with Gulf for three years before she married a geologist from San Antonio and moved, never to resume her geological career. She still has fond memories of developing prospects in Louisiana, Arkansas, Mississippi and east Texas and is pleased to have found her good share of oil in that short time. She, like Jeanne, was frustrated at not being able to do wellsite work.

One of Ros' memories was about a female geologist who told her that she always had to get a man to go to the supply room and get her pencils with erasers on them. In the pre-computer days, when geologists tirelessly drew with pencils, all their contour maps (as well as updating them with each new well), they went through lots of erasers. However, the company this woman worked for had a policy of never giving women pencils with erasers because they did not want the secretaries to erase on top of the carbon copies. This was before photocopy machines, when all correspondence had one to three carbon copies typed with the original. If someone tried to erase a mistake, it would just smudge the carbon in all the underlying copies. Consequently, if the secretaries made a mistake, management wanted to insure the correspondence was completely retyped and error-free. This female geologist could not convince the supply room that she was NOT a secretary and, therefore, entitled to pencils *with* erasers. She gave up trying and just had a male colleague bring her the pencils she needed.

In 2009, Ros' son, Albert Haertlein (B.S. Geology, 1978, The University of Texas at Austin), decided to honor his mother and aunt and established the Rosamond Allen Haertlein and Jeanne Allen Ferrin Junior Faculty Fund. Ros' daughter, Deeny Haertlein, followed the Allen tradition and became a geologist.

Jeanne Flavia Allen Ferrin was born in 1927 in El Paso, Texas. She earned her B.A. in geology from The University of Texas at Austin in 1950 and married Charles Ferrin in 1953. She is widowed and lives in Austin today. Rosamond was born in Laredo, Texas, in 1925 and graduated in geology from The University of Texas in 1947; she now lives in Fredricksburg, Texas.

Betty Russell Van Norman

Betty Russell always devoured numbers and took every math course she could in high school and college. The unsolvable equation was what was she going to do for a job? In 1949, from the view of working her way through Middle Tennessee State College, Betty's job choices seemed to be nursing and teaching. She wasn't interested in either. Betty dropped out of college and headed to her dream city, New Orleans.

Hard work and skills with numbers led Betty to jobs in the insurance business, where eventually she became, and worked as, an underwriter for several years. But, her friends knew she loved and lived for numbers. In 1955, one of her friends hounded her for weeks to answer a newspaper ad looking for a "girl" who had lots of mathematics. Betty noticed that it did not say "degree" and thought, "Oh, why not try?" She applied at a company called Schlumberger and got the job.

The job was to calculate dips for a new downhole tool called a "Dip Meter." Schlumberger put Betty to work computing (by hand because there were no computers) the "dip" for rocks as indicated by tools run in open wellbores. They wanted her to create a "dip meter" log, a paper display of the angle from horizontal of the rock layers in a hole that had been drilled. The layers would range from flat-lying or "no dip" to sometimes vertical (90°) dip. Schlumberger's recordings in wellbores could be used to calculate not only the angle of the dip, but also the compass direction of that dip. The recordings required careful, tedious measurements and calculations. All calculations were done by hand, using a slide rule and her command of geometry and trigonometry.

It was laborious work, but for Betty, it was the most fun she could imagine. The pace was frenetic with data coming in from wells at all times of the day and night, seven days a week. Well completions were waiting, mud was circulated in the well to keep the hole from caving in, and operators were charged large fees while they waited. It was expensive waiting while the data was being rushed to Betty to compute. As fast as she could, but careful to be accurate, the answers were rushed back to the well for decisions on whether to continue to drill, or not! Betty couldn't complain, as fast-paced as it was, because she was finally using the math she loved. She also enjoyed the interpretive geology work —strata, sands, shales, faults, dips and strikes, and chaotic bedding that she was learning on the fly. Betty soon learned that wellbores were rarely straight holes, instead, they often would worm around and deviate from a straight hole. The angle of the wellbore had a major effect on the accuracy of the dip meter she was plotting. Betty added the appropriate structural formulas to her interpretation process to bring the "apparent dip" back to the "true dip." All by hand. After a few years, Betty decided she could write a program to do this on the new computers, and then could eliminate the "darned slide rule." She loved the logic involved in writing programs.

Schlumberger rented time on Chevron's "big computer" to try out her program. It worked! Soon, Chevron got very interested in hiring her as a computer programmer, and Betty was amused when she learned that it took Chevron six months to decide to hire her because they feared "a female" couldn't bear up to the stress of the job. Stress? Different from her years of "24-7" (24 hours a day-7 days a week) stress with Schlumberger? That was laughable.

Part of the deal to work with Chevron was that Betty was asked (or told) to finish her college degree, started 20 years prior. Chevron's employment structure required that she have a degree, any degree, in her personnel files. Betty started night courses at Tulane and ended with an English degree. Probably the only logging engineer ever with English as a credential. Another benefit from working at Chevron, Betty met her husband, Gene Van Norman, a reservoir engineer. They were kindred souls for dips and dipmeters, for talking about reservoirs, and unitization over the dinner table. They both loved travel, language, and art and bought a lovely old home in the heart of New Orleans together.

After programming for several years, Amoco Production Company approached Betty about coming to work for them full-time doing nothing but dip meter interpretations. She welcomed the chance to get back into the wellbores and the rocks again. Programming was fun, but interpreting dipmeters was more so.

Figure 15. Betty Russell Van Norman parlayed her love of numbers into a career as a dip-meter "computer," then as a computer programmer before returning as a Gulf Coast specialist calculating and interpreting dipmeters. (Photo: Betty Van Norman, Baton Rouge, Louisiana.)

During an Amoco restructuring a few years later, the company offered to give Betty all the equipment needed for her work and set her up as a consultant, instead of as an employee. That led to a more exciting phase of her career, where she worked dipmeters for Amoco and many other clients all over the U.S., South America, and the North Slope. By 1985, as Gene retired, Betty started to slow down her consulting and finally retired in 1989. She and Gene learned French and started spending a month every year in Paris, indulging in their art interests. Back in the States, they took up sailing more frequently, and then, motorcycles, and even bicycling. (Fig. 15)

Retirement life was good. Then Katrina hit. They lost their home, entirely, and Betty and Gene moved to Baton Rouge to start a new life. Gene passed away in 2011 and she barely survived a burn accident that hospitalized her for two years. She is well today and now actively works to improve the Baton Rouge General Regional Burn Center. As a woman who loved math and had no college degrees, Betty solved her career equation by becoming a world expert in Dip Meters.

Betty Russell Van Norman was born in Tennessee in 1928, and attended Middle Tennessee State College from 1946 to 1948. She earned her bachelor's degree from Tulane University in 1970, and married Eugene Van Norman in 1972.

Joan Marilyn Fleckenstein Mizer (1930-2014)

The 1950s were years in which women were not very enthusiastically received into the geology fraternity. As an undergraduate at the Massachusetts Institute of Technology (MIT) in 1953, Joan Fleckenstein's first hurdle came when she was not permitted to accompany her sophomore classmates to the summer field camp at Crystal Cliffs, Nova Scotia, because the Ministry of Mines did not approve of MIT having women in the camp. Joan had to satisfy the field training requirement by working alone in several areas in suburban Boston, not a very comprehensive or satisfactory way of getting field experience, especially since she had limited instruction and supervision compared to what she would have experienced at Crystal Cliffs. She would face this field camp situation, again, when she began graduate work at the Colorado School of Mines (CSM). CSM did not approve of women at their summer camp either, so Joan did her summer fieldwork at the University of Wyoming's camp.

Returning home to Michigan after graduation, Joan found work in nearby Grand Rapids as a "mathematician, electrical engineer, and draftsman." On the side, she was hired by a local "wildcatter" to work up a report on several drilling sites. Her comments to the Alumni association at MIT talked about the attitude toward females at the time,

> I didn't even apply for the job--the man just heard of me and hired me, and he asked me to use only my initials (and not my first name) on all the maps, and the report, so that no one would know I'm a girl. Maybe if I mask myself behind my initials, I'll be able to get a permanent job in geology someday.

Joan continued her correspondence back to MIT:

> I think of the future and of what I want to do. I realize that I could go back to school and take up some course other than geology if I cared to do so. I have spent a great deal of time wondering what I really wanted to do. I finally made up my mind. I want to be a geologist! I love geology and I love the out-of-doors. I know now that I will have to take any job in geology at any salary doing anything, that it will take what might seem to be terrible sacrifices on my part, and that it will take years of time to get where I want to be.
>
> I was very tired, very unhappy, and very discouraged. I remember quite vividly one night during my junior year when [a friend] and I drove out to Dr. __'s house for a visit. Dr. __ explained to me the facts of life in regard to women geologists. I returned to my rooming house that night and cried and cried. My heart was

broken. But I convinced myself that Dr. __ was wrong and that I could succeed where other women had failed. I really hit rock bottom with my job interviews at school. They were the straw that broke the camel's back. Well, the camel's back has mended now. I want to try again. When I worked as a mathematician in Grand Rapids, I learned one thing—once you get a job you can always hold it so long as you are willing to work hard, to put in many extra hours, and to do the job well.

Joan subsequently entered Colorado School of Mines and, in the summer of 1954, put in 80 hours a week in the field learning how to survey. She and fellow student, Charles Mizer, decided to marry that fall; unfortunately, one of them had to drop out and go to work for financial reasons. Because she already had one degree and he did not, it was decided she would forgo her degree efforts. Almost immediately, she found an excellent position with the exploration division of the British-American Oil Producing Company in Denver, and one of her letters to MIT rang with joy at being so employed, "I feel that I was very fortunate to get a job as a geologist at all because there is still a great deal of prejudice against women in the oil industry. I must have a great many guardian angels looking after me lately because life has been more than kind and generous to me."

Sadly for Joan, the good fortune did not last. Her husband completed his degree at Mines and accepted a position with Standard Oil Company of California. She reluctantly resigned her position with British-American and went to California. For the next 10 to 20 years, Joan tried to juggle working in the oil industry, being a wife, and starting a family with more than frustrating results (Fig. 16). The marriage ended in divorce, after which, Joan returned to school in Michigan and finally "settled" for a degree in education.

She wrote to MIT, "a promising geological career for a well-trained and highly motivated young woman scientist seems to have come to a halt ...."

But, as a single parent with a son and a daughter to raise, Joan moved to Riverton, Wyoming, and took a teaching job. Her son, Clay Mizer, of Cody, Wyoming, today remembers his mother using her summers to work part-time with Riverton oil man, John D'Annunzio, developing prospects and getting them drilled. She also worked with another oil man, Gene Baker, doing the same.

Clay's fondest memories of his mother were of her teaching him to hunt and fish and spending considerable time as he was growing up doing so. He was 13 years old when he bagged his first antelope. At first, he frightened it away when he shot prematurely because he had accidentally crawled onto a bed of cactus. But, then he continued shooting and ended up putting a bullet through the antelope's heart. Joan had never field dressed an animal before, but came prepared with a book describing how to do so. Clay was a little queasy about doing the butchering, so he read the instructions and she dressed the antelope. After that, there were many hunting trips, most successful, for deer, ducks, and pheasants—all that Wyoming offers. Joan took him fishing, too, as she felt children needed that exposure to the out of doors. Her young daughter, Carlee, was not so interested. Joan was frugal and taught her kids that if they wanted something, they needed to get a job and earn it. Clay, like many, started with a paper route and bought duck decoys with his first money.

When the kids were grown, Joan Mizer moved back to Michigan and built a house for herself in the woods near Baldwin, where she lived quietly with her English setters and some memories of good times in the oil business (Fig. 17). Joan Fleckenstein Mizer was an AAPG member for 39 years.

Figure 17. Joan Fleckenstein Mizer, enjoyed her English setter hobby. (Photo: Joan Mizer, courtesy of her friends at the Belton English Setter Club.)

Figure 16. Joan Mizer often had to compromise her career with wife and mother responsibilities. She taught her son to hunt and dress his kill, to fish and appreciate the fish for sustenance. (Photo: Clay Mizer, Cody, Wyoming.)

E. Ann Butler

Ann Butler was very motivated to finish her degree in record time at Millsaps College in Jackson, Mississippi. She was divorced, had a baby girl to take care of, and did not want to overly burden her parents with this endeavor to reboot her life. The geology department at Millsaps, which had only one professor, worked well for her, except for the final advice she received, "You better take shorthand and typing, Susie! Or you'll never get a job!" He called every girl "Susie."

She said, "No thank you. I am going to be a geologist!" Thinking, "I didn't suffer through all that math and peripheral science to be a secretary!"

Because her family knew Grover Murray at Louisiana State University, Ann applied there for her master's program and was accepted. In 1955, Ann was urged to specialize in micropaleontology if she wanted to work in the petroleum industry and that advice worked well for her. When Ann finished her degree in 1957, industry jobs were scarce and she felt fortunate to get a job at the Louisiana Geological Survey to continue her research on the Gulf Coast Miocene microfauna. Ann became active in AAPG and especially in SEPM, publishing technical papers and developing a network of colleagues in industry (Fig. 18).

In 1962, Sinclair Oil contacted Ann and made her a very compelling offer to work in their paleontology lab in Tulsa, Oklahoma. She and her young daughter, Barbara, moved to Tulsa and started a new life. At first, Ann was Manager of the Paleontology group and continued work on the Miocene of the Gulf Coast, but eventually she went on to became Project Manager for Sinclair's Gulf of Alaska program. Ann's role as manager entailed visits to their Alaska field party in the area, something she looked forward to and cherished, especially the helicopter field trips. Once, as she sat on a mountain peak not too far from camp, shooing away mountain goats and thankful to have no bears in sight, she started busting up geodes in the Pool Creek Formation. Ann was astonished to open a geode and find a perfectly preserved foraminiferal specimen of a *Marginulina* species, millions of years old. She thought, "Could life be any better?"

After the Arco-Sinclair merger in 1969, Ann was transferred to Dallas to the Arco Lab where she concentrated once again on the Southern Louisiana Miocene. Working for Arco's Lab, her assignments also required that she travel to other parts of the world, and she especially enjoyed her trips to Jakarta. Pertamina, the Indonesian national oil company, had a mountain retreat that Arco employees were invited to use. On these trips, Ann was bestowed with the nickname "Texas Toucan" because she was so adept at bargaining with the local craft sales people who were referred to as "toucans."

Figure 18. Ann Butler, 1982, with a "toucan", a local crafts salesman, in Indonesia. She was humorously called "Texas toucan" for her bargaining abilities. (Photo: Ann Butler, Gleneden Beach, Oregon.)

In the early 1970s, Ann had the opportunity to move to Arco's corporate headquarters in Los Angeles to evaluate company-wide exploration activities for the executives of Arco. The domestic and international travel was exhilarating and Ann felt she learned a lot about strategic planning, techniques that she continues to use today in her civic activism. Her final move was back to Dallas to manage geological support for Harry Jameson, President of Arco Exploration Company. Ann Butler would end her Arco career on this pinnacle assignment when the next "restructuring" developed about seven years later. She found throughout her career, by coincidence, things happened in seven-year increments.

From the mid-1950s well into the 1970s, Ann was the only woman along on business trips and at meetings and was treated with great respect. She also was aware that many young women might come behind her in the business and thought it was essential, for their sake, that she leave a legacy of good comportment and professionalism. Ann had to occasionally deal with embarrassing situations, as most women do, when a colleague would make unwelcome advances. Sometimes they were peers, sometimes they worked for her, and sometimes they were above her in rank, but she found that a very firm, "No, no way, not now, not ever."

worked wonders. Though it might be a little awkward around that person for awhile, if she just moved on, Ann found that they got over it. Many remained life-long friends.

Compensation was not discussed during most of Ann's career and it wasn't something she gave much thought to, as long as she made a comfortable living and did work she loved. Ann did learn she was paid less than the guys in her earlier years; however, by the time she retired, she was equitably compensated. Ann's motivation, to the end, was the joy of the work, the people she worked with, and the feelings of accomplishment wherever she landed. Ann Butler has been an AAPG member for 60 years and is retired in Gleneden Beach, Oregon.

Ann Butler was born in 1932 in Meridian, Mississippi and earned her bachelor's degree in geology from Millsaps College and her masters from Louisiana State University in 1957.

Peggy J. Rice

I was born in 1935 in the Cretaceous hills of Montague County, Texas. I recall as a small child seeing the lights of a drilling rig in those hills and, later, being taken by my father to visit the wellsite. The well was plugged as a dry hole, however, there is now Barnett Shale production in that very area. In college (University of Tulsa and University of Colorado), my professors were very considerate. In most classes I was the only female, although there was another woman in several classes. Kay Smith and I were partners in Field Surveying, a two-semester ten-hour course in Tulsa. Somehow, we got the heaviest stadia rod (birch wood), but we managed fine. At the end of the course, each person had to do a walking survey of a section. The detail in my map of one area was sparse because it was home to a bull and his harem!

My becoming a geologist was not on the horizon when I finished high school in 1952. In fact, I doubt that I had even heard the word "geologist." The only options I was aware of for women were to be a nurse or teacher or, if college was not an option, then one could be a secretary or a waitress. I chose secretarial school, which led to a job (at age 17) with a small oil operation and drilling company in Wichita Falls, Texas. The oil industry was interesting. A Tulsa consultant especially impressed me, Glenn S. Dille, whose reports were infused with humor. While working full-time, I managed to juggle my courses, labs, and work and finally graduated in 1961.

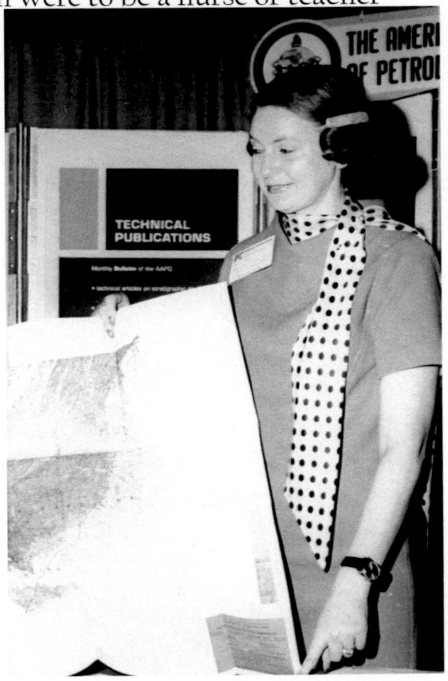

The next phase of my career was at AAPG, where I worked on the Bulletin, but more often on books, and was named Special Publications Editor after several years. I had wonderful co-workers, some of whom became long-lasting friends. I became acquainted with many noted individuals in both industry and academia and enjoyed the opportunity to work with people such as Mike Halbouty, Marshall Kay, and Gerald Friedman. Editing papers on such a wide range of specialties kept me abreast of what was going on in the geologic world. Art Meyerhoff oversaw publications most of my time at AAPG; his breadth of knowledge was remarkable, and I learned a lot from him. (Fig. 19)

Figure 19. Peggy J. Rice, 1971, showing off AAPG's new geological highway map at an International Petroleum Exposition meeting in Tulsa, Oklahoma. (Photo: Peggy Rice, Austin, Texas.)

The only gender discrimination I experienced during my career was when I was at AAPG—and it was subtle. Men lunched with men and women with women. Women therefore were not a part of casual conversation about policy, politics, and just plain gossip. Of course, we had our own gossip sessions! At one point (maybe the early 1970s) I decided to use my vacation time and attend the AAPG annual convention at my own expense. It was very helpful to meet authors in person and to schedule some work sessions at the convention. That changed things—after that, one or two female editors were sent to the annual conventions and some sectional meetings.

Contacts made at AAPG led to the next phase of my career, at Conoco in Houston. My writing and educational skills were appreciated and utilized. Also, my work in editing prepared me to handle reserves reporting at Conoco. One of my favorite assignments, which lasted several years, was with a joint-venture with a Japanese company.

Figure 20b. Close up of Peggy when she was President.

Figure 20a. The first female president of the Houston Geological Society (1982-83), Peggy was working for Conoco in Houston at the time. (Photo: Peggy Rice.)

Both in Tulsa and in Houston I was active with the local geological societies. Once, as I was registering at a Mid-Continent Section meeting in Tulsa, the [female] secretary of one of my fellow Tulsa Geological Society officers recognized my name and said: "You don't look like a stodgy old geologist." When I moved to Houston, I started helping Chet Baird with the Houston Geological Society (HGS) Bulletin, which at that time was a "cut and paste" operation. I was elected to several offices and, in 1982, to president of the Houston Geological Society. [Peggy was first woman president of HGS, sixty years after nine women helped to found the association; 12% of the founding members were women]. Board meetings were in the evening after a full day's work, so I tried to conduct them efficiently. At the transition meeting when "old" officers were being thanked for their service, one of the Board members made a tongue-in-cheek comparison of me to Margaret Thatcher. I took it as a compliment! (Figs. 20a and 20b)

I loved participating in field trips such as those offered pre- and post-convention at AAPG Annual Conventions. One was in the 1970s when the convention was in Anaheim. The trip was led by John Kilkenny to view geothermal sites. We stopped by the Salton Sea on the way to a site near Mexicali, Mexico. Winnie McGlamery, a paleontologist with the Alabama Geological Survey, was on the trip (Fig. 21). She was over eighty at the time but still clambered up steep stairs to view the geothermal facility. We ate at a restaurant in Mexicali, where we were served pitchers of margaritas with our meal. On the return trip, Winnie, the bus driver, and I were probably the only ones not napping.

Another trip was to Guatemala from the AAPG Annual Convention in New Orleans. The field trip leader, Hugh Wilson, had in-laws who lived in Guatemala City. They graciously invited us to their home for a reception and beside the lovely home and gardens, I remember the largest bowl of guacamole I had ever seen--wash-tub size! I also remember our sleep was interrupted one night in Guatemala City by an aftershock from a large earthquake that occurred months earlier. Next we took a flight to see the Tikal ruins in what I was told was a revamped "flying boxcar" of WWII vintage and I could see daylight around the emergency door. Fortunately, we flew low enough not to need a pressurized cabin.

Overall, being a geologist was a good career for me. Today's young women have opportunities through career counseling and many other avenues to learn what possibilities are awaiting them. I wish them well.

Peggy J. Rice was born in New Harp, Texas in 1935 and earned her B.S. degree at the University of Tulsa in 1961 and attended the University of Colorado in 1956-57. She retired from Conoco in 1993 and now lives in Austin, Texas.

Figure 21. Peggy in the mid-1970s on a Salton Sea field trip with a real pioneer, Winifred McGlamery (1887-1977) who was with the Alabama Geological Survey prior to her 1961 retirement. (Photo: Peggy Rice.)

Carolyn Miracle Ross

When Carolyn Miracle was a young girl exploring the hills and hollows on the family farm in Arkansas with her collie dog and playing on the lichen-covered rocks on the hillsides, she had no idea that she would someday be exploring areas of the world she had never heard of. But that exploration would be mostly subsurface looking for petroleum, not critters skittering through the woods.

Carolyn had international pen-pals as an adolescent and was always interested in science, history, and faraway places. In high school, Carolyn thought she would like to be an archaeologist with the unrealistic hopes of discovering another ancient Troy. She knew, however, there was little chance of her going to college, despite top grades all through school, because her family could not afford to send her to college. But an article in *Science Digest* in 1952 opened a surprising possibility for her, and that one article changed her life. It described a project that The National Science Foundation and Westinghouse conduct jointly every year for high school students across the nation, The National Science Talent Search. It required taking a science-oriented test and submitting a scientific paper to the National Science Foundation.

Carolyn took the test, and submitted a paper titled, "A Brief History of Man and His Common Ancestry with the Ape." A few months later she learned that she had placed first for the state of Arkansas. No monetary rewards were given with the Talent Search awards, but they provided strong recommendations for scholarships to universities and colleges everywhere. Based on that award and being valedictorian of her graduating class, Carolyn applied for and was offered several scholarships. However, she could not afford out-of-state tuition and other costs, so she chose the University of Arkansas.

Carolyn learned from the scholarship catalog that the highest paying scholarships were first, in football and second, in music. Since she was not qualified for either, she applied for the next highest one, a four-year, privately-endowed scholarship with a choice of majoring in either chemical engineering or geology. She chose geology. Fortunately, she fell in love with the subject during her very first course. So, what had started out as a financial means of getting a university education turned into a life-long love and appreciation of geology; one that after a long and frustrating delay, developed into a career in international petroleum geology. A woman working in international petroleum geology is not unusual today, but in the post WWII, pre-Affirmative Action years, it was exceedingly rare.

In 1953 it was especially rare for four-year scholarships to be awarded to female students in "men's fields." So, Carolyn entered the University as the only female in her geology classes and came in for a bit of hazing, particularly in the labs. Her sense of humor prevailed and she became good friends with the guys and maintained friendships long after graduation. Fieldwork was done in the Boston Mountains in northwest Arkansas, and was usually done in pairs. The head of the department chose to pair Carolyn with two of the married male students, no doubt assuming "safety in numbers."

After her sophomore year at the university, she still needed additional financial assistance beyond her scholarship. There were no government college loans at the time. So, she persuaded the Dean of Students at the university to defer her scholarship for one semester at the beginning of her junior year to allow her to earn additional money. She had been offered a job traveling to South America selling magazines and although the job didn't appeal to her, the adventure of her first trip to a foreign country did. And there were indeed many adventures.

Carolyn married her fiancé, Bill Ross, a chemical engineering graduate, during the summer of her junior year. He was finishing his Army service in Alaska while she was completing her university degree. Carolyn graduated from the University of Arkansas in January 1958 with a B.S. in geology with honors, Phi Beta Kappa, and on the Dean's List. She was also the first and only geology student in the newly established Honors Program in the department.

Anticipating starting her career in the oil business as did her engineer husband, Carolyn was very disappointed to discover that there was a big difference between the acceptance of female science students in academia and the attitude in the corporate world. She was met with, "Oh this is great, we can really use a good geological secretary." There was no regard for her geology degree, her academic achievements, nor the fact that she couldn't type. Another prevailing attitude for not hiring women professionals was, "If you're married, you'll get pregnant and leave." If a woman was not married, then the attitude was, "If you're single, you'll get married and leave." That prevailing attitude was not at all concerned that *men* often leave too, for a better job, more money, or for family reasons.

It was eight years before Carolyn managed to get a job as a geologist. Subjected to the prejudices of the times and, like so many other post-WWII female geologists, she had to work through jobs as a draftsman and as a technical librarian before finally, with mentoring from an "insider," to the position of geologist. The exploration manager of the international department of Phillips Petroleum Company where Carolyn was "a librarian" recognized her underemployment status and her potential. He moved her into the job of "assistant geologist," then later to geologist. This began a fascinating career covering many areas of the world, including the North Sea, northern Africa, western Africa, the Middle East, Central and South America, and the Gulf Coast of the United States.

Carolyn's international career experience began at Phillips Petroleum with the excitement of being able to view the first seismic line ever shot in the North Sea. It was a very long line that ran from Denmark to Scotland and the paper print had to be laid out in sections up and down the floor of Phillips' large gymnasium. In the ensuing years, the North Sea has been thoroughly explored by many companies and countries, and major petroleum fields have been developed. Being able to see the beginning of exploration of this major oil and gas region of the world is still a point of pride for Carolyn.

She was the first woman geologist ever hired at three large companies in the 1960s and 1970s, beginning with her Phillips Petroleum employment. After Phillips, she continued her career working for several companies both as an employee and as a consultant. Carolyn is proud she left a positive track record for other women. Each of the early jobs presented frustrating situations for a female geologist. Even though she got along well with all the men and formed many very good friendships, the attitudes of the time were challenging. While newly hired men were assumed to be capable from day one, with each new job Carolyn was at first regarded with skepticism and had to prove herself, over and over. Sometimes her managers felt compelled to "explain" her presence, and, in some cases, apologize for it.

At one company, the manager introduced her to a partner in a joint operation saying, "This is our woman geologist."

The man's amused response was, "Yes, I can see."

Another time, the manager telephoned a joint partner about a meeting that was going to be held and said, "I hope you don't mind, but I am sending a woman geologist to the meeting."

At lunch, shortly after they had hired her away from another company, he told Carolyn that the only way she could be more valuable to the company is if she were also black and disabled. Another limitation being female, was that even though she worked international frontier exploration (new ventures) for several of her employers, none would send her overseas by herself, even when her expertise was requested by the overseas managers. Once when she was requested to substitute for a geologist in Algeria for a month, the Vice President responded, "What? Send a woman to Algeria? Are you CRAZY?!"

Carolyn's brief Gulf Coast experience with Shell Oil in the late 1960s did not present these complications, since Shell had a long history of employing women geologists as stratigraphers and paleontologists—dating back to the 1920s. She was sent on all male field trips, but never out for wellsite work. In all her jobs, from the beginning, some people just never seemed able to accept the fact that she was in a so-called "man's" profession and that she, as the only woman, worked with, lunched with, sometimes traveled with, and was friends with her male colleagues. Despite the friendships, it was discouraging that her salary was never the same as that of the men. It was substantially less, even compared to her male colleagues with less experience.

Carolyn was amused with one job offer in the late 1970s, when an older man from Pakistan, along with his adult son, had come to Houston to look at getting into oil exploration in Texas. Carolyn was introduced to him, and after a few lunch meetings, he tried to persuade her to do consulting for him on Texas drilling prospects. He was reportedly the richest man in Pakistan. Carolyn was a bit skeptical, so she checked with a friend from Pakistan who told her that, yes, the gentleman actually *was* the richest man in Pakistan, and was very, very rich indeed. Carolyn turned down the offer, primarily because she had no expertise in Texas drilling prospects and she was already employed by another company. But the irony was not lost on her: her interests and experience had been primarily *foreign work for American companies*, and here she was being *offered American experience for a foreign company* (Fig. 22).

The 1980s brought a very welcome change in general attitudes toward women in the profession. For the first time, Carolyn had an opportunity to work with other professional women geologists and geophysicists. Until then, she had been the only woman geologist in the international departments of the companies where she worked. But in the 1980s women geologists were being sent overseas on assignments and even moved into supervisory or managerial positions with many of the major corporations and a few independents.

Figure 22. Carolyn Miracle Ross, 1972, working internationally for Texas Eastern in Houston. (Photo: C. M. Ross, Houston, Texas.)

Also in the early 1980s, Carolyn had an opportunity to work with a former boss in his international consulting group. He was French, and like many other Europeans, seemed far more "enlightened" about hiring women and putting them into overseas assignments. In fact, he admitted his surprise at how much discrimination women in America seemed to face. This consulting work involved some projects developed through the World Bank for international areas, such as Liberia in western Africa. It was a risky but very interesting project, working with both the World Bank and the government of Liberia. It so happened that a long and bloody revolution had begun in Liberia about the time the project got underway, a revolution that lasted for many years. Some of the Liberian Ministry people in charge at the time the project was negotiated were killed by the revolutionaries and a relationship with a new group of Ministry officials had to be established. She recalled that after the multi-year geological and geophysical project evaluating the petroleum potential of Liberia, a public presentation of the results was made to the Ministry and various American oil company representatives in Monrovia. Carolyn and her two colleagues made the presentation while being surrounded by revolutionary soldiers in camouflage holding submachine guns. Some were even standing onstage beside the presenters while more were sometimes running up and down the hallways outside the auditorium.

During the 1980s, Carolyn formed her own company, Miracle Exploration, Inc. But, because the petroleum business had not picked up again by the end of the 1980's, she reluctantly decided to change careers. She took several courses in administrative law and began her new career in the environmental regulatory field by joining the law firm of Vinson & Elkins in their environmental department. Carolyn continued to work there until the age of 70, when she retired to look after her husband, who had developed Alzheimer's disease and needed her more and more as time went by. He passed away in 2012, after more than 56 years of a happy marriage they had shared.

Carolyn was a founding member of the Division of Environmental Geosciences in AAPG and a member for 39 years. In 1982, she founded an international professional society, the *International Explorationists*, which continues to be successful to the present day. This contribution to the HGS was the basis for her receiving the Distinguished Service Award from HGS in 1990.

Carolyn was a docent at the Houston Museum of Natural Science (HMNS) when the large, world-class collection of gems and minerals was first sold to the Museum by Perkins Sams, a Midland oilman, in 1985. She also was able to finally fulfill at least part of her early interest in archaeology. Carolyn was part of a small group that helped to revitalize the Houston Society of the Archaeological Institute of America and served on the board for several years.

Carolyn Miracle Ross has enjoyed an interesting and fulfilling life, thanks to geology. She has met many fascinating people from various areas of the world, made many interesting friends, overcame obstacles and outmoded attitudes and the perspective of many men in the profession. She has been delighted to see the opportunities for women geologists expand, and she hopes she has left a positive impact as a woman geologist.

Carolyn Miracle Ross was born in Clarksville, Arkansas, in 1935. She earned her B.S. in geology at the University of Arkansas in 1958. She and Bill Ross were married in 1956. She is retired and living in Houston, Texas.

Rena Bonem

Rena Bonem decided on geology while in High School because she had entered science fairs, had placed 4th, and, received an award from AAPG at the 1966 International Science Fair in Dallas. She began her undergraduate work that same year at the University of New Mexico and studied with Sherman Wengerd, but once she realized she had an interest in macro paleontology she transferred to New Mexico Tech (School of Mines) and finished both her B. S. and M. S. degrees working under the direction of Dr. Christina Lochman Balk on Cambrian trilobites. Rena received her Ph D from the University of Oklahoma, where she worked with on Pennsylvanian bioherms.

This time she spent in the mid-continent of the U.S. also afforded her an introduction to the petroleum industry. She recalled, "I interviewed with Chevron in the early 1970s and was told that they did not want to hire women, especially PhD's because they would just get married, get pregnant, and would quit after the company had spent money training me. I was so upset by that one experience that I did very little more with petroleum. Perhaps, a couple consulting projects..."

Rena also shared this story from a friend who was getting her M.S. in geophysics during the same time, "[she] was told after sending résumés to several schools, they [oil companies] might hire her as a secretary, but not as a geophysicist. She quit school and never finished her degree."

Rena Bonem taught at Hope College in Holland, Michigan, from 1975-79, TCU 1979-81, and has been a professor at Baylor since 1981. Despite the unsupportive attitude toward women in industry in the 70s, Rena has taught and trained students who have become petroleum industry summer interns, and, eventually, employees.

Rena Bonem is a professor at Baylor University. She received her B.S. in 1970 and M. S. in 1972 from New Mexico Institute of Mining and Technology. She earned her PhD in 1975 from the University of Oklahoma. She has been a member of AAPG for 46 years.

Susan Ann Burton Longacre

Susan Burton Longacre remembers her father, Gerald "Gerry" Burton, a geophysicist for Shell Oil in the 1940s when seismology was a new technology, spreading out long rolls of paper on the living room floor looking at hundreds of markers and making something of the single line of squiggles on those rolls. This had a lasting impression, as did his arm-waving out the car window at passing landscapes as the family vacationed each summer in national parks of Wyoming, Colorado and Arizona. By 1954, Gerry Burton was picked as head of the new Shell marine division to help manage its growing offshore empire and Susan attended high school in New Orleans where her father was posted.

Because Susan thought the local atmosphere far too provincial, she wanted to attend college outside of Louisiana. To gain her parents support for out-of-state tuition, she researched the possibilities in Texas. Susan was very good in physics and math and learned The University of Texas (UT) had a Van De Graaff generator, so she used that as an argument to head to Austin. It worked. They agreed. However, upon arriving, Susan decided to try another science since she already had completed courses in biology and chemistry—she signed up for geology. It was love at first class. Then Susan agonized about how to tell her parents at Thanksgiving that she had already changed her major.

When Susan picked geology as her major, she knew she would meet with skepticism from her father. In his experience, women were not valued in industry because so many got married and quit or had babies and quit, after the company had spent resources on their training. He knew Shell's pioneering woman geologist, Doris Curtis, had done so, but perhaps he did not know that during her first employment with Shell she had been *forced to quit* because of Shell's nepotism rule. Eventually, once Gerry Burton realized his daughter was dead set on being a geologist, he became her greatest cheerleader.

The UT Geology Department had only two or three women in their undergraduate program in 1959, and most professors were very accepting of women. Only one professor had a reputation for not wanting any women in his classes, and Susan avoided him. Another skeptical professor completely changed his attitude when she "aced" his class. When she finished her undergraduate work, Susan approached Dr. Charles Bell about doing a master's degree with his supervision. He thought she would do well to go directly for a PhD and had the perfect project to combine Susan's math and geology skills, statistical predictive stratigraphy using several Cambrian trilobite zones from Central Texas.

In 1968, when her dissertation was finished and published, Susan moved to Houston and sought a job. She found that her father's position with Shell was a big drawback to finding employment. By then, Gerry Burton was the first President of Pecten, U.S. Shell's International Exploration Company. Shell would not hire Susan because of nepotism rules, and another major company would not hire her because her father was an executive for a competitor. A third major did offer her a job, but at a salary lower than her male fellow graduates.

Having very limited success with the majors, Susan was advised to try Getty Oil. She had no idea J. Paul Getty had an oil company, but a Getty executive and friend of the family recommended that she try to get a position in their research lab. That proved to be the start of a very rewarding career for Susan. As with most women hired before Affirmative Action, she was hired making 15% less than the men. That was soon remedied with the changes in the 1970s and a promotion to a managerial position; Getty equalized her salary.

The Getty job was somewhat risky for her, as Susan was told she would be doing a lot of engineering and engineering was not part of her academic background. Continuing education and on-the-job training established her as a person who understood both and their application in exploration and exploitation. For the rest of her career, she could rely on having the vocabulary, the understanding, and the mindset of the engineers to integrate geology into their side of the equation. In later years, Susan often taught geology for engineers and others in the company, and always found that rewarding.

Five years into her career, Susan had grown into positions with great responsibility. For example, she was the first carbonate geoscientist in Getty's Offshore Division. Although most of their offshore work was in the Gulf of Mexico, lease sales in three basins offshore of the eastern U.S. coast were on the horizon. The east coast basins had carbonates in their Mesozoic stratigraphy and Susan's skills in these types of rocks were needed. Many companies were drilling in Baltimore Canyon at that time, and a consortium was formed to prepare for other big offshore lease sales. C.O.S.T. or the Continental Offshore Stratigraphic Test program cored several wells in Georges Bank and the Southeast Georgia Embayment. Susan was Getty's technical representative and she thoroughly enjoyed the interaction with peers from other companies, forging lifelong friendships.

After several years completing the basinal studies, Susan started thinking about returning to Getty's lab, wanting to get back to "rocks," her first love. This coincided with a time when the EEOC was putting pressure on companies to have more diversity in their company management, and Susan was subjected to a lot of pressure to go into management, with opportunities to substantially advance in the company. Susan had a tough decision, "go back to geology, which she really missed and loved? Or, turn her career toward managing and dealing more with people, budgets, strategies?" She had always tried to stay out of office politics. She never wanted to worry about who had a nicer office, better views, bigger desk, or bigger salary—she knew she did not want to have to deal with those kinds of issues within the company. Should she "take one for womankind" or do what she wanted to do and avoid what she viewed as the quagmires of management?

Susan chose the return to science and never looked back. She still had to deal with budgets and people, but she excelled at finishing projects on time and under budget. Life was good. And then, in 1984, came the merger between Getty and Texaco. The cultures of both companies were vastly different. Getty was an open and communicative community: they were encouraged to share ideas, they encouraged employees to stand up and say what they thought without trepidation, and they valued thinking outside the box. In contrast, Texaco, at that time, did everything by the book: each person seemed to work with blinders on, not talking to each other either within the company and certainly not to people outside the company. There was little socialization and people were secretive. At first, the Texaco hands were leery of the "free-wheeling" Getty people, but gradually they found it refreshing, like they just got out of jail! As a result, Texaco became much more inclusive and comfortable and nowhere was this more evident than in the lab where Susan worked.

Interestingly, by 2001 when Texaco and Chevron merged, Susan felt that Texaco was the more open and communicative company and Chevron's people were more staid and process-oriented. Company cultures do make a difference and they can change.

Teaching became an important aspect of Susan's career. She was dedicated to teaching geologists and engineers alike to "read rocks." The most successful way to do that is at the elbow of someone else. She loved taking the time to walk colleagues through the process of reading rocks and transferring that knowledge from cores and well logs to their understanding of petroleum systems

One of the most rewarding things that happened as Susan worked for Texaco was their establishment of a "Texaco Fellows" program in 1998. Susan (the only woman) and four others were chosen the first year to be Fellows; a recognition of exceptional technical performance honoring their accomplishments and contributions to the company and to the energy industry. In later years, the Texaco Fellows were provided with the resources and administrative assistance needed to mentor young professionals in the company. The positive effect of this Mentoring Excellence in Technology (MET) program on young technologists was dramatic.

With the merger, ChevronTexaco adopted the MET program as a best practice, and it continues to this day. About 25 Fellows work with 80 high-potential young technical professionals in a year-long mentoring program. Susan felt so dedicated to the program that she stayed very involved with it long after she retired in 2002. One of her favorite parts was the casual evening gatherings that seemed to form around her after the formal programs of the day were over. This was a setting where the heart-to-heart Q&A was rich and fun. In recent years, other technical women have joined the Chevron Fellows and continue Susan's tradition in the MET Program. Although other earth scientists are among the Fellows, none of them are women, yet.

A critical aspect of becoming a Fellow was Susan's contribution to professional societies. Her technical "home" was principally in the publications of SEPM and AAPG, as well as among the technical professionals who published research results on sedimentology, stratigraphy, paleoenvironments and diagenesis, particularly as they applied to carbonate rocks. Participation and leadership in technical committees of both societies were part of Susan's career that was exceedingly rewarding, especially when she was elected the Editor of AAPG's technical publications, including the *Bulletin*. The first woman to do so (Fig. 23). As such, she also served on the AAPG's Executive Committee for the years 1989-1993. Again, strong friendships were forged and the volunteer work of reviewing and approving publications was phenomenal. It was both challenging and invigorating. Advice she always gives young professionals is to become involved in your professional societies and stay involved. She had also contributed to publications and committees of GSA and SPWLA. All rewarding, she says, but hands down, being AAPG Editor was the best.

Figure 23. Susan Burton Longacre, first woman to be AAPG Editor, 1989, and first woman to Chair an AAPG committee. (Photo: AAPG Archives, Tulsa, Oklahoma.)

To bring the story full circle, petroleum pioneer Doris Curtis was one of Susan's mentors during the 1980s when Susan worked on SEPM committees and convention programs. During a social gathering at an AAPG/SEPM Annual Meeting, Doris and Susan had a wonderful conversation about Susan's Dad. Susan remembers Doris remarking how ironic it was that "I have been working on Gerry's perceptions of women in the industry from the outside, and you, Susan, have been working on him from the inside!" He did realize that gender didn't make a difference – a good geologist is just that – a good geologist. Industry can't afford to ignore that segment of the talent pool.

Susan married law student, Ken Longacre, while working on her PhD., and had two wonderful daughters while jockeying her career, never having to quit, as her father once worried. Ken loved socializing with the AAPG crowd and created his own legacy. In Susan's "retirement" she has become a Texas Master Naturalist, continuing to teach geology in the Central Texas hill country to students with a wide variety of backgrounds, technical, professional, and domestic. She also is working diligently to portray "rocks" in another pastime: creating art quilts, including several with a Grand Canyon theme.

Susan Ann Burton Longacre was born in Los Angeles, California. She earned her B.S. in geology at The University of Texas at Austin in 1964, and her PhD in 1968. She is retired to Kerrville, Texas. Susan Ann Burton Longacre celebrates 50 years, a half a century, in AAPG in 2017.

Mary Beth Cooper

When I was growing up, I wanted to be a nurse. My Dad had been in the Navy, and I wanted to be a Navy nurse and see the world. I was a candy-striper in high school, was in the Future Nurses Club, and knew that a nurse is what I would grow up to be.

In college, I needed a basic science course and I had already taken chemistry in high school, didn't want to take Botany, and that left geology, which was totally new and looked to be interesting. Freshman geology at The University of Texas (UT), was taught by Dan Barker and Charlie Bell (Fig. 24). It was a whole new world, and populated by so many *cute* guys. I was majoring in math at the time, so I decided to minor in Geology. My grades went down in math and up in geology, and, when the trends crossed, I switched my major to geology. All thoughts of nursing were totally forgotten. There were few women in the geology department at that time, and I still remember meeting Robbie Gries (then Rice) outside the old geology building when she came to UT in 1966.

Figure 24. Mary Beth Cooper, 1980, river rafting in the Grand Canyon. (Photo: Mary Beth Cooper, Denver, Colorado.)

My vision of a career in geology was giving fireside talks on geology in National Parks, and working outdoors. Instead, I ended up working in offices with masses of data. In retrospect, I realize I went into geology for all the wrong reasons *(see previous note on cute guys)* and without any firm knowledge of the field of geology and the science as a whole.

In job interviews, both after my B.A. and then after my M.A., I was told that I could be hired as a secretary or a bug-picker, but not as geologist. It wasn't until after the civil rights legislation passed and companies had quotas that I could be hired as a geologist. In 1970, then husband, Dick Waitt, and I moved to Seattle. I had to look for a job where my science and math background would not go to waste and found a position in nuclear medicine at hospitals. My marriage ended about the time the Civil Rights legislation had passed and after living in Seattle for five years I decided that, if I wanted to use my geology degree, the time was right to try to the petroleum industry again. I moved to Houston and found a job right away and worked for Pennzoil for a year, but, Houston was not a good fit. I interviewed in Denver and got job offers from Chevron and Amoco. I moved there in January, 1975, and worked for Chevron as a geophysicist, not a geologist—without one single course in geophysics! Times had truly changed. For the next ten years, I worked for Chevron, then Kansas-Nebraska Gas, Page Petroleum, and Lear Petroleum.

I was active in RMAG and AAPG, and enjoyed serving on AAPG's Education Committee where I was sent to review a course offering in Miami, Florida, in 1980. There I had the good fortune to meet Ted Fons, a geophysicist working in Alaska. One year later, he moved to Denver, and, in 1983, we were married. Ted soon went to work consulting and using the Canadian Geophysical Microcomputer Applications (GMA) exploration software. He opened Excalibur Geophysical Consultants to represent the GMA products in the USA. In 1985, I took a leap of faith and left my job to join him at Excalibur. Soon, I was insisting that we purchase one of those new "portable computers" so that Ted would not have to install the GMA software every time he went to a demonstration for a client. The computer weighed 25 pounds and we had to borrow $6,000 to buy it. Initially, we worked out of our home, and, in 1988, we opened our small office in Union Station, bringing on several employees over the next few years.

In 1996, we sold our business and felt good about selling it to our employees to reward them for years of hard work and service. A couple of years later, another company bought GMA, and expected they were buying both the Canadian and U.S. rights. When we first started working with GMA, I wrote our initial contract which stated that our company, Excalibur, had exclusive rights to the USA sales and marketing. GMA made noises a time or two about wanting to renegotiate the contract, but they never did. Therefore, when the purchase time came about, the buyer discovered Excalibur still owned the U.S. rights and they had to purchase them from our employees, Jeff Saul and Jan Engelkes. Jeff and Jan made enough from the purchase to buy into another company and gave us a tidy check as a "thank you." What goes around, comes around. And, I felt it was very confirming to me, a geologist playing like a lawyer, writing our contracts.

Upon retirement, Ted began making pottery full-time and I decided to fulfill my childhood dream and started Nursing School so that I could work with people instead of data. I feel fortunate to have fulfilled two career goals and dreams in one lifetime.

Mary Beth Cooper was born in Pleasanton, California. She acquired her B.A. at The University of Texas in Austin in 1967 and her M.A. in 1969. Mary Beth is retired and living in Denver, Colorado, and was an AAPG member for 26 years.

Gwenn Jensen

My introduction to geology came in a seventh-grade science class. To this day, I am convinced my teacher was a frustrated geologist who couldn't get a job in geology; she spent an inordinate amount of time on geology compared to the other sciences that should also have been covered. She challenged us to interpret a series of increasingly complicated block diagrams. Being able to see in 3-D came easily and I turned out to be a whiz at interpreting the sequence of events that were represented by each puzzle. Sadly, there was never a mention of geology in any subsequent classes all the way through high school.

In the summer of 1964, on the cusp of transferring to the University of California Los Angeles (UCLA), I happened upon *Giants of Geology: The Story of the Great Geologists* (Fenton and Fenton, 1952). I was hooked. The small liberal arts college where I had spent my freshman and sophomore years had no geology courses, but UCLA did. To enroll in classes though, I had to have an advisor sign off on my program. I walked into the office of Professor Charles Corbato, the departmental advisor, and asked for his approval.

The first thing he said to me was, "Don't major in geology, you'll never get a job."

I was taken aback.

No one had ever told me I couldn't do something before, and I sat there for a few moments before I replied, "Well, that's okay, I'll do it anyway."

With that, he signed off on my program and I launched into my studies in geology.

I signed up for the first class of the major, Mineralogy 6A. Walking into the lab, I saw eight or so guys and two other women besides myself: Jan Clemens (Blacic) and another very sturdy looking woman who came to class with a rock hammer hanging from her belt. There was a bet that Jan and I would be the first to drop out, but instead it was Ms. Rock Hammer and two of the guys who left before the month was out. By graduation, Jan racked up lots of honors and earned a "University Scholar" designation from the entire university, and I managed to graduate with a B.S. in geology. The eight of us who made it through Mineralogy 6A went through the whole program together, probably one of the smallest classes for a UCLA department.

UCLA was big on fieldwork, what they called their "UCLA style of detailed geologic mapping." That meant to graduate you had to complete a full year of fieldwork, two semesters plus summer field. And every geology graduate student who had not graduated from UCLA had to take at least one semester of fieldwork, preferably Tick Canyon. This turned out to be excellent training as later in my career I ended up doing fieldwork in almost every area that I evaluated as a student.

The first semester started with plane table surveying, mapping the topography at the Janss Steps hill next to Royce Hall and then moved on to Bouquet Canyon. I took my sister, Cheryl, one day to finish my mapping. She had stayed at the bottom of a hill and complained she was hungry. So, I tossed the car keys to her so she could go back to the car for our lunch. Big mistake. We spent the next several hours looking for the keys. I never used a plane table again.

After Bouquet Canyon, the eight of us spent the rest of the semester mapping Rainbow Basin in the Mojave Desert. Every weekend we drove 150 miles to Barstow and back. The first night Jan invited me to toss my sleeping bag in the back of her station wagon while the guys camped out on montmorillonite mountain. That was their big mistake. It rained that night and they awoke in a slimy, slithery mess; they and their sleeping bags were encased in mud. Layers of the mountain clay had literally slid down on them while Jan and I awoke dry and refreshed.

We spent the second semester mapping Tick Canyon, a misnomer if ever there was one. It should have been called Rattlesnake Canyon. Every weekend, one or more of us encountered a snake. Someone left a coiled-up toy rattler in a narrow gully where everyone had to pass by. Just as I was about to step, I saw it, yelled, and jumped a mile only to find several of the guys chortling at my reaction. The very next day, Else returned at the end of the day to the parking lot with her hands behind her back. Slowly she revealed the headless snake with its blood dripping down her back side. No one topped that one.

Summer fieldwork, the final peg in our yearlong slog, we mapped part of the San Luis Obispo quadrangle. And unfortunately, half of us contracted poison oak. I was one of the lucky ones who didn't while Bob Sweeney had the worst case. One day when I was paired with Sweeney, we agreed on a spot to meet to catch the van back at the end of the day. As I sat on the boulder waiting for him, I saw this figure racing down the hill, map case and rock hammer flying in different directions, with a herd of cattle chasing him. He barely made it over the barbed wire fence and was incensed when I couldn't stop laughing. It was quite a sight. Apparently, the cattle thought he was there to feed them, and they were hungry. At the end our mapping, Bob held a bonfire ceremony in the parking lot where he torched his rock hammer. As a geochemist, he didn't need it again (Fig. 25).

I put myself through school working half-time, first for a year in the Geology Department, then two years for California Division of Mines and Geology. When the oil company recruiters came to interview, I signed up with all of them. I had taken Ted Bear's, (AAPG President 1984-85) petroleum geology class and loved it. This is what I wanted to do. Of the several recruiters that I spoke with, most said they didn't hire women, period. Only Amoco offered any encouragement. Their recruiter thought they might hire me as an "assistant," but I never heard from them again. So when I graduated in 1967, I had no job and no prospects. But Ted Bear gave me a reference and an introduction to two retired geologists running an oil and gas employment agency. They sent me to interview with Cities Service Oil and Gas.

Figure 25. Gwenn Jensen (middle) in the field with Jan Clemens (left) and Juhn Liou, 1966, San Luis Obispo. (Photo: Gwenn Jensen, Centennial, Colorado.)

Cities had two job openings, receptionist and draftsman. The lead draftsman, Charlie Hoefer, told me he would hire me only if I would stay two years. After thinking about it, I decided to take the receptionist job with the intention that I would go on to graduate school in a year. I called the next day and told them I would accept the receptionist position and their response was one of surprise. I don't think they thought they had offered me a job, but I started with Cities on February 1, 1968.

After several weeks of sheer boredom on the reception desk, Alaska geological manager Bob Thompson and others asked me to do a variety of literature searches and geological summaries for them. Within a few months, I was promoted to geologic aide tasked with creating a West Coast geological library and conducting short projects.

In late 1969, management decided to move the office from central Los Angeles to Thousand Oaks where most of the professional staff lived. I would have either had to relocate, as did a few others, or spend hours commuting. I said I wouldn't go unless I was promoted to geologist. At the time, John Wilson, a friend in the UCLA class after me, had hired on six months after I. He heard that they were looking for a geologist, and said, "You've got one here working in the library, and she's a better geologist than I am." That point is debatable, but I was offered the position of geologist, the first woman in the company since World War II.

My first assignment was to evaluate a package of prospects in the Sonoma-Orinda-Livermore basins. Over the next several years, I spent a total of three months field-checking the surface structures and collecting rock samples for lab analysis. My boss, Gus Keller, came to my office only once to see how it was going. In the end, I recommended only one prospect: the #1 Gumpert became the deepest well in California at the time, and a dry hole. It was my first well-site experience, three weeks on with one week off, for nearly six months. When it came time to log the well, log analyst Bob Colby and manager Vernon Hill arrived to oversee the operation. They offered to take me to dinner the first night, asking me to meet them at their motel room. When I knocked, they invited me in to sit on the bed. In an instant, the bed began to vibrate from the quarters they had slipped into the "Magic Fingers" mechanism. Only after they managed to contain their guffaws at my red face did we go eat (Fig. 26).

In the three years after the 1969 Santa Barbara Channel oil spill, the political and economic climate in California had deteriorated and the decision was made to close the office and relocate to Denver. Prior to the move, I had been dating Cities fellow geologist, Jeff Heller, and we decided to marry. Knowing most companies refused to employ husband and wife teams, we decided not to say anything until we were settled in Denver. I thought this might be the end of my career in the oil business as most companies considered it a confidentiality risk to hire the spouse of someone employed with the same or another company. How things have changed. Once there, we made the announcement and were pleasantly surprised to learn we both could continue working there. Land manager Bob Pasque came up to me and said if they had tried to fire me, he would have testified for me.

The following summer was truly a once in a lifetime opportunity. I joined four other Cities geologists for six weeks on the North Slope of Alaska doing geology via jet helicopter. On arrival in Anchorage, our first sojourn was a visit to see newly hired Randi Martinsen (AAPG President 2015-16; See Chapter 13) who was sitting a Cities' well on the north side of the Cook Inlet. Randi was the first and only woman to sit a well for Cities in Alaska, and I was the first and only woman to do fieldwork on the North Slope with Cities (Figs. 27 and 28).

Figure 26. Gwenn on the #1 Gumpert well, the deepest in California at the time, 1972. (Photo: Gwenn Jensen.)

A day sightseeing in downtown Kotzebue, population 1700, and off we flew north. The first three weeks' camp was a Head Start building in the Inupiat village of Noatak, 50 miles north of Kotzebue and 63 miles north of the Arctic Circle. As the first order of business, we were required by the BLM to set up the giant "fecal burner" and the second order was to learn how to shoot a .356 Magnum rifle and handgun. Bob Thompson, an avid gun enthusiast who loaded his own shells, advised me to place the butt of the rifle firmly against my shoulder when firing. Failure to do so could result in the recoil breaking my collar bone or shoulder. I passed the test intact but failed to hit anywhere near the target. One of the more accomplished

Figure 27. Gwenn with an Inupiat neighbor when working in Noatak, Alaska, 1973. (Photo: Gwenn Jensen.)

sharpshooters took over carrying the rifle on all excursions as protection from the bears.

The village was a delight. The children were out of school and played volleyball outside our building. This turned into a less than desired activity with the midnight sun. As the weeks progressed, their circadian clocks lengthened until they were playing at three in the morning.

Figure 28. Gwenn moving about the North Slope of Alaska, 1973. (Photo: Gwenn Jensen.)

We had made a free stop in Hawaii on our way to Alaska and brought four pineapples to the camp. We served them to the villagers who had never tasted it before and, in turn, they gave us *muktuk* (whale skin with blubber attached). They chew it like bubble gum. The oil seeping out of the blubber and the sensation of a mouth full of rubber bands is an acquired taste and we weren't there long enough to acquire it.

For the second three weeks, we set up a tent camp located on a sand bar at the confluence of the Noatak and Kelly Rivers. Each day we would climb into the helicopter and head to locations in the Brooks Range to collect reservoir and source samples of mostly Permo-Triassic rocks. One day returning to camp, we spotted a mama bear with two cubs nearby. We circled until we could see that they were headed away from camp and went on in.

I spent the next four years working California on the Central San Joaquin to Sacramento Basins and evaluating leases for the 1975 Federal Southern California Offshore Sale. Each of these involved combinations of field and subsurface investigations. In my brief foray into the Sacramento Basin, I developed a prospect which turned into my first discovery, Southeast Dunnigan Hills, 2333 MCF/D, drilled and completed in 1982.

It was an unusual trap and when I showed the prospect to my supervisor, Roger Wolff, he shook his head and said, "How do you come up with these things?" I can see in 3-D as I discovered in my seventh-grade science class.

Looking for a change, I requested a transfer to the Production Department, primarily to get Rocky Mountain experience. At the time, Cities was developing acreage in the Hartzog Draw oil field in Wyoming which Randi Martinsen oversaw. There were so many wells drilling that everyone in the department had to pitch in and sit the wells, one week every month. Before she moved to Exploration, Randi showed me the ropes on sitting a well without a mud logger. I inherited her 5-gallon bucket to wash the samples. It lasted until I left it filled with water overnight during winter, and it burst its seams when it froze solid. Late one night waiting for the objective zone to be reached, an old driller on the night tour (pronounced tower) offered me some of his coffee. Why the pay always comes in the wee hours of the night, I never figured out. Rather than be ungracious and hurt his feelings, I took a couple sips, and then noticed he had practically no teeth.

In Production, I oversaw Cities' efforts on the Minnelusa play of the Power River Basin and the Overthrust Belt, which was hot at the time. Then on January 20, 1979, I headed to a well just outside of Evanston, Wyoming, in the Yellow Creek Field. This was supposed to be a short visit as mudloggers were onsite. I was going to oversee the proposed coring job. The very next day I spent reviewing samples, drill times and such and drove back into town for dinner. On the dirt road into town, two oil field guys driving in opposite directions had stopped to chat completely blocking the road. They didn't move when I came up behind them, and I thought about honking but just waited patiently. I was glad I did as one of the guys pulled out a handgun and shot a winter colored white jackrabbit sitting on a bale of hay, red blood oozed over the white snow. He took one look back at me and then drove off into town.

That evening I returned to the well to wait out the core point. About 10 pm, I needed to take a leak. I told the mudloggers I would be right back and walked behind the engineer's adjacent trailer to squat down out of view. I didn't make it. Since there was some moonlight, I hadn't taken a flashlight and did not see the hole. I fell straight into a "rathole", bouncing off the walls as I went down and down. Shock turned to dismay immediately. I had never encountered a hole like that on any of the many wells I had sat before. It was cold, but not as cold as above ground where the wind chill was about -50°F. After a few minutes, I started to shinny my way out of the hole. It didn't work very well as I couldn't get my legs horizontal, the hole wasn't wide enough, and the side of the wall left nothing for a foothold. I managed to get within a foot or two of the top only to encounter the ground frozen solid with no purchase. I tried to get past it only to slip and fall to the bottom once again. I waited awhile yelling for help but the noise of the drilling rig drowned out my calls. Once again, I tried to climb up and yelled my heart out when I reached the frozen layer of soil, to no avail, and soon I tumbled back down again.

A bit of paranoia set in: what if the bottom of the hole is only bridged over? If I tried to climb out again, would I break through and fall deeper? Protected from the cold only with a down vest, at least I was wearing decent shoes, so, I settled in to keep myself as warm as I could and wait for crew change in the morning. Fortunately, I had a watch and as the tour change approached, I started back up the hole. It was daylight then, and I had been in the hole about nine hours. Back near the top again, I wedged myself in as best I could, and started screaming. Nothing.

Then, I heard a voice from inside the trailer, "Gwenn? Where are you?"

"I'm outside, in a hole," I screamed.

Slowly, the company hand came around to the back and looked down the hole, "What are you doing down there?"

"Get me out of here!" nearing the end of my rope.

"Wait, while I get some help."

"Hurry, I don't think I can hang on much longer."

"Well, don't fall back."

Within minutes, he returned with help and a rope. I grabbed on and they pulled me out. I could not have been more relieved to leave my abyss. (Fig. 29)

The first thing I asked when I was safe was, "What is that hole doing there?" though maybe more colorful language.

"Oh, we were going to hook it up with the trailer's bathroom, but it's been too cold and the pipes all froze."

So, there was one positive note, the hole had never been used as a latrine.

When I inquired about him looking for me, he told me that when he made his morning report, the Operations Manager asked where I was, since I hadn't called in. When he said he didn't know, he was ordered to go find me.

I later asked the mud loggers why they didn't come searching for me, and all they said was, "We thought you had gone into town with the core hand."

Figure 29. The "rathole" that Gwenn fell into, over 20 ft. deep and about 24 inches wide (see hammer for scale), could have been her grave. A scary situation she barely escaped alive. Yellow Creek field, Wyoming, January 1979. (Photo: Gwenn Jensen.)

"And leave my car here?"

That was met with a shrug, and I left disgusted at their incompetence and stupidity.

Our drilling engineer drove me to Evanston's hospital where I was ushered back to an examining room and a man in a white coat. I had hurt my knee and shoulder from bouncing off the walls of the hole and he checked them out. Seeing nothing critical, he gave me a tetanus shot in my rear and told me to soak my swollen knee in warm water. I returned to my motel room and filled the tub.

Meanwhile, our log analysts and my boss were on their way to Evanston. When they arrived the next night, they called and invited me to dinner.

"Meet us at our room," said the log analysts.

So, I did. I knocked and heard someone yell, "Come on in."

As I entered, I was greeted by SOB (Sweet Old Bob) and the 'Round Mound of Sound', aka Bob Colby and Wally Wahlstedt, standing on their heads, giving me the "Mork from Ork" hand gesture, and bellowing, "Na-nu, na-nu." *Mork and Mindy* was Wally's favorite TV series, and he would regularly greet someone with the salute, a handshake with a scissors motion that separated the middle finger from the ring finger.

I don't know how long it took for me to stop laughing. But, that was the point.

The three of us joined my boss, Vernon Hill, who took us to the finest steak house in Evanston. Vernon suggested we start with his favorite drink, a Rusty Nail, which we did, many times over. Somewhere close to the third or fourth round, Colby and I started arguing.

"I could have gotten out of that hole," Colby opined.

One way or another, I told my good friend, Sweet Old Bob, that no, I didn't think an overweight man in his fifties who smoked could have gotten out that 20-30 foot hole. And as the argument progressed, our language got saltier and louder. After awhile, the restaurant manager came over and asked us to please leave. We managed to stumble out of there and get back to our rooms and I have never had a Rusty Nail since.

The fall down the hole and subsequent fight with SOB taught me two things. First, to appreciate life as it can be short. It was the first time mortality entered my consciousness and how easily things could have had a different outcome. And secondly, that no matter how hard I worked or how I felt I could do things on my own, gender issues would always be there, even with colleagues I knew and respected. Over the next few years, I changed my outlook on many things. I had been affiliated with the AGI-Women Geoscientists Committee since 1975, but it was oriented to academic women and I had very little contact over the years beyond a newsletter from time to time. So, when women from Mobil formed the Denver chapter of the Association for Women Geoscientists, I joined and became active with them. I marched for the ERA and cried when it didn't pass.

Having completed my two-year stint in Production, I returned to Exploration. Minnelusa geologist, Paul Slack had just quit and I inherited his area and a few of his prospects. Paul had delineated a fractured Niobrara play in the Powder River Basin and after I evaluated it, I proposed that Cities drill deeper and go for the Dakota. When we cored the Niobrara, you could see the fractures were self-healed with pyrite and there was nothing, but the Dakota did come in with oil. Sitting the well was a disaster. The rig had come from North Dakota and the sour gas up there had created holes in the drill pipe. The crew was constantly tripping for "hole in pipe." And something was way off. Their depths did not tally with what I saw when I correlated the drill time to the section. About three times when they tripped, I asked that they strap out of the hole and check their measurements. Each time they could find nothing wrong. As the well progressed, the crew were getting frustrated and angry at my requests. Strapping out is a huge hassle and takes a lot of extra time.

When it came time for the first core, the crew asked me to wake the core hand, and, as usual, most things happen in the dead of night. I went down and knocked on his trailer and he kicked open the door and I found myself confronted with a double barrel shotgun pointed at my head. I guess I had woken him up. I backed off and told him it was time to core and left. When it came time to do second core, again late at night, I refused to get him again.

I left the well when they prepared to set casing in anticipation of the Dakota. Back in Denver, I went straight to the Engineering Manager to show him how the footages we measured going in and out of the hole just were not right and warned him to watch out when they drilled into the Dakota. They ordered another strap out and, finally, discovered that they had been strapping out with a tape that was one foot shy of the standard 30 feet. I later heard the drill stem test flared half way across the field when they tested the Dakota. It was completed at 293 BOPD, 350 MCFD.

Over the years that I worked at Cities and then Oxy after the merger, I felt fortunate to have worked with a great group of people who were good at their jobs and decent human beings. I learned a lot from them. When Oxy decided to close the office and move us to Oklahoma City, they had laid off almost everyone in the office. My husband, Jeff, and I were two of about 20 who were asked to relocate. In preparation for the move, a manager of the Oklahoma City office came to meet us remaining souls. We sat around the conference table and listened to him welcoming us to join his team. In his efforts to be helpful, he proceeded to tell us where we should look for a place to live.

He pulled out a map of the Oklahoma City area, and said, "Don't look here or here or here, that's where all the blacks live."

Jeff and I decided we did not want to make the move. The next day we declined the transfer. My last day was January 31, 1987, nineteen years to the day I started with Cities. Within a few years, all of the Cities explorationists from the Denver office had been laid off. We have never regretted our decision, even though it meant that I left the industry and a job I loved.

Gwenn M. Jensen was born in Los Angeles, CA, June 24, 1944. She received her B.S. in geology from UCLA in 1967. She returned to school and earned an M.A. in anthropology in 1992 from the University of Colorado at Denver and her PhD in anthropology in 1997 from the University of Colorado at Boulder. She currently consults as an oral historian and medical anthropologist.

Josefa Cuevas de Sansores (1920-2011)

The First Mexican Woman in Petroleum Geology

Doña Josefa Cuevas de Sansores, was the first Mexican woman to enter the field of petroleum geology and geology in general (Fig. 30) fifty years ago. Before that, petroleum geology in Mexico was exclusively practiced by men.

Josefa Cuevas was born in Merida on the Yucatán peninsula in 1920, the youngest of four sisters. Her mother was Professor Andrea Aguilar Arguello, founder of several kindergartens in Yucatán, one of which currently bears her name. Her father was Filiberto Cuevas.

At that time, Josefa's high school had a third-year option where she could choose a specialty and she chose law. However, Doña Josefa later told her friends and family, "I wanted a life where I fall in love with an engineer and marry him, so I went back to high school and did the engineering special."

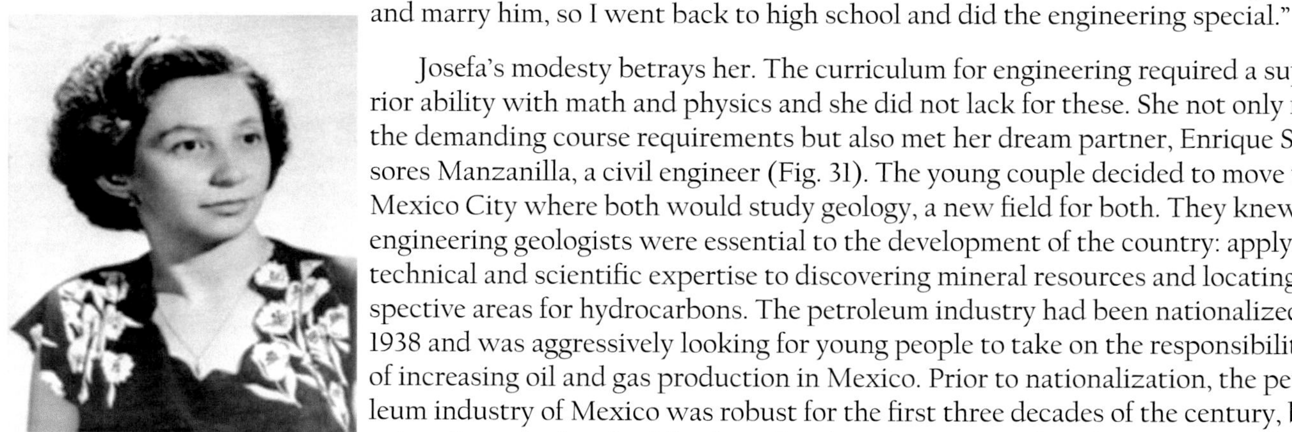

Figure 30. Doña Josefa Cuevas de Sansores, about 1945. (Photo: Luis Enrique Sansores Cuevas, Mexico City, Mexico.)

Josefa's modesty betrays her. The curriculum for engineering required a superior ability with math and physics and she did not lack for these. She not only met the demanding course requirements but also met her dream partner, Enrique Sansores Manzanilla, a civil engineer (Fig. 31). The young couple decided to move to Mexico City where both would study geology, a new field for both. They knew that engineering geologists were essential to the development of the country: applying technical and scientific expertise to discovering mineral resources and locating prospective areas for hydrocarbons. The petroleum industry had been nationalized in 1938 and was aggressively looking for young people to take on the responsibilities of increasing oil and gas production in Mexico. Prior to nationalization, the petroleum industry of Mexico was robust for the first three decades of the century, but primarily in the hands of foreign oil and gas investors and geologists. Some of the most famous geologists who founded AAPG gained their field experience working in Mexico; among them were Everette DeGolyer, Alex McCoy, and Sydney Powers.

Figure 31. Doña Josefa Cuevas de Sansores with her husband, Enrique Sansores Manzanilla. (Photo: Luis Enrique Sansores Cuevas.)

Josefa and Enrique enrolled in the school of engineering of the University National (UNAM). Josefa had to start from scratch. It was 1944 and few women were studying for university degrees at all, let alone in geological engineering. There were three women in the program when Josefa joined and she was the only one to finish. In 1947, she also earned the first medal for University merit, a great distinction in her school. Her professional exam was in 1950, which she passed with unanimous approval and was given an honorable mention. Her Synod included Eduardo Guzmán and Federico Mina, both in management for Pemex exploration, professors Harmión Larios, Manuel Álvarez and Ramiro Robles Ramos, and as President (Presidente del jurado que realizó el exámen profesional) engineer Teodoro Flores.

Josefa went to work at Petroleos Mexicanos (Pemex) in 1946, the first female geologist in the company. She started as assistant paleontologist and by 1949 was transferred to the Southern region of Mexico in charge of the Paleontology laboratory. In 1949, Josefa was transferred to the Southern region—southeast Mexico, to take charge of the paleontology laboratory, working primarily on Tertiary strata. Several promotions and years later, she was transferred back to headquarters where she worked from 1953 to 1966. Josefa's career expanded to new geological provinces in Veracruz, Tamaulipas, San Luis Potosí, Coahuila and Baja California when she moved to The Northern Tampico Zona, to continue as the head of paleontology and work on the Tertiary and Cretaceous.

In 1969, Josefa made her final transfer, back to Mexico City where she was placed in the Mexican Institute of Petroleum (IMP), as Chair for the Department of Tertiary Micropaleontology. At the IMP, she analyzed all sedimentary samples from the country, which enhanced their knowledge of the microfauna and stratigraphy of Mexico.

For the last nine years of her career, she was responsible for preparing catalogues of planktonic and benthic foraminifera and their interpreted environments. This was used to build paleogeographic models as they related to hydrocarbon habitats.

Post-retirement, Josefa worked with her husband consulting for Petroleos Mexicanos training new geologists and working on staff initiatives for exploration. In 1990, Doña Josefa Cuevas de Sansores was recognized for her contributions to geoscience with the Earth Sciences Award by the Mexican Geological Society.

Information for Doña Josefa Cuevas de Sansores was provided by Paty Ortiz Gomez who also presented the story of Doña Josefa in the History of Geology Session, 2016, "The First Mexican Woman Geologist," at the 2016 AAPG/SEG geological conference, Cancun, Mexico.

Cecilia Martin (1921-2005)

Venezuela's First Woman in Petroleum

Cecilia Martin was independent-minded as a young girl and with other girls at the women's Colegio Catolico de Caracas in the 1930s, she formed a group called the Las Castanuelas (The Castanets) and protested the dictatorship governing Venezuela at that time.

Women studying geology in Venezuela in the 1940s was completely unheard of, but, Cecilia Martin de Bellizia became the first woman to graduate from the Universidad Central de Venezuela (UCV) in 1947—and graduated Cum Laude. She and her classmate, Alirio Bellizia, were married during these college years and after graduating they were awarded a scholarship by Humble, now ExxonMobil, to study at the University of Oklahoma. Cecilia earned both her Masters in Geological Engineering in 1950 and PhD. degree and returned to Venezuela where she worked both at UCV and at the Ministry of Mines and Hydrocarbons.

Eventually, Cecilia became a full-time employee of the Ministry and was a dedicated field geologist, exploring for economic mineral resources, including petroleum. She coordinated and participated in many field campaigns across the company. Cecilia Bellizia was one of the main authors of the Mettalogeny Map of Venezuela, yet was denied credit for her work when she divorced.

Figure 32. Cecilia Martin doing field work in Argentina in 1982. She was the first woman to graduate in geology in Venezuela and worked on petroleum resources for the Ministry. (Photo: Juan Rios, Caracas, Venezuela.)

After a divorce, Cecilia returned to her maiden name, Cecilia Martin, and expanded her work for the Ministry to include countries outside of Venezuela, including Peru, Chile, Argentina, and El Salvador (Fig. 32). She was appointed to the position of Special Studies Division Chief. The Venezuelan government, recognizing Cecilia's important contributions, bestowed two medals upon her, the Order del Libertador and the Orden de Andres Bello. The last phase of her career was spent as a Senior Researcher at INTEVP, the Research Institution of Petróleos de Venezuela South America (PDVSA). She successfully combined raising a family of four children with her career. Cecilia was a member of AAPG for over 20 years.

The information about Cecilia Martin was from an interview done before her death in 2005: Furiati Paez, C. (2006) Cecilia Martin Franchi: Emprendedora de Jornadas Teluricas. PUNTAL, Year 12-Number 20, p. 18 - 21, Fundacion Polar. Caracas, Venezuela. Additional information was provided to Maria Antonieta Lorente by Juan Rios who worked with Cecilia at the Ministry.

Daisy Pérez de Mejia

First Venezuelan Woman in Oil Business

Daisy Pérez de Mejia graduated from the Universidad Central de Venezuela (UCV) in 1961, the 4th woman to be awarded a geology degree, and the first Venezuelan woman to enter the oil business. In 1962, she began working for the Corporacion Venezolana del Petroleo (CVP), the Venezuelan national oil company, after a short stay at the Ministry of Mines and Hydrocarbons. For a brief time, 1967, she returned to the Ministry to work with the team that conducted the first geological assessment of the Orinoco Bituminous Belt. (This was later presented to the World Petroleum Congress by team leaders J. A. Galavis and H. Velarde.)

In 1977, she was transferred from CVP to Corpoven, another unit of Petroleos de Venezuela SA (PDVSA), and assigned as an advisor specializing in Western Venezuela. In 1978, she was sent to Lagoven (Exxon's former oil operating company) to participate in the Maracaibo Basin Cretaceous Core Study, a joint project with Exxon. In 1979, she worked with PDVSA´s Inter-Affiliate team that collaborated with the Schlumberger on a study of Venezuelan geology, completed in 1980. In 1981, she became Assistant to the Manager of Regional Studies Group in Lagoven, and was soon promoted to Supervisor of that group. (Fig. 33) From 1982 to 1984, she was part of PDVSA´s Inter-Affiliate "Ad Hoc" Committee that prepared the Country's estimated total reserves (proven and unproven oil reserves including the unproven probable gas reserves).

Figure 33. (Left to Right) Maria de Lourdes de Gamero, Professor Gonzalez de Juana, Daisy de Mejia, and Mireya Bolivar de Sancio, 1981 in Caracas. (Photo: Daisy de Mejia, Caracas, Venezuela.)

In 1984, she coauthored a paper on the Gulf of Paria, and in 1989, she participated in PDVSA´s Inter-Affiliate Group that prepared the description of the major Venezuela's Oil Fields for the publication. From 1990 to 1998, she again participated in PDVSA´s Inter-Affiliate Committee for Hydrocarbons Resources Evaluation and was member of the Group for Evaluation of Exploratory Risk. In 1995, she contributed to the Post-Mortem evaluation of the Perija Exploration Campaign. Before retiring, she became involved in the publication of the 3rd Stratigraphic Lexicon of Venezuela and was responsible for Cretaceous Formations of Western Venezuela.

Daisy recalled, "In the late sixties into the early seventies, when the CVP offices were moved from Caracas to Maracaibo, I was left in Caracas at the consulting office, Thoms and Dallmus, who were doing a project for CVP's Exploration Department. I did not want to move from Caracas and neither did many of my colleagues. As time passed, my Exploration manager, Gorgias Garriga, was under a lot of pressure to transfer me. So, every time that he was questioned about the date to move me to Maracaibo, he replied, "When Daisy finishes preparing a Geological Column for me in Gothic letters!"

Figure 34. Daisy de Mejia, the first Venezuelan woman in petroleum industry, paved the way for future generations. (Photo: Daisy de Mejia.)

So, it was going to take a lot of time! And, I was never transferred and my entire career was spent in Caracas, where I wanted to be."

Though Daisy was asked to supervise the Regional Studies Department whenever the position needed to be temporarily filled—as she knew all the responsibilities and was very capable, she was never promoted to that position. A large disappointment in her career. Daisy´s advice for the new generation of women geologists in the oil industry is to "follow the examples of the pioneers, those that faced pressure, misunderstanding, and male chauvinism but that managed to overcome difficult situations and gain the well-deserved respect for all women in our profession." (Fig. 34) Daisy was an AAPG member for 35 years.

Daisy Pérez de Mejia was born in September 1939 in Los Teques Edo Miranda, Venezuela. She graduated as Geologist in 1961 (after Cecilia Martin, Maria Natera and Cecily Kavanagh de Pezal) the 4th woman to graduate as geologist in the country. She obtained her M.A. in 1977 from The University of Texas at Austin with specialization in carbonate facies and diagenesis, under the supervision of Professor R. Folk.

Nicola "Nicki" Barker

First Female Petroleum Geologist in the United Kingdom

In 1967, S. Nicola "Nicki" Mounteney found herself questioning the joys of having being born a girl, as Imperial College (IC), part of London University, was the sole university in the United Kingdom (UK) to offer a course in petroleum sciences and she was barred from attending. The world of rocks was going through a very exciting time in Britain, thanks to the emergence of the North Sea as a serious hydrocarbon province, with civil engineering firms dogged by geology related disasters, and with plate tectonics bouncing in on the scene (Fig. 35).

She says,

IC at that time was exclusively a science and technology university within which the Royal School of Mines held all the earth science disciplines, including petroleum. I arrived in London fresh from the rural provinces, and for three years, with just a single girl in mining and two of us in geology we had an absolute ball in what was pretty much an exclusive 500 strong male college. The only downside was that that my longing to break the barriers into petroleum geology was consistently resisted. Oil rigs offshore were strictly male provinces – no suitable accommodation, no loos etc. – a total red line that could never be crossed.

At the time this seemed a decidedly permanent setback, so, in my desperation to get into industry, I moved from soft rocks into engineering geology. In 1970, with a first-class honours under my belt I started out in the civil engineering world creating Rendel Palmer and Triton's first engineering geology department. One girl and a desk. It was new and fun, but geology within civil engineering did not sit easily with lateral thinking, like mine. Engineering projects then were still heavily constrained by "tick box" methodology—and a year on I still could not truly warm to their world of 'mice and men' [Scottish poem about a mouse carefully building a winter nest only for it to be destroyed in the spring by a ploughman].

Ever impetuous, I responded to an advert for a hydrologist in Australia in 1971 and it precipitated me into the petroleum world of the North Sea by the back door.

London-based Exploration Consultants Ltd. (ECL) was a vibrant, recently formed oil consultancy consisting of just three bright ex-oil company guys, a draftsman and a secretary. With the UK government

Figure 35. Nicki Barker, first UK woman in petroleum, checking out a core on the Shell Miri Well #612 in Sarawak, Borneo in 1980. Her husband, Ken, a petroleum engineer with Shell Sarawak, is working with her. (Photo: Nicki Barker, Dorchester, Dorset, England.)

releasing new rounds of licences in the North Sea, their young business was on an exponential upward curve and they needed a new recruit. Since I was clearly barred from joining any major or even small oil company, this was the very next best thing. Life became one huge learning curve, but then the North Sea was going through one huge learning curve itself. Schlumberger taught me how to read well logs, seismic was so full of noise that interpretation was a bit of a black art, and the rest I picked up in-house or from fellow members of the Petroleum Society of Great Britain.

In the early 1970s, the oil world in London was still totally a male province. But it was a small world and my fellow colleagues in the industry were very decent and went out of their way to accept me and my work. Nonetheless it was at least a couple of years before I dared come out of the "closet" and sign my reports with an obviously feminine name.

Throughout the 1970s, London became the base for many of the major oil companies operating outside the USA with interests not just in the North Sea, but also wider Europe and offshore western Britain. When staff were limited, they tended to turn to consultants to fill the manpower gap, hence we were regularly thrown in at the deep end. Work was often intense with long hours and a rapid pickup of a new regional and company dynamics.

Desperately in need of a break from this, in 1973, I took myself off to New Zealand (NZ) and spent 10 laid-back months working on an entirely non-oily project for the New Zealand Geological Survey before returning to the hectic pace of London and my old firm of consultants at ECL.

London during the 1970s was a fantastic place to be young and in work, but an impossible place to save. By 1975 I was married (to a petroleum engineer) but even on two professional salaries, any thought of buying a home was a pipe dream and it became clear that to make any headway financially, we had to escape the UK tax system.

So, in 1976, we slipped the bounds of the London oil scene and became direct employees of the National Iranian Oil Company (NIOC) operating out of Ahwaz in Iran at the northern end of the Arabian Gulf. What an experience! As a consortium of international oil companies from both the USA and Europe, it encompassed a wealth of differing company expertise, all hosted under the Iranian national oil company umbrella. There was oil and gas everywhere in uncomplicated anticlines. But the limestones were typically tight and one needed to understand the fracture patterns. Here, luck again served me kindly, as fold related fracturing had been a hot topic in the structural geology department at Imperial College.

It was in Iran in 1977, thanks to a fellow American geologist spurring me on, that I joined the AAPG and with delight found that I was far from alone as a female petroleum geologist. Iran was a remarkably liberal country before the fall of the Shah and although NIOC was a 2000 strong male company, life was never entirely conventional there which helped me greatly in being accepted. Sadly, it all came to an end, somewhat violently, with the Iranian revolution three years later and all expat employees and their families, minus pets and baggage, were evacuated to Athens before eventually being disbanded.

By fortunate chance, 1979 was a time of great manpower shortage in oil companies. So, for us "direct employees" with no parent company to go back to, job offers abounded, alongside an offer from Imperial College to join their petroleum lecturing staff. The IC offer was attractive, particularly as it was such a "volte-face" from my time there a decade earlier, but the London housing situation and the idea of commuting made it a non-starter. So, as a couple, we joined Shell hoping for a return to the Middle East via their operation in Oman. It was not to be, as even at the beginning of the 1980s, Shell Oman, whether company or country policy, found it impossible to have a woman on their staff. Our first Shell overseas posting ended up being the jungle coast of Borneo, with their complex, highly faulted and thrust offshore fields of the Baram Delta.

In 1984, we left Shell, returning to the UK to start our own small consultancy, which ironically did eventually take us back to Oman several years later, by which time even the Omani women had become big in the workforce scene.

Susan Nicola (Nicki) Mounteney Barker was born in the county of Devon in the UK. She received her B. Sc. Honors degree in Geology with a specialisation in Engineering Geology in 1970 from Imperial College of Science and Technology, London University. Susan has been an AAPG member for 39 years.

Chapter 12. Sources and References

AAPG Archives. Susan Burton Longacre. Photograph. 1989. Tulsa, Oklahoma.

Allen, Jeanne Flavia. Austin, Texas. Interview with Robbie Gries, 10/2014).

Barker, Susan Nicola "Nicki." *Bookham Farmhouse*, Bookham, Alton Pancras, Dorchester, Dorset, England. Personal autobiographical writings and photograph as cited in figure caption.

Berg, Madeline. "Everything You Need to Know about the Hollywood Pay Gap." *Forbes*. Web. 12 Nov 2015. http://www.forbes.com/sites/maddieberg/2015/11/12/everything-you-need-to-know-about-the-hollywood-pay-gap/#59eca8881fe5. Accessed 01/28/2017.

Bonem, Rena. Waco, Texas. Personal autobiographical writings.

Butler, E. Ann. Gleneden Beach, Oregon. Personal autobiographical writings and photograph as cited in figure caption.

Cage, Susan Kiefner. Georgetown, Texas. Personal Communication, 2013 through 2016; source of photographs as cited in figure captions; Video Interview, July 25, 2015, archived at AAPG, Tulsa, Oklahoma.

Cooper, Mary Beth. Denver, Colorado. Personal autobiographical writings and photograph as cited in figure caption.

Coury, Anny Buchstab. Denver, Colorado. Personal communication (2013, 2015, 4/2016). Video Interview, 8/9-10/2016, archived at AAPG, Tulsa, Oklahoma.

Coury, Rina. Denver, Colorado. Source of Coury family photographs as cited in figure captions.

Fenton, Carroll Lane, and Mildred Adams Fenton. *Giants of Geology: The Story of the Great Geologists*. Garden City, New York: Doubleday Dolphin, 1952. 318 pp.

Fried, Richard M. *Nightmare in Red: The McCarthy Era in Perspective*. New York: Oxford University Press, 1990. As quoted in Hartmann. 1994. "Women's Employment and the Domestic Ideal in the Early Cold War years." p. 85.

Gomez, Paty Ortiz. 2016. "The First Mexican Woman Geologist (abs.)" AAPG/SEG International Conference & Exhibition, Cancun, Mexico. Search and Discovery Article #90260. http://www.searchanddiscovery.com/abstracts/html/2016/90260ice/abstracts/2474746.html.

Haertlein, Deeny. Fredericksburg, Texas. Interview with Robbie Gries about her mother, Rosamond Allen Haertlein (11/2016) and source of photograph as cited in figure caption.

Hartmann, Susan M. 1994. "Women's Employment and the Domestic Ideal in the Early Cold War years." In Meyerowitz. *Not June Cleaver*. pp. 84-102.

Holt, Jennifer. "The Ideal Woman." California State University, Stanislaus. Soundings. 4pp. https://www.csustan.edu/sites/default/files/honors/documents/journals/soundings. Accessed 12/22/2016.

Jensen, Gwenn. Centennial, Colorado. Personal autobiographical writings and photographs as cited in figure captions.

Longacre, Susan Burton. Kerrville, Texas. Personal autobiographical writings and interview with Robbie Gries (10/2016).

Magnolia News. "Are you a help or a handicap to your husband." August, 1957. pp. 5-8. Mobil Oil archives, Briscoe Library, The University of Texas at Austin.

Magnolia News. "Married Women No Longer Employed by Magnolia." May, 1957, p. 8. Mobil Oil archives, Briscoe Library, The University of Texas at Austin.

Meyerowitz, Joanne. *Not June Cleaver: Women and Gender in Postwar America, 1945-1960*. Philadelphia: Temple University Press, 1994. 411 pp.

National Manpower Council Report. *Womanpower*. New York: Columbia University Press, 1957. As quoted in Hartmann. 1994. "Women's Employment and the Domestic Ideal in the Early Cold War years." p. 91.

Perez de Mejia, Daisy. Caracas, Venezuela. Personal autobiographical writings and photographs as cited in figure captions.

Renzetti, Claire M. and Daniel J. Curran. *Women, Men, and Society*. Boston: Allyn and Bacon, fifth edition, 2002. 497 pp.

Rice, Peggy. Austin, Texas. Personal autobiographical writings and photographs as cited in figure captions.

Ross, Carolyn Miracle. Houston, Texas. Personal autobiographical writings and photographs as cited in figure caption.

Shrock, Robert Rakes. "Women in Geology at M. I. T." Chapter 13. In *Geology at MIT 1865-1965: A History of the First Hundred Years of Geology at Massachusetts Institute of Technology*, Vol. II, Departmental Operations and Products. Littleton, Massachusetts: MIT Press, 1982.

Suzanne Takken working at Mobil Oil in Tulsa. ca 1950. Photograph. With permission. Suzanne Takken Papers, MS 523, Archives of women in Science and Engineering, Special Collections and University Archives, Iowa State University Library, Ames, Iowa.

The Home Economics High School Text Book of 1954, http://www.colorado.edu/AmStudies/lewis/film/homecbook.pdf.

Van Norman, Betty Russell. Baton Rouge, Louisiana. Personal communication (12/6/2016) and source of photograph as cited in figure caption.

Wikipedia. "Exploitation of women in mass media." 28 Jan 2016.

(Photos on page fronting Chapter 12 from "Classic Stock/Alamy Stock Photo," from the Coury family and from Doris Malkin Curtis archives-Susan Suchman Simon.)

Chapter 13

Early Affirmative Action, Diversity, and the Oil Business

Affirmative Action finally came to the oil and gas business in full force in 1973. Affirmative Action plans and Diversity Plans had been implemented for years by U.S. governmental departments, and gradually contractors with the government were "forced" to implement plans. But in 1973, the Equal Employment Opportunity Commission (EEOC) was given "teeth" to enforce antidiscrimination efforts. Roland Theriot, a retired Amoco Human Resources director, shared his recollections,

> I retired from Amoco in 1989 so I've had 27 years to forget a lot about Affirmative Action in the 70s. After we talked, I sat and tried to remember my involvement and what I recalled of the process we used in Amoco. In the mid-70s, President Lyndon Johnson issued an Executive Order that squarely put the onus on Federal Contractors to eliminate discrimination in the hiring process. This followed an earlier Executive Order by John Kennedy on Civil Rights [1964], but this one had a lot more "force." It established the Office of Federal Contract Compliance Programs (OFCCP) to monitor each contractor's efforts.

Theriot recalled that,

> Federal contractors had to have
>
> 1) a written nondiscrimination policy that was disseminated and enforced throughout the company;
> 2) a written Affirmative Action Plan that was subject to audit by the OFCCP, and,
> 3) hiring goals for minorities and women.
>
> The hiring goals were based on statistics provided by the OFCCP organized by SMSA's (Standard Metropolitan Statistical Areas). The contractor's work force at a particular location needed to reflect the SMSA statistics–primarily based on percentages in that location. That was what gave rise to "quotas" – a word that was hated equally by contractors and the EEOC.
>
> In answer to your question, the OFCCP regulations were written, widely distributed and included a pro-forma of how the Affirmative Action Plan should look. There were audits by the OFCCP followed by written reports of their findings. [A company] did not want to be in "noncompliance" [as the company] might not be included in the next round of bidding for offshore leases.
>
> In Amoco, the Affirmative Action Plan was administered by the Human Resources Department—adding greatly to our already "unpopular" reputation.
>
> As to management meetings, Affirmative Action was an integral part of our college recruiting program. I can recall many meetings to determine which colleges would be visited based on the availability of women and minorities in our disciplines. Think for a minute on the impact this had on college scholarships for minorities and women. (Roland Theriot, personal communication, 2016.)

Patricia Santogrossi, a geoscientist hired as a 1975 summer intern for the Bellaire Research Center and as a direct consequence a permanent hire in 1976, recruited young geologists and geophysicists for Shell Oil in 1980-84. She was their only female geoscience recruiter at the time and echoed much of what Roland Theriot says. She recalled that the "goal" in her recruiting days was for Shell to have 8% minorities and women within about 50 geology and 50 geophysics recruits per year. There were published social studies at the time suggesting that, if ever the percentages got over 15% because of high acceptance rates, the corporate system would "naturally" seek to reduce the number of women and minorities. This came to pass as women and minorities seem to make up a disproportionate number of those let go in the mid-eighties. Patricia recalled that the recruiters were then accused of having "lowered the standards" to hire women and minorities, but she says that just did not happen. In her time, the same high standards were applied to all recruits. She did ask that standards be equalized where they were not equal. For instance, male recruits were given "extra-points" in their evaluation if they were veterans. She protested that since women were not allowed to be part of the military at the time, this was an unfair standard. Her alternative proposal was that men should be given "extra points" only if their military service was in some way especially pertinent to their geoscience work sphere.

But the "extra-point" trait that she most objected to was that male recruits were given extra points if they were *married*! Women were discounted for being married; because they might quit to have children. Or, discounted for being single; because they might get married and quit. The pervasive attitude was that "men needed the income and women did not."

Further incentive to the oil and gas industry to comply with the EEOC was the 1973 and 1974 settlements between two large companies and the government. These were a "wake up call" to all large corporations. AT&T, the nation's largest private employer, signed a landmark consent decree to eliminate discriminatory recruiting, hiring and promotion practices against women and minorities. The action began in 1970 when EEOC petitioned the Federal Communications Commission to reject a substantial long distance telephone rate increase sought by AT&T. Under the decree, AT&T was to distribute $15 million to 13,000 women and 2,000 minority men. The company also would provide approximately $30 million in immediate pay increases for 36,000 women and minorities whose advancement in the AT&T system had been hampered by discrimination (https://www.eeoc.gov/eeoc/history/35th/milestones/1973.html).

Likewise, in 1974, the largest steel companies in the nation were penalized in "... a consent decree providing for approximately $31 million in back pay to be distributed to about 40,000 minority and women employees. The companies and the union also agree to a set of goals which include hiring women and minority persons for half the openings in trade and craft jobs and for 25 percent of the vacancies in supervisory jobs. The decree also provides that seniority will now be determined on the basis of plant rather than departmental seniority permitting women and minority access to the better paying and more desirable jobs" (https://www.eeoc.gov/eeoc/history/35th/milestones/1974.html).

Additionally, in 1974, with Richard Nixon's departure and Gerald Ford's assumption of the presidency, for the first time in 10 years, the EEOC was fully funded to the amount requested by the president. In the absence of funding, a backlog of 80,000-100,000 cases had accumulated. Four years later, in 1977, Carter expanded the EEOC structure and program extensively, and appointed the first woman to run the program (https://www.eeoc.gov/eeoc/history/35th/milestones/1975.html and 1976/html).

The effect of the EEOC on the Oil and Gas business can be seen in 1973 with the record hiring of women; many more than had been recruited during WWII. It was a new world, and for the most part, unlike all previous eras, *women were making equal salaries for equal work*, though occasionally, some found they were underpaid compared to their colleagues.

It was clear to most women geologists hired in 1973-1974 that there were "quotas" and their hiring was part of that. Hiring of women and minorities started before the Energy Crisis began in November 1973, but the timing could not have been better. High oil prices encouraged most companies, large and small, to increase their exploration staffs. This meant many more opportunities for jobs for women and minorities coupled with the dictate for equal pay. The energy crisis also resulted in more jobs for men, too, if the quotas had been met. It was a "Golden Age" for exploration geologists.

Recruiters for companies varied. Most recruiters provided a vision to young women of an exciting career ahead with equal treatment. Yet, there were those, although smaller in number, that were still stuck in a mode of discrimination, making discouraging remarks to women applying at that time. Fortunately, because so many companies were trying to hire, female geology graduates usually had several good interviews with the only the occasional bad interview.

By 1975, most companies had reached their "quota" of women and minorities. When Cindy Crawley Stewart interviewed at Conoco with Max Pitcher that year, he told her they were no longer looking for women and minorities, just the best qualified geologists. That suited her and was comforting to her and to most women hired in the late 1970s and the 1980s. Many of the women hired later had no knowledge of this hiring stimulus and were under the impression that they were hired strictly for their competence. And, likely that was true by then. But, had the EEOC not compelled oil companies into nondiscriminatory hiring in the early 1970s, would that have been the case? We will never know, but it is important for this history to be written, to be recognized and to be appreciated.

Early Hires and Affirmative Action

Robbie Rice Gries

"*Can't* never did anything." This southern saying my grandmother used on me has guided me all my life.

I was raised in the 1950's "Ideal Woman" era and was convinced that lifestyle was the path to a perfect life. My family had a "place" in the semi-desert, oak-tree filled, dune sand environment of south Texas. We were sixteen miles north of Corpus Christi, sometimes without indoor toilet facilities and, if pressed, easily categorized as "poor white trash." My father was happiest the years he spent as a shrimper or as a boat captain on the water. The closest he came to the oil business was ferrying offshore rig crews when the shrimp were not running. My mother grew up in an educated, middle-class community in San Antonio but was a rebel and threw off the "yoke of conformity." She did little in the way of housekeeping and scorned "society." I rebelled against being like her, though, no doubt, she gave me permission to be myself. When we got a television in 1958, I suddenly saw how I wanted life to be—like the perfect housewife June Cleaver in "Leave it to Beaver" or Margaret Anderson in "Father Knows Best." Now I could see how life was supposed to be. I was determined to go to college, to marry a college graduate, and build a home like *that*.

Working my way through high school and into Del Mar Junior College by babysitting and waiting tables was a good beginning to my "June Cleaver" goals. My sophomore year (1963), I took an Introduction to Geology course because I was trying to get out of a chemistry class. I had heard the German chemistry professor was so tough she scared off majors in chemistry, let alone me—who had almost no high school chemistry. I asked around for suggestions for another science class and someone suggested "geology" because it boasted an excellent instructor. At age 19, I responded with, "What in the world is geology?" I had never heard of it in my tiny high school with a graduating class of 30 students. When it was explained that geology was the study of the earth, including rocks and fossils and such, I recalled how much I had liked rocks on my family's singular vacation away from the Texas Gulf Coast.

Figure 1. Ruth Roberta "Robbie" Rice, 1966, at Colorado State University, geology field camp on the White River Plateau, Colorado. (Photo: Robbie Gries, Denver, Colorado.)

My first day in Hugh Doney's geology class totally swept me away. He was an exceptional teacher and I found my calling. I soon switched my major to geology as I headed to Colorado State University (CSU) in Fort Collins for my Junior year. Immediately upon walking into the department, the Chair called me into his office and told me I would have to find a geology field course at some other school because they did not allow girls on the CSU six-week course; however, they did *require* me to take a field course for graduation! Fortunately for me, the Chair went on sabbatical the next year and the rest of the staff voted to let women into the field course (Fig. 1). The benefits worked two ways, I became the camp cook and worked my tuition off over an open campfire in addition to the weekly shopping an hour's drive away in Glenwood Springs. Upon completion of the field course, I was to be the first female to graduate in geology from CSU.

A funny story happened getting ready for field camp. There was a Saturday field-methods course the semester before the summer field camp. One Saturday, I was mortified to start my "period" during class, and I had an embarrassing day completing our assignment. I had heard that the newly "invented" birth control pills would enable a girl to regulate her period so that she could control when they would occur (it was 1966 and "the pill" had been approved for contraceptive use in 1960). So, I made an appointment with the university infirmary doctor and asked him about getting a prescription for these pills. He asked, "What is your reason for getting this prescription?" I was fumbling around trying to figure out how to tell him about my embarrassing experience and said, "I am going on a six-week field course with 20 men, and...." Before I could say another word, he jumped in, interrupting me, and said, "Ok, Ok, say no more!" I never got to finish telling him my "reason" as he shooed me out the door with prescription in hand.

There were marked differences between the guys majoring in geology and myself. I always wondered how they ended up with summer jobs for oil companies and I ended up waiting tables, tending bar, cleaning hotel rooms, babysitting—anything to make a living. I assumed they must just have family connections that my shrimper father did not have. Later, I learned the guys were introduced by faculty members to intern programs with oil companies. Because I was a woman, it was assumed that I would never work in geology. Even if I were interested, there were likely no jobs for me. Therefore, I was never told about internships at oil companies.

In graduate school at The University of Texas at Austin (UT), the well-meaning Dr. Sam Ellison took me aside and told me that my only chance for a job after graduation was to study micropaleontology. I loved paleontology (I did my research on bio-stratigraphy) but did not want to be a micropaleontologist, so I ignored his advice. I loved sedimentology and stratigraphy and stuck with what I loved. I admit that at the time, I also believed I might not need a job, that I might just get married and be June Cleaver! I wisely kept that possibility to myself. I decided to study whatever I wanted and, like Scarlett O'Hara in *Gone with the Wind*, I would worry about jobs tomorrow.

I did get my degree, got married, and had a baby; but, I soon found I was not cut out for the housewife role. The daily, repetitious work maintaining a household was frustrating to me after the fun and excitement of research and work in the UT geology department. Intellectually, I felt stuck, especially being in a new town (my husband and I had moved from Austin to Wichita, Kansas) where I knew few people. I told my husband I just had to go to work, at least part-time, and that I would use my salary to hire a maid to do the housework. He said, not once, but several times, "... if we get a maid, then I don't need a wife!"

Shockingly, it took several repeats of his statement for it to sink in. Click! Finally, in 1973, I decided he could get the maid and I would get a job. I moved away with our 2-year-old daughter, Lynn Margaret Gries, to Houston. My poor husband—he married June Cleaver and divorced Gloria Steinem. Despite that, we remained friends.

Miraculously, I quickly landed a technician job with a geophysical company for several months while I did a more serious job search. I calculated gravity data with an old hand-crank calculating machine and made out punch cards to feed into the "main frame" computers that filled an entire room. While cranking out gravity data, literally, I searched for a "geological" job and specified that I wanted to be in Denver, Colorado. As a kid raised on the flat coastal plain of the "Ingleside Sand Bar" in South Texas, and having discovered topography and seasons in Colorado, I knew where I wanted to live.

The fortunate coincidence during my job search was the onset of Affirmative Action and the diversity demands being made on oil and gas companies. Starting that year, the EEOC demanded oil companies have diversity plans. Every major oil company was scrambling to fill their "quotas" of women, people of color, veterans, and disabled employees.

By chance, Texaco Inc. was one woman short of their quota in the Denver office (Fig. 2). I was hired. I packed up my child, my belongings and headed off to start my oil industry career armed with the unfortunate and incorrect academic warnings about how "unscientific" a career in the "grease" business was. At that time, even at UT, several professors had a disdain for geologists who entered the oil business. How wrong I found them to be!

Figure 2. Robbie, 1973, her first week at Texaco in Denver, Colorado, 1973. (Photo: Robbie Gries.)

I immediately discovered that oil companies were often on the leading edge of new ideas and creative thinking. I learned that, as a petroleum geologist, I would do constant research. Every project was like a new college thesis project. And, I could give talks, publish, and share ideas with other professionals. These academic pursuits were coupled with the applied science drama of testing ideas with a drill bit. No one had ever told me how exciting a career in petroleum would be!

My first boss at Texaco, Jim Uhrlaub, cognizant that I had acquired my job at Texaco through Affirmative Action, quickly nicknamed me "Token." He would yell down the hall at me a couple of times a week, "Hey! Token! We're having a staff meeting, so get down here to my office!" Of course, today that would be grounds for a harassment suit, but I recognized immediately that it was his way of addressing the "elephant in the middle of the room." He was humorous and his actual dealings with me were equal and fair. I benefitted from his many recommendations for raises and promotions as well as his mentoring and guidance. He encouraged my love for "thinking outside the box" and supported and celebrated such thinking; I still enjoy flexing my mind this way.

I had several amusing experiences while working for Uhrlaub (Fig. 3). One summer he let me hire a young man to do fieldwork on a San Juan Basin project in New Mexico. The fellow came into the office and I instructed him as to where I needed samples collected. I lined him up with a company car, maps, and expense account, and sent him on his way for three months of field work. A week later he came back to the office and told me he was going to have to quit. He had just gotten married and his wife was not happy with him being away. I looked him in the eye and said, "You know, that's the trouble with you young men, we hire you and you just get married and quit!" Unfortunately, he didn't have the history to appreciate the joke, but, fortunately for me, I made this joking remark in the days *before I* could get into trouble for harassment myself.

Women were not allowed, for the most part, to do any wellsite work in the 1970s. Texaco women, just like women from Amoco, Chevron, Shell, and many others, took their companies to task over this and had to fight for the right to sit wells. One of my funnier career moments came in our District Affirmative Action meeting where Uhrlaub was reading from a list of questions prepared by upper management to let the EEOC know what kind of handicapped people we might be hiring. He asked all the professionals to own up to any "disabilities" they might have as he read from the list. These ranged from serious things like epilepsy to the ridiculous, like nearsightedness. He asked us to raise our hands if we had any of the disabilities as he read the list aloud. At the bottom of the list, he asked the final question, "Do any of you have any physical disabilities that are not on this list?" I immediately raised my hand and said I thought I was suffering from a physical disability that was not on the list. I said I did not have the genitalia that were needed to do wellsite work. Uhrlaub (and everyone else) laughed and he quickly added this to the list and sent it back to upper management to see if it could be added to the corporate list of disabilities. Not because of this incident, but because it made sense, shortly thereafter women were allowed to do their share of wellsite work—a change that greatly relieved our male colleagues who had been carrying the full burden of wellsite work; a legitimate cause for them to resent the hiring of women.

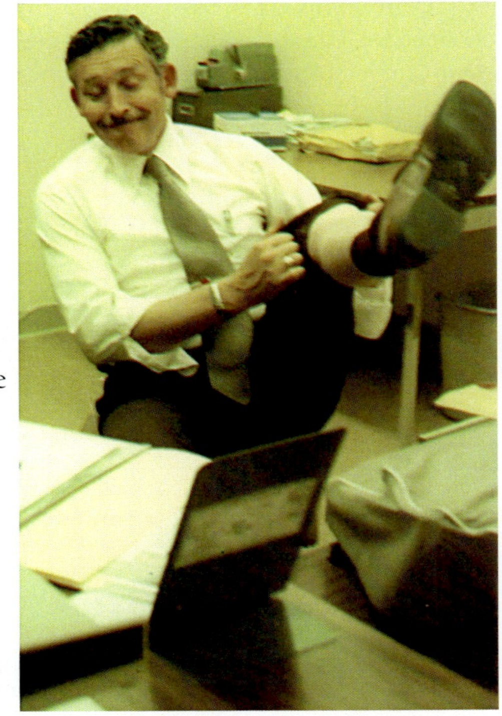

Figure 3. James Uhrlaub, 1975, Robbie's first boss at Texaco, showing a little leg for his staff. He named Robbie "Token." (Photo: Robbie Gries.)

My first trip to a wellsite to be trained by another Texaco geologist, Bob Anderson, created an awkward experience. All the companies in Denver were struggling to figure out how to get women trained without aggravating the male employee's wives. The solution in my District office was to have Bob's wife accompany us to the well for the week I was trained, then they would return to Denver and leave me for another week on my own. As it turned out, Bob's wife did not want to stay at the rig which was a four-hour drive (one way) from Vernal, Utah, so she took a hotel room there. Bob drove me out to the well where I had a very nice trailer. He had to drive out each day to train me. Poor guy—eight hours on the road every day, while his wife laid around the pool and joked around with the oil field hands who were on their days off.

While I was at Texaco, the Oil Boom of the late 1970s into the 1980s engulfed us. Geologists were quitting the major oil companies in large numbers—taking jobs with smaller independent oil companies (Independents) that offered overriding royalty interests, cars, expense accounts, petroleum club memberships and large salary raises. Uhrlaub took me aside after yet another geologist quit (and incidentally just before Uhrlaub himself quit to work for an Independent) and said, "You are going to witness a complete change in demographics within oil companies." He predicted that Independents would never hire women because they were *not required to* under Affirmative Action; that soon, the Majors would evolve into mostly female and minority exploration staffs, and the Independents would be all men. Within the year, all three Texaco women "tokens" were hired away by Independents. Independents had learned to look for talent, not gender!

I went to work for Reserve Oil Inc. with all the typical bonuses and perquisite (perk) packages including my main incentive—overriding royalty opportunities. Bill Leroy, a feminist at heart, hired me. He hired women—treating them fairly and standing up for them—but you would never have known it to look at him, with his white-tasseled loafers and his "ladies-man" presence. I was pleasantly surprised as I got to know Bill and work with him. He was never inappropriate. Bill demonstrated his support of women and insisted that ALL his geologists and geophysicists should have memberships at the Denver Petroleum Club (DPC) regardless of gender. Reluctantly, the Club gave in and changed their long-standing policy. Geophysicist, Louise Bridges, and I became the first women members of the Petroleum Club in Denver. The first time Louise and I tried to have lunch in the "Men's Dining Room" at the DPC, we were stopped by the maître d' who refused to seat us; he had to make many calls before he was instructed it was ok to seat us. No one had informed him about the rule change. It reminded me of a joke in the newspaper about that time where two women are in an exclusive men-only dining room and the maître d' says to them, "I'm sorry, we only serve men in this room." One of the women quips right back, "Good! Bring us two!"

Denver was far ahead of Casper, Wyoming; Farmington, New Mexico; Houston and Dallas, Texas; and Oklahoma City, Oklahoma and perhaps all the Petroleum Clubs in the U.S. Even though we had reciprocal memberships to Petroleum Clubs in these other cities, they refused us entry and we were repeatedly asked to leave their premises. Of course, I repeatedly tried to enter those other clubs. I wanted them to know how progressive Denver was.

In the 1980s, as more women geologists came into exploration, I noticed that many of the guys would have regular coffee meetings, lunches, or after work "happy hour" gatherings with close buddies in the business. We thought of them as "good ole boy" groups, but recognized they did "business" in these informal settings. Mary Beth Cooper, Penny Frush and I had lunch at The Broker in downtown Denver and said, "Let's start a luncheon group once a month like that—it can be the 'Good Ole Girls' and no doubt we'll generate lots of business ideas." We thought of a few other oil and gas women to invite, limiting the group to no more than ten as a lunch group and expecting that maybe six or seven would show up regularly. We quickly changed to dinners—lunch was too short for us to all to have our say! And it seemed that all ten always attended! We did very little official business, but deep friendships were created with great empathy and support for both professional and personal trials.

After working for an Independent for several years, I went "out on my own" and started consulting and generating prospects to sell. My most opportune consulting work was done for John Mason of Fort Worth, Texas. He was probably the smartest person with whom I have ever worked. John taught me much about the oil business and about life. Once, when we were strategizing about how to approach a project, I suggested that if our company was extra aggressive drilling, we might be able to force our partners to give up their interests because they could not keep up with our program. John, in his quiet and gentlemanly way, said, "It is very important in business not to get too greedy. It helps a play, especially in a frontier area, to have several companies operating and making progress." I am sure that I blushed and felt ashamed of myself. He was right and I learned yet another important lesson from working with him. That spirit of sharing and working together has made my independent ventures

Figure 4. Robbie and daughter, Lynn Margaret, 1978, doing fieldwork in the San Juan Sag, southern Colorado. (Photo: Robbie Gries.)

all the more pleasant. On a contract basis for John Mason, I was encouraged to do very exciting and creative exploration including work sub-thrust and sub-volcanic plays in the Rockies (Fig. 4).

I was fortunate not to have suffered from a lack of consulting in the early stages of the oil bust in the 1980s. I kept working because of the many contacts made through involvement in professional geologic organizations and through publishing. Yes, "networking." Though that term was not widely used then, networking proved to be invaluable. However, the oil bust did hit me in 1992, and it hit hard. A characteristic that has always carried me through hard times was perseverance. During the bust, one of my friends called me on an Easter Sunday and said, "Wow, you have convinced me never to go independent—you are always working." It was true. There were years of 12- to 15-hour days, seven days a week, often on holidays, just to survive. But, it didn't seem all that bad at the time. I was always convinced the deal would sell, the play would work, and the bust would end. I woke up every morning eager to get to the office again.

I sold one prospect three times and never made a cent from it. All three companies turned it back to me because they lost their funding. All three of them! This was the time, many will remember, when we could easily present a drilling prospect 70 times before finding a buyer or partner. Another time, I finally sold a prospect and hoped to make some extra money sitting the well. I was stiffed (not paid) for my three weeks of wellsite work. Next, I took a consulting job on a water case in the San Luis Valley and got stiffed on that job too. That year, I mortgaged my almost-paid-for home and sold some property to survive. I decided to change course in my petroleum career and took several classes in acquisitions and divestitures, mergers, and raising funds (public offerings and production payments, etc.).

These courses led to my work putting together the merger of two companies. I learned a great deal, working with lawyers on the purchase and sale agreement and then setting up the paperwork for a public offering (IPO) stock to finance the merger. While on a whirlwind national tour of brokerage firms promoting the IPO, I was introduced to another new world. When the merger was complete, I became Vice President of Exploration and enjoyed the next year running the office in Denver with about 30 fantastic employees.

However, soon I learned my partners were not following our business plan, and, in my opinion, were spending money haphazardly. I knew our bank would not approve, and, of greater concern, the partners were running us into the ground. I complained and tried to change the behavior, but at the next Board meeting, my "colleagues" announced that they were reducing my salary and increasing the salary of the accountant 20 years my junior. It became obvious they were trying to push me to quit. I left the meeting distraught about the situation; soon, I did quit but not before I consulted a lawyer and threatened to sue them for gender and age discrimination. We settled on a package that enabled me to resume my consulting for a year or so. It wasn't much, but the company did not have much; they went bankrupt within a couple of years, just as I feared they would. My stock options were worthless. I started my own company, Priority Oil & Gas LLC, that year (1995).

During my initial consulting and deal-selling days, I was with a group hosting a visiting geologist from Texas, a "good ole boy" standing for AAPG executive office. He sat across from me at dinner and, after lots of chat about what he and I did in the oil business, he said, "Well, I have to tell you, young lady, I cannot fathom taking an oil deal from a girl!" I thought, "Okay, his loss." But what shocked me and aggravated me even more was when we were walking down the hotel hallway after dinner, he asked if he could accompany me to my room. Good grief! I told all my friends about the incident. He lost by about five votes in that election. He later apologized to me, and said he often wondered if he lost due to his misbehavior. He stood for Executive Office again a few years later

Figure 5. Robbie with Melissa Gray, COO of Priority Oil & Gas, and Kevin and Jessica Andrews, longtime Priority workers, 2015. Hydraulic fracturing Niobrara wells in Cheyenne Co., Kansas. (Photo: Robbie Gries.)

and did win. And, I will say, by then he seemed to have considerably improved his behavior toward women professionals. I still did not vote for him.

Priority Oil & Gas LLC, struggled for about five or six years with the industry still in a downturn, but finally, my gamble buying some money-losing gas properties in Kansas paid off. In 1999, when prices started climbing (from 66 cents to $2.50/mcfg), I made a deal with my friend, Jane Woodward, whose company purchased natural gas royalties. Her company took a substantial royalty interest in the project, enabling me to run "poor man's 3D (2D swath)" seismic and drill a large inventory of wells. Soon, the company was solid and I was no longer economically dependent on consulting. Perhaps more significant, I had an all-female office (Jessica Trevino, me, and later, Melissa Gray), with a female financial backer. We ran all the operations—geophysical, drilling, and supervising production (Fig. 5). We did have men in the field pumping wells and maintaining the compressors, but it felt good to have such a unique (though unplanned) organization. We never had any problems with contractors or landowners. "The times they are a changin'."

Oh, the excitement and joy of looking back on the creative years of prospecting— whether it was finding a sedimentary basin under a volcanic field against the prevailing dogma, questioning source rock data when it didn't make sense and finding there *were* different and valid answers, or challenging the semi-dogma of "vertical uplift" on Rocky Mountain foreland uplifts and having the drill bit prove the thrusted mountain fronts by drilling through Precambrian rocks over and over—into sediments. And, nothing thrills a geologist more than driving out to a location where your idea is being tested—topping a hill in the night and being greeted with the lights of the drilling rig, then arriving on location to the sounds of the rotary table, the scream of brakes when a porous reservoir is penetrated, excited about what lies ahead in the next few hours! I've experienced the exhilaration of finding oil, finding gas. And, the despair of the dry hole—everything was right, but the oil wasn't there— and the long drive back to the city with tears pouring down my face, wondering if I will ever generate another idea as good as that one.

The highlight of a financially more comfortable period in my career was the economic ability to take time off and serve as the first female president of AAPG. The time and travel commitment was enormous, but immensely rewarding. My election coincided with AAPG's establishment of International Regions and I visited about 60 geological societies and 70 universities in almost 50 countries to reinforce AAPG's emphasis on international growth (Figs. 6 & 7). Meeting women geoscientists all over the world was exhilarating.

Figure 6. Robbie with Dr. John Kaldi, former President of the Asia Pacific region, who organized parts of her three-continent tour through Australia, Asia, and back to Africa in 2001. (Photo: Robbie Gries.)

When I was elected AAPG president (Fig. 8), it was tempting to translate my election victory into some personal ego-boosting accomplishment. But, I

Figure 7. Visiting Port Harcourt, Nigeria, in 2001, Robbie with Tunde Afolabi and Kunle Odusina on the left and Adebayo Akinpelu on the right—three past presidents of the Nigerian Association of Petroleum Geoscientists. (Photo: Robbie Gries.)

Figure 8. Robbie, having fun with other AAPG Past Presidents at the Annual Meeting in Houston, Texas, 2014. Robbie was the first female president of the Association in its 84th year. (Photo: AAPG Staff.)

had a reality check when I asked the right question at the right time to the right person. After my election, I was attending an Eastern Section meeting where I was relatively unknown. A young man came up to me at a cocktail party and congratulated me on my win and carried on a bit about how he had voted for me and was so happy and excited that I had won. I was flattered and decided to find out what was behind his vote. I wondered if it was my speech to the Eastern Section the year before that had convinced him, or, if it was my résumé of hard work for AAPG, or, just my "good looks." So, I asked him point blank, "Why did you vote for me?" He looked at me seriously, eyes opening wide, and said, "Oh, nothing about you. I just didn't like your opponent!"

My journey into geology was accidental, but who can argue with the success of a life well lived? "*Can do*" describes my career. And, the richest adjunct has been exposure to a class of people who *ROCK*.

Robbie Rice Gries was born in 1943 in San Antonio, Texas. After two years at Del Mar Junior College, she transferred to Colorado State University and earned a B.S. in Geology in 1966. She has her M.S. in Geology from The University of Texas at Austin, 1970. She is semi-retired and splits her time between Denver and Tucson with her husband, David Bailey; daughter, Lynn, lives in Tucson and is a trauma surgeon.

Randi Martinsen

In 1973, I was one of three women and about ten men finishing our graduate program in geology at Northern Arizona University (NAU) who were actively looking for jobs (Fig. 9). It was shortly after Affirmative Action had been implemented and just before the big boom in the oil business. Our department chair had worked hard promoting our department and we felt fortunate to have quite a few companies come to campus to recruit. We were all confident about getting a job. Even so, I followed the advice of one of my early and very influential mentors, Pete Rose, and sent out my résumé to every company whose address I could find. This amounted to something like 200 letters with a résumé that had to be individually typed—no small task in the pre-personal computer era. However, Pete—who had taught me Introductory Geology, inspired me to become a geologist, and advised me on graduate schools—had been a recruiter for Shell, so I was strongly motivated to follow his advice.

Figure 9. Randi Martinsen, 1973, field trip in the Valley of Fire, Nevada. (Photo: Randi Martinsen, Laramie, Wyoming.)

It was a good thing I did send out résumés because I wasn't having any luck with the companies that recruited at NAU. Neither was my roommate, Christine Turner (Peterson). The guys were getting offers, as was the third woman graduate student, Emily Bradshaw. In fact, the companies were falling all over themselves courting Emily. I think she got an offer from every company that interviewed her. Christine and I were totally baffled. We had good GPAs, we knew our professors liked and respected us, and we were both outgoing and fun-loving. Except for one particularly obnoxious Amoco recruiter who sat with his feet on the desk and blew cigar smoke in my face the whole time, I thought I had handled my interviews reasonably well. I'll admit Emily had a 4.0 and had been a captain in the Army before graduate school, but she was kind of aloof, seldom smiled and seemed a bit stern, a possible affectation from her military training, and, her attire was usually, well, prim.

So, what was our problem? Christine contacted a friend that had graduated and gone to work for Exxon to see if he could find out why neither Christine nor I were getting ANY offers, and Emily was getting so many. He called her back after having chatted up the Exxon recruiter and found out that the recruiter thought Christine and I were "too marriageable." The recruiter told him, "If we hired them they would just get married and quit." Whereas he thought Emily was un-marriageable! Trying to be attractive, friendly, fun-loving, and outgoing was exactly the wrong approach to take. Shortly after learning of this, my résumé-sending efforts bore fruit, and I received an offer, sight unseen, from Texaco in New Orleans, and I thought seriously about what our Exxon recruiter had said.

Over the next few months, I received a couple of additional "sight unseen" offers, but the first one from Texaco took the pressure off and gave me a shot of much-needed self-confidence, as well as the confidence to try a crazy idea. We had one last company, Cities Service, coming to campus and I decided to test the Exxon recruiter's opinions and interview as an "Emily" look-alike. I wore a very severe, dark-blue suit with a high, "mandarin-type" collar and capped the new image with a pair of cat-eye shaped, rhinestone-laden eyeglasses from the local Salvation Army store. I wore no makeup and pulled my hair back into a tight bun. I sat with my knees tightly together, holding a clutch purse, and did my best not to smile. Well, there were two recruiters from Cities and they both loved me! They loved me so much they immediately offered to bring me to Tulsa for a second interview and they spent the rest of the interview "selling Cities" to me. I liked their sales pitch and thought it would be great to have the possibility of another offer. I agreed to the Tulsa interview.

When my department head at NAU found out what I had done with these recruiters he was very angry with me. He thought I was ridiculing and mocking these companies after he had worked so hard getting them to come and interview, and he worried I might jeopardize his efforts. But it was too late. My charade was a fait accompli. When I went to Tulsa for my "in-house" interview, I continued my charade with the severe blue suit, no makeup, funny glasses, hair in a bun, clutch purse, and no smiling. I arrived a bit early and, as I was waiting in the reception area before my interview, I saw an *Oil and Gas Journal* on the coffee table. Because I cannot stand to sit and do nothing, I picked up the magazine and began to read an article on the recent offshore Eastern Gulf of Mexico (Mississippi, Alabama, Florida or MAFLA) lease sale that described what a frenzy the sale had been, how promising this enormous structure appeared and how companies had made enormously high bids. It also listed what companies had acquired leases, and Cities was not one of them. Fortuitously, the subject of the sale came up during my interview and the recruiters were astounded that I knew so much about it. I was "golden." Nowadays advisors routinely tell students to read about the company and encourage the students to ask questions and be knowledgeable about company activities, but in the early 70s it was rarely done.

I had a job offer within the hour—any job I wanted, anywhere they had an office. I told them I'd like to work in Denver and they said, "Great!" They wanted to make sure I'd be happy in Denver and arranged for me to visit their Denver office, look around and meet my co-workers. Although I had a firm offer from them, and the Denver trip was to encourage me to accept their offer, I felt it best to continue my "Emily" charade during my Denver visit.

In Denver, I told them I'd be finished with my graduate work in about 6-8 months. Cities was so concerned about losing me during those months that I received three raises before I even showed up for work. However, there was absolutely no way I could live my life as "Emily" so on my first day of work, I showed up with my hair down, my not-so-conservative regular clothes, no glasses and I was smiling and laughing as I met people and started to work. Several of the bosses took me out to lunch that first day and it seemed they were a bit uncomfortable, and were staring at me. Finally, my boss looked at me and said, "There is just something different about you, did you change your hair or something?"

The best part of the story is that Emily, from her numerous offers, chose to work for Chevron in Denver as well. She was married within six months (we never even knew she had been dating) and worked only a short period before she quit geology altogether to follow a life-long dream—to write romance novels! She did this and became a wildly successful romance novelist. She was so brilliant at applying her research skills for historical accuracy that her success was phenomenal. Her author's photo on her books shows the "hidden" Emily, a very attractive, sexy woman. I've read several of her books and they are "hot!" Not one of us would have predicted that she had these hidden talents—certainly, not the recruiters. (Emily has won awards for her writing; she has 22 novels and novellas.) In contrast to Emily, Christine and I did not marry for many years, and have kept up our careers in geology to this day. *Recruiters, beware your impressions and judgments!*

There is an interesting side story related to my interviewing as a graduate student. I was especially perplexed by not getting an offer from Exxon (marriageable or not) because several months earlier while attending the Rocky Mountain Section meeting of AAPG in Salt Lake City, Utah, the President of Exxon had made me a job offer. He had attended because he was standing for President of AAPG. During the initial reception for the meeting an Exxon geologist came up to me, one of maybe 2-3 females present, and asked if I would go to dinner with him and the Exxon President. In addition to a free meal, which as a student I never declined, I felt it was a great opportunity, so I said I'd love to.

That evening, I also got a little insight into "Big Oil" because the Hotel Utah's dining room was opened, after closing for the night, just for the Exxon group. We were the only people there and about five waiters took care of about 8-10 people. I sat next to the President and we had a nice conversation, although, I have no recollection of the details—except for one. He told me if I wanted it, I had a job with Exxon and had his assistant write down my name and contact information. So, when Exxon came to NAU, interviewed me, and rejected me, I was quite surprised. Just before I went to work for Cities, I attended a Geological Society of America (GSA) meeting in Miami Beach, Florida. The only other person from NAU who attended the meeting was NAU's Geology Department Chair (who had forgiven me my interview charade) and he invited me to go to dinner with him and the head of Exxon recruiting. Again, happy for a free meal, I said yes. Sometime during the evening I decided I'd ask the recruiter about not getting an offer from Exxon after the President had told me I had a job with Exxon. I did and he stared at me, went white-faced, and said, "You're the one?" Apparently, the assistant lost the paper with my name and contact information. The President had instructed all the Exxon recruiters to find me. Then, after regaining his composure, the recruiter asked if I'd come work for Exxon. I smiled and said, "Sorry I already have a job."

Shortly after I started working, and after the Cities Service Denver office had adjusted to the "new me," my boss came in and said he had a field project he wanted me to work on along with the one of the research center's sedimentologists, Rod Tillman. The project was set up in February and scheduled for June. Shortly after the project was set up, various people started coming into my office and telling me about Rod. They'd say things like, "Do you know Rod was recently divorced?" and "I've heard he has a round bed with mirrors on the ceiling?" and all sorts of other unfounded gossip. Suddenly I had inherited coworker "fathers" who were concerned about my welfare and that I not be unfairly taken advantage of by this potential gigolo. I don't know whether it was because my boss was concerned about my safety or because my boss just wanted to get out into the field, but he went into the field with Rod and me, bringing his 11-year-old son and a geo-tech for good measure! Chaperones in abundance. Well, there was no need to worry because Rod was always the gentleman. He and I became close colleagues and went on to collaborate on several projects over the years. I count Rod as one of my important mentors—he taught me how to apply sedimentology to exploration.

One of my strongest supporters and most important mentors was Cities petrophysicist, Bob Colby. Bob had a reputation as a bit of an eccentric, but he was highly regarded in the company. His reputation as an outstanding petrophysicist was so high, I remember Schlumberger used to come to him for advice. Because he often traveled to the field, he had a company car. Cities policy was that employees who had company cars would provide car pool duties. Bob always wanted to be in the office by 6:30 am for the morning report and normal work hours were 7:30 am-4:30 pm, so no one wanted to ride with him, except me. As his only "car pooler," Bob and I got to know each other better than we would have otherwise.

One day Bob asked me, "How serious are you about your career?" I answered, "Pretty serious, I love what I'm doing and I can see myself doing this for a long time." He then told me I needed to get into Development, to find out where the data comes from and how it's collected. I told him that would be fine with me. Several months later

I was given notice that I was being transferred down to Development (Exploration was on the 9th floor and Development on the 8th). I was elated! My exploration colleagues all came to me and asked who I had pissed off to get demoted and transferred to Development. Their responses perplexed me, but I responded that I had asked for this. And, career-wise, it was a great choice.

At that time, development geologists were expected to "sit wells," and there was no question within Cities that I would sit wells as a development geologist. However, there was a bit of awkwardness around the question of who would go out to train me in wellsite work. My colleague's wives were not enthused to have their husbands spend time in the field with me. My boss, Vernon Hill (another very important mentor), creatively decided to hire a consultant. The consultant, Dick Model, was considered one of the best wellsite geologists around, and he taught me well.

Dick was happy to have been selected to train me, and on every new well we went to, he proudly introduced me as, "Randi Martinsen, Cities' new girl geologist." After a few of these introductions, and after I felt he and I had developed a good relationship, I said to him, "Dick, I can understand that it is not obvious that I work for Cities or that I'm a geologist, but if they can't figure out I'm a girl, I'm in deep doo-doo." I understood that he was always proudly introducing me and that his introducing me as a girl was because he thought it was wonderful girls (women) were now going into the field, but because I respected him so much I wanted to let him know he could drop the girl part, which he did. I learned a lot from Dick. He was among the best.

Soon I was sent out to sit a well on my own in the Powder River Basin, Wyoming. I was now a development geologist, and development wells at that time never had any mud-loggers or company trailers. If the situation allowed, I'd head to town to sleep and, if not, I'd sleep in my car. One morning after a night in my car, I headed out to find a place to go to the bathroom. Now, there isn't a lot of cover throughout most of the Powder River Basin, so I just started heading down the road away from the rig. I walked about a mile and thinking this was far enough away from the rig, squatted down and started to do my business. I was looking back at the rig and not really paying much attention, when I realized a vehicle from town in the other direction was nearly upon me. As they passed, I saw the morning tour (rig crew) driving by. Later that morning, when I called into my boss, Vernon, to report on the well, I told him I had met the morning tour. He responded "Really? How did that go?" Or, something to that effect. I responded that I had been squatting by the road doing my business when they drove by. Vernon was quiet for a few moments, and then asked, "So, what did you do?" I replied, "Well, what could I do? I waved." Vernon later told me that after that call, he never worried about how I'd handle things in the field again.

Another story, not as humorous but much more rewarding, relates to when I submitted an abstract on Hartzog Draw for the Rocky Mountain Section(RMS)-AAPG meeting. I felt confident it would be accepted because Hartzog Draw was a recently discovered giant oilfield in the Powder River Basin of Wyoming and a hot topic. I was totally surprised when my abstract was rejected. Rather than protest, I submitted it to the Annual AAPG meeting where it was accepted. However, shortly after I had received notice of being rejected for the RMS meeting, a member of the technical committee called me and told me that my abstract had been rejected because the Technical Program Chair thought Hartzog Draw was too important for a female to present. The person who called me did so because he objected to the Chair's behavior.

After thinking things over for a bit, I started calling the geologists who were working Hartzog Draw for other companies. Throughout my work on the field, I had developed good relationships with most of them. I explained what had happened and asked them if they would refrain from sharing information with the "speaker selected by the Technical Program Chair." To a person, no one shared anything and that speaker had to go back to the Chair to say he couldn't put together a presentation. Consequently, the Chair came back to me and asked if I would present the paper. The strong support I received from my Hartzog Draw network who stood by me and "tight-holed" the other speaker is one of the most rewarding and confirming experiences of my career. When I received the Levorsen Award for best presentation at the meeting, it was "icing on the cake" (Fig. 10).

After just a short time in Development my boss, Vernon, who appeared to be always looking for "barriers" in the oil patch for me to break, decided when Cities started to drill a well in the Cook Inlet of Alaska, I was to be the wellsite geologist. The well was onshore but remote and the only access was by plane. There really weren't any separate facilities to accommodate a female living on site and I was to share quarters with the toolpusher. Cities was concerned about how the toolpusher and the unionized roughnecks would respond, and as far as anyone at Cities knew, a woman had never sat a well in Alaska, so they were quite nervous about the whole setup. There were consultations with lawyers and talk of sending a lawyer with me. As it turned out, there were no difficulties, although I do think it was a bit rougher on the toolpusher than on me as he was frightfully concerned he'd walk in on me naked, or I'd walk in on him, neither of which ever happened. I loved being in Alaska and one of my main thoughts while I was there was "I can't believe I'm getting paid to do this!"

Another duty of development geologists was to provide expert witness testimony in relation to developing fields. Vernon saw to it that I got my opportunity for that and helped me prepare so that I would shine during my testimony before the Wyoming Oil and Gas Commission. Afterwards, to celebrate my becoming an expert geologic witness, Vernon took me to the Casper Petroleum Club. However, at the door to the club, we were told females were not allowed. Vernon explained that I was a Cities geologist, that I had just testified before the Wyoming Oil and Gas Commission and that he was a member of the club, all to no avail. Right then and there, Vernon tore up his membership card and announced he was dropping his membership. More than 20 years later when I was at a Wyoming Geological Association (WGA) function, Don Bascoe, the former Head of the Wyoming Oil and Commission walked up to me and said, "I remember you. You were the first woman to be sworn in as an expert geologic witness before the Commission."

Back in the development group at the office, I, of course, had to interact with engineers. For the most part, I was always made to feel welcome, and developed a good relationship with many of them. Of course, they all knew I was a "Colby protégé" and that held me in good stead. After awhile, however, I decided that many of them needed to see the impact of their office décor on women. I have never been easily offended, but I found walking into engineers' offices where pictures of naked women on Rigid Tool calendars was disconcerting to say the least. I knew I couldn't complain, so, I decided what's good for the goose is good for the gander and I put pictures of naked men from *Playgirl* magazine up in my office. I also found some pictures of mistletoe and discretely put these over certain parts so as not to display everything. I can still see engineers walking into my office, seeing the pictures of naked men on the walls and doing a 180 and walking out. It was amazing how fast the Rigid Tool calendars came down, and I didn't have to say a word.

Figure 10. Randi receiving the Levorsen Award for her Hartzog Draw paper in 1979. (Photo: Randi Martinsen.)

With the calendars and other things, I have always found that humor is a powerful tool, and that keeping my sense of humor about things eased my way through many potentially uncomfortable situations. I was used to being a lone female among a group of males since my first year as a geology major. I had had time to adjust and become comfortable with being in the company of males, while for many of my male colleagues, change was put on them abruptly and they often had difficulty trying to figure out how to interact with me. It was always clear to me, however, which men were trying to make me feel like one of the boys by telling dirty jokes because they wanted to be inclusive, and those who were trying to embarrass me. With the rare exception of a few younger colleagues, I always felt the guys and especially the "older guys" were on my side.

Another time during my development days, I contacted a colleague at Davis Oil to see if I could stop by one of their development drill sites. He had told me no problem, so after checking on my Cities well, I went to the Davis well. Before heading up to the doghouse I put on my hardhat with the Cities logo and headed up to chat with the driller. I entered the doghouse,introduced myself, and told him I worked for Cities and that so-and-so with Davis had said it was ok to see how their well was doing. The driller kept looking down at some records, refusing to look at me and told me, "We don't want any magazine subscriptions." Well, I wasn't sure how to respond to that—why was this guy talking about magazine subscriptions? So I just went through my whole introduction again. His response was the same "We don't want any magazine subscriptions." After several futile attempts to explain I wasn't selling magazine subscriptions, and that I was a Cities geologist wanting information about the well, I gave up and left. Back in the office as I was relating this strange story to my "lunch group" including Bob and Vernon, they all started laughing. I asked ok, what's so funny and they told me the driller thought I was a prostitute—that buying a magazine subscription was code for wanting the services of a prostitute. I never did see any prostitutes while I was sitting wells, although maybe I just didn't recognize them, but my attire—jeans, flannel shirt, hard hat, and steel-toed boots—sure weren't what I would have considered typical dress for a prostitute.

I really enjoyed sitting wells. I loved the singing of the drill string as it made its way through porous, permeable, and oil-saturated rock. As a development geologist, I never drilled a dry hole. I also never experienced any pranks by the rig crews, like putting pipe dope (grease) down the wellbore to contaminate cuttings and make false hydrocarbon shows that some of my male colleagues experienced. I always treated every roughneck with respect, most especially the "worms," who were responsible for collecting samples. I would tell the driller that I was relatively new to wellsite work and would ask him and the rest of the roughnecks if they would teach me and help me. The response was always positive. I wasn't insincere. I knew I could learn a lot from them. As a female, I also seemed to be offered more promotional items from rig and service company personnel, like hats and coats. My most memorable and valuable gift was a miniature, diamond-studded core bit from Christensen Diamond Products Co. that was made to be put on a tie pin that could be worn on a necklace. It was beautiful. However, I felt I had not earned it, so I gave it to my boss, Vernon, whom I thought was much more deserving. He was so appreciative. In my ignorance, however, I thought I would easily get another one from Christensen. However, they were a lot rarer gift than I realized and I never received another one. Although I'd love to have such a pendant, I still believe Vernon was much more deserving.

After about two years in development, Vernon came into my office and told me I needed to go back to exploration. He told me if I stayed in development any longer, I'd be labeled a development geologist and not be able to get back to exploration, and that I deserved to keep all options open. I had learned so much from Vernon and he was such a great boss, I hated to leave him, but I trusted his judgment, and was transferred back to exploration. To my surprise, when I returned to exploration, I was given a 20% compensation raise to get my salary up to the level of the average exploration geologist with my years of experience. During my two years in development, I had outstanding evaluations and maximum raises, therefore, I don't think this had anything to do with gender and everything to do with the fact that Exploration geologists were viewed with higher esteem than development geologists. Hopefully that bias, along with any bias towards women in the oil patch, has mercifully ended.

Interestingly, as I mentioned, the only people I felt some resentment from were male geologists my age. The older guys all seemed to like and accept me. I suppose the younger guys felt I was competition and the older guys did not. For example, generally a geologist only got to go to one meeting a year. I got to go to several professional meetings a year because I gave talks and the company liked the public relations exposure. I remember complaints and whining from some of my peers about my getting to go to so many meetings. Another time, this animosity became apparent when I was out on a rig. I was with one of my young peers, and he was staying at the same motel. He got roaring drunk, came to my door in the middle of the night, and started banging and yelling that he wanted to "f— me." I felt badly that my peer had such anger toward me, but not badly enough lose sleep over it that night. He finally gave up and went away. Another time, as I was being transferred back to exploration, my boss brought in my replacement and asked me to fill him in on everything. As soon as my boss left, my replacement walked out of my office. He clearly didn't want to hear a thing from me. Overall, these incidents were minor compared to all the positive experiences I had working in our male-dominated industry (Fig. 11).

After working for Cities for about five years, I fell in love and married. I met my husband, Jim Steidtmann, at an AAPG conference. Jim was a Professor of Geology at the University of Wyoming (UW) in Laramie. We had a commuting marriage between Denver and Laramie for about six months when I decided that arrangement simply wasn't working. I had a house in Denver, Jim a house in Laramie, and we had an apartment in Fort Collins. I could never remember where anything was, and I decided, if I could make any money as a consultant, it would be better to have only one residence. This was 1979 and the oil business was booming. I was fortunate to obtain a retainer with a small company that didn't care where I lived and so I moved to Laramie to prospect in the Laramie Basin. I loved my job with Cities and hated leaving it, but Jim had obligations in Laramie that really didn't allow him to move. I felt I was putting my career on a bit of a back burner when I moved away from Denver, but was going to give it five years. If after five years I was not happy, then Jim and I would have to work out something else.

Shortly after I moved to Laramie, the Chair of the Department of Geology and Geophysics at Wyoming came to me and asked if I would teach a course in petroleum geology. I was busy but I liked the idea of having an affiliation with the department and having library privileges as well as an office on campus. I said yes and began my academic career. I believe the reason the department was interested in hiring me, even though I didn't have a PhD, was because I had been very professionally active in the petroleum geology community—writing papers, giving presentations, putting on workshops, and leading field trips. My practical experience and network as a working petroleum geologist could be an asset to the department.

Instead of putting my career on a back burner, moving to Laramie may have saved it. A few years after I moved, the industry experienced the major downturn of the 80s and consulting dried up. Fortunately, the UW Geology and Geophysics Department liked my teaching and asked if I would teach more classes. Eventually, my position evolved into a full-time position that included teaching, advising graduate students and research. As projects came up I was also able to continue consulting, but my main job was with the University. I had never had any desire to be an academic, but I enjoyed teaching and mentoring students. I loved seeing the "light bulbs go on" in their heads when they made discoveries.

The Department was especially appreciative of my industry activities when I started the student job fair at UW—based on the concept pioneered by Susan Morrice (Chapter 17) and Mary Beth Hatteberg. We called it the Rocky Mountain Rendezvous (RMR), and for the last 15 years that I was a faculty member, I brought recruiters from 15-30 companies to campus to interview geoscience students from as many as 60 different universities. Although most students were from the greater Rocky Mountain region and within a day's drive from Laramie, many came from across the U.S. It was greatly successful giving so many students exposure to industry without having to travel to Houston, and of course, helping students get jobs. The RMR also benefitted the small companies and independents that are active in the Rocky Mountain region and who don't have budgets to visit multiple universities.

Figure 11. Randi on a drilling rig in the Powder River Basin, Wyoming, 1993. (Photo: Robbie Gries.)

I honestly don't believe my career as an academic was as exciting as my time with Cities, but it had some definite advantages. For one thing, I had children, and Jim and I raised them. Yes, we had babysitters, but usually for only a few hours a day, at most. The flexibility of academia, where you are only on campus for the hours you are teaching, allowed Jim and me to work at home a lot of the time, sometimes late into the night after the children were asleep, but still, we had a great amount of flexibility. We never taught at the same time, so we did not have any problem when our children got sick. I wasn't exactly the proverbial "soccer mom" although I did coach all three of my kid's grade school soccer teams. So, overall, I feel very fortunate and proud to have been part of the Department at the University of Wyoming.

I never dreamed when I moved to Laramie that my career would evolve to academia. I also never dreamed I'd become AAPG President. As I think about my career path, my advice to young people is to never be afraid of taking a new or a different path because you never know where that path will lead. I have so many stories, so many memories, some of which I suppose could be viewed as negative experiences, but when I remember them, they always bring a smile to my face.

Randi Martinsen was born in New York in 1950 and earned her B.S. in Earth and Space Science at Stoney Brook University, in 1971, and her master's in 1975 at Northern Arizona University in 1973. She is retired from teaching petroleum geology at the University of Wyoming, where her husband, James D. Steidtmann, was also a professor and distinguished geologist. Randi and Jim have three children, David, Dana, and Matt, and two granddaughters, Lauren, and Kaya. Randi was the second female President of AAPG.

Cindy Crawley Stewart

What a difference just a few years can make with Affirmative Action—by the time I interviewed in 1975, many companies had already filled their "female" quota with recently-hired geologists. I was at Tulane University in New Orleans, a very small Geology Department, so there weren't enough graduate students to keep the recruiter occupied for the scheduled visit. My professors asked me to interview despite my undergraduate status. The oil business was booming and I didn't want to miss out. If I could land a job, I planned to obtain a master's degree later. The Conoco recruiter was interested, but he said he didn't have authority to offer a position to anyone without a master's degree. However, for some reason, he was eager for me to meet the Chief Geologist who was visiting the Lake Charles office. I had heard several stories about Dr. Max Pitcher and was a bit apprehensive about the upcoming interview.

When Pitcher's secretary called to confirm the details of the trip, she reiterated that Conoco did NOT have a policy to hire people with just a bachelor's. To open the interview, Pitcher stated up front that "Conoco is not looking to hire women or blacks, and it is not our policy to hire bachelor's candidates." In my somewhat brash manner, I asked, "Then why would you fly me to an interview in Lake Charles?" His point, poorly articulated, was that they were looking for good geologists. I took him at his word that I was likely unqualified, and relaxed, figuring I was obviously just at this motel restaurant in Lake Charles for a free lunch.

He asked about my strengths and weaknesses and I talked about all my strengths. Then he said, "I know a lot about your strengths, but I don't know about your weaknesses." I paused a moment and then admitted the only weakness I could think of was in not recognizing my weaknesses, yet!

Dr. Pitcher pontificated a bit about his position as head of all geologists and training, etc. His final point was that he was in a position to offer me a job with Conoco. This was exciting because I already had a job offer from Texaco, but I preferred Conoco's training program. Having had a summer with Texaco in their geophysical department, I knew the right experience was more important to me than just the highest pay check (Fig. 12).

Growing up poor and not having a mentor in business, I didn't realize that I knew the correct answer when Pitcher asked what salary I wanted. Savvy interviewees would ask to match the salary of their current offer! Naively, I thought I would give Pitcher the opportunity to "be generous." I gave him the minimum salary I would work for, as in, $50 *less* and I'd go back to being a waitress. Of course, I was disappointed when Pitcher offered me only $50 over my measly request. He was taking advantage of me, and sadly, I knew it! The right job AND the competitive salary didn't need to be mutually exclusive, but my business naivety made it so. I had a lot to learn about negotiating.

Figure 12. Cindy Crawley offshore Mustang Island on a production platform, 1978. (Photo: Cindy Stewart, Denver, Colorado.)

At my first-year review with Conoco, my boss told management that I was doing the work equal to that of a geologist with a master's and should be paid as such. My first raise in 1976 was a hefty 30% and Dr. Pitcher was surprised that I wasn't overjoyed with such a substantial raise. He said, "Conoco doesn't give many of these." I knew what my starting salary with Texaco a year ago would have been—considerably more, and replied, "30% of nothing is still nothing." But, my experience was worth it, as I was an "Explorationist", interpreting both the geology and geophysics of my plays. Again, I thought the right experience was more important than chasing the highest pay.

How did I get into geology? In high school I loved debate. Arguing was entertainment for me. I thought I wanted to be a courtroom lawyer. My high school counselor recommended Duke and Tulane because "they give good scholarships." Attracted to Duke because of the gothic architecture, I wanted to meet with the Financial Aid officer to emphasize that I wouldn't attend their college without significant support. During my junior year of high school, at age 16, I drove alone from Florida to North Carolina over the Christmas break. I loved the Duke campus; although it was devoid of students, it was not devoid of the stereotypes. Jokes about the East Beasts (Women's campus) and the West Pests (Men's campus) were discouraging to someone like me who enjoyed working with men.

I was offered a full-ride from both Duke and Tulane and didn't know how to choose. I liked working with guys and was concerned about the Duke "Pests" comment, plus the Tulane scholarship was $50 more than Duke and I wondered if that meant Tulane wanted me more. Arbitrarily, I chose Tulane sight unseen.

As for selecting the "best fit" college, maybe this wasn't it. The humidity in New Orleans was brutal in August in the un-air-conditioned freshmen dorm. Furthermore, Louisiana is under French Law—out of all 50 States, as a budding lawyer, I pick the only one under French Law!

While I contemplated this hitch, I continued to take classes for general requirements. I needed a science, and since I was not pre-med, I wanted to avoid the chemistry and biology classes. That left only two choices: astronomy that was favored by football players, and, geology, a total unknown. But, studying Introduction to Geology it became clear that this science was going to be fun. In geology, we argued for our interpretation and never had to quote someone else's "case law" or prior arguments. It was a science with few hard facts, lots of unknowns, and you couldn't be proven wrong until someone drilled another data point. I had found my niche—I could argue all I wanted and not be bothered with tomes of legal examples.

Figure 13. Cindy Crawley in geology field camp (Univ. of Nevada, 1975), when a bee flew up her shorts! (Photo: field partner, John Battie, provided by Cindy Stewart.)

As a new major, I reviewed the course offerings with an eye to my four-year scholarship. Tulane's Geology Department was so small that some critical classes were only offered every other year. If I was to major in geology, I needed to take petrology before the prerequisite Mineralogy to graduate in four years. I talked the professor into letting me take petrology without the prerequisite. This was a bold move because the relationship of mineralogy to petrology is like letters of the alphabet are to words. Over Christmas, I studied the seven basic minerals, or just the "vowels," and that's all I knew going into petrology. In retrospect, I think it helped on some exams as I never "indentified" pink rhodocrosite in granite, because I didn't know anything about rhodocrosite. With only the basic minerals, statistics were on my side for identifying rocks. With an "A" in petrology, I launched into my new major.

Structural geology was another major requirement, taught by the only Tulane Professor with oil industry experience. I loved his different perspective on geology, but it also came with his standard chauvinistic view, "Women can't see in 3-D and the only job you will be able to get is in a library." (Fig. 13)

There were only two students in structure class, and yes, it took me a minute longer than the other straight-A student, but I did get it. This was the only time I was truly the "bottom" of the class, my A was lower than the guy's A. As for the Professor's opinion of women and 3-D visualization, I'd point out that it probably wasn't genetic. If a girl played with Lincoln Logs instead of flat paper dolls, she could develop spatial sense like a boy. I don't think Dr. Cal Badon ever changed his opinion of women; it was just easier for him to think of me as more of a guy.

Figure 14. Cindy Crawley Stewart, 1984, a discovery in the Paradox Basin of Utah using new seismic integration. This discovery was followed up with the first 3-D seismic program in algal mounds of Paradox Basin (January, 1985, Seis-Port semi heliportable). (Photo: Duane Moredock, BWAB partner in discovery, provided by Cindy Stewart.)

Dr. Badon went back to work in industry, a loss for Tulane. When he departed, he said he would offer me a job upon my graduation. After my first year with Conoco, he did call from Anadarko and offer me a job. My position with Conoco, working both geology and geophysics, seismic modeling and working offshore lease sales, was too exciting to leave. Again, for me the experience was always worth more than the paycheck. [Comment from Robbie Gries: Cindy's combined geology and geophysics expertise led her to several oil discoveries in the Paradox basin, using creative seismic processing techniques, which were developed by colleague, Louis Willhoit (Fig. 14).]

Cindy Crawley Stewart was born in 1954. She graduated summa cum laude, Phi Beta Kappa with her bachelor's degree in geology from Tulane University in 1975. Cindy is retired and lives in Denver with her husband, Tom Stewart. Her daughter, Christine Paaverud, is married and lives in Minnesota.

Marsha Findlay Bourque

Marsha Findlay's earliest memories centered on books, and an abiding curiosity about the world. She was born in a now-gentrified part of Brooklyn, New York, to parents who gathered their resources to move the family to Huntington, on Long Island, where their children would grow up in a multi-cultural school district whose high school graduates were regularly accepted to highly competitive colleges and universities, and received appointments to U.S. military academies. As a woman of Caribbean heritage, Marsha had a different perspective of society and race relations from Blacks who grew up in the U.S. South.

A high achiever academically, she attended Vassar College, funded by an assortment of scholarships and jobs. The courses she chose reflected her plans for a career in law. But her geology classes were compelling, and her career path was permanently altered with a visit from a Chevron recruiter during her senior year.

Marsha earned a bachelor's degree with a double major in geology and political science. Historically, Vassar had a strong but small roster of geology majors who went on to become not geoscientists but rather dentists, physicians, lawyers, judges, and teachers. Those who wanted to do geology graduate work first had to be accepted for field camp, many of which did not consider admitting women. To provide its geology majors a full field experience, the Vassar geology curriculum included two rigorous field courses which paved the way to some graduate schools.

Marsha earned her master's degree from the University of South Carolina (USC), where she had a very positive and encouraging major professor in Dr. William H. Kanes. Bill Kanes was the architect of an NSF-funded study of the opening of Tethyan Seaway during the Mesozoic. Marsha's chapter in the story included an examination of the carbonate stratigraphy in Tunisia. Dr. Kanes wanted her to stay on at USC for a PhD, but she found herself feeling "less than safe" living in ultra-conservative Strom Thurmond's South Carolina, and she was also eager to begin her career. She accepted a position at Chevron in New Orleans, in 1976. She had interned with Chevron in New Orleans following graduation from Vassar, and with Exxon in Houston during graduate school, and looked forward to starting her career.

And there was much to look forward to, and much to learn. Petroleum geoscience was then, as it is now, an apprenticeship-driven profession, requiring attention to detail and mentorship. Marsha was a "first," and for many of the people she worked with, a challenge to their perception of women and minorities. For some, there was the unease attached to a new situation and for others, resistance. The positive experiences were memorable, but always resided within the context of prevailing social and business culture such as: the senior geophysicist who spent his lunch hours working with her, only to be reprimanded for "wasting his time because she won't last"; the joy of having an interview with a potential new employer, only to have her headhunter excoriated for sending "someone like her" to a job interview; a Mobil manager who placed her on a list to be promoted for her solid contributions who was therefore reprimanded – and sanctioned—by the Chief Geologist. It was difficult not to notice.

The attitude of some colleagues in the early years was a challenge to navigate, with disrespect ineptly manifested; certain co-workers would stand outside her office door and state that the industry had been forced to hire "unqualified people" to fill Affirmative Action quotas. Too often, those comments were voiced by colleagues who had not yet completed their M.S. degrees. Proud of her academic performance and her alma mater, she found the comments to be doubly offensive. To this day, the term "Affirmative Action" brings up vivid memories of those old comments and the negative impact on her work environment. She prefers the terminology "Post-Civil Rights Era" to describe the times, and the challenges of her early years in the industry. This phrase doesn't push any buttons.

Navigating these barriers was also different for Marsha. For most people, if a company did not suit them, they could just move to another company. But, in the 1970s, a change of venue was no guarantee of a better work environment for minorities. Marsha had additional factors to consider and influence her career decisions. After six months in her first job, a hate letter, stapled to a routing slip bearing her name, was intercepted by the company's security department. She was told not to share the information with anyone while an investigation took place, and was offered to have security monitor her home and office telephones. Whomever sent the letter clearly felt comfortable with his behavior. Marsha could only wonder, "What's next?" For her, she decided the next move would be to further develop her skill sets, write a résumé, and leave that company.

But something wonderful also happened in the first year of full-time employment. The American Geological Institute (AGI) had created the Minority Participation Program (MPP) in 1974, and invited Marsha to join its Advisory Scholarship Committee in 1976 seven months after she began working. This, for Marsha, was an opportunity to not be an "only." Even better, she could make every effort to give the next generation of minority geoscientists the information, contacts, and resources to develop a strong academic background and interpersonal skill set for the exciting and challenging careers ahead of them. She could make a difference.

The AGI MPP Committee was dedicated to ensuring its scholars were solidly prepared, and their credentials unquestioned. Marsha spent more than 30 years as a volunteer on the committee, reviewing scholarship applications and mentoring undergraduate and graduate Native American, Hispanic and Black U.S. citizens. Scholars from the program have gone on to become academicians, researchers, U.S. Geological Survey employees, hydrogeologists, meteorologists, and petroleum geologists, with some reaching the highest levels of management at major companies. Many of the student applicants were non-traditional, and included veterans, people in their twenties and thirties, community college students and those who attended reservation or rural schools with limited resources. Most were the first in their family to seek an education beyond high school.

For many, the coaching and mentoring from committee members (largely minority geoscientists themselves) was as valuable as the funding received through AGI. Along the way, committee members found that some students of color did not want to apply for several of the designated scholarships that promoted diversity because they were concerned that such scholarships could stigmatize them as "not qualified to compete" with majority students. Marsha and other committee members couldn't dispute that possibility, given their collective experiences and observations.

Confidence gained by working on behalf of others–future minority geoscientists–carried Marsha through her professionally challenging times in industry. In 1980, Marsha married Michael Bourque and continued to work hard to build her technical skills at Chevron.

All the while, Marsha continued to look at other job opportunities. A highly-placed colleague at Amoco arranged an interview, and things appeared on track for a job offer. But just as a final offer was to be made, Marsha received a letter. She was turned down. Her contact at Amoco said they had learned that "someone" at Chevron had filed an EEOC suit. The assumption was that the Black woman must have been the one, and if so, she could be a "trouble-maker." Marsha was unaware of the EEOC complaint and later found out it had been filed by a female landman, but the damage had been done.

Figure 15. Marsha Findlay Bourque, 1984, exploration geologist with Shell Oil. (Photo: Bartholomew & Tillery, 1984, p. 403.)

Marsha continued her job search, and accepted a position with Mobil, where she thrived under an excellent boss, who was a Canadian expatriate. She was a team leader in Production Geology, and was assigned a field, which because of her work, soon became a "Crown Jewel" – the nickname for the top moneymakers for the company. As good fortune would have it, Marsha became pregnant with her daughter during this time. She had a determination and desire to maintain her career and be a wife and mother—in part, to provide a good role model for her daughter. This was not easy as she was confined to bed rest the month before her daughter's birth, but having time off with a reduced salary and an understanding boss, she managed. She was back at work as soon as possible. Later, when her boss wanted to promote her, the Chief Geologist sanctioned him. A short time later, he returned to Canada. Her new boss, whose mentality was aligned with the business culture set by the Chief Geologist, ignored her work and she was laid off within a year.

The oil business is volatile, and the mantra borrowed from the Girl Scouts– "Be Prepared"–always rings true. Marsha knew that, having survived many rounds of layoffs, one should always be aware of new opportunities. At the time of her layoff, she had two job offers, both in Houston. She chose to work with BP. (Fig. 15)

Moving to Houston was important, both professionally and for her family. Her husband, Michael, was an exploration geologist with Shell and Houston was a desirable place to be. They had enjoyed their time in New Orleans, but they wanted to have the best possible educational and cultural environment for their young daughter. Marsha continued her career at BP, where she had the pleasure of reuniting with several colleagues from New Orleans in her new workplace.

Marsha spent her years at BP growing her skill set in offshore operations. After seven years, she moved to Statoil, which had just begun to spread its global outreach to the Gulf of Mexico. Statoil's first office in Houston did not last, succumbing to a severe drop in oil prices in the late '90s. The office was closed, and it was difficult to find another job so Marsha learned another skill set and consulted in risk analysis. Then she joined Conoco in Lafayette as their Deepwater Geoscience Manager. She commuted to Lafayette from Houston for a year until the decision had been made to close the office and bring the Deepwater team back to the Houston campus. But on her first day, as she logged on and checked her email, she read a congratulatory note from Human Resources, "As of today, all employees are fully vested in the company stock plan."

Marsha exchanged looks with another, experienced new hire. They had an idea what this might mean. "Wait for it...."

Three months later, Thanksgiving weekend, came another email announcing the Conoco Phillips merger. The office in Lafayette closed, as scheduled. But Deepwater Operations did not survive the merger. Layoffs connected to the merger took place in September, one year after Marsha's first day with the company.

Marsha took stock of her industry, her goals, and her work-life balance. Time to reinvent! Her work experience was valuable. During her career, she had observed a great deal of dysfunction, the result of poor communication, poor listening skills, impatience, and misdirected ambition. Along with Dr. Susan Peterson, her petroleum engineering colleague from her risk analysis consulting days, Marsha developed technical training courses for those entering the petroleum industry. The first course, delivered through the Nautilus organization, led to other classes for individual companies. Tailored to the needs, culture and history of client companies, the courses were popular and remain popular.

As her technical training work was gaining traction, Marsha's husband was transferred to Shell's office in The Hague, where he was the Team Lead, for New Ventures in Russia. They decided that Michael would live as a bachelor for The Hague assignment because he would be retiring at the end of the assignment. But a year into his assignment, Marsha was invited to apply for a consulting position in Shell's Learning Center in Rijswijk. At the same time, Anadarko was aggressively pursuing her to lead their technical training division in the Woodlands, Texas. Again, time to pivot and regroup. The Anadarko position was a dream job, something Marsha would have embraced at another time. But the opportunity to live in Europe, with her husband, and have meaningful work was undeniably the better choice.

Figure 16. Marsha Findlay Bourque, 2002, running for the Houston Geological Society Board. (Photo: Marsha Bourque, Houston, Texas.)

Time marched on. Michael retired, and Marsha continued her work with Shell for four more years, and continued to work with Susan Peterson to develop and deliver classes to client companies. Then, another change; as the conditions began to change at Shell, Marsha terminated the relationship and made the decision to seek a different client. As has been said, unless you are the lead sled dog, the view never changes! Marsha started teaching courses in Saudi Arabia and, today, enjoys a deep sense of reward and satisfaction working with the Saudi young female engineers and geoscientists (Fig. 16). She enjoys mentoring them and encouraging them. She feels she is providing them with career tools and advice that was sometimes a challenge to find early in her career. Like her, *those* women are pioneers, the first in their generation to play a role in the development of their most valued natural resources. For her, this makes everything worthwhile.

Marsha Findlay Bourque was born in Brooklyn, New York in 1952. She acquired her B.S. in geology from Vassar in 1974 and her M. S. in geology from University of South Carolina in 1976. She has been a member of AAPG for over 40 years. She and her husband, Michael Bourque, are the parents of daughter, Veronica. They split their time between Houston, Texas and Santa Fe, New Mexico. Marsha has chaired the Teachers' Day Program for all but one Houston AAPG meeting since 1992, and is involved in the planning of the expanded 2017 Houston ACE Educators' Program.

Debra Kimiko Nishida

I decided to become a geologist one sunny summer day on Malibu Beach in California. It was 1975, and this seemed like a natural choice. As a kid, I loved collecting unusual and colorful rocks on family vacations to the Sierra Nevada Mountains and Utah. I was already a student at the University of Southern California (USC), and a meeting with the geology department chairman, appropriately named, Dr. Stone, sealed the deal.

During the next three years of earth science course work and field trips, it was clear I had made the right decision. I especially enjoyed the camaraderie with my fellow geology students. We made many good memories; one highlight was a six-week summer field camp in the White-Inyo Mountains of eastern California. The camp's water was supplied by a dusty old tanker truck that was parked up the hill to allow for gravity feed through a garden hose. This hose was also our shower source. The shower enclosure was built on the edge of a small escarpment. For privacy, there was orange plastic sheeting on three sides. The fourth side was open to the UCLA geology field camp down the hill. The six of us young ladies complained that the UCLA students could see us take showers. Our field camp professor just laughed and said in his Texas twang, "Don't worry girls. If they've never seen a woman before, they won't know what they're looking at. And if they have seen one before, you all look the same anyways!"

We lost the argument.

The USC geology department had many professional contacts and for two years I had a part-time job with the California Division of Mines and Geology (CDMG, now the California Geological Survey). This is where I learned how to hand draft graphs and maps with now antiquated tools such as a Leroy Lettering Set and Rapidograph pens. I also became a skilled log and map splicer and colorer using Prismacolor pencils.

In the fall of my senior year, recruiters from major companies came to interview students for jobs in mining and petroleum. Thanks to recommendations from my professors and CDMG mentors, Texaco offered me a job in their Los Angeles office. As the first person in my immediate family to go to college, I was thrilled and grateful to have full-time work upon graduation.

Both sets of grandparents were immigrants from Japan to California. They entered the US before the passage of the Immigration Act of 1924 that restricted the number of immigrants who could enter the recession-hit United States after WWI. This law had many provisions, including the total ban of immigration by Asians. It was feared that immigrants would increase U.S. unemployment.

My grandparents were farmers, gardeners, and housekeepers who, with their children (my parents), suffered the displacement and indignity of World War II relocation (internment) camps at Poston and Gila River in Arizona. Among these hardworking and practical people, going to university to study geology was an "untraditional" choice. My younger sister also made an untraditional decision to study petroleum engineering. Looking back on our respective decisions, we weren't trying to be trailblazers. Instead, we were guided by our situation, namely we did not have a financial safety net from our families and we wanted satisfying and challenging professional careers. And, we were determined to independently support ourselves. We were both good in science and math, and these fields offered our best options.

I first heard whispers about "Affirmative Action" (AA) and the "Equal Employment Opportunity Commission" (EEOC) during the recruitment process. They said, "Hire Debbie. She's our best Asian female student."

The truth is, I was the ONLY one. My employment gave my new employer the opportunity to fill two AA categories: women and minorities. However, I was not treated as a "token" because it was 1978 and there were already many female geologists and geophysicists in the office. Times were good in the oil patch. During the late 1970s and early 1980s, oil prices were high, and there was a push for increased staffing and drilling operations.

New hires had wellsite geology training in the Central Valley of California. After receiving safety instructions and hard hats, we toured a drill rig. An interesting area, besides the drill floor, where lots of action takes place, was the driller's doghouse. The walls were posted with nude and scantily clad women on promotional calendars. I was young and naïve and I can't remember who was more embarrassed—me, or the drill hands. I could feel tension and the men staring at me to see my reaction. The next time I went into the doghouse, all the "special decorations" were gone. Perhaps my non-judgmental reaction caused them to rise to their "higher selves" and discreetly clean up their shack.

New "green" employees were easy targets for mischievous rig crews. At my first wellsite training experience, we called the tool pushers (drilling managers) the "I Brothers." They were good old boys who talked incessantly and bragged about their successes and experiences, as in, "I did this..." and "I did that..." One evening they invited me down to their tiny rusty trailer for a game of cards. When I arrived, they made room for me around the crowded dinette. I lost $20 in a flash. I felt it was as if I opened my wallet and said to the sharks, "Here, take my cash!"

Although I enjoyed the two weeks of training, my geologic mentor and the tool pushers knew I was eager to return home. I made a courtesy visit to their trailer to say good-bye and thank you. I excitedly got back in my truck and started it. Suddenly, smoke billowed out from under the hood. In a panic, I shut off the ignition, and ran back to the shack to get help. The guys were just as I left them: sitting back in their chairs with feet propped on desks, rocking back and forth, and smoking. They feigned concern about my automotive problem, and came out to check underneath the hood. "Hmmm...it looks like someone planted a smoke bomb in your engine!" The guy with the biggest twinkle in his eyes, my geologic mentor, had done it. And, of course, they all were watching out the window chuckling at my panic.

In 1980, the oil and gas boom provided me with an opportunity to work in Calgary, Alberta, Canada. My first day of work at Hudson's Bay Oil and Gas (HBOG), I met members of my team and landman, Dennis, poked his head around my office door, then slid into the chair opposite my desk to chat. He was an extrovert, all questions and cheeky fun. But, when I told him I was the geologist from California, he became crest-fallen. I figured out exactly what had happened—prior to my arrival, there was excitement about a new hire, a female geologist from California. The hopeful assumption was she would be a blonde-haired, blue-eyed surfer girl. I blew his expectations. I teased him, "They grow Asian girls in California too, Dennis!" We had a huge laugh and became great friends.

Our team explored for gas in the Devonian carbonates of NE British Columbia (BC). In this area, drilling occurs in winter after the muskeg freezes. To get to the well site, I flew north to High Level, Alberta, and picked up a 4x4 rental truck. I drove on roads to Zama City and then followed rig signs on specially built ice roads across the Alberta-BC border to Thinahtea Lake. In the frigid north, safety was a life-or-death matter. At a minimum, vehicles carried a shovel, tow rope, Arctic parka and gloves, sleeping bag, candles, matches, and extra food. For the most part, the roads up north had little traffic. So, I was surprised to see a very large equipment truck barreling down the road towards me. The road wasn't wide enough for the two of us. To avoid a collision, I was forced off into the steep ditch. Fortunately, the snow bank cushioned the impact, and the driver stopped and winched me out. He was apologetic; vehicles can't stop quickly on winding icy roads. This was certainly a change from the freeways of southern California.

Winter logistics in the far north could be a challenge, too. It was so cold that I had to keep the truck running or it would freeze. There were two sets of keys, one for the ignition, the other to lock the truck while you had a meal at the restaurant. Parking lots were so filled with billowing clouds of vehicle steam and exhaust that it was hard to find your truck after a meal.

One frigid night, curtains of green and pink Northern Lights crackled in the sky as I sat in the truck, shining headlights down a frozen lake "runway." Oil-fueled smudge pots lit the edges of this makeshift landing strip. We were waiting for the mud man's small plane to land at the appointed time and deliver rig parts. Drilling had been suspended for a week due to mechanical issues. Because drilling was behind schedule, the rig was on location longer than planned and the water supply from a nearby beaver pond was close to depletion. We were getting down to the brown "bottom" water. Thankfully, it tested "safe" by the onsite medics. Though the kitchen staff did their best, the mashed potatoes and rice were hazel-colored. Towards the end, it was so disgusting, we brushed our teeth with soda pop.

HBOG's takeover by Dome Petroleum in 1981 created another opportunity in the Beaufort Sea of the Canadian Arctic. Initially, only male geologists were called upon for geologic wellsite supervision responsibilities on the Canmar drill ships. Women were told that accommodations and appropriate facilities were unavailable, due to the ship's tight quarters. But, we also knew about the superstition that it was bad luck to have women on board at sea. Finally, necessity and management decisions convinced the drillers to include women. Soon, we were in Sikorski helicopters landing on the drill ship helipad. There was no hint from the crew that women were unwelcome. Everyone was totally professional.

Geology took me overseas to Jakarta, Indonesia, in 1989. As Head of Development Geology at Australia Gas Light (AGL), I supervised a group of three geologists and one technician. My boss, the General Manager, and I were the only ex-pats, so it was a wonderful window into Indonesian culture. The friendly and warmly welcoming staff enjoyed sharing their traditional food with me because I was fearless in trying everything.

One of my fondest memories took place at AGL's camp on Seram in the Maluku Islands of eastern Indonesia. A few camp hands went into the forested mountains on their day off and brought back gunny sacks of wild durian, infamously atrocious in its odor. After dinner, two guys with machetes cracked open the spiky, thick-husked fruit as all of us gathered around and enjoyed the smelly, buttery delicacy in giddy happiness. To this day, I only like to eat durian with friends, never alone.

One morning at the Jakarta office, I was struggling to hang a map of our oil field on the wall. Local geologist Rudi rushed into my office and politely informed me that standing on a chair was not appropriate for the leader of the group, so please step down. It was a blanket-sized map, so I was grateful for his offer of help. But, as I turned to thank him, he was gone. He had gone to find our technician, Gani, to put the map up on the wall because hanging a map on the wall was beneath Rudi's job level, too.

After six years in Indonesia, I returned to Calgary at a time of low oil prices. Thanks to my network of friends, I started a consulting position in Alberta Energy Company's (AEC) Northern Alberta group. Six months later, I learned that the Southern Alberta group wanted to hire a geologist with heavy oil experience to replace a retiring geologist. Initially, I was turned down for the job because I didn't have the right experience, which included planning horizontal well locations, working with drillers to "steer" the drill bit to intersect the best oil pay, and plotting coordinates of the drill path on maps and cross-sections. I told the manager that I understood why I did not get the job, but if given the proper training, I knew I could do it. He was silent, and asked if I would give him three hours, and he would get back to me. He called back with good news: I got the job!

Figure 17. Debra Nishida, 1988, in the High Atlas of Morocco. (Photo: Debra Nishida, Houston, Texas.)

Don, the retiring geologist, said he was delighted I was hired. It turns out that during the months of searching for his replacement, he told the managers that this detail-oriented job was perfect for "old men and Japanese ladies." When my résumé appeared across his desk, he instantly knew that he wanted to hire me. He was the "old man." I was the "Japanese lady."

My work at AEC (which became Encana Corporation) was rewarding for many reasons. As a team, we met the challenge to reach our stretch production targets and acquisition goals. We also played hard and had amazing team-building activities. These included golf tournaments with special beverage carts and celebratory parties with mandatory leg wrestling for the guys. We worked earnestly to keep costs down, yet the engineers could not understand why geologists were always going on "boondoggle" field trips. We invited them to join us on a field trip to the Oregon sand dunes, a model for our subsurface reservoirs. In the field, they saw and understood the depositional environment and spatial context of the sand dunes. They also saw potential vertical and horizontal permeability barriers. You could see the light go on in their heads. Later, when planning wells, engineer colleagues began to ask, "Don't you want to cut more core?" This scores as a victory for geologists!

In summary, my decision to study geology changed the course of my life. As a child in Los Angeles, I never would have dreamed of having a career that opened the doors to the world. I lived and worked in the U.S., Canada, and Indonesia, carried dual U.S. and Canadian citizenship, and love multi-cultural and ethnic experiences of all types (Fig. 17). And there's something more—I, belatedly, married the young man I met on my first day of USC geology classes, Neil Hurley.

My Japanese American and Buddhist traditional values are no different from anyone else's: harmony, respect, and hard work. We try not to let others lose face, to listen more than talk, and to be sensitive to nuance. While it was better to "blend in, and not stick out in a crowd," I was an anomaly as an Asian woman in the oil patch. I cannot say whether or not this helped or hindered me, but my cultural "roots" served me well with regards to teamwork and getting the job done.

Debra Nishida was born in 1955 in California. She earned her bachelor's degree in geology in 1978 from the University of Southern California. Debra is retired and lives with her husband, Neil Hurley, in Houston, Texas.

Joan Burnet Bruns

Figure 18. Joan Burnet Bruns, 1991. (Photo: Joan Bruns, Oklahoma City, Oklahoma.)

"Having graduated with a master's in geology in 1980, I became a petroleum geologist with a major oil company. After I had been working for several months, my boss and the person who hired me, commented to our team that I was the perfect hire. I came at the right time, I had the needed qualifications and I was female. This broke my heart a little. I would have felt better thinking that the fact that I am a woman had not played a part in my selection. A wave of sadness *still* comes over me when I think about it. My boss was great. He meant no harm by this statement. After the company succumbed to a hostile takeover, he and I were employed elsewhere, we remained friends." (Fig. 18).

Joan Burnet Bruns was born in 1955 in Terre Haute, Indiana. She has both an B.S. in geology (1977) and an M.S. (1980) from Iowa State University.

Denise M. Stone

My life direction appeared to me on a fall day in Fort Worth, Texas, in 1975 when I went on my first geology field trip. As an 18-year-old college freshman, I arrived at Inspiration Point overlooking Lake Worth. The sun was shining; there were several miles of visibility across the lake. The air was crisp. The weather, rocks, and camaraderie with others in the van combined to make me realize that I love geology. My life course was set.

The instructor and his graduate students herded us around and showed us how to look at stacked beds of Cretaceous sediments loaded with fossils and depositional structures. When someone spotted something interesting, we'd hear, "Hey, look at this!"

And we'd all clamber over to see it. At the outcrop that day, observing and sharing your observations was encouraged and rewarded with enthusiasm. With bedding planes clearly exposed, we scrambled around several localities for a few hours measuring strike and dip with a Brunton Compass. How cool is this, I thought. "Lightbulb" moment: *sedimentary layers have attitude. They continue for distances. There is a grand organization to the solid earth beneath my feet.* Geology had grabbed hold of me!

My intended major when I arrived at college was a new discipline at that time called International Relations. It combined Political Science, Economics, History, and Foreign Languages. I love languages and had studied both Italian and French while living in Rome, Italy, for my sophomore and junior years of high school. After living outside the U.S., in both Australia for some of grade school and Italy for high school, I had this vision that I would become a diplomat for the U.S. State Department and work in an American embassy somewhere in the world. I knew that I loved to travel. My dad's foreign assignments with his job had our family moving frequently, in fact, it wasn't until I got to college that I would attend the same school for more than two years in a row.

Figure 19. Denise M. Stone, in Arches National Monument, always happy to be in the field. (Photo: Denise Stone, Houston, Texas.)

All that planning went out the window on this field trip to, aptly named, Inspiration Point. When I called my parents, and broke the news I wanted to change my major to geology, they were cautiously supportive. "You'll have to take a lot of math, physics, chemistry, computer science, etc. Are you ready for all that?"

I replied, "I don't know. All I know is that I REALLY LIKE GEOLOGY!"

And so, the journey began. (Fig. 19)

After declaring myself a geology major, the coursework intensified, the field trips got both more serious and more fun, and the geology jokes started, especially about my last name. People would say, "Your name is Stone and you're majoring in Geology? Ha, ha, ha. That's some kind of joke, right? What's your real name?"

My response, "No, it's the truth, I am a Stone and you now know someone who has been divinely preordained to their profession."

There were also odd funnies, newspaper clippings, etc. that would be posted, usually anonymously to the geology department bulletin board. One, in particular, I remember was a letter to Dear Ann Landers, that went something like this:

> *"Dear Ann, my husband is a geologist and frequently goes to remote places to do fieldwork. Recently, to my surprise, I learned that he's planning to do "fieldwork" with a female geologist. They will be alone together in remote wilderness for days. I don't like this at all. Please help, what can I do?"* Signed: Concerned Wife.

Ann's sensible and reassuring answer to this plea was to encourage her to talk it over with her husband and make her feelings known. But, below Ann's response, there was also a reader response. It went something like this:

> *"Dear Ann, please tell Concerned Wife who doesn't like her geologist husband doing "fieldwork" with female geologists that she doesn't have a thing to worry about. My husband is a geologist and all the female geologists he works with are "ugly as a stick." It's totally impossible that any of them could steal him away. He would never be interested."* Signed: Calm Geo-Wife.

Well, as you might imagine, this Dear Ann Landers exchange prompted a good deal of chatter in the department. The female geology majors got ribbing from the guys. Calm Geo-Wife planted the idea that, if you are female, when you become a geologist, your ability to attract men would drop to zero. I'd hear, "Denise, are you sure you know what you're getting yourself into? Women are measured by their looks and, when you get your degree, it's all downhill."

Hmmm, I thought. The flipside of the issue to my way of thinking was that *being a female geologist was going to be anything but boring.* Not only is the subject of geology fascinating, but just trying to do your job, once you start, carries with it a boatload of social challenges I had no idea existed.

When I was a geology undergraduate at Texas Christian University (TCU), several recruiters from industry came to campus looking for summer hire geologists. I was delighted to receive an offer from Union Oil of California. In the summer of 1978, at 19 years old, having no idea what a geologist did inside an oil company, I would soon find out.

The job worked out well, and Union kept me on for three summers as I continued working toward my master's at Memphis State University. They also generously sponsored my thesis. My summer projects were great training. I read scout tickets, picked tops on logs, posted them on a base map, and contoured the data, all the while learning the stratigraphy of the Gulf Coastal Plain. Handmade contour maps were the norm—the kind with the contour lines smooth and equally spaced using 10 point dividers. It was typical to do a lot of erasing before the map was finished and to your liking, and an electric eraser was essential. In those days, the late 1970s, all geological work was done in a 100% computer-free office!

When I presented my maps to the Union geologists I worked with they were well received but typically lead to more questions and the need for more mapping. My understanding of the industry began to take shape while listening to morning coffee room banter and discussion in meetings about wells currently drilling, preparation for the upcoming budget, etc. There was much I didn't understand, but I soaked it up and filed it away.

The highlight of my time at Union was a day trip to an offshore platform in the Gulf of Mexico drilling a Union operated exploratory well. I went with another geologist; I'll call him Mike. His mission was to shoot sidewall cores and bring the samples back to the office for analysis. I got to tag along. It marked my first ride in a helicopter and first time to an offshore platform. Mike had prearranged with the Union company man for a full tour of the rig for me which was a gigantic semi-submersible—an environment of loud machines and steel, an hour flight from land. It floated at the mercy of the sea and whatever the weather would bring. I asked a lot of questions that day, "What's this? What's that?"

The most amazing thing about the rig visit was an elevator ride that the company man, Mike, and I took down into the bottom of one of the legs of the platform. Inside the leg, we descended about 60 feet to see the pumps that controlled the ballast water volumes that stabilized the huge floater. When the elevator stopped at the bottom, the company man told us to look up. About 50 feet above us was a sea-level marker. Awesome!

The floating steel structure and sheer immensity of a semi-submersible rig in the middle of the Gulf of Mexico made a lasting impression on me. However, the tour and hospitality that day came as a bit of a shock. At that time, company policy dictated that women were only allowed to go offshore during the day, and were not permitted to spend the night, as there were no accommodations. Given this, the hospitality seemed weird. After my tour, it seemed to me that there was plenty of space on that rig and enough money flying around in the operation to "fix" that problem. To me it was like saying, "We'll hire you to do a job, but the rules we make will limit your ability to do it."

I felt that, if my male peers and I were doing equivalent jobs, we should have equivalent support from the company. The platform had about five different decks, loaded with equipment. A bit of extra thought could solve the accommodation issue in a hurry. Later, when talking to the recruiter that hired me, I asked him, "How can I do my job as a geologist if my project work requires that I go offshore, for say, a coring job, and the company doesn't allow me there beyond daylight?"

It was the ultimate Catch-22. "We're working on that," he said. "That hasn't been an issue for us until recently. We're working on it."

When I finished my master's degree in 1981, the petroleum industry was doing well, jobs were plentiful and oil prices were climbing. It was at the height of a boom. After several interviews and office visits, I received job offers from five companies: Union Oil, Exxon, Texaco, Amoco, and Superior Oil. This number of offers was not unusual for the time. Companies were competing for geologists. The starting salaries plus benefits seemed enormous. It was a heady time. My income would rocket from that of a poor graduate student to an industry geologist, literally overnight. Of all the offers, Superior Oil's was a stand-out. It was an Exploration Geologist position in their North Sea Exploration Group, located in downtown Houston. The idea of learning the geology of the North Sea, of which I knew nothing, and traveling to the London office occasionally sounded very exciting and I grabbed it.

After four years at Superior, filled with great project work and many training courses, I began to really settle into my role as an Exploration Geologist. Alas, it was not to last as the Mobil Oil Corporation acquired Superior in 1984. I worked for Mobil in Dallas for about six months and then resigned to return to Houston.

Many of my bosses at Superior were former Amoco and Mobil geoscientists and seemed to have a broad view on the industry—an international perspective acquired when they were at a major oil company and I wanted to follow a similar path. My mentor at Superior encouraged me to pursue an Amoco interview. (Mentors are great at any age, if you don't have a mentor, get one!)

In 1985, Amoco had built a very aggressive acreage position in East Africa. Building on their success finding giant oil fields in the Gulf of Suez, Egypt, Amoco was pushing exploration southward into East Africa, looking for more giants. I interviewed with Amoco, managed to convince them that my North Sea rift experience was just what they needed to explore in East Africa, and accepted Amoco Production's offer for a position as an Exploration Geologist. From 1985 to 1990, I worked in the highly remote frontier areas of East Africa: Kenya, Tanzania, and Burundi. No exploratory wells had been drilled in this part of Africa, no oil and gas production existed. Amoco was hoping to be the company that would launch exploration success and open a new petroleum basin.

On the western shore of Lake Turkana, a desolate equatorial desert, I was the only woman on a three-person geological field party. It was 1987, and our geologic efforts were in full swing. Our party was to quality control geological maps I had made using satellite imagery back in the Houston office. We were also going to document the geology that cropped out where we were shooting seismic lines. Our overnight accommodations were at our seismic contractor's basecamp, and consisted of about nine very basic insulated industrial-style trailers set in place on sand dunes that dominated the area. There was very little vegetation save for an occasional palm tree which could barely survive the wind. What might be considered desolate to some, was beautiful to a geologist because the rocks were clearly exposed for 360 degrees and unmarked by human activity.

Each trailer handled a different camp function: kitchen and dining, bathrooms, seismic operations office, equipment storage, communications, sleeping quarters, etc. Despite its simplicity, by normal standards, it was a true oasis to return to after a day in the field where the winds and the heat were unrelenting. It offered water, soap, food, and human comforts, all welcomed at the end of the day when everyone was exhausted, weather-beaten, and ready-to-get cleaned up. Meal time was eagerly anticipated and was entertaining as everyone shared their day's experiences.

When I arrived, the only female among the ten guys, the camp boss assigned me my own room in one of the trailers (the visitor's quarters). It had air-conditioning, was comfortable, and best of all I got some solitude at day's end. But I still faced an issue with the toilet and shower facilities, there was just one facility. The camp boss and I agreed that I would use the same facilities as the guys—I would knock on the door before entering, something the guys wouldn't do, so if they heard a knock they'd know it was me. I would take my shower after 10 pm because usually everyone else had taken their showers. The arrangement seemed to work just fine for the first few days, however, one night, after 10 pm, totally unsuspecting, and tired from the long day, I knock at the door of the bathroom trailer. Hearing no answer, I open the door to enter and there in front of me, naked in all his manhood, is (I'll call him Jason) the camp electrician, Jason, a very proper and mild-mannered British gentleman. He was still towel drying after his shower. He saw me and gasped! I scared him and he scared me. It was the ultimate deer-in-the-headlights moment. I quickly stepped back and shut the door.

"Oh, no," I said to myself.

"What just happened there? I think I just saw Jason totally naked."

It was like a scene out of a movie, spontaneous and uncomfortable. So, processing all this, I stood there, outside the bathroom door, still wanting and needing a good shower, waiting for him to exit, so I could have my turn.

Finally, the door opened, he stepped outside, wearing clothes this time, and the apologies started. He said to me in a very British accent, "Oh, Denise, I'm so sorry I didn't realize how late it was. Please forgive me for not honoring your time."

In return I said to him, "No, it's my fault. I should have knocked much louder on the door. I'm sorry I barged in on you."

Apologies were sincere, awkward, and accepted. All I wanted, at that point, was to get my shower and go to bed, which I did. Unlike the guys, I always locked the door when I was taking my shower so no one could enter. After "the scare," I was extra sure to do it, so the reverse wouldn't happen to me!

The next morning at breakfast, rested and recovered, we both looked at each other and chuckled. Jason says aloud to the group, "Denise and I had a surprise encounter in the shower last night. She has seen everything I've got."

Somebody chimes in, "Well, no worries, that ain't much."

A second later Jason got up from the table and as he left said, "When I get home, my wife's not going to believe this story."

In the early 1990s, evolving technology and technical know-how were king, and smart people were everywhere working hard to learn it. After being on the Kenya Team for four years, I was transferred to the Egypt Field Studies Group. October Field, offshore in the Gulf of Suez, was my introduction to development geology and working with very brainy reservoir and production engineers. Computers were appearing in offices and spreadsheets became the tool of choice. The work of two petrophysicists in the group really got my attention.

About that time, the Research Center in Tulsa was taking applications for the coming year and I applied. To be accepted into the Petrophysics Program, one requirement was that you had to bring conventional core from an Amoco producing field coupled with a technical question with high business relevance. That was a challenge. The core I would study was from a new reservoir in Egypt's October Field, a serendipity discovery above the main producing zone. I had to pinch myself many times at my good fortune to work on a complete conventional core of a reservoir interval that amazingly tested 14,000 BOPD! Who knew 200 feet of sandstone could liberate liquids at that amazingly high rate? The equivalent formation of the cored interval cropped out onshore in the western Sinai where there was easy access for further field work. This discovery I was studying was a new play opening in the Gulf of Suez that was getting a lot of attention from competitors. My petrophysics project was a success at characterizing the technical merits of this new reservoir.

When I completed my work in Tulsa, I was invited to present the results at an industry conference in Cairo. It would be in a large theater-like auditorium that would seat several hundred geoscientists and engineers. I had prepared and prepared my delivery, spending hours rehearsing it so I would speak only within the allotted time. No detail was too small to worry about. I wanted to get the talk perfect. On the day of the conference, Egyptian men dominated the audience and listened attentively. After I finished speaking, I got a very healthy round of applause. Feeling relieved that it was over and that it went well, I walked off the stage and took a much-needed deep breath. However, I was only to find out a few minutes later that my talk wasn't what had their attention. An Egyptian geologist colleague of mine, in the presence of several of my co-workers, said to me in his charming Arabic accent, "Denise, your talk was very good. Everyone in the audience now wants to *marry with you*!"

That comment got around the company in a hurry and followed me for the next several years!

In 1994, I joined Amoco's Colombia Exploration Team anxious to use my newly-developed petrophysics skills. We were evaluating an over-pressured gas, thrust play in the eastern Middle Magdalena Valley. My job was wellsite geologist on the second well being drilled which included describing the reservoir as we drilled through it, calling a coring point, and recommending when to stop drilling. It would become my most technically challenging wellsite experience because there were many drilling issues, safety hazards, and concerns about managing high pressures. After a short flight from Bogota, I arrived by helicopter. The landing pad was inside a fenced location in a dense jungle clearing. The only colleague I knew in the project was the exploration manager back in Amoco's Bogota office. Everyone on the rig would be new to me, and, unbeknownst to me when I arrived, that wellsite would become my home for the next seven weeks.

I headed for the Amoco company man's trailer and introduced myself. After a brief update on how the well was doing, I asked him, "Where will I sleep, and keep my things?"

I'll call him Fred. Fred said with a straight face, "We're pretty short on accommodations around here, I'm going to have to put you in the bunkhouse."

"OK," I said, not knowing what that meant.

"Just show me where that is."

He took me to a trailer across the location downwind from the diesel engines—not the most desirable place to be for sleeping. He showed me to a trailer with about eight guys sharing it. He pointed to an upper bunk, which would be mine and showed me the bathroom down the hall. He watched me for a reaction. Without missing a beat, I threw my stuff on the upper bunk and said, "OK, thanks."

And, I headed back to work. The whole time I'm thinking: "Oh brother, I guess I need to make this arrangement work for the next month, especially if it's all there is. It's going to be rough sharing a small trailer with eight guys. I'll be lucky if I get any sleep at all."

The room smelled like dirt and space was tiny, it was like living in a submarine. I decided to just deal with it—being here was ten times better than being back at the office because I was very excited to see the results of this well. Doing any complaining, at all, might bring an end to the good assignments I'd had with the company. It wasn't worth the risk to make a fuss. I decided to just endure some hardship, after all, some things just come with the territory. The hardest part was not having much privacy. And, the great awkwardness of sharing close sleeping quarters was only surpassed by sharing the mirror-less, airplane-cabin-sized bathroom. And, with a bunch of strange guys whose names I didn't even know!

The next morning, after getting zero sleep in the bunkhouse the first night, mainly because of one guy's loud harmonic snoring, I staggered into Fred's office. Not only was I without a mirror, I couldn't find my hairbrush in my pack. Fortunately, bad hair is easily hidden under a hard hat. It was 6 am and Fred was all showered and shaved—he looked fresh as a daisy. We both worked on our morning reports to send back to Bogota. He poured me a cup of coffee and said, "How'd the bunkhouse work for you last night?"

Filtering out truthful details, I responded, "Not so good, too much snoring in there!"

Short pause, and I added, "I don't want to be any trouble around here, but is there a vehicle on location I can sleep in instead? Those guys don't want me sleeping in there with them any more than I want to be there."

Fred turns to me as if a light-bulb idea had just occurred to him and said, "I have a solution! You can sleep in the visitor's room in the Amoco trailer — no one sleeps there. It's used only when we have visitors."

It turned out the bunkhouse night was him testing me to see what I was made of. He admitted to me later he was totally stunned when I didn't fuss about it. After he got to know me better, the fact that he didn't offer me the visitor's room to start with made him feel bad. However, the bunkhouse night did give me some useful leverage in future situations. By not fussing, I was taking him at his word that *that was the only accommodation he had to offer* me, which turned out not to be true. When I didn't object, and make a stink, the joke was on him! After that, we had a great working relationship and I credit much of my knowledge of drilling to this day to his explanations during challenging moments on that well. In the end, the well was a technical success and, the project, complete with bunkhouse experience, dirt smell, and mirror-less bathroom was one of my most memorable assignments.

Forty odd years have passed since the day at Inspiration Point on Lake Worth when I first realized geology was the career for me. Since then, technology has greatly empowered geologists to do more in less time with more data. Learning in our profession is a constant and I still enjoy that. And when I think of my original goal of studying "International Relations" in college—having become a global petroleum geologist—in the bigger picture, I have accomplished just that. I help produce the energy the world needs to keep itself going, and I am very proud to be a part of that.

And, furthermore, what "Calm Geo-Wife" wrote so long ago to Dear Ann Landers, about female geologists, "they're ugly as a stick" is a big lie. We are all beautiful.

Denise M. Stone was born in Summit, New Jersey in 1957. She has a B.S. in geology from Texas Christian University and an M.S. in Geology from Memphis State University. She consults in geology and petrophysics and resides in Houston, with an aim to move to Denver.

AAPG and the Paradigm Shift, 1982-83

Because the American Association of Petroleum Geologists (AAPG) is the largest and most important professional petroleum geoscience society in the world, it makes an enormous difference to professional careers to have been involved in and recognized by this august group. AAPG was complicit in, consciously or unconsciously, holding women back from participation and recognition. Women, for decades, were not seriously considered for leadership roles on committees, on the Executive Committee, and for many awards. Often, the role given to female geologists for Annual meetings early in the life of the organization was taking care of spouse events.

In 1982-83, John A. "Jack" Parker served as AAPG President, took notice of the absence of women in AAPG leadership and decided to do something about it. Jack and Robbie Gries had finished only a couple of years earlier, serving on the Rocky Mountain Association of Geologists (RMAG) board together and he confided in her about his goal to change AAPG. As they discussed the absence of women on AAPG committees and consequently leadership, she concurred with him—this had not been a "deliberate" exclusion. It was the result of "who do you know," or, some might say "good ole boys" network. When volunteers were looking for others to help with committee work, they thought first of the men they worked with, the men they knew. They did not know many women, in fact, many had never worked with a woman. And, without thinking about it, the male domination of committees and leadership was perpetuated.

Jack recognized this pattern, and, perhaps because at RMAG he saw that women in leadership positions were getting things done, he realized that AAPG's "consciousness needed to be raised." Men needed to be pushed out of their "comfort" zone, with their old friends and acquaintances and into the new world of finding and inviting women and minorities to participate on AAPG committees and in AAPG leadership.

As President, Jack issued a "dictate" to AAPG's Committee Chairs—they were all male (one cannot easily be appointed Chair having not even served on the committee), that he wanted to see women on their committees, *now*! Every Chair had his feet held to the fire about acquiring women for their committees. Jack asked Robbie Gries to join the Distinguished Lecture Committee and within a few years, she Chaired that committee. By about

1990, AAPG could boast of 25% female Chairs of AAPG committees. Jack Parker deserves a lot of credit for his initiative.

In 1987, 70 years after the birth of AAPG, Martha Lou Broussard was the first woman to serve on the AAPG Executive Committee by way of becoming the first woman elected to Chair the AAPG House of Delegates. By 1989, AAPG had its first female Editor, Susan Longacre. The first woman elected to the Executive Committee (Treasurer) was Susan Landon in 1992 and, in 2001-02, Robbie was elected the first woman President of AAPG.

On the 100th anniversary of AAPG, 33% of the Committees are chaired by women, in comparison to the 15.7% of AAPG's voting membership being female. Obviously, women have become good working volunteers for the association.

Chapter 13: Sources and References

AAPG Staff. *AAPG Past Presidents at the Annual meeting in Houston, Texas, 2014.* Photograph. Tulsa, Oklahoma.

Bartholomew, Rolland B., and Bill W. Tillery. 1984. *Earth Science.* Lexington, Massachusetts: DC Heath and Company 1984. 624 pp. [Source of photograph of Marsha Bourque]

Bourque, Marsha Findlay, Houston, Texas and Santa Fe, New Mexico. 2016. Personal communication 12/15/2015-12/10/2016; source of photograph as cited in figure caption.

Bruns, Joan Burnet, Oklahoma City, Oklahoma. 2016. Personal autobiographical writings and source of photograph as cited in figure caption.

Gries, Robbie, Denver, Colorado. Personal autobiographical writings and source of photographs as cited in figure captions. Video interviews (8/5-7/2016, 9/16/2016, 1/19/2017) archived at AAPG, Tulsa, Oklahoma.

Martinsen, Randi, Laramie, Wyoming. 2016. Personal autobiographical writings and source of photographs as cited in figure captions. Video interview (8/7-8/2016) archived at AAPG, Tulsa, Oklahoma.

Milestones in the History of the U.S. Equal Employment Opportunity Commission. 1973. EEOC, the Department of Labor, the Department of Justice and AT&T, the nation's largest private employer. https://www.eeoc.gov/eeoc/history/35th/milestones/html. Accessed 1/20/2016.

Milestones in the History of the U.S. Equal Employment Opportunity Commission. 1973. EEOC, the Department of Labor, the Department of Justice and AT&T, the nation's largest private employer, sign a landmark consent decree to eliminate discriminatory recruiting, hiring and promotion practices against women and minorities. https://www.eeoc.gov/eeoc/history/35th/milestones/1973.html. Accessed 1/20/2016.

Milestones in the History of the U.S. Equal Employment Opportunity Commission. 1974. EEOC, the Department of Labor and the Department of Justice file suit against the nation's nine largest steel producers for discriminatory hiring, promotion, assignment and wage policies directed against women and minorities. https://www.eeoc.gov/eeoc/history/35th/milestones/1974.html, accessed 1/20/2016.

Milestones in the History of the U.S. Equal Employment Opportunity Commission. 1975. Congress approves President Gerald Ford's budget of $63 million for EEOC, marking the first year since EEOC opens its doors 10 years earlier that the Agency receives the full amount requested by the President. https://www.eeoc.gov/eeoc/history/35th/milestones/1975.html and 1976/html, accessed 1/20/2016.

Nishida, Debra Kimiko, Houston, Texas. 2016. Personal autobiographical writings and source of photograph as cited in figure caption.

Santogrossi, Patricia, Houston, Texas. Personal communication, September 30, 2016 to December 12, 2016.

Stewart, Cindy Crawley, Denver, Colorado. 2016. Personal autobiographical writings and source of photographs as cited in figure captions.

Stone, Denise M., Houston, Texas. 2016. Personal autobiographical writings and source of photograph as cited in figure caption.

Theriot, Roland, Houma, Louisiana. Personal communication, February 24, 2016.

1 24 85

Chapter 14

Wellsite Work—A Part of the Job

Deborah Shaeffer King Sacrey

Gulf Oil had no female geologists in their Oklahoma City (OKC) office in 1976 and made Deborah Shaeffer an offer that lured her away from the master's program at the University of Oklahoma (OU). She had hardly been in the office any length of time, and had no real training under her belt, when her boss called her in to his office and said they needed a geologist out on a well in North Texas where their operating partner was about to run a drill stem test (DST). Deborah's preparation for wellsite work consisted of her boss telling her to get a hard hat, some steel-toed boots and pick up a company car from the company fleet.

Deborah drove south to the Texas town near the wellsite where their partner had an office. She entered the office and knocked on the president's door, introduced herself as Gulf's geologist arriving to witness the DST. He told her he was just going to the store to buy groceries for a big barbeque at the location because a ton of people were coming to witness the test! She politely offered to help and he asked her to bring along a big, fresh salad. She, too, headed to the store and bought the supplies, prepared the salad, and headed to the location where it was already getting dark.

By then dozens of people were hanging around as big steaks were being grilled and cases of 1964 Chateau Laffite Rothschild were opened and being served with abandon. The DST was run over the course of the night and when Deborah could, she caught periodic sleep in one of the trailers. The test resulted in a gigantic (and dangerous!) flare. By morning they were done. As she was leaving the wellsite, the partner suggested she take a couple of the left-over bottles of Rothschild with her. Knowing nothing about wine at the tender age of 24, Deborah decided to take two, one for herself and one for her boss—she had no idea the wine was both exceptional and expensive.

When Deborah got to her boss's office back in OKC she gave him the bottle of wine, but he was visibly upset and said, "Come into my office and shut the door!"

Once inside, he proceeded to chew her out for, a) letting their partner run a DST at night (for safety reasons they are usually run during daylight hours), b) participating in a party/barbeque on location, and c) driving a company car with alcohol in it.

Deborah didn't take long to defend herself saying, "No one told me any of these rules! So, if you are going to fire me, I'll just take that bottle of wine back!"

Well, he quickly said, "No, no. Leave the wine, just don't do anything like that again."

She contrasts that with an experience two years later when she was a Senior Geologist (their youngest ever) with Michigan Wisconsin Pipeline. She was, again, asked to go out to a well near Wilberton Mountain in Oklahoma. By then she knew the ropes a great deal more, but when she got to the tool pusher's trailer and introduced herself, the fellow leered at her and said, "There are only two kinds of women that come out on rigs! Wives or the kind of woman that brings other services to the men!"

Deborah handed him her business card and said, "Well, here's a third kind of woman—the kind that can fire your sorry ass if you give her any shit!"

During the energy downturn of the 1980s and early 1990s, Deborah overcame many challenges to keep working and stay in the business; she was resilient and persistent beyond imagination. After a tough couple of years in menial jobs trying to stay afloat, she saw an ad in the paper for a geologist with Arkoma Basin experience. Deborah's network of friends saw the ad and several of them also sent it to her. Hers was one of 600 applications—a sign of the times during the downturn. She got an interview when they narrowed the list to 16 applicants. The president hired her as their Chief Geologist on the spot after she had expounded on her experience.

Having been out of "real work" for almost four years, Deborah put her heart and soul into the new job. Within six months though, she had a new challenge. One of the engineers, who sported a rotund 5-foot by 5-foot figure, became sweet on her and started trying to date her, which Deborah always politely refused to do. He would yell at her in the office, then send her flowers and love letters to her home. She was wary and nervous and started keeping records in a leather notebook of everything he said and did toward her. As she was dating someone at the time—Emmett Sacrey, whom she would later marry—they both recognized that the fellow was stalking her house, keeping track of Emmett's visits and her comings and goings. She emphasized to him, again, that she wouldn't be interested in dating him even if he were 100 pounds lighter. He proceeded to lose 100 pounds and kept harassing her. When nothing worked, he apparently convinced the boss that he should let Deborah go; things were untenable to him with her in their office.

The boss came to her and hemmed and hawed before just saying it appeared things were not working with her and he was going to have to let her go. Deborah did not want to lose her job. She pulled out her journal and said, "Maybe you want to read this first."

He read several pages and looked at her, "What are you going to do with this?"

Deborah said she thought she wouldn't have any trouble getting some legal help with that documentation. He came back to her later and said, "Okay, here are three options I want you to consider instead of a lawsuit: one, I can get you a job with Mobil Oil [that had a reputation for hiring lots of women because they 'worked harder and took less pay']; or, two, we'll give you $50,000 to leave; or, three; we'll get you an equivalent job in Houston with a subsidiary company."

She took the job in Houston, which turned out to be a wise decision (Fig. 1).

Deborah, an attractive redhead and single in 1978—like other women in the Affirmative Action era—had to deal with the occasional "jealous" wife. When the, now famous amongst female geologists, 'Dear Ann Landers' geo-wife column was published that year, one of her colleagues assured her it was written by one of her fellow geologist's spouses. She could only laugh. This may well have been true, but every female geologist working for any oil company in the U.S. at that time wondered if it was one of her own colleagues' wives.

Figure 1. Deborah Sacrey, 2000, doing what she loves best—looking for oil on a 3D seismic work station. (Photo: Deborah Sacrey, Houston, Texas.)

Deborah Shaeffer Sacrey has a B.S. in geology from the University of Oklahoma (1976). She is the owner of Auburn Energy. In 2012, she was the fourth woman to serve on AAPG's Executive Committee as Treasurer.

Quote from the Ann Landers Column: "Husband's duties training woman irks wife"

Dear Ann Landers: *My husband is a geologist for a major oil company. Recently he had to take a young woman geologist out to an oil well to train her. They were together for three weeks, traveled thousands of miles alone in the car, ate all their meals together, even slept out on the rig.*

I'm not worried about the physical attraction, because most women geologists are so ugly they could go lion hunting with a switch. I do resent the proximity between the two of them for that length of time and have told him so. He swears everything is strictly business.

Why should women who choose to stay home and be wives and mothers have to put up with such stuff just so these liberated women can prove themselves in a man's field?

What about the oil companies? They profess to care about the welfare of their employees. Why not their employees' wives? I wonder how other wives feel about these situations and how they deal with their anxieties. –Geologist's Wife.

Dear Wife: *for a woman who is "not worried" you sound pretty upset. Cool it, dear. If your husband's job consists of training new crew members, you'd better accept the fact that some of those crew members are female. What you describe is the result of women's insistence that there be no discrimination on the basis of sex. So, we have to take the bitter with the sweet.*

P.S. Before I get clobbered by a few thousand lady geologists, I want to go on record as disassociating myself from that comment about their looks. Please don't put the wife's words in my mouth. I make enough gaffes on my own. (*The Sun-Telegram*, 1978).

Debby Sycamore

Debby Sycamore was a New Hampshire girl, armed with her bachelor's degree in geology from Lawrence University when she arrived in Denver, job hunting in the fall of 1980. The Wild West was totally new to her. Given the good fortune of job hunting coincident with the skyrocketing price of oil, within ten days Debby had eight job offers. She accepted a position with Union Texas Petroleum (UTP), a subsidiary of Allied Chemical, and started on her steep and exciting learning curve becoming a petroleum geologist—a career she had never anticipated when in school (Fig. 2).

In March of 1981, it was determined by UTP management that it was time for Debby to gain some wellsite experience. She was scheduled to go out on her first well with a senior company geologist, however, at the last minute he couldn't go. There was a highly experienced mudlogger on location, and Debby got the green light to head out on her own. Her boss said, "Here's a company car, an ultraviolet blacklight, microscope, well site kit, topographic map with the well location and a highway map! Good luck!"

Away she went at first light – new blue jeans, brand new hard hat, UTP logo stickers to hand out on location, steel-toed work boots, colored pencils all sharpened, and her new business cards – and, because it was off the beaten path in Wyoming, she packed a sleeping bag, a cooler of food, water, and extra warm clothes.

Figure 2. Debby Sycamore, a greenhorn from New Hampshire, reported a "stampede" when sent to her first wellsite. This photo is on an offshore rig in the Gulf Coast, circa 2000. (Photo: Debby Sycamore, Denver, Colorado.)

Debby drove her new, white Ford sedan north on I-25 to Cheyenne, then east on I-80 to the small town of Pine Bluffs, then headed north on the Pine Bluffs Albine road toward the rig site, conveniently marked with a prominent red dot on the topographic (topo) map. The rolling topography took her up and over low hills and swales and as she topped a hill, she saw cattle all over the road in front of her and as far as she could see in the entire panoramic view.

She thought to herself, *stampede!* Debby had never seen so many cattle in her life. She didn't even know what to call them—they were all "cows" to her.

Being a civic-minded scientist, she stopped her car, took out the topo map, plotted the exact location of the loose cows and turned around to report the situation to the nearest authorities. Debby pulled back into Pine Bluffs, population 1000, give or take, where at the corner of Main and Second street there was a small one-story red brick building with a sign "Pine Bluffs Police Department." A man was standing outside the door as she got out of her car. She approached him, telling him why she was there, "I'd like to report a stampede."

She took out her map and showed him where the stampede was, handed him her business card and asked if he needed anything further.

He looked at her very intensely and then said, "Just a minute, I need to get someone else."

He went into the building and brought out another gentleman. The new fellow was a big man. He was chewing on a large wad of tobacco and wearing a cowboy hat. The first gentleman turned to her and advised her, "Now tell this man what you just told me."

Debby, thinking this was the guy in charge of loose cows, again opened her map, showed it to the man wearing the cowboy hat and told him about the stampede. By the time she finished, Debby couldn't help but notice that the first man was visibly shaking and making odd noises. Why, it appeared he was laughing! Then "cowboy hat" started laughing, too!

After regaining some semblance of composure, "cowboy hat" shifted the wad of tobacco from one cheek to the other and said, "Little Lady, where are you from?"

She pulled out another of her fresh business cards and said, "I'm from Denver, I'm a geologist with Union Petroleum and we are drilling in the area."

He said, "No, no, no, where are you REALLY from?"

"Okay, okay," she confessed with a gnawing sense of unease, "I'm originally from New Hampshire."

Now, both gentleman were laughing so hard, they could hardly get any words out. "Cowboy hat" finally managed to say, "Little lady, if you are going to spend any time out here, you need to become familiar with the phrase 'Open Range.' These 'cows' can go where they want, when they want, and however they want!"

Debby was aghast. She asked, almost in tears, "Well, how am I supposed to get to my wellsite?"

"You just drive through them!"

She said, "I can't drive a brand-new company car through all of them!"

"Oh, yes, you can. Just keep your hand on the horn and they will eventually move."

Having relinquished all shred of her dignity, Debby turned around, got back in the car, and headed back on the county road to find the rig site. It was very tenuous at first. The "cows" just looked right through her. It didn't help that the company car was a sedan and was, therefore, at the same eye level as the cows. She also couldn't find the horn on this new car: it was located on the turn indicator stick and needed to be pushed in to make a sound. That took a while to figure out. Who would engineer such a thing? Finally, pushing repeatedly on the stick-horn, and moving along at a snail's pace, she managed to successfully navigate through her "stampede" and, now that it was completely dark, she could see the tell-tale Christmas-like lights of the rig ahead in the distance. It was Debby's first and last stampede report.

Deborah Sycamore was born in Hanover, New Hampshire in 1958 and earned her bachelor's in geology at Lawrence University, Appleton, Wisconsin, in 1980. She has worked in Denver, Colorado, most of her career, employed with several independents. Debby was a key person working on the establishment of the first International Pavilion at the 1984 AAPG annual meeting with her colleague, Susan Morrice. (Fig. 3)

Figure 3. Debby Sycamore, right, 1994, working on the first AAPG International Pavilion in Denver, CO with her friend, Susan Morrice who originated the concept. (Photo: Debby Sycamore.)

Paty Ortiz Gomez

Paty Ortiz Gomez was in the oil business for 41 years before retiring, having joined PEMEX in 1975. Her first year out of college, she worked in hydrology. (Fig. 4) With PEMEX she spent ten years doing exploration, including eight years of wellsite work. Paty loved wellsite work. The crews were especially good to her; sometimes they decorated her room with plants and often built nice pathways to the rig.

The first time she went to an offshore floating drilling rig, she was having a terrible time walking on the undulating rig floor. Her engineer was obviously uncomfortable and tried to politely advise her on how to walk more safely on the rig floor without falling. He tried unsuccessfully several times to give her safety hints. Finally, he just gave up and said, bluntly, "You must spread your legs!"

Walking "like a lady" had kept her too unbalanced, and he taught her to "walk like a sailor!"

Figure 4. Paty Ortiz Gomez, 1980, fieldwork in San Luis Potosi. (Photo: Paty Ortiz Gomez, Mexico City, Mexico.)

Paty Ortiz Gomez received her bachelor's degree in geology from Universidad Nacional Autonoma de Mexico (UNAM) in 1973. She is now retired in Mexico City.

Jean B. Kulla

The year is 1983 and I have worked at Exxon since graduating with my PhD from the University of Illinois in 1979. I am at my desk working on some well logs when my supervisor, Kumar, comes in with the Vice President of Exploration and asks how long it would take me to pack a small overnight bag and get to the Sydney airport to catch the company jet to go down to the heliport near the Bass Straits of the Tasman Sea. They wanted me on the next helicopter out to one of Esso-Australia's seven off-shore platforms in the Bass Straits. Thinking this was another emergency, like the time eight months earlier, where I had been rushed out to a platform with gas bubbling up around it to oversee a noise log designed to find a hole in the well casing, I replied that I could be at the airport in less than two hours (Fig. 5).

Figure 5. Jean Kulla, 1979, had to handle both dangerous operational and inappropriate behavior on an Australian rig. (Photo: Jean Kulla, Lake Forest, California.)

Well it seemed like it must be a terrific emergency or something really important because the VP coming to my office just never happens. And, that was the beginning of a four-day experience, which would try my patience, call on my creativity, and test my abilities in diplomacy, which had nothing to do with exploring and producing oil and everything to do with being a female geologist working for Big Oil.

My story really begins in 1979 when I landed my dream job, doing research at a major corporate research facility in Houston, Texas. I was one of five women hired by Exxon Corporation in the U.S., as it was known in those days, into a "Professional" position as they were called – i.e. non-secretarial and not as a lab technician. I was hired into the Petroleum Geochemistry Division of Exxon Production Research Company; my PhD was in stable isotope geochemistry. I loved my job and the people I worked with. Things went really well and I was promoted several times in the first couple of years, which put me on the "fast track." I was involved in a couple of research projects that really helped the company and they sent me around the world to Exxon affiliates to teach the new techniques I had developed with my team. On these travels, I also got to see "operations" and learn a great deal about exploration in different locations. Therefore, when asked if I wanted to spend several months on some assignments, I eagerly agreed. I had opportunities in London working on North Sea exploration, in Bordeaux, France, and on projects in Alaska. In early 1983, I was asked if I wanted to go on a two-year assignment at ESSO Australia.

My first 24 hours in Australia included my first case of real "jet lag," starvation at midnight, falling asleep and almost having my head in my soup at lunch with my new team, and not understanding a word any one said to me, though I knew they were speaking English. When "Stralian" is spoken fast, it is totally incomprehensible and the inflection is up at the end of a sentence so it sounds like you are always being asked a question. After about four days, I was beginning to become adjusted to the time change. That was when I had my first experience being helicoptered out to a platform in the Bass Straits for the gas issue. There were only ten of us humans on the platform at the time, because everyone else had been evacuated when a casing rupture sent gas bubbling up, threatening the platform. Very scary stuff. But, we quickly ran the noise logs, found the rupture, and I was off the platform as a cement crew came in to shore up the problem. Science and engineering to the rescue.

This second rescue trip was a bit different! As we landed on the helideck and I disembarked, the petroleum engineer greeted me with a red face, a lot of hand gestures and yelling. My quick take was that it seemed like he was trying to deal with a *mutiny*. And, one quick look below the helideck told me that things were indeed near riot conditions. I also noticed what seemed like the cause of the problem. Standing in the middle of 60 huge men was one beautiful blond woman that I "sort of" recognized. She was a relatively new Esso Australian exploration geologist. And, she was *topless* and wearing blue jean short shorts! Some might say it was a "good teachable moment."

Well, there was no way I was going to descend into the mob where she was, so I told the company engineer to go down to the lower deck, throw a shirt on her, and bring her up to the helideck. I didn't care whose shirt or what shirt—but get her covered up and out of the crowd. Now, at that time, the crews on the off-shore drill ships and platforms were from the U.S., mostly Texas. They did a schedule of two weeks on and two weeks off. When they were off, most went back to Singapore where they were based. Societal customs in the U.S. and Singapore were different from those in Australia—in Australia, young women often sunbathed topless on the beach.

Once the young female geologist was up on the helideck, I yelled at her, "What were you thinking!" She responded that she had some time off, a break, and she was sunbathing in a relatively secluded spot on the deck. I had to calm down and decide whether to "boot" her off the platform—ok, well not literally, though I was tempted—or whether she could continue to do her job. If I took her off, I knew her job with Esso would be in jeopardy; but, if I let her continue, I would have to stay on the platform with her for 48 hours to make sure things went back to normal. We sat on the helideck for several hours talking and I decided to give her another chance. Things calmed down, and she was able to stay on the platform and continue to do her job.

I wish I could say she went on to make a major contribution to the company, or to geology, but I didn't keep track of her and I have no idea what happened to her. I hope that if she had the opportunity sometime in her career, she also gave another female geologist a chance.

Jean Kulla received her PhD from the University of Illinois in 1979. She is with K2 Energy & Environment in Lake Forest, California.

Lyn Wethington George

Lyn George was the first female president of the Wyoming Geological Association (WGA) in Casper, Wyoming. She tells a story about sitting a Mission Canyon well in Montana around 1978. Having encountered shows and a drilling break, Lyn thought a drill stem test (DST) should be run. Company management approved the test and because it was after business hours, she called the partners to give them notice. One of the partners started asking Lyn questions about the shows, the samples, the drilling break, and more. In the middle, he paused and said, "You're not a secretary, are you?" She responded, "No, I'm the wellsite geologist." They laughed and continued with the details.

That was then, this is now. At a recent Rocky Mountain Section meeting for AAPG, Lyn, Julie LeMaster (another female past-president of WGA and president-elect for RMS), and Marron Bingle-Davis (the current WGA president) were attending the AAPG House of Delegates breakfast. They reported on what WGA was doing. After the meeting one of the AAPG officers remarked that he thought they were AWG (Association for Women Geoscientists) representatives, since they were all women. And, after all, AWG is similar to WGA!

Lyn Wethington George was born in Denver and earned her B.S. (1974) and M. S. (1976) at Texas Tech University. She started her career with Union Oil of California in Casper, Wyoming. When she began her family, Kirkwood Oil & Gas allowed her to work part-time until her second child was born in 1985. After the oil price crash of 1986, she earned her MBA, worked outside the industry, and was fortunate to return to geology in 2001 with Goolsby, Finley and Associates. She has been an independent consultant since 2005.

Elizabeth Bartow "Betsy" Campen

It was 1979 and I was trying to fight my way into the oil business. A total "newbie" at age 43! With no experience and at the onset of a downturn, I did everything and anything to get a foot in the door. Bruce Benson, from Colorado, had opened a small gas exploration business in Billings and I went to work for the manager, Duane Estelle as a geotech. Shortly thereafter, Billy Lane of Helena, an engineer, hired me to help finish well reports. Billy had a consulting company that supplied wellsite geologists for operators in the area and he was so busy with the plethora of wells drilling in the Tyler oil play, that he did not have the time for the paperwork.

Billy, and everyone else in Montana, would not let a woman sit a well—it was considered "bad luck" to have women on a rig. It was also said it was considered "bad luck" to have a Jewish person on a rig. I wondered where these weird superstitions came from. When I wasn't helping with reports and doing clerical work, I would look at samples and try to teach myself something about wellsite geology (Fig. 6).

Figure 6. Betsy Bartow Campen, determined to get "on top of the business" as fast as possible when she entered the industry later in life than most geologists. (Photo: Betsy Campen, Billings, Montana.)

Finally, my break came. It was Christmas and, suddenly, Billy was short of wellsite geologists. He asked if I wanted to go sit a well. Of course, I said, "Yes!" expecting him to send me out with an experienced wellsite geologist to show me the ropes. Instead he gave me a microscope, directions to the rig, and sent me off. I didn't even have a place to stay. I knew nothing when I arrived and headed to the rig floor. They were in the process of running a drill stem test (DST) so I walked into the dog house and introduced myself. Then I ripped off the sheet from the geolograph and grabbed the sample bags and headed to the mudlogger trailer. It shocked everyone of course! The geolograph plots the drill depth as the drilling pipe is turning and cutting new hole. Now, because of my mistake, how in the world would we ever know how deep we were! I was truly a novice. I found the trailer a mess, mucked it out, and started teaching myself how to be a wellsite geologist.

Fortunately, I was fearless about asking questions. No matter how "dumb" the question might seem. The more I asked, the more people taught me. I became a very good wellsite geologist. I continued to sit wells through that intensive Tyler drilling, sleeping in Schlumberger logging trucks, toolpushers' trucks, my car, and other awful places because there were just no facilities. I was 43 years old. I was recently divorced and was determined to be a successful geologist. To my mind, no one could be a real petroleum geologist without being capable of sitting a well.

When I earned my bachelor's degree in Geology at Smith College in 1958, my professors told me that women could not work in petroleum. I floundered around, traveling, and trying to find a career. While working toward a nursing degree to become a mid-wife (that is another story) the son of a Montana dude-ranch owner came to Boston to visit. My family had visited that ranch and I knew him just superficially, but when he proposed to me, adventure beckoned, and I suddenly saw myself as belonging to the big skies of Montana. I wanted to get away from "proper" Boston. Not a great underfooting for a marriage, but I did as well as possible for 17 years, locked into the role when three children rapidly arrived in our lives; a daughter and twin sons within 18 months.

Once my children were grown, I knew that I had to get back to a world where I was more intellectually stimulated. I moved to Billings, got a divorce, and started to learn everything I could about geology again and also began to learn about the oil business. For years, it was common for me to fall asleep with a text book on my face.

The first thing I did in Billings was to take a Montana Geological Society (MGS) sponsored class in fluvial systems. I befriended a woman who mentioned her boss was a geologist. She asked if I wanted to meet him. "YES!"

I soon met Jack Warne and he said, "We have a workshop this weekend on fluvial systems. Why don't you attend?"

"YES!" again.

And then the wonders of serendipity began to take over.

At the class, I sat by a friendly geologist, Erv Kranstler, and, during a break, I asked him if he knew anyone looking for help. He took me over to meet Duane Estelle, who was just setting up a new consulting office. Duane said, yes, he was looking for someone and to come around on Monday. I had a job! I worked for two years before I ended up on that first wellsite.

One delightful thing I discovered right away was the "old timers" in Billings, who were so very knowledgeable, were always happy to answer questions. And, I was always asking and more importantly, listening. These guys were my teachers, tutors, and mentors. Right away they insisted I join the MGS. Hard to believe, in 1977, I was the only woman! It remained that way for over a decade more.

The first assignment they gave me was to be the MGS "Social Chairman." Of course, it had always been done by a man in the past, but I took on the task and did it for years. One of the first challenges I had to overcome was arranging the Annual Men's Poker Party at the Petroleum Club. No women were allowed to play, but I had to set it up and because women were also not allowed in the Petroleum Club, I had to meet the personnel from the Petroleum Club outside the club to arrange all the details! Finally, I moved up to secretary of the MGS and eventually became the first female president.

My industry network grew and I loved it when I finally got to meet and associate with female geologists from Denver. I was older than all of them, but we hit it off terrifically. I never will forget listening to Robbie Gries speak at a conference about the San Juan Sag and I thought, if she can do it, I can too! Susan Landon (Chapter 16), with Amoco Production, and I had become acquainted through field trips and meetings, so, when she was drilling a well in the Montana thrust belt she hired me and my husband (I had remarried) to do the wellsite work. A full summer in the Crazy Mountains—that was heaven. When we were nearing one of objectives in the well, Susan and another female geologist came flying in on a helicopter. After updating them on our situation, Susan offered to fly me around to see the thrust belt geology from the helicopter. I thought, "This is the life!" Here I was, with two other women in exploration, flying around in a helicopter. Had I died and gone to heaven?

I also enjoyed having other women show up on a drill site. Another time, a female Schlumberger engineer and a female cement engineer were working with me, and, of course, I always had my dog with me, a blue heeler. We were standing by my trailer discussing our next procedure when the tool pusher came around the corner and stopped short. He blasted out, "There are more goddamn women and dogs on this location than an Indian reservation!" Then, he turned around and left!

My second husband and I worked up prospects together; he had years of experience and I was learning as fast as I could. When ready, we would take the ideas to companies in Denver and try to sell them. One year we had several Eagle sandstone prospects to show and went to Denver. I remember showing them to Penny Frush (Chapter 15) at CSX in Denver, and for some reason I got completely nervous. Penny was so smart and she spoke her mind. When I started talking, for the first time in my life I started stuttering, and couldn't control it! I was so embarrassed. They did not take our deals, but fortunately, I got over my nervousness and by the time we left Denver, we had sold all of them.

One of my most satisfying projects was in the coalbed methane play when it was hot in the 1990s. I had been reading about that activity in Colorado and other places and decided to start looking at coal data in Montana and northern Wyoming. No one else was working on it in our area and I thought I might develop a niche for me and my engineer husband, Ted Campen. I practically memorized Fred Meissner's paper on the subject and hit the libraries, learning all I could. One bit of research I conducted was bizarre but fruitful. I went to the Bureau of Mines and read all the literature about deaths in coal mines. I thought if there was enough gas in a mine to kill someone, that was good evidence of ample methane! I ended up with five or six prospects through those efforts. Somehow *World Oil* got word of my research and called me, asking if I would write an article for them. I did, and two remarkable oil men, Sam Bibler and Les Harrington from Kalispell, read it and contacted us. They ended up financing the lease acquisition on these plays, hundreds of thousands of acres, and eventually we had some successful drilling results (Figs. 7 and 8). But not before we got initiated into the world of anti-oil and gas environmentalists. One

Figure 7. Betsy lived and breathed for drilling and thought, to be a petroleum geologist, well-site work was part of your DNA. (Photo: Betsy Campen.)

of our prospects was on Bozeman Pass, where a subdivision of "McMansions" was being developed for wealthy people wanting a second home in Montana. We lost that five-year battle, and they now have a covenant in the subdivision, "No Coal Bed Methane and No Pigs."

Figure 8. Betsy with her late husband, Ted Campen, 2010, a partner in life and in business. (Photo: Betsy Campen.)

My late and rewarding career was facilitated by the wonderful people and associations that helped me along the way. I took every course AAPG offered that I could and read every book that helped with my studies. The great geologists in the MGS and others at AAPG truly have made my geological life fulfilling and gratifying, and, oh, the treasured friendships that have sustained me. What a life—supported by friends and the earth we stand on!

Betsy Bartow Campen was born in 1936 in Massachusetts. She earned her bachelor's degree in geology at Smith College in 1958. Betsy served on the AAPG Executive Committee as secretary from 1996-1998. She has been recognized with AAPG's Distinguished Service Award and Honorary Membership.

Valary Hogg Schulz

Valary Hogg was seven years old and amid a derelict mine muck-pile in northern Saskatchewan, when her father gave her a geologic hand lens and showed her what gold looked like. Then he said, "See what you can find!" and left her picking through the ore tailings while he did his geologic reconnaissance.

Fast forward to Valary's first summer in college, when she was majoring in English and couldn't find a summer job. Her father hired her and took her into the Canadian bush; this time Valary was camp cook and his field assistant. While running mining reconnaissance lines which had been cut in the winter—the stakes marking the grid had fallen into the brush when the snow melted—her job was to trudge ahead of her father looking for stakes every 100 feet. Valary would reset the stake, march another 100 feet, and find the next one. He would map any outcrops and they would both collect geochemical samples. At noon, they would locate a sunny outcrop, light a smudge to keep the black flies at bay, and sit down to a lunch of sandwiches and canned peaches. She looked around at the peaceful beauty of the scrub pine bush, and said to herself, "This is the life!" When Valary got back to university that fall, she changed her major to geology and never looked back (Fig. 9).

Valary's first job out of college was with Campbell Chibougamau Mines in northern Quebec, Canada, in 1971, before she moved on to Rosario Resources Corporation in Honduras in 1973 as a mining geologist. Though there was no prohibition to her efforts in Quebec, in Honduras, the longstanding superstitions about women in mines limited her access to the information she needed. Valary was trying to calculate reserves extrapolating between stopes, crosscuts, and diamond-bit drill holes, and needed to map between the data points to be more accurate. She would have to ask another geologist to grab samples for her in specific locations. It was an inconvenience for them, as well as for her.

Figure 9. Valary Schulz, Zortman, Montana, 1970, geology field camp. (Photo: Grag Cave from Valary Schulz, Dallas, Texas.)

To facilitate her access to the physical data she needed, Valary petitioned her boss. At that time, the mine was not operating on Sundays and there was just a skeleton crew. The mine manager allowed her to go underground on Sundays to sample and record strikes and dips, but only if accompanied by one of the mine captains. Eight weeks later, after each one of the captains had volunteered a Sunday, there had been no accident or loss of life. Superstitions were put to rest. The captains were increasingly reluctant to give up another of their sole days off for the week so, from then on, Valary did both surface and underground mapping with no impediment.

She went on to work on other Central American mining projects, several where she was the supervising geologist. One of the more exciting aspects for her was following up on "leads" which came about when a prospector would come into their camp with a hand sample, asking if it was valuable. If she thought it warranted a closer look, Valary would hop on a mule and head into the jungle with the fellow and evaluate the prospect. Those were the best of times.

But the mining business took a downturn in 1977 about the time the oil business started the big up-tick in the U.S. Valary interviewed with Tom Mairs in Dallas who worked for Rosario's oil and gas subsidiary, .

He offered to train her in petroleum, saying, "Just bring a sharp pencil, because you are going to be on a steep learning curve!" She did and it was!

Valary was in shock and awe after having been the only woman in every mining camp for the prior six years; there were *lots of women* in the oil patch! Affirmative Action had paved the way a few years ahead of her arrival.

On one occasion, Valary was sent out to a location for a midnight logging run in the deep East Texas thicket. The operator, Delta Drilling, sent out the prospect originator, also a woman, to witness the logging, and a third partner sent out their geologist, Queenie Mungen-Davis. It was a Cotton Valley well with lots of pay so when the logs came off the printer, the three women started calculating while the guys, geologists and engineers alike, settled into the back of the trailer and played cards. About five in the morning the gals finished, and everyone agreed to recommend running pipe.

"So, now, let's get some breakfast!"

And they all headed into a Nacadoches breakfast diner. They took a couple of tables, but the waitstaff looked at Queenie and indicated that she would not be served. Everyone just sat there and stared down the staff until Queenie was served along with everyone else. In a good natured, blasé manner, Queenie remarked, "I never know if I'm being discriminated against because I'm a woman, black, or a geologist!"

Earlier that evening, a knock on the trailer door brought them to open the door to a bride of one of the fellow geologists who was playing cards. The bride had never been to a well before and was surprised to see all these women in the trailer. When her husband got home from that job, the bride said she hadn't any idea that was his working environment, and she did not approve of it at all. (Fig. 10)

Figure 10. Valary Schulz, 2010, consulting form her office in Dallas, Texas. (Photo: Valary Schulz.)

Valary experienced the typical baptism-of-fire on one of her first drill stem tests. The crew and everyone else on the rig knew they were pulling a wet string of pipe (meaning the pipe was loaded with drilling mud/water) but didn't let on to the "weevil." When the pipe unloaded the water, they were all out of range of the spewing muddy water, but she was not. It hit her right at the waist. She tried to go down the steps, only to realize, too late, that now she was wet from head to foot! As a weevil, Valary also made the common mistake of rushing through the doghouse to the rig floor early in the morning, not realizing it was a shift change (tour change) and catching all the roughnecks in their skivvies as they changed for their tour. She just closed her eyes and kept moving!

As Valary gained more experience, she was often out on locations in West Texas, Louisiana, and Oklahoma for extended periods, and was the "company man," meaning she was in charge. As company man on one well, Valary remembers being dubbed "rabbit" by the crew. She was on location and suddenly heard a rumble, felt the rig floor begin to shake, and knew what was about to happen. Within seconds, Valary was off the floor and down on the ground 100 feet from the rig, watching a fountain of salt water drench the location. She also recalls that no one could wake the toolpusher to get the "blow out preventer" functioning; he had a reputation as a sound sleeper!

In another episode when Valary was the company man on a different well, an off-duty driller showed up extremely drunk and had a rifle visible in his truck's gun rack. She knew she had to run him off location as that was the company man's responsibility. Valary did it, but it was tense for awhile, and he was really upset about it. Several days later when one of the engineers driving to the rig had potshots taken at him, Valary was pretty sure she knew who was doing the shooting.

Valary has many other fond memories of when she was just learning the wellsite routine. She would take her toddler, Beau, out to nearby locations and set up a playpen in the shade for him while she got some practice running samples. Once, when she looked up from her microscope, she saw a couple of roughnecks over at the playpen playing with her baby! "Ya gotta' love it!" she says. Valary has been part of the oil business family for 35 years.

Valary Hogg Shultz was born in Regina, Saskatchewan, Canada, and received her B.S. in geology from the University of Saskatchewan, Saskatoon, in 1971. Valary has been President of the Dallas Geological Society, Chair of the AAPG House of Delegates, President of AAPG Southwest Section, DPA President, and has received many awards for her contributions.

Constance "Connie" Nuss Knight

Constance (Connie) Nuss Knight has delightful memories of her early years in the oil business working for Amoco Production Company in Denver, Colorado (Fig. 11), and later as an independent geologist. What makes her "delightful" memories phenomenal is how, in 1970, she overcame early trauma while she was completing her first semester of graduate-school studies at the University of Arizona (U of A) in Tucson.

Connie was brutally attacked in her home by a rapist who had been stalking her. The rapist's plan was to surprise her by entering her small living quarters while she was in the shower. However, after hearing a faint warning noise, she exited the shower and surprised her masked assailant as he entered the back door. After one single scream, he took her into a choke hold and threatened to kill her if she screamed again. She knew he was serious and held little value for her life. She desperately tried to recall the advice she had been given in a self-defense lecture she had attended a year and half earlier and forced herself to appear calm despite intense panic. She started acting as though compliant while looking for a chance to escape. Her attacker violently tore the phone out of the wall as he repeated his threats to harm her, but because of her apparent compliance, he did not use the phone cord to tie her up. As he threw her on the bed and got on top of her, Connie tried talking him down and succeeded in convincing him that she would not resist. He relaxed a bit and moved away from the bed so that (apparently) he could secure the back door and turn out lights.

Figure 11. Connie Nuss Dodge, as she went to work for Amoco Production in Denver, in 1973. (Photo: Connie Knight, Golden, Colorado.)

Judging the time it would take him to reach the door and the distance between her and another exit door, she leapt up and ran naked into the street where street lights might help. She KNEW he would kill her if he caught her in the thirty feet of dark between her door and the street. From the street, she made it to a nearby home where, thankfully, neighbors let her in. Quickly covering her up, they called the police, who arrived and were helpful and respectfully professional.

The next morning, still in shock, Connie went to the Chairman of the Geology Department, Dr. Edward McCullough, and shared this experience. She was a teaching assistant and knew she was in no shape to teach her class that day. Dr. McCullough handled the situation with grace and compassion. He first praised her for her bravery and for being smart throughout the ordeal. He told her to leave Tucson a little early for Christmas break so she could be with her family. Her teaching assignments would be covered in her absence and her position would be ready for any decision she made. It was not until she was enroute to her home in Colorado that she broke down in tears for the first time.

NOT keeping this ordeal a secret in the department and university proved to provide great support to Connie. The faculty and students took it upon themselves to offer their support and to tell her they hoped she would return to the U of A. After her Christmas break, she knew she had to be brave and go back, even though the rapist was unidentified and at large. When she returned to Tucson, her fellow graduate students and the faculty continued to offer support and concern.

Within only six months of the attack, and ignoring her fears and feelings of vulnerability, Connie took a summer position working at an early-stage mining operation in Safford, Arizona. Her primary responsibility was field mapping with the company geologist, Don Ross. She was the only woman working at the site. She lived in a nearby town, and recalls getting up at 4:00 a.m. to beat the summer heat and begin field work before sunrise. The summer job was a great success. She learned a lot, made great friends, and earned good money for graduate school.

About nine months after the rape attempt, Connie learned that she had been the first of a series of young victims who had been brutally attacked by someone the police called the "red rapist." A year and a half after the attack, the red rapist was shot and killed by one of his victims. At that time, the police and Connie discovered that she and this criminal had simultaneously attended Western State College in Gunnison, Colorado, though she did not know him during her undergraduate studies. Connie completed her M.S. field work and thesis, and she graduated from the U of A during the summer of 1973. Upon graduation, she published her first technical paper.

In 1973, Connie took a job in Denver with Amoco, hired by Ed LeFaye, along with another woman geologist. This occurred before the Amoco office was delivered their federally imposed "quota" for hiring women, and Ed was pleased to report to his superiors that he had already hired two women.

Connie fell in love with oil and gas exploration, and she particularly enjoyed the Amoco sponsored short courses and field seminars. A career highlight for her was being included in the "trial run" carbonate field seminar presented by famous biostratigrapher Alan B. Shaw. Alan had expressed concern about accommodating women geologists on field trips, but after her attendance in his course he let her know that his mind was changed. He said that when the groups were all men, there was a heightened sense of "boondoggle" and a lot of partying. Her presence prompted the guys to work harder, and perhaps not play as hard. Shaw said he wanted more women in his courses.

Connie helped "break the barrier" for women going out on wells at Amoco (Fig. 12). Her first trip, like those of the rookie men, was with a seasoned geologist, Pete Matuszczak, who let her know that he was chosen because the assignment did not upset his wife. He supplied invaluable training, and they became friends. However, in her wellsite days, she still made the common mistake women made of losing track of the time for tour (pronounced tower) changes and she had a couple of experiences walking in on the rig hands changing clothes. She said they were "culturally different."

Figure 12. Connie Knight, always amenable to hearing from the drill hands and engineers on a rig, was delighted with well sitting. (Photo: Connie Knight.)

In Kansas when a Hispanic crew found Connie in the doghouse, they were too shy to ask her to leave and went back outside to change their clothes in the freezing wind. She felt terrible when she realized what she had done. In contrast, in Colorado with a Caucasian crew, the roughnecks just proceeded to start undressing while she was in the dog house. She watched tour changes more closely after that. The only time she observed someone actually changing clothes was with Pete on that first trip. A shy, core-lab consultant chose to change his clothes behind the geologist's trailer rather than in the more public doghouse. Pete delighted in calling her over, "Connie, come quick and look out this window!"

Then, Pete had an afterthought, "What if the poor guy found out she had seen him and couldn't do his job?"

So, Pete covered his tracks by meeting up with the core hand and explained: "You know, we have a woman geologist on this rig, and women on rigs will become more common. Don't worry, she didn't see you, but you might want to be more careful about where you change your clothes in the future." The core hand thanked Pete profusely, not realizing Pete had set him up in the first place.

Connie always seemed to be able to create good, friendly, and professional working relationships with rig hands. One time a mudlogger made it difficult for her by playing a little joke. The driller was a huge, burly man, and when he bent over, apparently, a tattooed butterfly was visible—as well as his ample butt crack. Of course, no one teased him about it because he was formidable.

Connie was due to get the next set of samples when the mudlogger said, "By the way, I told the driller that you really like his butterfly."

When she looked out the door up to the rig floor, there he was in the moonlight provocatively waving her sample bag back and forth, just coaxing her to "come and get it." She "ponied" up. With head erect, Connie marched up to the rig floor, smiled politely, took the sample bag and said, "Thanks."

Then, she marched back down. After that the driller always greeted her with a polite smile.

On another early wellsite, the wives of the drilling crew decided they wanted to see who this "girl geologist" was and drove to the wellsite, parking near her trailer. Only one of the women got out of the car and knocked on her door, muttering some excuse to visit. Connie invited her in, showed her what she did, and how she ran samples. She was as friendly and as harmless as she could possibly be. This apparently was sufficient to satisfy the carload of curiosity. The woman said thanks, got back into the car and they all drove off.

Connie once had a toolpusher who continually made remarks indicating he was not happy with women on drilling rigs. But, one day he brought his young daughter to the rig and Connie took her into the trailer and showed her all the things geologists did. The next day the toolpusher said, "Damn! Do you know what you did? Now my daughter wants to be a geologist."

On another occasion, Connie had to get a roughneck to NOT be so willing to please; he was washing the samples so thoroughly for her that she feared he was washing away any potential shows. She had to tell him not to be so enthusiastic.

When in the field, the memory of the Tucson attack kept her on her toes and reminded her to be cautious. On one well, a roughneck started to linger around her trailer. He became emboldened and started to make comments about how he had raped his wife, and how she had provoked him to rape her. He asked whether Connie ever messed around on her husband (she had married during graduate school). She experienced a jolt of concern and was uncertain about how to handle the situation. If she complained and he lost his job, would she be at risk of his retaliation? She remained silent during all his comments. Sensing something was afoot, the toolpusher, protective like most men she worked with, asked if there was a problem with this guy. She was hesitant, and then said, no. He seemed not to believe her; he indicated that the whole crew thought the fellow was strange and that she should be careful. She was. She never left the location when he was not working on his tour, thus assuring herself that she would not "run into him" on the way to or in town. One night, Connie observed someone in a car watching her as she left the wellsite. The next day she learned from the crew that her observer was the toolpusher, and that the entire crew was watching out for her. She experienced no further harassment from the roughneck.

Many of the Affirmative Action hires suffered great setbacks in their careers as did their male colleagues when the big oil bust of the late 1980s and early 1990s hit. Connie was fortunate, partly because of a choice she made in 1977 while working for Amoco. When she had a baby after four years at Amoco, managers bent over backwards to give her ample maternity leave so she would continue to work with the company. Her immediate supervisor asked if she could return to work as soon as possible. Connie was willing to return early if she could work "parttime" for awhile, because not only was she dealing with a newborn, her mother was dying of cancer.

Amoco policy at the time could not accommodate the part-time request, to the regret of her immediate superiors and colleagues. Therefore, in 1977, Connie established herself as a consulting geologist. She paired up with experienced consultants, first with geologist Jim Rogers, and landman, Bob Schulein, developing Kansas prospects for Sam Gary, a Denver oil producer. She was compensated with pay and overriding royalty assignments. She remembers those years with great joy, recalling that as soon as they developed a prospect, Schulein would acquire the acreage, and Gary would drill it. They had discovery after discovery in the Morrow, Lansing, Viola, and Mississippian reservoirs. She felt "like it was Christmas, over and over!" During the 1980s, she consulted in various areas in the Rockies. She also generated, leased, and sold several self-funded prospects.

It made her day when, in the late 70s, she received a letter in the mail from her old Amoco boss, Lou Bortz. He sent her a copy of an Amoco newsletter showing the development on an exploration opportunity she had put together in the Anadarko Basin for Amoco. Lou remains her friend today. Another "day maker" was when she was in the hospital recovering from her C-section delivery. She received a call from the rig. The wellsite geologist, toolpusher, and drillers called to congratulate her and to wish her good luck.

In the early 90s, Connie cross-trained and worked in the environmental industry for several years. And, she remembers, it was in a cross-training program at the Colorado School of Mines (Mines) that she met her second husband, Roger Knight. She worked at Rocky Flats, a Department of Energy (DOE) facility, from 1991 to 1995, where she managed the "Sitewide Geoscience Characterization Study." In 1993, while still employed, she completed a Professional Degree in Hydrogeology at Mines, and began work on her PhD. In 1995, she accepted a buy-out from EG&G Rocky Flats so she could concentrate full-time on her PhD program. At that time, she was a single parent and sole provider for herself and her daughter. She earned her PhD with a petroleum geology dissertation in 1999. Having income from her overriding royalties not only helped Connie through the terrible industry downturn in the late 80s, but it also helped to provide financial means to pursue her PhD.

During her career, she has served as a "resource" to many of the local public and private schools in Colorado. She has supported the Math Engineering Science Achievement (MESA) program and particularly enjoys teaching in elementary schools. She has presented workshops for teachers, executed camps for young students, and she currently volunteers at Dinosaur Ridge as a guide. During the petroleum downturn in the 80s she took some time to design and produce an educational earth-science kit, consisting of four teaching modules and an instructional manual. In 1988, she transferred her copyright to Wards National Science Establishment, who produced her product as *The Ward's Discovery Kit for Rocks and Minerals* in exchange for a royalty to her. Wards presented Connie with the first kit they produced, and she uses it in classrooms today. Today Wards continues to produce and sell Connie's kit, and she still receives annual royalty payments. Also in the late 1980s, she established a Rocky Mountain Association of Geologists (RMAG) speaker's bureau as a resource for local elementary and secondary schools. Within a two-month period, various RMAG members made over 100 presentations. Many of those geologists continued, by invitation, to resource school classrooms for years afterward.

Connie has found that sharing her early attack experience has helped many other women address similar horrific experiences. At the age of 22, she refused to allow that incident to define her, even though she experienced lingering fears for years afterwards. She maintains that dealing with this early trauma "cemented her to her career" by making her stronger and even more committed to succeed. During the industry downturn of the late 80s, and early 90s, many of her colleagues were changing careers, but she was committed to remaining a geologist. She says: "Courage isn't 'not being scared.' True courage is being scared to the limit and forging ahead anyway."

"Staying in Tucson in the face of tremendous fear, to complete my M.S. Degree, is the bravest thing I have ever done."

Constance Nuss Knight was born in Scottsbluff, Nebraska, in 1948. She received her B. A. in geology from Western State College in Gunnison, Colorado, in 1970 (even though she entered the school with a four-year music scholarship) and her M. S. degree in geology from the University of Arizona in 1973. She completed a professional degree in hydrogeology from the Colorado School of Mines in 1993, and, in 1999, she received her PhD in geology and geological engineering from the Colorado School of Mines.

Monica Sue Donellan (1948-1977)

The First Female Fatality in the Oil Business

Many male geologists have lost their lives to exploration; this is part of the risk taken when entering this profession. Monica Donellan was likely the first woman to die on the job as a petroleum geologist.

Monica went to work May 1, 1972 for Texaco, Inc. in their Denver office. Mindful that the Equal Employment Opportunity Commission (EEOC) was soon to make diversity demands in major company hiring, Texaco had begun to fulfill their requirements to hire more women and minorities (Fig. 13).

Monica was the fourth of eight children. Her older brother, Bux, was deaf so Monica learned sign language at an early age. Her father, Joe, worked at a refinery in Baton Rouge. Monica was a Louisiana State University (LSU) graduate, obtaining both her B. S. and M. S. degrees there by 1972. Her sister, Kathy Donellan Hayes, remembers that their parents were quite distressed about her attending geology field camp in Colorado, the first woman to do so from LSU. They did not want her at risk with all those young men. Monica's professor reassured her parents by letting them know his wife would be along to chaperone.

Figure 13. Monica Donellan her first day at work for Texaco Inc. in Denver, Colorado, May, 1972. She may have been the first female geologist to die on the job. (Photo: George Vandersluis, Montrose, Colorado.)

Monica had been accepted at Stanford and other schools to work toward a PhD, but decided to work in the petroleum industry for awhile because she could not afford continued graduate school expenses without putting away some savings. A friend from the New Mexico Institute of Mining and Technology where Monica had also been accepted for a PhD program wrote to her, "Do a PhD—this is required for most government jobs, and there is less discrimination there."

Monica was a soft-spoken "Southern girl" but also a passionate red-headed geologist who had no trouble quietly, but determinedly, speaking her mind. When she brought in a houseplant to lighten up her drab office décor, her boss told her that it would have to go as it wasn't SOP (standard operating procedure). She didn't know what SOP stood for, but she knew it wasn't good. Monica challenged the dictate. More profoundly, in 1974, as a novice with 18 months under her belt, she indicated to upper management that she thought there were problems in the way Denver ran their office. They asked her to put it on paper.

Monica wrote a two-page memo (Donnelan archives) suggesting changes, prefaced by, "I have further evaluated what was said, and I still think the same as I did yesterday, and many yesterdays before that. I realize some of the issues to be discussed below have been behind many of my friends' and acquaintances' decisions to leave the company."

A synopsis of her suggestions reads:

"...Management has too many levels of command with little authority, and power struggles between geology, land, and geophysics at all levels are detrimental to the company. At the District level, Monica suggested that all three aspects be under one manager and unified in their work effort, data dispersal and credit for work done (an exploration department concept that was soon to become the working norm in most exploration companies). She felt the division manager above the district manager should be chosen for having expertise in all three departments."

Monica continued, "...geologists are discouraged because they were not allowed to present their own prospects to managers, nor were they allowed in budget meetings. This needed to be changed."

She also told them she believed the method of communication in the current system led to misinterpretations and incorrect instructions because it was all verbal, and as it moved down the line of command it became garbled or, at best, unclear, by the time it reached the geologist. She insisted that these communications needed to be put into writing.

And finally, Monica thought performance appraisals should be more often than twelve to eighteen months and should include "company" status, so that if raises were not forthcoming, the employee would know it was a company-wide policy instead of a performance issue. Basic evaluations of day-to-day performance and suggestions for improvement were noticeably inadequate, in her opinion.

Monica's comments, apparently, did not have a negative impact on her Texaco career, but two years later, she, too, resigned from Texaco when the "Boom" brought her an excellent offer from an Independent.

Monica actively 'campaigned' with Texaco management for women to be allowed to do wellsite work, just as the male geologists did. Most the major companies were in the same deliberation about their female hires and the issue of women sitting wells. The fact that women had sat wells from the 1920s into the 1970s had become a lost part of history. Long deliberations were held in management offices. George Vandersluis, a fellow geologist at Texaco (and later to become Monica's fiancé), was an assistant district geologist at the time and recalled meetings where management tried to discuss all possibilities regarding the safety and welfare of women on the wellsite. Laughingly, he recalled, "Someone suggested the women might have a pregnancy test before and after they went out on a well. Some worried about the women, some worried about the men who would be with them."

By March 1973, Monica was responsible for exploration in Lincoln, Sweetwater, and Uintah Counties, Wyoming; and Summit and Daggett Counties, Utah. Finally, the day came when Monica succeeded in getting a well sitting assignment, July 7, 1973. The first trip was always a "training trip" accompanied by an experienced geologist who could show the ropes to the new person. She was sent out to be trained and oversee the drilling of the Texaco No. 1 Leo Unit at Table Rock, Wyoming (Figs. 14 and 15).

Figure 14. Monica and her dog, Zach, out on a well, 1975. (Photo: George Vandersluis.)

These letters from Monica to her father (Donellan archives) in Louisiana while on her first wellsite training job for Texaco provide a perspective that is both unique and typical:

July 13, 1973, Dear Daddy--The last letter that you wrote me arrived the day or two before I left for Wyoming. Since then I've been so busy that I've hardly had time to sleep these last four days. I thought you might be interested in what is going on...

07/07 Left Denver with Sid, another geologist who is about 50, drives like an old woman, is very slow mentally, is LAZY, and smells like B. O. plenty. I didn't find out most of this until I had to be in close quarters with him for a while. Anyway, we drove 2 cars with all the equipment we need to well-sit, run the samples (the rocks which we drill through), and set up a trailer for geologists to live in for a year, that is, several geologists who will rotate on 2 week shifts. We got to Green River and ate dinner, and Sid said he was too tired to go to the Rig. So, we didn't get out here until Sunday. That guy is really a lazy SOB.

Figure 15. On a rig in the Denver Basin, 1973. (Photo: George Vandersluis.)

07/08, Sunday--We drove out to the Rig and looked at the geologist's trailer—it was pretty old and dirty, but not unlivable for summer. Sid had a fit! He couldn't stand it. So, we had it halfway cleaned it up, but Sid decided to try to switch it for a better one. OK—but it wouldn't get to the site until Tuesday & it would be only 1 BR instead of 2BR. All in all, we wasted a lot of time while Sid piddled around & smoked about 5 packs of cigarettes—he is ====!!

07/09, Monday, The well was supposed to Spud—start drilling, but the Rig wasn't quite all together. So, we drove down to Flaming Gorge—which is quite beautiful. The reservoir is 91 miles long & about 500' deep at the dam. I'll send the map of it & some pictures if you would like. On the way back—about 5 pm, we drove out to the Rig & they still weren't drilling. So, wasted or rather had a day of vacation, sort of, but I was anxious to get started to work.

07/10, Today, Tuesday—Sid decided the well probably wouldn't spud again so he said we'd go look at some more geology—up to the Wind River Mtns through Sinks Canyon and Riverton. This took all day—and he was too tired when we got back to go out to the Rig. So, we went to eat dinner at this nice restaurant—with the wife (Claire) of the drilling foreman, Norm Johnson. She didn't know anything [whether the well had spudded] because Norm hadn't come to Green River from the well all day. So, on the way in we saw some service hands & Sid was going to ask them what was going on at the Rig when 3 of the top managers of Texaco stopped him. They were out checking some field operations where we have producing wells & wanted to know what was happening at Leo #1. Sid didn't know & acted real dumb, and would have been in trouble if the other guys hadn't had a few drinks. I was really mad—just before leaving the restaurant I met them by myself as I was going to the restroom. They didn't recognize me, but Norm Johnson's wife stopped them. They asked me how I was doing well-sitting and some stuff about the well. I knew the answers because I talked to the service guys before I saw them (the Texaco managers). It wouldn't have mattered if I didn't because they were rather inebriated, I'd say drunk, but you're not supposed to say that about your bosses.

Since we managed to bluff our way out—I thought we had better go on out to the Rig since we had found out that it had spudded & they were 300 ft. into the ground already. I mean, that is what we were sent out to do! It was 10:30 pm and Sid was too tired again—well, I told him I was going by myself & Norm's wife said she would go with me. By this time, Sid decided he would go—so out to the Rig.

By 12 pm—they had drilled to about 400 ft. & so Sid said he would stay out & start working. I was to go back to the motel & turn in the key to his room, and to turn in mine the next day. Also, he wanted me to buy groceries so we could stay at the Rig.

07/11, Wed. I got out to the Rig about noon to find Sid had done no work & had gone to sleep right after I left. Norm Johnson doesn't think he is teaching me anything! Norm is an OK guy who has worked on the rigs all the way from roughneck, to driller, to tool-pusher, to foreman. I think you would like him. He doesn't say much—but you know what he thinks. He & Claire asked me if I wanted to stay in the 2nd BR in their trailer, and I was very grateful. Besides them—the tool pusher, Hub Dubolt, has a trailer. Both of those trailers are new. Anyway, I didn't have to worry about 1 BR & dumb Sid at night—we also had to clean out the exchanged trailer on Wed, and this made us even further behind in our work.

So, all evening on Wed, all day (6 am – 12 pm) Thurs., and today, Friday (6 am to 6 pm/now), I've been running samples, washing them, looking at the rocks under a microscope & writing down what type rock is found at what depth—like 280' – 290 ft. Sandstone, white; 290' – 300 Shale, gray etc. And, noting if the sand has any oil or gas stains. Then I have to draft all this on a piece of plastic film with pen & ink so we can have a paper print made of the whole depth of the well.

Right now, I'm only 250 ft. behind where they are drilling—about 1350 ft. deep. This hole is 17 ½ inches across in diameter. It is much bigger than normal, but this well has to start big because it is going down so deep—20,000 ft. Ok, I forgot the 3 big shots came out to the Rig, Thursday (yesterday) & Sid got busy for about the 1 hour they were here.

He argues with me every time I ask a question, because I say, "Are you sure, couldn't it be this way?" He said I was always on my high-horse—well, I don't like people giving me dumb, textbook answers when sometimes I don't know the answer, but I know that the answer they give me isn't complete, or maybe not even correct. Well, I feel better being able to tell someone my problems—sorry to take it out when I am writing you. This would be a great job if I were just able to do it myself, without having to ask this Jerk for his OK on everything because he is "supposed to be training me."

Love, Monica

Figure 16. The ultimate outdoors person, Monica Donellan was also a dedicated prospect generating geologist. (Photo: Robbie Gries, Denver, Colorado.)

Monica did wellsite work under brutal conditions and often alone. In the winter of 1973 she sat a well in Wyoming, in exceedingly cold and difficult conditions, and returned to well sit again from January 2 to January 17, 1974 for that same deep well. In 1975, she well sat alone at Table Rock, Wyoming from January 16 to February 1.

Like every other geologist during the oil boom of the late 1970s, she was offered a great job with Benson Minerals Group (the same Bruce Benson who opened the office in Billings, who ran for Governor in Colorado) (Fig. 16). In 1977 Monica was sitting several wells simultaneously in Kansas, having to drive from location to location, all separated by long drives. The closest towns were Scott City, Garden City, and Dodge City. Sleep-impaired, she started toward Denver on a much-needed break when she lost control of her vehicle and rolled it, ending her life at the young age of 29.

Monica Sue Donellan was born on February 7, 1948 in Baton Rouge, Louisiana. She received her B.S. in geology from LSU in 1970, her M.A. in geology in 1972. Monica was the consummate geologist and outdoors person, who traveled every free moment with fiancé, George Vandersluis. They visited 16 different states with geologic guidebooks, collecting fossils and minerals, climbing peaks, hiking the Grand Canyon, skiing, camping, and canoeing.

Mentors in the 1970s

Many of the men who hired and fired and worked in the Post War era, like women of the time, also bought into the societal propaganda of the Ideal Woman—her place was in the home. Consequently, their attitudes when forced to live with "quotas" were often negative.

On the positive side, when most women hired during this time arrived into an office with no female role models or mentors, most of the male geologists stepped up to the plate. They mentored, taught, encouraged, and set women of this generation on the right course—just as they were used to doing for new, young male geologists. Most successful women who I have talked to from that era have great appreciation for the men who did this. It quickly became standard.

Another dynamic that we recognized with some of our male mentors was a new awareness in their lives; they had daughters. They recognized that the future for women, their daughters, could not be expected to be as "secure" as the way of life of their mother's generation. Divorce was becoming common, women choosing not to marry was becoming more common. The men, who previously had not thought about careers for women, were now embracing it, in part, for the benefit of their daughters.

Chapter 14: Sources and References

Campen, Elizabeth "Betsy" Bartow, Billings, Montana. 2016, Personal autobiographical writings, personal communication and source of photograph as cited in figure caption.

Donellan, Monica Sue. 1973-1974. Correspondence. Donellan archives with Robbie Gries, Denver, Colorado.

George, Lyn Wethington, Casper, Wyoming. 2016. Personal communication, 11/2016-12/2016.

Gomez, Paty Ortiz, Mexico City, Mexico. 2016. Personal communication, 9/2016; source of photograph as cited in figure caption.

Hayes, Kathy Donellan, Savannah, Georgia. 2016. Personal communication, 4/2016.

Knight, Constance "Connie" Nuss, Golden, Colorado. 2016. Personal communication, 8/2015-12/2016); source of photograph as cited in figure caption.

Kulla, Jean B., Lake Forest, California. 2016. Personal autobiographical writings and source of photograph as cited in figure caption.

Sacrey, Deborah Shaeffer King, Houston, Texas. 2016. Personal communication, 10/2016-12/2015; source of photograph as cited in figure caption.

Schulz, Valary Hogg, Dallas, Texas. 2016. Personal communication, 10/2016-12/2016); source of photograph as cited in figure caption.

The Sun-Telegram. "Ann Landers Column." Thurs., Jan. 26, 1978, p. C-2.

Sycamore, Debby, Denver, Colorado. 2016. Personal communication, (9/2016-11/2016); source of photographs as cited in figure captions.

Vandersluis, George, Montrose, Colorado, colleague of Monica Donellan. Personal communication, March 2016; source of photographs as cited in figure captions.

"Rock" Banta, Girl Scout Camp, 1974, horsemanship was one of her many specialties.
(Photo: Nancy Banta.)

Chapter 15

Dealing with the Bad

Sandra Jean Lindquist

As a little girl, Sandra Lindquist, was so shy and reticent she hid and ran away from both strangers and play dates but as an adult, she crossed North America giving talks as an AAPG Distinguished Lecturer (Fig. 1). The transformation happened when she fell in love with geology; geology gave her the passion and courage to do difficult things.

Sandra Lindquist spent her early years on her family's dairy farm replete with outdoor "plumbing facilities," and her best friends were other species, furry species. She likes to joke that she was raised by dairy cattle. School, though, was a place where she could excel—how many parents have to tell their children they are "*working too hard*?" Sandy's did.

After her valedictorian performance in high school, Sandy gained entry to the University of Illinois (UI) with scholarships, only to have acceptance ironically withdrawn to provide slots for "underprivileged" students in "Project 500." Only by "jumping through hoops" (as did other valedictorians affected by this initiative) and by fictionally realigning her intended study focus did she get into UI.

Figure 1. Sandy Lindquist in 1985 when she was an AAPG Distinguished Lecturer. (Photo: Sandy Lindquist, Estes Park, Colorado.)

Sandy's career and life journey has been defined by the ironies of major ups and downs, some related. Her career with Amoco Production Company began with ten years of exciting and rewarding accomplishments and contributions, but as the industry changed, that corporate career evolved into a second ten years of increasing disappointment and ultimate betrayal. Net experience at Amoco—less than zero from her perspective.

Joining the company in the mid-1970s as companies were hiring and on the economic upswing, Sandy had many choices and took an offer from Exxon for the promise of Denver. But, prior to showing up for work, Exxon closed their Denver office and told her she was needed, instead, in Midland, Texas. "Midland, Texas is a fine place for young unmarried females," they said.

"Yeah, right", she thought. Sandy quit Exxon before beginning employment and headed to Denver determined to find a job there on her own. She faced some "corporate fear" issues that companies seemed to have at that time, namely that she would marry a geologist in a competing company. An "expected offer" from Chevron fell apart when Exxon leaked that she had gone to Denver for a boyfriend. Though marriage was not on her mind, Chevron quickly lost interest (they even phoned her mother and asked if Sandy was getting married!) George Ecker at Amoco Production Company, on the other hand, seemed very impressed with Sandy's "ballsy-ness" to move to Denver without a job and he offered her the kind of job she wanted. And, Amoco promised more security to remain in Denver than a similar job offer from Mobil.

Her first decade at Amoco Sandy worked in Colorado, Wyoming, Utah, Alaska, and the Mid-Continent and externally published part of a regional Jurassic Nugget Sandstone study. When trying to publish, it was cumbersome and time consuming to get around company proprietary concerns but, ultimately it worked and was rewarding. Her Nugget Formation work led to a 1983 Best Speaker award from the Rocky Mountain Association of Geologists and then a 1985-86 "Distinguished Lecture" tour for AAPG (two weeks each on three different occasions and geographic regions.) The title of her talk was "Practical Characterization of Eolian Reservoirs for Development: Nugget Sandstone, Utah-Wyoming Thrust Belt." Sandy describes AAPG's Distinguished Lecture tour as a petroleum geologist's closest equivalent to a rock 'n' roll concert tour. The daily travel, meeting people, and speaking "performance" was a blend of exhilaration and exhaustion.

She wondered sometimes if life just could not be better. Sandy was most proud of establishing, at Amoco, an applied geology field trip for both engineers and geologists in northern Arizona which included a six-acre outcrop laboratory and 120 feet of core and logs from the center of the outcrop. Many of those materials now have been donated to the Glen Canyon Visitor Center. (Fig. 2).

Figure 2. Coring the walk-around "reservoir model" outcrop near Lake Powell, Arizona, January 1986. (Photo: Sandy Lindquist.)

Not counting the "modern carbonate field trips in the Caribbean," work on Alaska's North Slope, beginning in 1985, was Sandy's most unique assignment location. Her North Slope work included a regional Mississippian formation evaluation and producing-field study, again, using thousands of feet of core (Fig.s 3). A related March wellsite assignment on a Beaufort Sea gravel island began with a pickup truck ride over the ice highway and a driver who made a point of telling her that, because of legal reasons, "he could never go back to Florida." She made sure not to antagonize him or appear nervous for the rest of that ride. (Fig. 4)

Figure 3. Sandy is prepared for huge mosquitoes or attacking carnivores in Alaska's Brooks Range, July 1985. (Photo: Sandy Lindquist.)

In the gravel island's pre-fabricated dorm, she shared a room with another female geologist who worked for the well's operator. The dorm's doors didn't have locks, and one day a guy (accidentally) started to walk into their room and said, "Sorry, I was looking for Lucky."

They replied rather matter-of-factly, "Well, you're not going to get Lucky in here!"

Boom times in the oil business led to many major company geologists quitting and trying their luck with Independents who paid more and offered attractive incentive packages, but Sandy didn't think she was cut out to be a "wildcatter" or business entrepreneur. She was very satisfied with the job she had and with meeting the challenge of putting out the best maps, reports, and applications that met the company's business goals within required deadlines. Advancement was faster than she anticipated – and WITHOUT any office politics and "undercover stuff." There was even a corporate intent to create and maintain a "technical career path" equal to a "managerial career path," which suited Sandy's strong desire to continue to do applied, hands-on rock work.

Figure 4. On the North Slope with colleague Valerie Krass in 1985, they enjoyed looking serious about guarding their field office and personal sleeping quarters. Transport helicopter in the background. (Photo: Sandy Lindquist.)

When oil prices plunged and "the bust" began, it could be distressing to sort through the work left behind by the exiting geologists ("culled deadwood" per corporate jargon) or from takeover acquisitions. Sandy didn't like changes that wasted so much brain power and creativity. As she recalled, Amoco's "technical career ladder" concept shrunk to more of a "technical step stool" when the world of Human Resource "continuous improvement" took over. "*If it's not broke, break it*" seemed to be a frenzied slogan around the office; another was "*don't miss the train,*" while she thought staying on the platform might be a better idea. Also, starting to dominate the company scene were "personality-strength evaluation programs, diversity sensitivity training, cubicles with incessant white noise, and searches for ways to prove everyone's continuing progress with creative "score-carding." Oh yes, and the regular meetings to "reilluminate" the staff about work ethics most people had already learned from their parents!"

For Sandy, the big turnaround from a good working atmosphere to bad, unfortunately, coincided with a violent physical confrontation during a home burglary in 1986. She recalls,

> I had come home on a summer Sunday around 4 pm to a burglary in progress by two males, age 15 and 18. The younger one escaped (temporarily) over the fence out back, but the older one had his car backed into my attached garage. They'd probably been in there 15 minutes or so and had some of my stereo equipment in the trunk and my high school ring in a pocket – causing some disarray, a broken kitchen window, and the insulting sense of extreme invasion and loss-of-privacy. Apparently, they'd cased my rather secure but visually private home several days earlier when I'd found a gate unlocked. "Why me?" The only answer was, "Well, why not?" Funny, how I can remember every thought and tiny detail in sequence.
>
> I rammed his car with mine (stalling his car) and jumped through his driver's window as he restarted the car. I ended up sitting on his open-window driver's door with my flip-flopped feet in his lap and my arms around the frame of the open sunroof. Initially screaming for help, no neighbors were outside. He pounded on me and tried to push me out of the car. Only the fact that I'd flattened his rear tire caused him to spin out on the main road and stall again – long enough for a neighbor driving by to recognize me and help apprehend him until police came.
>
> I didn't sleep much for the rest of the summer and sank into a multi-year clinical depression, which was only relieved with Prozac in 1990 or 1991 For at least a year, I had negative visceral reactions whenever coming home. To cap this off, the Rocky Mountain News (RMN) got hold of the story and published a "superwoman" account including my full name, age, street address, and the fact that "stereo equipment and jewelry" were stolen. After my indignant phone call, they admitted making a mistake in publishing all that identifying information from the police report.
>
> With advice, I filed an invasion-of-privacy lawsuit that was dismissed (summary judgment) one year later for "absence of malice" reasons, all while the asshole burglar was still being treated tenderly by the legal system (he continued a life of crime). Despite officially admitting no wrong doing, I noticed the RMN *did stop* publishing exact addresses of crime victims. I'd gotten a home alarm system right away, but I had a 2nd prowler (not apprehended) seven weeks after the burglary – which I witnessed occurring around 10 pm on a Friday shortly after returning home from an outing and having just opened all the doors and windows. This was only three weeks after the 18-year-old was released from jail on his (non-English speaking) parents' recognizance. No bail! That put me over the edge. I'm at war, but I don't know whom I'm fighting.

In 1996, Sandy was trying to evaluate her life and career as the Amoco changes were so discouraging to her. She applied for and was granted a year's unpaid leave of absence (LOA), partly for expanding her involvement in volunteer responsibilities. She had no worries about a job being there when she came back— Amoco had never rejected an employee from a LOA return. Her work reviews had always been stellar. But, things changed while she was away. She was prevented from returning as scheduled in late 1996, effectively being "locked out" and not offered any severance package or transfer, in contrast to other personnel. She and another colleague filed wrongful termination lawsuits, which, for her, dragged on for two years concurrent with other major family stresses. The legal settlement had to remain confidential but suffice it to say, the lawyers and IRS did well.

As this tribulation continued, Sandy submitted an ethics complaint to AAPG regarding the dishonest behavior of a former geologist supervisor during the lawsuit testimony. Provided with all the documents indicating the supervisor's dishonesty (legal deposition versus Sandy's Amoco performance evaluation), AAPG took about a year to decide not to pursue it. It was a blow to Sandy's confidence in her profession and *a confirmation of the contradictory way the world often works.* Small comfort that several years later this person was run off from being CEO of a non-profit for questionable behavior and finally was incarcerated for committing several felonies. AAPG did decide to cancel the woman's AAPG membership once she was convicted and in jail. Too little, too late for Sandy.

Sandy spent another decade consulting for industry and for the U.S. Geological Survey (USGS) on energy-related geology. Despite the mixed bag that defines her career, Sandy looks back to her great days in graduate school at The University of Texas at Austin (UT) where Professors Robert Folk and Earle McBride were inspiring and innovative teachers. Sandy reminisced,

> Most geologists were a raucous bunch who appreciated both giving and receiving when it came to insults and teasing. Gender didn't matter. Humor-cloaked, verbal sparring capability always came in handy, and offensive language is still a good way to vent emotions. It was at UT where my mentors Dr. Earle McBride and Dr. Robert Folk really made it likely I'd work in the geology profession – particularly after one became accustomed to Dr. Folk's aggressive and sometimes off-the-wall teaching style (which some of his students certainly tried to copy in their own careers!). Anything resembling today's (my opinion) often wimpy characterizations of teacher harassment in those days could be handled simply by picking up the diminutive Dr. Folk and carrying him out of the room. Gals learned through experience the vigilance required to keep his "Folk You" ink stamp from unexpectedly appearing on any areas of bare skin.

Recently, Sandy gave back on a larger scale to UT's Jackson School of Geological Sciences to honor these two professors, the work they have done, and the highly effective way they taught; setting up a "McBride of Folk-enstein" endowment. A requirement for the scholarship recipient is to include hands-on rock examination and research so that in this age of ever-increasing "remote" data evaluation, such basic descriptive and interpretive skills aren't lost.

Looking back, she submits, "The petroleum geology career certainly gave me a wide variety of life experiences and a self-established financial independence to retire from that world when and to where I wanted. In terms of the science, I like that I'm back to the casual joy of geology for what first drew me to it – the beauty and understanding of why things look like that! Not to mention loving to dabble in other sciences. It's all pretty selfish, really, but at least not harmful to others."

Sandra Lindquist has a B.S. from the University of Illinois (1974) and a M.S. from the University of Texas at Austin (1976). She lives surrounded by the peaks of the Rocky Mountains and with her photography avocation, she takes thousands of wildlife and nature photos every year (no "selfies," though). Her best friends, as in childhood, are still the four-legged furry ones! (Fig. 5)

Figure 5. Sandy Lindquist's oft seen visitors in Estes Park, Colorado, some of her many furry friends. (Photo: Sandy Lindquist.)

Mary Penelope "Penny" Frush

My most difficult career experiences centered around a very trying boss when I was at an independent company in Denver. Early on I was confronted by him making a statement to the effect, "I want to get rid of you, but the VP says you have been a good performer and that I shouldn't be hasty!"

I felt put down, scared, and, determined to not let this happen. I started seeing a therapist to try to deal with him and my emotions around this—as well as asking the therapist to help me develop coping mechanisms. The long and short of it was that I decided to completely insinuate myself into his needs. I made myself totally indispensable to him and developed a relationship where he would not do anything without me either helping or doing it for him. I was his right hand "man." I felt I had completely bamboozled him into thinking I liked him when in fact I detested him, disrespected him, and, found him to be totally incompetent. He ended up losing his job in a merger, whereas I kept mine and became the manager when he left. (Fig. 6)

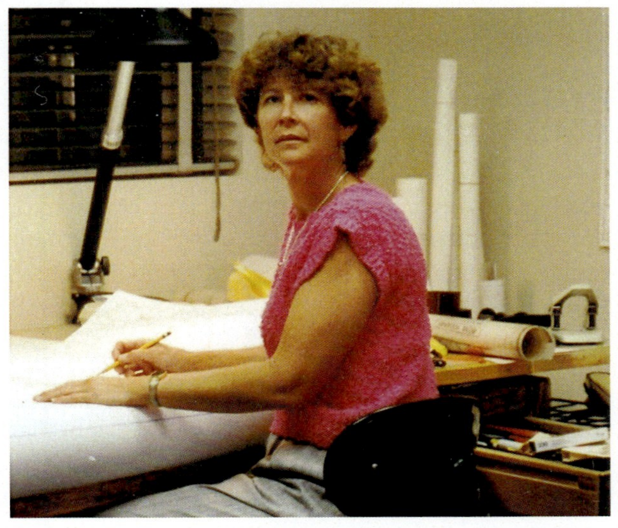

Figure 6. Penny at her company, LSSI, jointly owned with Richard Inden, satisfied to have her own company! (Photo: Penny Frush.)

I wasn't the only one who felt this way about him, it seemed everyone did. People would sit around after work sometimes when he was gone and share feelings about wishing he would never come back. In fact, his employees all shared pipe dreams about him going down in a plane or being run over or anything that would permanently eliminate him from our lives. That gives some perspective to the degree that he was disliked.

A couple of incidents come to mind to typify his behavior. Once in our weekly staff meeting, he asked me to make a particular map of an area—an isopach of some type and I responded that I did not think that map would address the problem and that it shouldn't be made. He burst out with a command that, "By God!" he wanted me to have that map made by Monday at our next meeting or else! So, I brought the map in on Monday, and he proceeded to say to all the staff, "This is a dumb map! It doesn't address the problem at all!" This was truly a "roll your eyes" moment to the rest of the staff who were as stupefied as I was.

Another time, he was challenging me on the stratigraphic plays I was working on in the Big Horn Basin, saying they weren't any good; what he wanted was another Oregon Basin field. I said, "That is a big surface anticline, those have all been mapped and drilled." He then proceeded to tell me to "find a *buried* surface anticline!" I could only stare at him in disbelief.

At an AAPG convention in New Orleans, Richard Inden (my life partner) and I were on one of the river paddle boats with a large group of fellow AAPG members. While Dick was off talking to some friends, I was standing by the rail soaking up the beautiful lights and scenery. Suddenly, the idiot stepped in beside me, so, to make conversation I commented on how beautiful it was. He looked at me and said, "Yeah, doesn't it just make you want to cum?" Horrified, I said, "No, actually it doesn't!" and walked away.

I continued with my therapy for five years while working with him. I always scheduled my therapy on Tuesday over the lunch hour. Somehow, he must have noticed I was gone regularly at that time, and he came in one day and said he was going to have a meeting at noon on the next Tuesday. I recognized it was not a crucial meeting, nothing working in the office was crucial for the staff, I knew. So, I told him I had an appointment that day. He started grilling me, "What kind of appointment?" "Where are you going?" "Who are you seeing?" So, I decided to tell him the truth and I said I was seeing a psychotherapist and had been for a while. He immediately said, "Why! Are you crazy?"

I held back from saying, "She is helping me deal with YOU!"

And, instead, calmly said, "I feel that I have some issues from the past and she is helping me work through them."

Then he said, "Huh, do you think I should see a therapist?"

Again, temptation put aside, I quietly said, "I think everyone can benefit from good counseling."

Whereupon he dropped the subject. I thought it over considerably and realized I could never have done that five years earlier. I felt that all the time and effort in therapy had truly paid off.

Another confounding incident while I was with that company involved a "dog and pony show" with the upper management. I was describing a project and mentioned the fossils and age dating we were doing and the CEO looked at me and said, "Well, Miss, this would imply that you believe in evolution! That the world wasn't created 4000 years ago?" Flabbergasted, I managed to say that indeed I did and that I thought the fossils and rock record could be used to our advantage. It was hard for me to respect people like that, though.

When Silo field was discovered in the 1980s everyone was interested and wanted to find another one. I started looking at it and tried to find a key. I looked at stratigraphy–no deal, structure–no, lineaments–not great and, finally, I started looking at various logs. I ended up, without any input from outside the company, realizing that the production seemed to be tied to well logs with high resistivities. I made a map of the resistivities and presented it to management only to have another manager say, "That is the dumbest map—nobody makes a resistivity map!" Of course, I was before my time, and resistivity WAS the key to the play.

In 1968, when I was fresh out of college with my undergraduate geology degree, I was in San Francisco and job hunting with other young "girls" who had other degrees. They were landing jobs at about $150 to $200 a month and happy about them. I interviewed at Bechtel and a wonderful manager, Cole McClure, took my application and interviewed me. I had hesitated to answer the application question about "expected salary," wondering what it should be. Finally, I thought being a geologist must be worth more than the secretarial jobs my friends were getting, so I put down $350. McClure told me that he wanted to offer me a job, but that he a problem with my salary request. Oh, I just cringed, thinking I had asked for way too much. Then he said, "Our pay scale for geologists doesn't go that low. Would you come to work for $450 a month?" Of course, I was pleased and took the job. It wasn't until YEARS later that I realized it never occurred to me to ask what men were offered!

He was a good boss, though, and was a woman's advocate. He only gave me work to do that was the same as the other male geologists. However, when he was out of town, *HIS* boss would come to me with a huge sheath of papers that he insisted I type. When my boss came back, he would look at what I was doing and ask about it. When I told him what happened, he just said, "I see." And then put me back on the geological work. This happened several times.

After graduate school, and for all the years I was with Texaco (Fig.s 7 and 8), Bolyard Oil & Gas (where I had an exceptionally positive experience and learned to prospect under the guidance of Dudley Bolyard) and with the difficult boss, I would not be caught dead near a typewriter—even when I could have done it better and faster than an incompetent secretary. In those days, even typing on a computer smacked of "women's work," and it wasn't until I went independent with Richard Inden in 1989, forming our own company, LSSI Ltd., that I felt I could publicly sit in front of a computer screen! A whole new way of approaching geology opened before me.

Penny Frush was born in 1945 in Iowa, and grew up in Golden, Colorado. She earned her B. S. in geology at the University of Colorado in 1968 and her M. S. in Geology at the University of Colorado in 1973. She and Dick Inden have enjoyed very successful consulting careers.

Figure 8. Penny in her Texaco biostratigraphic lab, 1975, with colleagues, Bob Rivers and Robbie Gries. (Photo: Penny Frush.)

Figure 7. Mary P. "Penny" Frush, 1974, when she worked for Texaco in Denver. (Photo: Penny Frush, Denver, Colorado.)

Jewel Fernandez Wellborn

Jewel Fernandez Wellborn's career out of California State University in Los Angeles started in the mining business with Arco Coal Company in January, 1979. This was a period when the mining business was just becoming accustomed to having women underground and the men finding that the presence of women did not cause mining catastrophes (also see Valary Shulz, Chapter 14). She was deep in a mine with miners around her one day, making her map and marking horizons on the walls of the tunnel, when suddenly the lights went out. She realized that, without noticing it, the tunnel had also gotten very quiet and she seemed to be totally alone. In the dark. Rather than panic—no screaming, no running–she just flipped on her head lamp and turned around to find her way back out of the tunnel. Soon her headlamp illuminated all the guys, waiting in the distance. They all just smiled and started laughing as she said, "Hey you guys. The lights went out!"

Soon they were applauding her. She had passed their test—no panicking, no screaming. They knew they could trust her underground. Jewel is still fond of that memory and knew that was the way they tested all newbies underground, male and female. (Fig. 9)

Figure 9. Jewel Wellborn at Red Rocks Amphitheater, Morrison Colorado. (Photo: Jewel Wellborn, Denver, Colorado.)

That incident is juxtaposed to a "worst nightmare" experience several years later when she was working for a major international oil company. She had transitioned from mining to oil and gas when jobs in mining became scarce. With this petroleum company, she was in their Russian Unit and had been to Russia once already to look at cores in a large oil field in the Timan Pechora Basin. No problems that trip, except to find that many of the core boxes were loaded with bricks instead of core. Apparently, the Russian drilling crew was paid by the pound for cores collected and bricks were a common discovery in the core facility!

On her second trip to Russia in November 1993, she traveled with her direct-line supervisor, a geoscience colleague, we'll call Chad, and, a translator from Houston. The mission was to present the results of their 3D survey and to look at planned drilling locations. She was the geophysical interpreter of the data.

As was usual, after work one day, they all went to dinner together with some of their Russian colleagues. A bus was their transportation mode, dropping them off and scheduled to pick them up later. After dinner, they were all sitting back, relaxing, chatting, and drinking vodka, except Jewel, who did not drink vodka. She just kept drinking water out of her own water bottle.

At one point she left to use the ladies room and when she returned she found that five women had joined the table, each sitting down between a couple of men. She was naïve about the women, not realizing until much later they were prostitutes. But, one of the ladies, a very tall and large blonde, sat beside her and kept putting her hands, inappropriately, on Jewel. Jewel would move away, and move closer to Chad for some protection. Each time she moved, the woman moved closer. The men at the table seemed to think it was very funny and kept egging the Russian woman on. Jewel didn't think it was funny and asked her boss if she could get a cab back to the hotel. He said, no, that they couldn't be responsible for her safety in a cab—which sounded reasonable but was frustrating. He said the bus would be back to get them at 11 pm, which was an hour and a half away.

She endured watching the guys and gals dancing and groping, all the while trying to escape the aggressive blonde who kept trying to take her water bottle and fill it with vodka. She asked her colleague, Chad, to step outside with her and, there she told him how uncomfortable she was and asked him to go with her to the hotel in a cab. He replied that he couldn't, the boss had told him absolutely he was not permitted to leave. She asked the interpreter to tell the blonde to leave her alone and her boss interrupted and ordered him not to tell the blonde to quit.

Finally, the bus arrived and Jewel went out immediately, got on the bus and waited for the others. Much to her dismay, they brought the women with them. Her blonde nemesis sat behind her and kept harassing her, trying to kiss her and messing with her hair. It seemed a nightmare ride. She was swinging her arms back and hitting the woman and telling her repeatedly to stop it. All the guys were laughing about it. When they got to the hotel, Jewel dashed up the three flights of stairs and asked the "floor lady" to let her in her room and lock the door behind her (only the floor ladies in their hotels had keys to the rooms). She braced a chair against the door for insurance. All night long she heard the fellows and some of the women going up and down the hall, pounding on her door, saying, "Jewel, come out and play!"

She was terrified they would break in—she was afraid she would be raped.

About 3 or 4 in the morning, it finally got quiet and she got some sleep. When she got up in the morning and opened her door, her boss and three of the women were asleep on the floor outside her door. Her boss woke up and got up, pushed her against the wall and said, "What we do in Russia, stays in Russia, understand!"

They flew back to Houston and the whole way she worried about what she should do. Jewel just wanted to be sure that she never had to go to Russia again in that scenario. Should she report it to their upper level management? To Human Resources (HR)? She sat on it for a week and then tried to make an appointment with management, the Vice President of the Russia Unit. He put her off, saying he was busy. Finally, as another trip to Russia was being set up, she went to HR in desperation. She did not want to travel with them again. That was what she told the HR woman—she didn't want to make a stink, she just wanted to be free from traveling with these same individuals on future trips. That turned out to be a big mistake. Immediately, the HR woman said, "Oh, we have to file a report."

Then the HR woman sent out a VOICE mail message to the entire Russia Unit saying there had been an incident and there would be an investigation. Her boss started coming into her office and glaring at her. She realized later that in the ensuing days, the men traveling with her got together and built 'their story.' Suddenly, SHE was the one being investigated. When Jewel was finally able to meet with the VP, he accused her saying, "I hear you were drinking so much they had to carry you out to the bus!"

More accusations came, "You are the one who invited the prostitutes and paid for them."

Protesting, she said, "What kind of person do you think I am?! There is no such thing on my expense account."

She told the VP, "I am not trying to make trouble for anyone, I just don't want to travel with these guys again."

He responded that she would then be considered as "not doing her job."

By this time, Christmas holidays rolled around and Jewel had a scheduled two-week vacation. She took her maps home with her to work on over the holidays. (That kind of diligence had gotten her high marks on all her evaluations to date.) Coming back into the office in January, she found her files had disappeared from her computer. She called in IT, and they could not find the files for the project. Jewel knew they regularly backed up so she requested the backup from three weeks before. The IT guys shuffled around and said, "We don't have a backup." Something was wrong, they ALWAYS had backups.

Then the plot unfolded. A meeting was called with the *entire* International Group, not just the Russia Unit, requesting that she present her materials. Jewel had only the maps she had taken home, crucial backup data was missing, but she muddled through the meeting as well as she could. The VP insisted, "Is that all you have?"

She explained about the data loss and the absence of the backup, but it seemed to fall on deaf ears.Out in the hall, a woman in the International Group cornered her and said, "Thanks to YOU none of us will get to travel! Why did you hire prostitutes?"

Other women would make derogatory comments when they saw her, and all seemed to disappear in the halls as Jewel would walk by. Her explanations were to no avail. Jewel again met with the HR department and pleaded to be transferred out of the Russia Unit. She was finally sent to a different Unit—but given no assignments there. A friend relayed to her it was becoming a big issue and confirmed that she had made a big mistake by going to HR.

She called a friend and colleague in the company's Midland office and told him what was happening. He came to her rescue. As he was trying to arrange for her to be transferred to Midland, Jewel's husband got a job in Denver. Her Midland friend said, "Great, I need someone in Denver. You can be our office there."

By this time, it was June, 1994. They made the move. Jewel got busy right away looking at prospects and deals for the company. During that summer her Midland boss ended up in the hospital fighting cancer. Out of the blue, another Permian Basin manager came to Denver in October and wanted her to sign some papers agreeing to be "let go." She asked if her Midland friend knew about this and found that he was unaware and still being treated for cancer. The manager said, "You are causing too many problems for the Houston office. Everyone was asking, "Why is Jewel allowed to work in Denver."

Going on the offensive, Jewel said she would not sign anything until she talked to her lawyer (which, of course, she did not have!). He was not happy about the thought of a lawyer and said he would talk to the office and be back the next day. Before he left, he asked her what it would take to get her to leave the company. She knew that many employees had been offered an early retirement "package", which had ended the week before on September 30th. She told him she would take a similar package and leave by January, 1995. He left for the day. She went home that night and got on the phone to find a lawyer. Luckily, a friend's son was a lawyer and agreed to meet with her that night. He listened to the story and then said, "You have an excellent case and would likely win a lawsuit. *But you would sacrifice your career*. You may never get another job in the oil business."

The next day the Permian Basin manager came back, agreeing to all her conditions and they agreed to put "closing Denver office" as the reason for her leaving the Company.

When Jewel started looking for another job, she found that every time she got close to final interviews, the companies would suddenly drop her. She had asked friends and colleagues in the Houston office if they would give her references and they had said yes and were very helpful to her, so what was going on? A woman in one of the companies where she had interviewed called her and said, confidentially, "We cannot hire you based upon the information provided by your former company."

Jewel went back to the lawyer and he suggested hiring a private investigator to check out the "references." The investigator found that when her references were called they stated they could not provide a personal reference. This is always the kiss of death, coming from a reference. The investigator recorded the discussions and had them translated into court records. A message went to the CEO, the President and the Vice President of Exploration for the company demanding a "cease and desist" from this activity.

Within a week of the "cease and desist" her interviews went smoothly and Jewel got a new job—the issues had disappeared overnight! Later, when she talked to her friend from that company who had agreed to give her a reference, he told her that he had been threatened with losing his own job if he did not respond as narrated by the company—"She worked from this year to this year, can say no more, we expect her to file a lawsuit." Later, too, one of the women who had been so critical of Jewel confessed to her that she could not come to her defense as "they had a gun to my head."

The actual incident in Russia was nothing compared to the agonizing two years that followed where she worried that her entire career would be ruined. It was small comfort when the Russia team was apparently back in Russia, having a good time again with more "ladies" and the boss, that same guy, got his eye damaged from popping a champagne cork and had to be evacuated back to the U.S. The VP was then

Figure 10. Jewel with the completion crew for a well in Belize. (Photo: Jewel Wellborn.)

asked to retire. A larger comfort was her Midland friend and former boss recovered from cancer, and quit the same month she did, saying he was disgusted with the whole episode.

Since that time, Jewel Wellborn has continued to enjoy a full and fruitful career in the oil business (Fig. 10).

Jewel Fernandez Wellborn was born in 1956 in Lancaster, California, and earned her bachelor's degree from California State at Los Angeles in 1978. After her work with Arco Coal Company, she married Tom Wellborn in 1980 and went to the Colorado School of Mines for an M.S. in geology in 1982. She currently is President of Hydrocarbon Exploration & Development Inc., a consulting company in Denver.

Nancy "Rock" Banta

Figure 11. "Rock" as she is known, Nancy Banta, 1974, working at the Girl Scout Camp near Ten Sleep, Wyoming where she got a call from Getty Oil. (Photo: Nancy Banta, Kansas)

Nancy Banta, her nickname "Rock," was in Wyoming with Girl Scout National Center West (NCW) working as a geology consultant for visiting Girl Scout troops in the summer of 1974. She was holding onto a horse, wind howling around her, trying to get an excursion underway, when someone handed her a phone (Fig. 11). Nancy thought it was some geologist she had met in a bar in the nearby town of Ten Sleep, then the wind died down for a second, and she heard, "We'd like for you to apply for a job..." She positioned herself to hear a little better and asked, "Now WHO is this, again?" The guy on the phone explained he was the Chief Geologist from Getty Oil Company's (GOC) International Exploration & Production Division. He wanted her to send a résumé as soon as possible and think about coming out to Los Angeles (L.A.) for an interview. "OK," she said, hesitantly.

Nancy did not have a résumé. But her other Girl Scout colleagues stepped up with a portable typewriter and said, "No problem, we'll whip one out." They helped and she sent it off to Getty thinking they must be trying to fill a quota by talking to a number of women and minorities, and she was fairly certain that it would come to naught. Everyone in camp treated it like the joke of the summer. "When you get this big job, we'll go with you."

Getty kept calling the Center's management. Finally, the director of Wyoming Trek, one of the programs at NCW, said, "I think you should take this more seriously." Soon, Getty called, again, wanting Nancy to come to L.A. for an interview. She and her friends from the Girl Scout camp convoyed to Denver. Having only field clothes and a farmer's tan, her camp buddies helped her shop for an "interview outfit." It was late August, 1974, and from Denver Nancy flew on to L.A., where a limousine picked her up from her hotel and dropped her at the door of Getty Oil Company where all the executives except for J. Paul Getty himself officed. She just knocked on the imposing wooden doors until a secretary let her in. Naïve as she was, Nancy was totally relaxed because she was still convinced this was not REALLY a serious interview. She was just going to kick back and enjoy a free trip to L.A., a city she had never visited before.

Nancy enjoyed the interview, talking with several very gracious and nice gentlemen, and she answered questions frankly and openly. At the end of the day, they shocked her further by offering her a job right on the spot! They wanted her to start on October 1st and the salary, benefits, and responsibilities all sounded enticing. She wanted to say, "Yes!" But, she had promised her Girl Scout friends that she would take them on a three-week trip to Mexico—Nancy being the only one who spoke Spanish. She told the Getty men that she had this obligation and could not break her commitment. They said that could be a deal-breaker. She said, "Well, then my answer has to be no! I gave my word." Bottom line—Getty agreed Nancy could come to work November 1, 1974.

Back she went to Denver to celebrate and soon thereafter, Nancy and her friends drove to Laredo, Texas, walked across the bridge and boarded a train for Mexico City. They had a wonderful vacation before she reported to L.A. as the second geologist of two covering Europe. The first geologist, a wonderful man with great skill and patience, taught her a lot. He, however, had a style of speaking that drove the upper management crazy. It was slow, very deliberate and took a long time to get to the point; whereas, Nancy had been on speaking tours previously, had a photographic memory and did not need notes. Soon everyone was happy to have her making all the European presentations and taking all calls regarding their activities. Her boss was glad to have Nancy take over that part of the job; he had been frustrated trying to communicate with his impatient superiors.

Getty's international exploration at that time consisted of three areas: Europe, Africa, and Asia. They would take non-operating positions with other companies, usually about 25%. The Occidental Group, of which Getty had a 25% interest, had just made two big discoveries in the North Sea—the Piper oil field and the Claymore field. Nancy joined this group and she was excited to learn her assignment involved helping to delineate about 60% of the latter field. Management called her daily for reports. Soon she realized they were getting the telexes from London before she did and she was at a disadvantage trying to field the queries. She remedied that by having Maria, her secretary, go upstairs to the Telex machine and get the morning report before it was forwarded to the executives. Now she could talk with data.

Those were the days of "three martini lunches" and Nancy became aware that the several of the highest level managers were often "three sheets to the wind" in the afternoon. One afternoon, she and a landman went upstairs to present to the Chief and he fell asleep in the middle of their presentation. They looked at each other dumbfounded. What to do?They did not want to waken and embarrass him. Finally, they just sat there until he woke up and then they continued their talking as if it had never happened!

Getty had made a deal with the Spanish national oil company. They had multiple meetings in Madrid, where they discovered the Spaniards did not speak English and she was the only who could speak Spanish. Nancy became the resident translator, a role she performed regularly for the company. To her disappointment, her considerable foreign-language gifts went unacknowledged and seemed underappreciated.

For part of her training, Nancy went to Canada where Getty had an active drilling program. It was January and February—cold, as one would imagine. The pilot light on the heater in her trailer kept going out, making life miserable. But, her Girl Scout attitude kicked in—be grateful not to be in a tent, to have good shelter, a bed out of the elements, and great food. She decided to focus on the "luxury" of shelter rather than hardship. The rig crew had been together a long time and the operation was well run—all three shifts were efficient. It was a great learning experience. However, on occasion a crew member would get drunk and try to crawl in bed with her. Nancy remedied the situation by explaining to the "drunk" that she couldn't possibly sleep with him or she would be obligated to sleep with everyone! This logic seemed to work with gentlemanly Canadians and she used the excuse several times—it always worked.

When Nancy first arrived in Canada, everyone warned her about "FBI." She was going to have to watch out for FBI! She finally learned that FBI meant "F---ing Big Indian," who was the toolpusher, meaning—the boss of the crew. She quickly made friends with FBI and found his trailer was the social place where she could watch "Gunsmoke" every night after dinner. FBI would not allow anyone to talk during the entire program as he didn't want to miss a word.

While working in Canada for Getty, Nancy learned she was working illegally. As it turns out, she was in that situation in EVERY country she worked in for Getty. It was standard operating procedure for them to skirt the visa processing and taxes of various countries by slipping people in and out, without going through the legal channels, because that often took years. Nancy was told if the Royal Canadian Mounted Police showed up, she was to say she was FBI's girlfriend!

One of the best things about the Canadian training was that she met a Good Ole Boy, Doyle, from Mineral Wells, Texas, who oversaw operations. Doyle later would be doing oversight work in Central and South America and always vouched for Nancy, smoothing her way with the crews. He was a godsend.

Nancy remembered her first trip to London, her first trip to Europe and she was to help the company sell a Spanish venture to their offshore partners, Phillips and BP. Her boss, a gem of a guy, came to her office on Friday afternoon and said she needed to be in London on Monday for presentations on Tuesday. She hastily readied herself and went as requested, but was considerably nervous, because it was first time presenting to partners. When they arrived at the posh hotel in London, Nancy's reservation was not found and the landman had to put his foot down and demand a room. Misinterpreting the role of this red-headed woman, the hotel quickly gave her an "adjoining room" to the landman! He was a gentleman and did not attempt to take advantage of the situation. They all agreed to rest and meet in the bar at 4 pm for drinks before dinner.

Before the appointed cocktail hour gathering, the Senior VP called her and said everyone was meeting in his room. When she got there, Nancy realized she was the only one in this invite and there was a large bottle of scotch on the table. Not her drink. Not her idea of a good time. Fortuitously, the landman appeared—saved! Soon down to the bar they all went.

Some British guys stopped her as she was going into the bar and asked her if they could "check her purse." Nancy was totally puzzled and tried to understand their version of English. Did "check your purse" mean "check it into the cloak room?" She answered, "No." They insisted. Back and forth, until they *demanded* to look inside her purse. Finally, she let them, and they relaxed. This encounter ratcheted up her already-soaring anxiety level and gave her a sense of being watched. Just because you are paranoid, it doesn't mean they aren't out to get you! Later, she finally learned that the hotel bombings in London were done by nice "Irish girls." Nancy and her red hair, again! Her purse was being searched for bombs!

Nancy continued to be nervous about her presentation to BP and Phillips the next morning, wondering if she would be regarded as a young fraud, a young upstart. BP arrived as a team with "Dr. So-and-So", and "Dr. So-and-So" and carried rolls and rolls of seismic data under their arms. She thought, "Oh my god, this party is over!" Now she was really nervous, but she had to lead off with her one map. She did her spiel. They sat quietly for a few minutes after she finished, then said, "We'll take the deal." Done. Her superiors were so pleased they gave her the next day off to see London—one of the rare times she had any sight-seeing time on a business trip.

Getty negotiated a deal in Central America and was organizing teams of two guys each to go down into the jungle, mapping, while she, the only one who could speak Spanish, was being left out. Nancy went to her manager and insisted she be part of a team. He said, "I would never send my daughter into the field in country like that!" She said, "Well, your daughter doesn't work for Getty Oil." He relented and let her go.

Just like her work in Canada, Nancy's work in Central America was without legal papers. At Getty's direction, she went in and out of the country without proper work documents. The job was to map a site in the middle of the jungle to determine where to drill. It was rough territory, with slippery red clay everywhere, and she thought it would be hard to convince authorities if they questioned her that she was on a "vacation." It was easy to get bogged down, either by foot or by tractor–they had a four-person basket on the tractor to carry the mapping team. There were poisonous asps and coral snakes to negotiate and, on one occasion, one of these snakes unexpectedly fell into their basket with them! The two Maya workers with her in the basket pulled out their machetes and started swinging. She levitated out of the basket into the swamp in a nano-second, not knowing which would get her first, the snake or the machete. If not in mud, they were in thigh-high grass where you also could not see the snakes.

Nancy finally mentally adjusted herself to "I am just going to die here, so get over it." The psychology worked. She had more focus. In camp, again, for a Girl Scout, the facilities were "luxurious." She had a tent, generators for electricity morning and night, and a "steward" who would clean their tents, make the bed, and do laundry. But then the poor fellow began to take grief from women at the river because he was having to wash (pound with rocks in the river) her underwear! His manhood was in question. Finally, Nancy paid extra so that he could subcontract a village woman to do her underwear. That worked. Regardless of who washed their clothes, they were always wet because it always rained every afternoon at the same time. The steward never got the clothes off the line before the rain. She wore wet clothes most of the time. And, he sometimes left her tent unzipped, which invited the tarantulas that usually clung to the outside of the tent waiting to enter. Nancy did a tarantula search every evening, beating them up with her rock hammer. Her leather boots were covered with mold within the first few days, so she was glad she prepared for that by bringing some military-style Vietnam jungle boots. It was dangerous in this country because you could be shot for wearing any kind of military attire, but there was little alternative if you wanted your feet covered. Weighing her alternatives, she thought, "Just shoot me, then."

The toilet facilities—outhouses—were a hike past the 40 hammocks under tarps that the Mayas used for sleeping. Everyone in camp worked from before dawn to after dark, every day. The Mayas mostly worked on the seismic crews. Nancy tried to be as nonchalant as possible, strolling to the latrine with her roll of toilet paper every morning, but the Mayas would all take off their hats and greet her with, "Buenos Dias!"

After the mapping phase, she took it upon herself to find jobs around the camp or on the rig for the Mayas, knowing how much they needed the jobs. Because she was the only one who spoke Spanish, Nancy became very friendly with the Mayas and developed a "brigade" that always went with her if she had to go to a village, or whenever she had to leave the site. Roving military, often drunk, were dangerous to be around.

The American men and, especially the New Zealand and Aussie workers, treated the Mayas very poorly and showed contempt for the indigenous people, which mortified her. Nancy started learning words in their native Maya language, Quiché (pronounced kay-chee)—one of twelve Maya dialects. One of her mapping colleagues was particularly obnoxious. He was always insisting she interpret his "demands" to native workers because he spoke no Spanish. She finally tired of his rude behavior toward the workers and just quit being his interpreter. He had started their tour together threatening her, "Just don't get in my way or you'll regret it!" Early on, they tried to report in on the "broken" radio, but she learned that to prevent her from joining him for the reports, he would sneak off to give daily reports by himself on said "broken" radio, which worked fine when he reconnected a few wires.

Another practice when away from camp was the tradition of using cemeteries as bathrooms—a local custom. All the free roaming pigs around knew it and would always follow them into that space. Scrawny turkeys were abundant on the small farms and would occasionally follow them, too. This became a game—every farmer maintained that their biggest, best turkey had disappeared with the crew and insisted on full payment. A similar thing occurs in the U.S.—where the bovine that dies in an oil mud pit is most definitely the county award-winning bull.

The nearest thing to "civilization" when they were mapping was a thatched roof hut—the Central American version of a "7-11" convenience store. When she stopped at this place with the crew, she treated the Mayas to cold drinks when available. These huts used kerosene-powered refrigerators which frequently weren't working. Warm Coca Cola or Orange Fanta were okay but warm mineral water was not exactly thirst quenching.

Nancy had been sent from L.A. on two mapping tours in this jungle. The last night of her second tour, she got into bed and thought, "Wow! I made it. I'm still alive!" Just then, she turned over in bed to face the tent wall. There was the biggest and nastiest looking spider she had ever seen. It was very fat, black, hairy, and bulging—about five inches across and only a few inches from her face. She grabbed her rock hammer and smashed it—only to learn the hard way about live-birth with spiders. The spider exploded into a thousand tiny spiders all over her, her bed, her gear. She curled up in the far corner of her tent, wide awake, for the rest of the night.

The next year they were back for drilling. This time, with the engineers in charge, Nancy went from her Girl Scout brand of "luxury" to THEIR brand of luxury. Hot showers, indoor toilets, air-conditioned trailers, a dining hall, TV room, and a cool X-Log mudlogging trailer with the fanciest of equipment for the geologists.

Soon shacks that functioned as bars appeared just outside their lease. To her chagrin, Nancy learned while visiting these "shacks" with the crew, that the back room separated only by a thin curtain, served as a whore house. Sitting in the bar having a drink, you would be treated to all the sounds one might expect from this activity, and sometimes the client (from their crew) carried on a conversation with the guys in the bar at the same time. "Men minus civilization," she thought.

After a few visits—it was the ONLY place to get a cold coke or beer—she came to know the "madam" who conversed openly with her in Spanish and told Nancy of the various venereal diseases both she and the girls had, including syphilis. Nancy thought it best to keep that information to herself.

As there were good reasons to think there might be hydrogen sulfide (H2S) dangers while drilling, everyone was trained on H2S alarms and procedures. The operator went around to the Maya villages and told them what to do if the alarm went off. Each person of rank had a heavy suitcase with an air pack and when the alarm went off, they were trained to take a deep breath, hold it while they put on their gear, and then run 100 yards away from the rig. The X-LOG trailer was narrow and long, with tight quarters and not much room to put on gear. Nancy and one of the X-LOG employees became friends as she enjoyed his amazing Irish wit and he kept her laughing a good deal of the time. Once, they were in the trailer laughing so hard they failed to hear the H2S alarm. A glance out the window alerted them to the alarm and the fact that everyone had retreated 100 yards away from the rig in their full gear. Quickly they tried to pull on their masks and get their gear on, but were bumping into each other and pushing everything around, still not able to stop laughing. Finally, they stumbled, very tardily, out to join the crew. The crew was obviously making their own assumptions about what had caused their delay which only made them laugh even harder. (Fig. 12)

Figure 12. Nancy at the binocular microscope, doing wellsite sample work. (Photo: Nancy Banta.)

Once, an "idiot" engineer, instead of throwing the training switch, mistakenly threw the H2S alarm switch warning the surrounding Maya villages. The Mayas scattered and the crew spent two days rounding them up and apologizing. Another time, there was a drilling break (which often indicated potential reservoir) and Nancy decided to run a core because the stratigraphy was getting very complicated. The driller did not want to do it, suggesting it might be dangerous because of the H2S. Nancy disagreed and they agreed to let the company man make the decision. A convoy of pickups went to find him. He was at the local shack involved in questionable activities and totally drunk. When he arrived back at the rig, he fell out of his pickup and passed out. Nancy said to the driller, "I think we can safely say that he agrees that we core!" The next morning when she telephoned in from his trailer with the morning report and described the core, they asked what the company man thought. As he was still passed out, she said, "Oh, he's right here and approves of the results!"

Camp was exciting in other ways. In Central America, there were occasional regime changes and it was common to hear automatic gunfire. Once, rudely awakened by the noise, Nancy looked out her window and 30-40 Mayas were gathered outside her trailer. She thought, "Well, I can hide under my bed or put my boots on and 'take it like a woman.'"

When Nancy opened the door, the Mayas all took their hats off, apologized, and pleaded with her for help, saying the army was going to kill one of their guys who technically owned the lease. She went looking for the company man, but he was drunk in the dining hall watching Football reruns—he had not even heard the shots. She then found the toolpusher and told him the situation. She asked him to leave by the back way, find the army captain in town, and ask him to help. The toolpusher was happy to leave because he was not keen on the erratic gun fire, anyway. The poor Maya man was finally rescued and lived to see another day.

However, there were not always happy endings. One ex-patriot (ex-pat) in charge of supplies found out that the local guard they hired was allowing people into the supply depot to steal fuel. The L.A. office told the Getty ex-pat to go to town and file a complaint with the authorities. They found the ex-pat shot dead in his pickup soon afterwards.

And then, the ultimate nightmare for Nancy—and nightmare of any woman working in dangerous environments—came one night when the drilling crew asked her to join them down at the "shack" for a beer. She rarely went there at night, this time she had mixed feelings. Her Maya brigade was gone for the day. She knew the crew meant the invitation as a signal that they accepted her, trusted her, and that she was "one of the boys." Going with them would help further develop a collegial relationship and show she could "get along." On the other hand, she rarely drank more than one beer and she knew they would be drinking more and drinking longer. Yet, on another hand, if she did not go, they might interpret that as her thinking she was too good for them. Finally, she agreed to join them. She grabbed her trusty mag-lite flashlight—a steel, 6 C-battery, long-handled, heavy instrument—and walked down the road with them. Unfortunately, as she nursed a polite beer, the crew was getting drunk and one guy started insisting the resident girls do a strip dance for them. As one might imagine, the girls did not want to dance in front of a lady, so Nancy agreed to leave and walk back to the rig. Alone.

When she was a considerable distance down the road, a jeep load of drunk military men drove up and passed her, then stopped and backed up. There were 6-8 of them—she couldn't tell in the dark—but verbal harassment quickly turned into physical approach, with very ill intent. Nancy started swinging her hefty mag-lite and hit several. She hit them again and again. She kept swinging and hitting as long as she could. She was sure she might have killed a couple—she was trying so hard—but, of course, she would never know. However, a machine gun in the ear trumps a flashlight on the head. In the end, they overcame her and she was raped and left unconscious in the foliage off the road.

Nancy woke before dawn and was shocked to be alive. Somehow, she made her way back to the rig and her trailer without being seen. Though she was injured, she felt she could tell no one. She might not be believed. She considered it would only bring bad judgments on herself, the company, and, be detrimental for the future of other women wanting to work in the field—an objective she fought so hard toward. She might even be arrested if she had seriously injured one of the assailants! Or, fired from her job? All for a stupid strip show! She sneaked into the shower and cleaned up, covered her massive bruises and went to work. When asked about some bruises and cuts she couldn't conceal, she gave the standard answer like so many other women, "I fell down the stairs."

When Nancy returned to L.A. her work situation was soon to change. Her good bosses who hired her were transferred or moved up the corporate ladder. New International Division management transferred in, with a different view on the role of women. She remembers one significant introduction to the new Vice President. All technical personnel were called to the conference room for a meeting and the VP was at the head of the table. Before the meeting started, an older black man in a utility apron stuck his head in the door. The VP waved him in and proceeded to visit with him as he shined his shoes for about 20 minutes in front of the entire division staff. Not a good sign.

Her junior "equals" were beginning to get promotions and transfers to Europe to take over the work she had been doing from L.A. What was more insulting, Nancy knew she had taught them all they knew about Getty's European projects! It was extremely disheartening and made no sense to her. Then one of her administrative friends dropped the real bombshell. It had always been her practice to treat the secretaries very equitably and friendly. She found them to be so helpful and always cheering her on. Executives sometimes told her, "Don't get too friendly with the secretaries, this is just not done." But she found it impossible not to show them appreciation and friendship, especially as she was the only female in the International Division in a professional scientific capacity. As a result of her friendliness, one of these secretaries provided her with the compensation information for her department and she discovered she was making $20-40,000 less than the guys—even before they took the jobs in Europe, where they would be given raises. For the first time, she wondered, was she a "token woman" after all?

During this time, Nancy continued to make trips to Madrid to work with the Spanish national oil company and/or Getty's partners. One amusing story was when they stayed at a very posh hotel - so posh that a young boy carried their room key ahead of them on a velvet pillow ahead of the bellman. She and her geophysicist colleague came off the elevator and noticed all the people in the lobby were on their knees. They followed the gaze of the people over to an elegant looking woman and realized it must be the Queen of Spain. What to do? They thought it was a little late to go to their knees, besides, it wasn't THEIR queen! They just eased themselves sideways out of the lobby.

Prior to his death, J. Paul Getty's home and European headquarters were once Henry VIII's hunting lodge in Sutton Place. After J. Paul's death, the household staff was retained and employees visiting from around the world continued staying at Sutton Place until a small office building could be completed on the estate. This plan would facilitate the continuation of a tax break given for the business office. (Though, after J. Paul died, his pet lions were gone. They had previously entertained other guests with nightly roaring like big cats on the back fence.)

When Nancy and her geophysicist were working an assignment in London, they entered through one of the gate houses and were greeted by a man with an Alsatian German Shepherd—he was carrying a shotgun and he asked them for IDs. The place was memorably plush, especially for a kid like her from "Plainsville," USA. This included butlers (who previously helped the Getty executives dress and undress; as in, "Let me hold your shorts for you, sir"), maids, and gardeners and furnishings (including gold bathroom fixtures), Delft tile bathrooms, luxurious four-poster beds, heated towel racks, etc. When Nancy blew out the current for the lights while using a hair dryer, the butler said ,"No problem, it always happened when Zsa Zsa was here, too." The butler, Bullymore, had to get used to the difficult chore of waking her up—knocking, then banging on her door. "Time to get up, Mum." Response, "ZZZZ." "Mustn't be tardy, Mum!" As she came down the sweeping staircase, the chauffeur took her briefcase to the car. "Just slap me!" she thought, "This is another world!"

Nancy's last year at Getty, before taking an educational leave of absence to go to The University of Texas at Austin for master's and PhD work, was very difficult. Still dealing with the new boss, who now seemed to be trying to get rid of her, she decided to have fun with him and his secretary, knowing his secretary was a little slow on the uptake. She had a friend from the Equal Employment Opportunity Commission (EEOC) call that secretary and "leave a message" for "Ms. Banta." The secretary had an annoying habit of always asking people to spell everything. She asked, then she repeated the spelling "E Q U A L--E M P L O Y M E N T—O P P O R T U N I T Y—C O M M I S S I O N" slowly, just outside the boss's office. Nancy could hear the secretary from her nearby office and laughed the rest of the day.

At one time Nancy's "evaluation" from her nemesis was written in two versions; one for her eyes and one for his file. But, this same ding-y secretary accidentally gave her the file version. It read, "...Nancy is acutely aware she is being discriminated against." The next day, the secretary was knocking at her door, trying to get the copy back, but she told her, "Sorry, I already threw it away."

Years later, Nancy started having flashbacks, screaming nightmares, and delayed trauma over the rape episode. She had totally repressed the event, but it was still there and after a certain time lapse, the door could no longer stay locked. She didn't want to discuss it with her parents and was afraid they would notice something was wrong. Only a few friends had been told. When the episodes became more frequent and more disturbing, she heard about a program for trauma victims at the Menninger Clinic in Topeka, Kansas (now part of Baylor University in Houston) and she went there for treatment. She was fortunate, she believes, as she got into a program with very good psychiatrists who were studying trauma and what became known as Post-Traumatic Stress Disorder (PTSD). One of her doctors theorized just what was happening to victims and why it could occur years later. He also asked for patient input about their trauma. It was reciprocal learning. The therapy helped her immensely and this doctor later published his research. She felt very fortunate to have found this program. Nancy says she would not trade places with any of the women she met there for similar traumatic events. She very much recognizes that too many victims blame themselves and/or are ashamed of what happened to them and do not seek treatment.

Nancy Banta has remained in the Kansas area and has continued her ties to her beloved Girl Scouting community. She has always relied on her early life in Girl Scouts for inspiration, strength, and confidence. Born into a military family that moved often, she was "'at home'" anywhere there was a Girl Scout troop. In her adult and retirement years, she has continued her work for Girl Scouts and was recently singled out as a recipient of the Girl Scouts Gold Award—their highest honor. Nancy continues to inspire girls and be an advocate for women in STEM. She's a member of Girl Scout's Daisy's Circle, GSKSMO's monthly giving program and a member of the Girl Scouts Trefoil Society. She recently received the Philanthropy Award from her council and is fundraising to build an amphitheater at Camp Daisy Hindman. She feels that singing around a campfire is a tie that binds Girl Scouts together. Her favorite song includes the lyrics, "We can find more meaning in a campfire's glow than we ever learned in a year or so."

Nancy Banta was born in 1952 in Cookeville, Tennessee. She received her B.S. in geology from Beloit College in Wisconsin in 1974. She worked toward her M.S. and PhD at The University of Texas in Austin in 1982-89.

Chapter 15 Sources and References

Banta, Nancy "Rock", Topeka, Kansas. 2016. Personal communication and interviews (7/2016 through 12/2016); source of photographs as cited in figure captions.

Frush, Mary Penelope (Penny), Denver, Colorado. 2014. Personal autobiographical writings and source of photographs as cited in figure captions.

Lindquist, Sandy, Estes Park, Colorado. 2016. Personal communication and interviews with Robbie Gries, (5/2016 through 10/2016); source of photographs as cited in figure captions.

Wellborn, Jewel Fernandez, Denver, Colorado. 2016. Personal communication and interviews with Robbie Gries, (9/2016 through 12/2016); source of photographs as cited in figure captions.

Chuck Bitgood, age 8, son of renowned wellsite geologist, Ellen Posey Bitgood, on location with his mother—a frequent occurrence with a "single mom."

Gert Burnley, 1938, Derby Dome, Wyoming.

Nancy Card and Narcissa Cameron, 1938, University of Missouri Field Camp, Camp Lander, Wyoming.

Gert Burnley, Kitty Moore, Ann Dorsey, 1938, Camp Lander.

(Photos: Elizabeth Watson archives, American Heritage Center, University of Wyoming, Laramie, Wyoming.)

Chapter 16

Diverse Career Paths—Opportunity Favors the Prepared

Ione Taylor

As Ione Taylor rushed to finish her morning breast pumping in the Amoco office ladies room, she tried to adjust her skirt which was too tight to zip after having her first baby eight weeks prior. She hoped her suit jacket would hide the gapping zipper. She grabbed her briefcase and ran down the hall for her first presentation to management since returning to work. Flustered, she tried to compose herself at the conference table occupied by bosses and potential joint venture partners. As she opened her briefcase and pulled out her files, a baby's pacifier popped out, bounced a few times, and then skittered across the polished conference room table, landing in the middle. All eyes locked on the blue plastic object with silent stares. Mortified, she blinked, took a deep breath, grabbed the pacifier, put it back in her briefcase, and launched in to her presentation. Sometimes you just can't avoid being embarrassed as the personal part of your life spills into the professional. But she swore to herself that she would never go back to work again while still breastfeeding! This was in 1987.

She didn't need to the next time. By the next child, Amoco had a much better family-leave policy that allowed her to take about eight months of unpaid leave, easing back into the job by working part-time from home. When Ione went back to work after her second child, having taken all the leave she needed, she desperately wanted the mental stimulation and reward of exploration. She had mopped all the kitchen floors and washed and folded all the laundry she could bear for awhile!

They say that "luck" is a combination of being able *to recognize an opportunity* and having the character *to take a risk*. Ione's entire career was enhanced repeatedly by just such "luck."

In 1975, puzzling over what she would do with her chemistry studies at Guilford College in Greensboro, North Carolina, Ione took an oceanography course on the Outer Banks run by Duke University. Her teaching assistant for the course knew she was struggling between the parts of chemistry she loved (inorganic), parts she hated (organic), and what to do about it. He suggested she consider geochemisty, a discipline within the broader field of geology. Ione returned to Guilford for her senior year and looked up geology in the catalog. Wow! It was very appealing. She included Physical and Historical geology in her classes and debated on whether to stay another year and take more geology classes, or to apply for graduate school and makeup all her needed classes while pursuing her master's.

As she would do repeatedly, Ione chose the "challenging track." She was accepted into the University of North Carolina (UNC) graduate program in Chapel Hill and caught up all the classes needed, including field camp. Much as she preferred lab work over field work, given her lack of direction, she embraced field work, too! Coming to a large research University from a tiny liberal arts college—smaller than her high school—was intimidating, but she would thrive. Interestingly, a decade later, the AAPG Explorer ran a career profile story about Ione and four of her undergraduate classmates from Guilford College; how unique it was for five people from this small class to excell in the oil business.

Ione was thrilled with geology and knew she had found her calling, but her start at UNC was less than illustrious. Upon arrival, she found all graduate students had to pass a qualifying exam. Having so little geology coursework and no self confidence, she studied like crazy for the exam. The day of the exam, the students filed into one of the geology 101 labs. The proctor handed out the exams and noted that some of the questions referred to items on the table at the front of the room. To Ione, this looked like the standard rock and mineral sample identification exercise. But he also held up an illustration that had to be identified. Her glasses were still in her backpack, so she squinted trying to see it. She penciled in "stegosaurus" with a note to check back on this once she had gone through the other questions. Her time ran out before she could get to the front of the class to examine the samples and that illustration. On her way out of the room, she glanced at the illustration that the proctor had held up and found it was a photomicrograph of tiny radiolarian! Figuring she was doomed, she was relieved that she passed the exam by 2 points. From then on during her Carolina days, she often wondered how long and how loud the faculty must have laughed at her "mistaking" a radiolarian for a stegosaurus!

Wanting to add geology of the Western U.S. to her experience, Ione opted for graduate work on research that North Carolina shared with the New Mexico Bureau of Mines (NMBM) and developed both master's and PhD theses on Cenozoic rocks in New Mexico. She worked with co-advisors Dr. Paul Ragland, Dr. Larry Benninger from UNC, and the phenomenal field geologist, Dr. Charles Chapin (NMBM), whose careful instruction and inspirational leadership she relished. She worked on nested calderas and the geochemisty of the volcanics in the San Juan volcanic field. Ione aspired to be a professor, too, but only after she worked with "hard rocks" in industry for a few years.

However, when she graduated, mining was in a terrible slump and there were no jobs in academics for her specialty. Ione had half-heartedly interviewed with a few oil and gas companies just for practice, so now she had to take a serious look at possible employment in that field. As she considered several major petroleum companies, she decided at Amoco she would have more say in "charting her own course." Friends from college and graduate school had also gone to work for Amoco and recommended it. She planned to work for two years, tops, then she would go back to her geochemistry professorship dream.

When Ione arrived at Amoco's Office in New Orleans, she was thrown into operations with a "learn it on the job" plan. Her first day, there she was assigned to an offshore barge rig in the Louisiana marsh. She did not even know what a "scout ticket" was, let alone the terminology used on a drilling rig—WoW (waiting on weather), P&A (plug and abandon the well), etc. But, learn it she did. More surprisingly, she found she LOVED the challenge and excitement of the work. Drilling rig personnel were getting used to working with women offshore by that time, and she found their only challenges came by way of testing her attitude. Would she be an arrogant "college kid?" Or, would she be down to earth? One of the team? She quickly realized that their years of expertise and "knowing the rocks" were her best resources for learning how to navigate, and Ione made sure they knew she wanted to learn from them. There was no trouble once that was established; she knew she needed them more than they needed her.

Another early professional learning experience was when Ione was paired with a very senior geophysicist to develop a prospect. She was on a steep learning curve and nervously practiced her part of the joint presentation they would make, relying strongly on his long experience, guidance, and knowledge of the way things worked. She practiced her presentation at home with her husband (also a petroleum geologist). He played the role of management, barking from across the table, "What's your point? Get to the point!" *That was another important lesson to Ione—recommendations should be concise and not waste a manager's time.*

When she and the geophysicist were ready to present, they filed into the conference room and placed their maps, cross sections, and seismic lines in front of multiple managers sitting stone-faced around the table. The geophysicist was a seasoned story-teller with his own style and pace. He immediately wandered totally off the script. The managers kept interrupting him and tried to get him to move on to the bottom line. He told them to just wait, he would get there! She was wringing her hands, wondering where this was going. Again and again they interrupted him and he, in turn, refused to be rushed and told them to just wait and listen. They wouldn't. He grew tired of their impatience and finally collapsed his pointer and told the group, "I'm going back to my office. When you fellows are ready to listen to what I have to say, come and get me!"

He walked out. The managers were livid and Ione was left standing there in the middle of her first committee recommendation. She lingered uneasily on her side of the table unsure of what to do as the managers, paying no attention to her, unloaded with both barrels about her colleague. She finally realized she was dismissed and went to her office. Soon, she saw the managers heading down the hall to the geophysicist's office. During her years with the company, Ione found that to be the worst behavior she would encounter and she resolved never to treat anyone that way!

Her two and a half years in operations were fun and she relished continuing, but, when Ione was pregnant with her first child, she knew she couldn't continue with the multiple demands of operations. Fate intervened. Amoco asked her if she wanted to transfer to the Petrology Lab and work the Eastern Region. It was a godsend. She showed up at the lab, with her lab coat on, and no one knew she was pregnant until well into her seventh month. The only drawback was that her new supervisor could hardly speak to her for awhile—he was so upset about her eight-week maternity leave (afforded in 1987). She thought about quitting, but one great project after another kept her too enthralled with the job—new rocks to see, new sections to examine.

When Ione had her second child in 1990, she was working international and had exciting projects in the Mediterranean, offshore Madagascar, Indonesia, Myanmar, Ukraine, and the South China Sea. Finding good childcare had its ups and downs, but Ione's husband, Al Taylor, who was also with Amoco, was an ideal partner sharing all the challenges of parenting and housekeeping. Together they juggled lunch boxes, ear infections, Donuts with Dad, bathtime, and storytime—learning to make the most of every minute of family time (Fig. 1).

Figure 1. Ione Taylor with her two children, 1991, learning to juggle job and child care—made easier with a participating husband. (Photo: Ione Taylor, Toronto, Ontario, Canada.)

Ione's next career challenge came because of a joint move within Amoco involving her husband. He was offered a position in petrophysics at the Tulsa Research Center that he really wanted. Amoco offered her a position there, too, as a Research Supervisor. She had *NEVER* aspired to be a manager, being suspicious of managers after hearing about some of the crazy training they had to take. But again, she made the choice to "just go for it"—opportunity and risk. Ione learned on her feet and found, just as she had in operations, if she welcomed input from the staff and put in her best efforts, it worked out. And, she ended up taking some of that crazy training herself—making an aircraft carrier out of cardboard, being propelled in it around an obstacle course in a hotel pool in Galveston, playing touch football blindfolded, and making masks to explore your "inner leader" (Fig. 2).

Figure 2. Management training at Amoco required some questionable exercises, but, in the end, worthwhile. (Photo: Ione Taylor.)

About three years later, when all the Majors began to significantly downsize and were eliminating, or completely restructuring, their research and development (R&D) function, Amoco, too, changed their corporate views. It was the end of a proud 50-plus year history of strong support for research. Now they wanted Ione to integrate research with technical services. The new department would have to gain funding from business units by competing with all other investments, including leasing, drilling, seismic, and even salaries. With the outstanding work of her exceptional colleagues, the effort succeeded. This led to her relocation back to Houston, rejoining her former peers, but now as their boss. Never had she imagined this could happen, but her experience in operations, again, served her well; she would integrate the research lab into an applied integrated rock-fluid systems department with the help of her talented and resourceful colleagues.

By 1996, Ione was ready for another "silo change," a process that Amoco used to continually develop their employees. Again, with the move came some huge demands. She was to oversee a recently restructured version of World Wide New Ventures, looking closely at areas which were not in Amoco's current "core assets." The group was given two years to evaluate the rest of the world (RoW) using full cost accounting and developing projects that would generate a 5-to-1 return. Otherwise, the Vice President of Exploration hinted, the group would be disbanded. She was to supervise very senior and experienced geoscientists who were world-caliber. She knew they could have legitimately resented her, but they proved to be first-class. Her major challenges came instead from upper management. The group recommended opportunity after opportunity for new country entries thinking, *management will love this!*—only to have it rejected. Management would poke at it and poke at it and finally say, "No! Too much risk!"

Time was passing and their deadline loomed. Ione and the team decided to fall back and regroup. Out of a brainstorming session, they decided to develop a "Portfolio Options Expert Choice System." The geologists and geophysicists integrated all the technical data and then added the critical country data for all worldwide opportunities. Then it was overlain with carefully extracted key management decision parameters derived from their earlier recommendations. As part of the data acquisition stage, the team worked with the U.S. Geological Survey (USGS) World Energy Project on worldwide basins and developed an excellent rapport with those geoscientists, each side collaborating with data and thoughts. When her team next presented their proposed areas for new country entry using their Portfolio Options System, multiple opportunities were approved—it was a big success.

Then everything changed. And she met her next challenge. Amoco was merged (or acquired by) British Petroleum (BP) in 1998. Ione was consumed with helping find positions for Amoco geoscientists within the BP structure and fought hard to prevent professionals in her group, who were often just a few months short of retirement eligibility, from being laid off. The process was frustrating for everyone, especially dealing with poor to ineffective lines of communication. In the end, only she, one other professional, and her secretary were retained. It was a very difficult experience having to let her colleagues go. (Years later, when those colleagues examined the documented evidence of Ione's battle on their behalf, they called her and thanked her for all her efforts. This was emotionally profound for her.)

Many of the Amoco people, both men and women, retained by BP suffered from "survivor guilt" and Ione's struggle was no exception. She and her husband, Al, had been thinking about a move back to the East Coast where their families were. She turned to her colleagues at the USGS, where she had formed such good working relationships, and found a job at their headquarters in Reston, Virginia. Al was excited to try his hand at consulting, so they moved back across the country with two kids in tow—their tenth move in eight years. When Ione was asked about her motivation for this move, she responded, "We're from back east." Her kids, in true *Go Texan* style, would jump in to say, "Mom, YOU'RE from back east, not us."

In 2000, Ione started a new phase of her career as a federal employee, a "fed," something she would NEVER have predicted. She worked in a range of projects including geological research and assessment programs for energy and mineral resources. Her background lent itself to evaluating future energy and mineral supplies and the potential environmental impacts associated with their development.

By 2009, when she entered the Federal Senior Executive Service, her interaction with Congress and the White House increased, including serving as Co-chair for the White House Office of Science and Technology Policy Working Group on Critical Mineral Supply Chains in 2013. This was during the period of tense international relations due to the rare-earth element (REE) supply scare. At the time, China produced virtually all the REE's which are so essential for high-tech and green technology applications. The Chinese announced (for reasons still debated) that they were going to greatly decrease or end export of REEs. Countries, including the U.S., dependent on this supply, panicked, and the American President went to the World Trade Organization and demanded action to prevent the Chinese from stopping exports. A multi-agency working group comprised of high ranking representatives from key U.S. Federal Agencies was established to develop solutions to the potential shortage problem.

At Ione's initial meeting with the group in her role as co-chair, she began with the geologic overview – everything starts with the geology – right? Where are REE deposits? How much of what element is there? How are they to be mined, etc.? As she went through this requested material, she noticed the representative from Department of Defense restlessly shifting in his seat, his military uniform covered with ribbons, medals, braid, and shiny buttons. She looked at him and stopped, but he did not say anything, so she continued. Finally, apparently tiring of her techno-babble, he exploded, landing his fist loudly on the table, "You want rare earths, little lady, we can get you rare earths"—and he did not mean by the scientific method. Ione decided she was out of her league on this one!

One day in 2013, as Ione sat in a stuffed armchair in her living room reading a book, she heard a ripping sound coming from the dining room table behind her where her husband was sitting. Then, from above her head, a large sheet of paper came wafting down, zigzagging back and forth, back and forth, before settling like an autumn leaf in her lap. Her husband then moved from behind her chair to stand beside her. He pointed to the full-page job posting in the AAPG Explorer and said to her, "You have been preaching about the need for better professional development for a decade. Here is your chance to do something about it." (Fig. 3)

The position was at a top-notch University in Canada to develop a professional master's degree program for early career professionals working in energy and minerals. The idea was to create an integrated learning experience with training in business, economics, geoscience, engineering, law, policy, regulation, and ethics. This would prepare future leaders to assess risk and make sound decisions. Wow – the opportunity to pack all of what she had learned the hard way into a program for the next generation in the resource sector – why not go for it?

Figure 3. Ione, at Queens University in Toronto, enjoys preparing students for industry. (Photo: Ione Taylor)

So, in 2014, after an almost 30-year diversion into a thrilling oil industry career and service as a "fed," she fulfilled her college dream and became Executive Director of Earth and Energy Resources Leadership at Queen's University in Kingston, Ontario, Canada. In this position and as a coordinator in the AAPG Visiting Geoscientist Program, she interacts with students constantly. As she helps prepare them for careers in the resource sector, she finds she has come full circle. When they are practicing their presentations, she sits stone-faced across the table from them, like her husband did for her, helpfully barking out, "What's your point? Get to the point!"

Another challenging position with steep learning curve? What else is new? For Ione, these are her life lessons: *Embrace change and challenges. Don't be afraid to take a risk and try something new. At times, you will be embarrassed as one part of your life spills into another part, but you will be learning and growing. Be patient; it takes time to get to where you want to go.* If "lucky" is recognizing opportunities and working hard at making them successful, then Ione has had a lucky life indeed.

Ione Lindley Taylor was born in 1954 and earned her B.S. from Guilford College in 1976, and her M.S. and PhD from the University of North Carolina at Chapel Hill in 1979, 1985. She and her husband, Al Taylor, currently reside in Kingston, Ontario, and will be relocating to the U. S. where their son, Carl Taylor, and daughter, Lindley Taylor reside.

Sherilyn Williams-Stroud

Sherilyn Williams was in elementary school in the days of school desegregation and later experienced the impacts of rapid school integration in the suburbs of St. Louis, Missouri. Her mother, being very light-skinned and sometimes mistaken for white, was a frequent witness to many remarks and attitudes her children would face in the 1950s and 60s, so she prepared them well. She made sure they knew the sky was the limit—her children could do anything they set their minds to, no excuses! She taught her five children to *never* worry about what other people thought, because people who judged you by the color or your skin were "just ignorant."

Sherilyn remembers the days when people routinely wrote checks for purchases and the store cashier would turn it over and put "N" for Negro or "W" for White on the back. Once, when a store employee wrote "W" on the back of a check Sherilyn's mother had written, she calmly informed that employee that she'd "better change that." She was not interested in being identified as white on her check! When Sherilyn's parents bought their first house and moved the family into a neighborhood just at the boundary between neighboring white and black communities, they experienced first-hand the results of realtors' open practice of "red lining." Shortly after realtors sold a house to a black family, they would inform the white families on the block that "a colored family had moved in," and they'd better sell their house before the property values went down—and soon the next block was all black, too.

As a teenager, Sherilyn dreamed of going to Oberlin College in Ohio to study music. She started her college years there, but the tuition was unmanageable for her parents with three children in college at the same time, so she ended up going to Seattle and enrolling at the University of Washington. By then, she had decided she wasn't going to have a career in music, and wanted something in science. (Fig. 4)

Figure 4. Sherilyn Williams, seated on the left, with her two sisters in 1970s; they were all heading to college. (Photo: Sherilyn Williams-Stroud, Pasadena, California.)

Having been active in outdoor sports, when Sherilyn found out that studying geology meant you got to be outside and hike and camp, it was enough to convince her it was the right choice and off she went. Needing to earn some income to help pay her way through college, she looked in the yellow pages for places in Seattle that might hire people doing geology and discovered something called the "United States Geological Survey" (USGS). She popped into their offices and was fortunate to run into Thane McCullough, a senior geologist who had convinced the Survey to let him open a satellite office in Seattle. She told him she needed a job and he said, "Come back tomorrow, we'll get you started!"

Sherilyn worked for the Survey for a couple of years and through that job qualified for in-state tuition. Early in the computer days, she was doing data input and laboratory rock porosity analyses on McCullough's mercury injection apparatus. She gradually grew into more analytical work on McCullough's projects, running the numerical analyses of his data and plotting the results on a computer. She completed her geology field camp in Washington, but still longed to graduate from Oberlin back in Ohio—she just liked the smaller school and the people there. Sherilyn had left Oberlin after her sophomore year still owing tuition, so she went back and negotiated with them to return and finish her degree in one year. She took on a ridiculously heavy course load needed to complete the requirements to graduate, and got it done. Finally, she had her Oberlin degree.

In 1982, she had a boyfriend in Baltimore, so when her two favorite Oberlin professors told her about their alma mater, Johns Hopkins, and encouraged her to apply there for graduate school—she was easy to convince. As the program dictated, went straight for her PhD. One of the professors learned there was NSF money earmarked for minorities and pushed for Sherilyn to apply for it. She got the grant! Four years of paid graduate work was welcomed, but she took some guff from one fellow student, with him taunting, "You're sitting there like a fat cat with all that minority money!"

She defended herself, saying, "It doesn't make any difference why I got it, because I still have to successfully do the work to keep it, and I am!"

She laughed gratefully when one of the other students of Italian descent chided, "Well, so what! I have an Italian-based scholarship!"

Her degree efforts became more complicated when she married her Ethiopian boyfriend and had baby Aysha while working toward her PhD. The clash of cultures—independent American woman versus more traditional Ethiopian man—raised its ugly head while she was trying to balance everything in her life, and soon her marriage ended. Finished with her course work, she returned to St. Louis with her toddler to live with family while she finished writing her dissertation.

A fortunate move it was because she met her future husband, Dennis Stroud, a physicist, whom she tried hard not to like because she thought, "I didn't want to marry a white guy!"

But love won out (her marriage is now in its 29th year) and they moved to Ann Arbor, Michigan, where he was offered a new and challenging job developing medical physics technology, and where he also pursued graduate studies. She had a hard time finding geological work there. Finding nothing in Ann Arbor, she had to expand her search and was offered a job with the USGS in Denver. She thought, "Denver? Is that cowboy land? Really?"

Figure 5. While working with the USGS, 1996, on the Yucca Mountain Project, Sherilyn was looking at fractured Tertiary welded tuffs, being evaluated for a nuclear waste repository. (Photo: Sherilyn Williams-Stroud.)

Balancing two very different careers with job opportunities became a very crazy part of Dennis and Sherilyn's lives and careers. She took the Denver job and he found work there (he had lived in Colorado before and grew up in Boulder). Their son, Nathan, was born in Denver. She had ten wonderful years working with Walt Dean, Bob Hite, and Tom Fouch and made many lifelong friends, including pioneering geologist, Anny Coury (See Chapter 12). Networks around the world began to build. She worked on evaporates in the Paradox Basin which led to her participation in a project studying large evaporite basins in the U.S. and Poland, and then fracture analyses on the Yucca Mountain Project (Fig. 5).

Then the USGS made a mistake—they pushed her toward administration. Sherilyn wanted to do science, so even though she had good reviews for her management skills, she wanted back in science. At the same time, Dennis was offered a great opportunity to complete a PhD in Minnesota, so he moved there and she started job hunting again from Denver—with no success. A professional colleague in Houston with Texaco respected her fracture expertise and coaxed her into applying at his lab. Sherilyn's entry into the oil business in 1998 was not only in a down market, but also, ironically, with the company that was two years into a class action lawsuit for racial discrimination. (The Texaco suit was not settled until 2001 – in favor of the minority employees who were awarded back pay.) No matter, because the Texaco lab in Houston turned out to be very exciting work and she forged great relationships with people like Susan Longacre (see Chapter 12), a highly valued, then Senior Scientist for Texaco.

Figure 6. Sherilyn, 2007, in the midst of purple heather near Bridge of Allen, Scotland when Sherilyn was with Midland Valley. (Photo: Dennis Stroud, Pasadena, California.)

In 2003, Dennis was offered a job in California and he commuted for a year while daughter Aysha finished high school in Houston. After that, Aysha and brother, Nathan, moved to California with Dennis; Sherilyn commuted back and forth to Houston for a year while looking for a job in California. She finally took a temporary teaching job at Whittier College—it was full-time, but paid like part-time.

Figure 7. While at Midland Valley, working with colleagues on new geologic mapping software. (Photo: Sherilyn Williams-Stroud.)

Uncanny things happen. After she had already accepted the Whittier College job, her contacts at Midland Valley, a small software and consulting company in Scotland, heard she was looking, and offered her a job that she and Dennis felt she should not refuse. (Fig. 6) Dennis found employment with the National Health Service (NHS) in Scotland and they moved the family to Glasgow—Aysha wanted to attend college there for the international adventure. Sherilyn would be the Geology Team Leader at Midland Valley for the next four years (Fig. 7). She brought her oil company "insider" perspective to the early-career geologists on the team, and helped them to understand industry problems and processes as they became proficient consultants. Sherilyn enthusiastically took on the role of software champion. She worked closely with the developers to improve the fracture modeling capabilities of the software, and did special projects, sales and consulting around Europe, the Middle East, and the United States.

In 2008, for family reasons, Sherilyn and Dennis decided to move back to the U.S., agreeing on the strategy that whichever of them finds a job first, that's where they would live. This time Dennis' network heard that he was looking, and they contacted him to encourage him to take his old job back in Los Angeles (L.A.). Now for the first time, it was hard for Sherilyn to find employment in her area of expertise! Again, the professional network kicked in and Sherilyn found a "commuting job" where she could work part-time in L.A. and part-time in Houston. Dual careers definitely created a lifestyle that few could handle as well.

Sherilyn joined the technical staff of a startup company called MicroSeismic, Inc. (MSI) as the only geologist among a team of geophysicists, turning seismic wiggles and "dots in a box", that represented microseismic events from hydraulic fracturing, into geological fracture networks. She had a productive and rewarding experience at MSI, helping to grow and improve products delivered to the industry. The CEO of MSI realized shortly after she joined, that Sherilyn was a good communicator and encouraged her to make technical presentations for the company. As a result, she further expanded her network until, after nearly five years with MSI, Sherilyn was made another offer she could not refuse – to work for Occidental Oil & Gas (Oxy) as the company expert in the areas of rock mechanics, structural geology, and microseismic analysis. Finally, after working for Oxy in Houston for over a year and becoming gradually more involved in California projects with a high degree of structural complexity, Sherilyn could live full-time *in* California and work for California Resources Corporation—very nearly solving her marriage and dual career problem. (Fig. 8)

Figure 8. Sherilyn Williams-Stroud, 2015, visiting geoscientist for AAPG, shares her expertise with university students in many countries. (Photo: Sherilyn Williams-Stroud.)

Sherilyn's career in the oil business has been rich with creative work, from software development to geochemical analyses. She has had experiences where she wasn't sure if "disrespect" came from her being black or being female, or both; such as when a new young employee addressed her as 'Sherilyn' while addressing the (white) male PhD's in the office as "Dr." There were also a few times where it was clear that men hired at the same time she was, with the same level of experience or less, having similar responsibilities and contributions to the company, were promoted much faster. Sherilyn takes this in stride, and always does her best as Thane McCullough advised her years ago; and if a move to something different is called for, she is ready to embrace change and challenges!

Sherilyn Williams-Stroud was born in St. Louis, Missouri in 1956. She earned her B.S. in geology from Oberlin College in 1981and her PhD from Johns Hopkins in 1988. She and Dennis Stroud were married in 1989 and live in Pasadena, California. They have three children, Aysha, Nathan, and Noelle.

Susan M. Landon

Susan suffered a debilitating head injury in 2006 in a ski accident, which shortened her career, but never dulled her enthusiasm for geology. She says, "I was always interested in geology, though when I was little I didn't know what it was called. I had a rock collection and I used to walk up and down the railroad tracks and pick up rocks. It was the start of whatever became "me." My mother worked for a geologist briefly before she married and the family joke was that I became a geologist because of early prenatal exposure. I think my mother probably told me what geology was when I was in grade school." (Fig. 9)

Susan Landon has almost no memories of any tough times or discriminating behavior as a geology student or an employee. One exception was when she was working for Amoco. One night the doorbell rang, and a visiting high executive of Amoco was standing at her door with a six-pack of beer. She was aghast, but invited him in. She had a beer with him while she found the words to say, "I apologize if I did anything to encourage you to think I was interested in any relationship except strictly professional, but I am definitely not." He must have felt a little sheepish, but left without any additional advances.

Robbie Gries met Susan at a Rocky Mountain Association of Geologists (RMAG) meeting in 1974 when one of her Amoco colleagues, Pete Matuszczak, was RMAG President and Susan was on the house committee setting up the slide projector. Robbie had not noticed her until Pete shouted back to her, "Hey, Twinkletoes! When are you going to have that projector ready!" Susan reacted by putting her fists on her hips, giving him a very reproachful look. But he was her good buddy and colleague and it was all in fun.

Figure 9. Susan Landon, 1973, in the field with her SUNY Binghamton professor, Don Kissling. (Photo: Susan Landon, Golden, Colorado.)

Susan remembers how her Amoco colleague, Lou Bortz, was so helpful to women. He would escort new, young female geologists around the RMAG meetings and introduce them to fellow geologists saying, "This is our new girl geologist," or, as with Robbie, "This is Texaco's new girl geologist." About the fifth time he was introducing Robbie she whispered to him, "Lou, I think they can tell I am a girl without your needing to point that out." He was embarrassed, but he never did it again. He was so well-intentioned and mentored many women and men and he adjusted very quickly to the suggestion.

Amoco, like the rest of the oil companies, had a hard time facing the issue of sending women to well sit. Susan remembers being told that she absolutely could not do that when she first arrived at work. Within a year, she was out sitting wells. Her colleagues, Cecilia Travis, and Larry McPeek, were instrumental in breaking that barrier. Larry best tells the story,

> Two of my supervisors came into my office one morning in about 1975 and shut the door. They began the conversation by saying that they were going to ask me to do something, but if I didn't want to do it, then they would go away and forget it, and there would be no adverse consequences. Above all, they wanted to make sure that what they were going to ask me to do was discussed with, and approved by, my wife, Kay, and that if I gave my OK then they would call her to make sure that what they were about to propose was really OK with her.
>
> I was baffled, so I asked, "What the hell are you talking about!" At this point, they disclosed that they wanted me to take Cecilia Travis out on a well for a few days training and they thought Kay might be the one wife they knew that would not object. I was dumbfounded. I thought the whole thing was being blown *way out* of proportion and that they didn't need to bother Kay about it. Nevertheless, they called Kay. They reported back to me that she thought about it a bit and replied, "Well, okay, but he better come back horny."
>
> After all of that, these supervisors were still apprehensive so they sent along another young male geologist from another district as a chaperone.

Figure 10. Susan Landon, 1983, Denver, when Susan was with Amoco Production Co. (Photo: Robbie Gries, Denver Colorado.)

Susan was an indefatigable volunteer for her professional societies and was the second female President of the Rocky Mountain Association of Geologists (the first, Ninetta Davis, was during WW II, see Chapter 9). Susan was the first female President of the Society of Independent Petroleum Explorationists (SIPES), the second female President of the American Geological Institute (after Doris Curtis, Chapter 10), the first female Treasurer of AAPG (Fig. 10).

Susan Landon was born in 1953, in Mattoon, Illinois. She received her B.A. from Knox College in 1972, and her master's degree in 1975 from the State University of New York at Binghamton. She still lives in the Colorado mountains and travels occasionally with her husband, Dick Dietz.

Nancy Darnell

I was born and reared in a small coal mining town in the southwest corner of Virginia. I went to the College of William and Mary (W&M), though one college looked like another as far as I was concerned. I did, however, know I wanted more out of life. I had no idea what that meant—just more—more life, more experiences, more places, more people.

At W&M I began as a history major. I loved history. I had read biographies and autobiographies beginning in the third grade when the bookmobile made its first monthly visit to Big Stone Gap. I loved the stories and getting to know the people and their situations. I read about generals and pirates, and every book that the librarian brought to me about women from Elizabeth Blackwell to Jane Hull, Clara Barton to Annie Oakley, and Martha Washington to Eleanor Roosevelt. When I went away to college I had no career plan. I didn't even know what a career plan was.

My freshman year at W&M I chose geology as my science course, because I had already had biology and chemistry and physics scared me. Plus, I thought— dinosaurs! I liked my young, very nice, and smart geology professors who encouraged me to take a second year, and so I did. During this sophomore year, I got mad at the history department when I made a "B" instead of the "A" I was certain I deserved. With as much forethought as I had had before entering college—none—I changed my major to geology.

I learned as much out of the classroom as in it. My father died over Christmas break in my junior year and I went home for a semester. I took a couple of classes at a small college about 30 miles from home, and returned to W&M for my final year. I graduated—a goal met! I flew from my graduation to West Point for June Week, and then found myself back in Big Stone Gap with a diploma in hand and no idea what I would do with myself for the rest of my life. I began sending out résumés and received replies that suggested I actually had to know something before I could be hired as a geologist.

My friend, Phyllis, who had moved from Big Stone Gap to Alabama when we were seven, called and said, "Let's move to Atlanta." We had kept in touch all these years, and she had a plan. So, we did. Now I had access to a major city newspaper with employment opportunities. I applied for a job to run a mud lab. I had mud experience; my senior project was entitled "Mud Cracks." Surprisingly, the very nice man who interviewed me suggested that I had to know a lot more than I did to get this job, but he also suggested I consider going to graduate school.

After more looking, and a bout with pneumonia, I "won" a job as a clerk typist for a collection agency. Within six months, I hadn't found more to life, but I did have more experiences, and I still had no plan—no vision. In my desperation, and with help from my hormones and help from the beautiful young lieutenant from June Week, I was engaged and back in Big Stone Gap taking classes at the same nearby college—this time to get a teaching certificate and become a good Army wife. Again, I sent out résumés aiming at a teaching job in Colorado Springs where Johnny would be stationed. This time I had a plan. However, six months later plans changed. I ended my engagement, packed and drove to Bloomington, Indiana. I began classes at the University of Indiana, re-teaching myself microscope skills by spending an inordinate of time looking into a microscope the first two weeks and settling into a routine.

I still had no plan but to work hard in school. I think I enjoyed "running away from home" in this manner and school was my comfort zone. Some highlights included: the professor who told me in the middle of class that there was no place for women in geology except as secretaries; My commitment to reach the top of the mountain during field camp inthe middle of the pack—exertion being a new concept as Southern girls did not sweat; Sleeping in a sleeping bag for the first time; and, applying myself to studies for the first time.

I went to class, studied, made new friends, and played volleyball on Friday nights. My new plan was to graduate and get a PhD. That is when I got frustrated with the department because they failed a not-so-bright guy after his orals but then proceeded to pass another less-deserving person—I didn't think it was fair. In a "snit," I signed up for oil company job interviews.

I didn't get the job with Exxon. My professor said it was because I told my interviewers that I didn't care about the business side of the oil and gas industry. In fact, I told them that I didn't even keep my checkbook current. I did receive an offer from Chevron (they didn't ask me about my checkbook). I was fortunate the job was in Denver. I was also fortunate that Chevron arranged to have my thesis typed, which included drafting the charts and graphs. I left Indiana a year short of a PhD.

I arrived in Denver in the early fall of 1973, not knowing a soul. When I walked into the Chevron office, I assumed I would intuitively know how to do whatever work I would be doing. That day I didn't know any more about what a geologist actually did than I had after my first geology course. I was fortunate again. Chevron seemed to have encountered this ignorance before and rotated new hires through three jobs—exploration, development, and geophysics. These were typically two-year rotations.

When I arrived at Chevron, there were already two professional women in the office. One was an older woman who was promoted from a geology technician to a geologist when the last man in her San Angelo, Texas office left for WWII. She, with her master's degree, replaced the men with their B.A.'s. (Ruth Sheldon commented in her 1941 article about women entering the oil business in WWI that most had master's degrees and were replacing men who had only a bachelor's degree, for less pay.) The other professional woman was the first woman engineer that Chevron hired in Denver. She was attractive, I assumed smart, but it appeared she was being fired for lack of interest. She missed a lot of work and was frequently late. The president of Chevron West was taking her out for a drink at Trader Vic's on her last day of work, and she invited me to come along. I had discovered, that only after completing the three job rotations, would there be a chance for promotions in Chevron. I began in exploration, and because I had no patience, I was already looking forward to my next rotation which typically would have been development. So over drinks at that happy hour, I asked the president,

"When am I going to get to go into the field?"

He looked at me, made a "teaching" gesture at me shaking his index finger, and said, "Oh no, I can't send you into the field."

"Why not?!"

"I need to protect the sanctity of your womanhood!"

I don't believe I had ever before heard anyone say "sanctity of womanhood." In an instant, I reached across the table and took his pointed finger, folded it back and then pointed my finger at him and shot back,

"Well sir, the sanctity of my womanhood doesn't need protecting, and besides, there is not enough left to protect."

Before long, I did get out into the field. In late 1974, I went out to my first well which was in Utah, north of Roosevelt in the Bluebell-Altamont Field in the Uinta Basin (Fig. 11). Chevron always sent a new person out with an experienced development geologist who introduced the "newby" to the field and wellsite. However, the day before we were supposed to leave, I was told to go on alone and John would join me in a day or two. Well, I said to myself, "Let me get this straight. I get to fly into Salt Lake, rent a car, find my way to the rig in the middle of a very large oil field along unmarked rig roads, introduce myself to whomever is in the mudlogger's trailer, whatever that is? Oh, great!"

Figure 11. Nancy Darnell, 1975, drilling in the Altamont Bluebell field in Utah for Chevron. (Photo: Nancy Darnell, Boulder, Colorado.)

I did find my way to the drill site by a circuitous route, found the mudlogger who showed me the mud pits, pointed to the privy, and then took me to the trailer so that I could begin to learn about the equipment and look at samples. Within the hour, the trailer door opened and a man looked in, saw me, said nothing, and closed the door. I asked who the man was. Billed said he didn't know, just someone from the field. All day long and through part of the night this "look see" continued—men from areas of the field drove in, stopped to talk for a couple of minutes to the tool pusher, looked over at the mudlogger's trailer, walked to the trailer, opened the door, poked their heads in and looked at me. Soon I began to say "hi" and I got some "hi's" back, but each one left without ever entering.

Things I learned at wellsites over the next few years:

> *Most mud loggers, engineers, tool pushers, and rough necks are interested in doing a good and safe job. No matter how much you try, an unripe avocado will not make good guacamole. No matter how fresh, a sage hen is not edible. No matter how far away the first hill, outcrop, or large bush is from a drill site, these locations are far better than using the wellsite privy. Drill sites are okay-places to spend Christmas, New Year's Eve, and your birthday. When sitting a well, sleep is the first priority—eating is a close second. Sometimes you are just lucky—by about 20 feet—not to be hit by a falling drill pipe. Sitting a well in the winter on top of Strawberry Peak, Utah, requires a snow cat and bing stuck in a trailer for a week at time. Even a "girl" geologist can win $175 in a Super Bowl pool on a wellsite. The best all-night religious conversations take place on a wellsite when the Schlumberger engineer is Latter Day Saints, the tool pusher is Catholic, and the geologist is a liberal Baptist. Having food poisoning in Midland, Texas, and the flu in Browning, Montana, are unpleasant experiences. Cedar City, Utah; Lemon, South Dakota; Rangely, Colorado; Browning, Montana; Roosevelt, Utah; and Evanston, Wyoming might be out-of-the-way places, but very nice people live there.*

The field experience that I still ponder occurred when I went to the Rangely Field located outside of Rangely, Colorado. The only space to stay in Rangely was in a six-room motel. The rooms all surrounded a sitting room with a TV. The first time I stayed there, my shower water ran out of the bathroom, through a corner of the bedroom, and under the door and into the TV room. The second time I was at Rangely, I was thrilled to be able to stay in the Chevron guesthouse in the field itself. Another development geologist who was maybe 30 years my senior was also staying in the guesthouse. That night I went to bed in my usual night garb, nothing. I was not quite asleep when my door opened and the other geologist came into my room. He walked over to my bed where, by then, I had my covers clutched up to my neck. He began to tell me how he just really needs to sleep with me! I began talking, telling him that would not be a good idea. I reminded him that he was married and he said, "Yes, but my wife is sick."

Finally, I convinced him to leave my room. The next day, we were in the company car, and he was driving me around the maze of field roads. I began to feel uncomfortable. I realized I no control and felt quite vulnerable. I need to say that he never touched me, but I had lost a sense of safe space. I never told anyone. I didn't want to get him in trouble. I didn't want to hurt his already difficult marriage. I thought of him as a friend. I didn't want to get a reputation as troublemaker. Looking back, I believe that I made the right decision for me at that time and place. I thought of my coworkers as friends. I made no distinction between colleague and friend. Today, my twenty-something-year-old daughter does know this distinction. However, I don't think I taught her this, I just think times have changed and expectations have changed. I am hopeful that corporate culture has changed. I believe today, I would have done things differently; to begin with, I would have locked my door.

All-in-all, I'm so thankful for the time I spent in the oil industry. I love Denver and the West. It is my home. In addition to many small oil and gas towns, company business sent me to New York, Dallas, Calgary, and San Francisco. I travelled to Yellowstone, Glacier, Yosemite, etc. for industry education. I met most of my long-time friends through oil and gas connections. I learned about business, "boom and bust." I left Chevron during "boom times" and worked for Nova Petroleum where I had the exciting benefits of overriding royalties, company car, and expense accounts. I had fun drilling my own prospects, tending the wells, and representing my company selling plays.

Nova began downsizing during the "bust" of 1980–90s. I then moved to Buckhorn Petroleum which was later sold to Harper Oil. I personally was downsized in 1985 or 86. I don't remember which, but I do remember that I was downsized the same day as John Hickenlooper, now the Governor of Colorado, who worked with me at Harper. John went his way, becoming a beer mogul and successful politician. I went to seminary and became an American Baptist pastor. I loved my new life work, but I missed many things about the petroleum industry. I was not able to keep up with many friends. I did not get to travel as much. I missed the pace. I missed the wide-reaching conversations.

I retired after 26 years in ministry having been able to co-pastor with my husband for most of those years. We now live in Boulder, Colorado, and our grown daughter is in Fort Collins.

Nancy Darnell was born on March 14, 1948 in Big Stone Gap, Virginia. Her B.A. was from the College of William and Mary in 1970, her M.A. from Indiana University in 1974. Her Theology degree was from Iliff School of Theology in 1989.

Donna Schmidt Anderson

I began my career in the initial years of Affirmative Action, graduating with a B.A. in Earth Science and geography from California State University Fullerton (CSUF) in 1974. At CSUF I had two very important women mentors, both professors: Dr. Margaret S. Woyski and Dr. Dorothy L. Stout. In 1973, I attended the AAPG Annual Convention in Anaheim. There ,I had several job interviews in which I realized that I had four strikes against me: 1) I had only a bachelor's degree; 2) I didn't have a geology field camp experience, because CSUF offered none, and many camps did not take on women students; 3) women in engineering geology, a field-based profession, were not initially allowed in the field; and 4) a recruiter from Union Oil of California informed me that I could only be hired as a geological secretary.

In June of 1974, I began my first career path in engineering geology working as an "information specialist" for a local engineering geology company in the Los Angeles (L.A.) Basin. They would not hire me as a geologist for reasons number 2 and 3, above, but I did finally get to go out in the field as an assistant. At that small company, I had my first experience with one of the two worst bosses I ever encountered; he loved to shout at and belittle his female employees, and he was clearly doing it on purpose. When the office moved to another city, he had his office sound-proofed by an acoustic engineer so the rest of the office couldn't hear! Today we would call that sexual harassment. I left that company as soon as I could.

I resolved to overcome my educational shortcomings and found some excellent mentors, all male, one of whom was the first male member of the National Organization for Women (NOW) in Orange County, California where I lived. My mentors helped me learn field geology by taking me out as a field assistant and then turning me loose. At one point, I took weekends and went out and mapped along the San Andreas Fault with one of my women friends who had the same field work deficiency as I did, and for the same reasons. I also unashamedly and frequently changed jobs, until my father sat me down and told me to stay somewhere two years to prove I wasn't a total job-hopper. My job-hopping was expedited by being engaged in professional societies where I networked into new jobs that gave better opportunities. When I got hired as a "real geologist" at a larger engineering geology firm in southern California, I stayed there exactly two years to the day.

I sought every bit of field experience I could, because I truly loved being out-of-doors. Being in the field often, and with drillers and heavy equipment operators—some of whom were the most down-to-earth people I have ever met—helped me develop a quiet but effective "take no prisoners" attitude. The guys I worked with gave me a great deal of guff, but fortunately most were very willing to take it in return.

On one drilling crew in southern California, the driller kept asking me how many freckles I had on my butt—I was a redhead with a ton of freckles. Getting quickly tired of that question, I started to look for an opportunity to tease him back. On a trip to pee in the bushes, I found a bleached cow jaw with all the teeth intact. I stuck the jaw in my safety vest and waited for an opportunity to use it. When a subsequent conversation turned to going to the dentist, I pulled out the jaw, suggesting that the driller get some new teeth. Touché! He laughed heartily and quit asking me about my freckles.

I also recall sitting on a drill rig for many weeks in the central San Joaquin Valley, drilling shallow boreholes for a nuclear power plant siting project with a crew from the Bay area. I had wanted to work stirring the mud pit, but for safety reasons was told no. So, in between catching samples, I read the *San Francisco Chronicle* out loud to the crew. I thought that was an acceptable alternative to playing in the mud, and it seemed paradoxically elegant! With all the field experience I accrued over four years, the field camp educational issue faded away.

One of my male mentors, along with my then-fiancée from an office romance, urged me to get a master's degree to alleviate further professional problems as a geologist. I got married in 1978 and started on my second career path, in which I went back to school at UCLA. I had an excellent experience with a good advisor and first-rate field geologist, Dr. Clarence Hall, who planted the idea of someday pursuing a doctorate, and Dr. Clem Nelson, another outstanding field geologist, with whom I got my first teaching experience as his assistant in his undergraduate California Geology class.

I attended and graduated from UCLA at the height of the 1980 oil boom. I had diverse job offers, but my husband was adamant about moving to Denver, because he hated southern California and thought that he could find a career opportunity in Colorado (which he ultimately did). Initially I had no offers for employment in Denver, so in June 1980, I went to the AAPG Annual Convention in Denver, staying with a friend who I had worked with at one of my jobs in California. She suggested that I call up the exploration manager at Mobil in the Denver office. I did that, had an interview, and had a job offer a week later, with a starting salary higher than basic starting salary because I offered four years of experience. Although all the companies I interviewed with thought my field experience was a big plus, Mobil was the only company that made an offer that included monetary compensation for that experience. I immediately joined the Offshore California team working on the offshore Santa Maria Basin lease sale. My ticket to the team and the position was my M.S. thesis topic on the onshore Santa Maria Basin and adjacent coastal areas. My career took a third change in paths.

At Mobil, I had a positive experience as a woman professional, largely due to the path that previous women had paved during the Affirmative Action period from 1973-1980. By 1980, Mobil was consistently hiring women. It was refreshing to work with women professionals and share experiences, especially having been one of only five in southern California!

Early on at Mobil I did a lot of wellsite work. One of the amusing stories was relieving one of my team members who had a family obligation. I went up to Gillette, Wyoming, to sit a well and meet with our wellsite consultant. He was an old-time, crusty guy who had to "train" a long line of new Mobil wellsite geologists. When he was informed that I was coming on location as the "lady boss," I can only guess what he thought. We were sitting in a café in Gillette chatting, well, maybe more like I was being "grilled." He was recounting his credentials and took out a card from his wallet and laid it on the table, saying, "I bet you don't have one of these."

It was a Professional Geologist registration card from California, the first and most highly regarded registration at the time. I looked at his card, reached into my wallet and pulled out *my* California registration card. As I laid it on the table, I said, "I passed the exam."

The entire conversation changed at that point. He looked pretty shocked and then he relaxed. From then on, he treated me more like a colleague and over the weekend, introduced me to his long-time ranching friends and showed me around the county. It turned out to be a positive, memorable experience.

As I look back on it, the nearly 12 years I worked at Mobil gave me a superlative technical background. I liked working in teams, and I had the honor of being a guest lecturer in the California Tectonic seminar led by Dr. John Crowell, a giant figure in California geology! I finagled three summers of helicopter-supported field work in the Wyoming Range, and I also gained management experience that sadly turned out to be awful as I had to lay off my colleagues. I also took prospects from concept to drill bit, but at that time only drilled dry holes. I learned many hard realities during the 1986-1992 downturn years, such as gaining "wisdom" can be very painful.

When Mobil closed the Denver office in 1992, I took a severance package and stayed in Denver, because my husband had a job that looked stable for at least 18 months. Seeing the downward spiral in the industry, by 1991, I had already invented my "parachute" and fourth change in career path: seeking a PhD in stratigraphy at Colorado School of Mines (CSM).

The five years I spent at CSM was an intellectual and professional leap. I was fully-funded in an active stratigraphy research group led by Dr. Timothy Cross. My thesis field area was in western Norway, the land of the midnight sun when it wasn't raining or snowing, and my first overseas endeavor. As my long-term goal was to become a consulting geologist specializing in stratigraphy for the oil and gas industry, I designed my research program toward that end. A CSM requirement at the time was to have a minor outside the geology department. I naturally minored in petroleum engineering (PE), emphasizing reservoir engineering. That turned out to be fortuitous through subsequent years, as I made invaluable contacts, learned a different way of thinking, and got my second teaching experience as a teaching assistant for Dr. Ramona Graves, a mentor, in PE field camp.

I also became very engaged in professional societies in Denver, serving first as officer for the Rocky Mountain Section of the Society for Economic Paleontology and Mineralogy (RMS-SEPM), then beginning as an officer for the Rocky Mountain Association of Geologists (RMAG). When I graduated in 1997, I recall my advisor, Tim, asking me what I was going to do as a consultant. I replied, "Everything." He said, rolling his eyes, "Good plan."

Tim put me on a part-time Post-Doc in which I went to northern Spain for field work and which also let me start consulting half-time. I immediately started one consulting project that took me to Myanmar during the monsoon season and then another to southern Chile in the middle of the southern winter. Career-path change number five was full of adventures!

Unfortunately, 1997 was the beginning of another deep recession in the oil industry. By the summer of 1999, I had zero consulting work, and had experienced the joys of "rubber checks" for insufficient funds from one of my clients. I recall standing in line at an RMAG luncheon bemoaning this fact to Robert Groth (husband and business partner of Jeanne Harris), who quickly pointed out the upside, saying, "Donna, it is summer. You live in the Rockies. Go hiking and camping and enjoy it."

So, I did. That turned out to be one of my most memorable summers ever for outdoor recreation! By fall of that year, I found myself back at CSM working on a consulting project in the Java Sea of Indonesia, and on my way to becoming a Research Professor with a Deep-Water field consortium in the Delaware Mountains of West Texas. Back to the field for career-path change number six!

From early 2000 to 2006, I spent six years as a part-time Research Professor at CSM on a fairly rocky path. I got extensive experience teaching undergraduate petroleum engineers the rudiments of sedimentary geology for five years, and I co-taught Petroleum Engineering field camp with Dr. Jennifer Miskimins for nine years, both because of my PE contacts that I made as graduate student. I got on the research grant and consortium funding treadmill, in which I quickly found out that I could support students, but not myself. While at CSM, I helped a group of women students try to establish a student chapter of the Association for Women Geoscientists. Although my involvement was short-lived, the effort was very rewarding as I could "give back" as a mentor to the women students.

I simultaneously consulted in the local petroleum industry with a goal to work for every company and in every building in downtown Denver, which fortunately never happened. I did, however, get a tremendous education in the different business models and cultures in various companies. I gained a sense of what I liked and did not like, and I established a professional reputation.

I also increased my activities in RMAG, serving as president in 2004. Afterward, I became active in AAPG, serving as President of the Rocky Mountain Section of AAPG in 2005, and then beginning service to AAPG on various committees and Divisions which lasted through 2015. Through these activities, I gained a tremendous network of friends and colleagues within the Rocky Mountain region and subsequently worldwide, all of which complemented the worldwide CSM network.

Career path twist number seven began in 2006 with the spectacular upturn in the petroleum industry in the Rocky Mountain region. Because of my professional network and exposure, I had several opportunities to return to the industry. Only one company, EOG Resources, was creative about making a job offer that I could not refuse. They set up a permanent part-time professional position in return which guaranteed a minimum of 20 hours a week of my undivided attention with the expectation that I find a major hydrocarbon accumulation. I accepted.

Probably the most humorous part of the interview process was trying to fill out their Human Resources (HR) experience form. The HR representative told me that it was a mess and complimented me for even trying. Recently I have heard my work history called "portfolio employment." EOG's offer allowed me to keep my part-time, mostly volunteer position as Research Professor at CSM, where I advised several M.S. students between 2004 and 2011. I also began teaching part of the undergraduate geology field camp in 2012—what a change from my undergraduate deficiency! I wanted to maintain the CSM connection because eventually I wanted to go back to academia after I retired. I recalled from my Mobil days how many retirees in the early 1980s had that vision. However, they were unable to accomplish it because they had never kept those contacts over their careers, plus they did not have the required credentials. (Fig. 12)

Figure 12. Donna Schmidt Anderson, September 2010, at the mouth of the Hoh River, Washington. (Photo: Donna Anderson, Golden, Colorado.)

My nine-year EOG career was wildly successful. I became a proven oil finder, a goal I had since leaving Mobil. I used all my educational and professional skills in an integrated team setting. I was on the ground floor of unconventional resource plays with nearly a free rein to be inventive. I worked with an exceptional group of people, saw the peak, and then saw the downturn. I retired in July 2015 as things were declining. I feared that I was seeing a repeat of 1986. I also thought it was time to make way for a new generation of geoscientists.

Career turn number eight. Now. I am semi-retired and engaged at CSM as a part-time, mostly volunteer, Research Professor, mentoring students, and teaching about rocks via the field and the core library. I aim to be a role model to the current generation as it learns the art of applied scientific inquiry and begins their careers during another downturn cycle in the petroleum industry. While I have my war stories, I try to focus on universal issues spanning generations. Our culture of diversity needs rigorous cultivation. It has progressed in some ways, but not in others.

Throughout this 40-plus-year journey, I give huge credit to my husband, Larry, who has supported me through thick and thin. We did not have children, a conscious choice in my late thirties abetted by modern pharmaceuticals and the turbulence in the oil industry at the time (refer to career-twist number four). We have shared our lives for over 38 years and look forward to doing so until we depart the earth.

Another bright light has been my small group of nine geoscience women friends, known as the Rockettes. We have been together for over twenty years. Our monthly luncheons only have two major rules: all topics (politics included) are fair game, and spouses are kindly reminded to disappear during lunch! As we have each twisted through our careers and are now retiring, we have supported each other with our shared experiences.

My career has been one of unpredictable twists and turns, traveling on many paths, with positive outcomes overall. My favorite saying has evolved to: "Opportunity favors the prepared mind."

Donna Schmidt Anderson was born in 1951 in Inglewood, California, in the L.A. Basin. She earned a B.A. in Earth Science and Geography with Highest Honors from California State University, Fullerton in 1974, an M.S. in geology from University of California, Los Angeles in 1980, and a PhD in Geology from Colorado School of Mines in 1997. She and her husband, Larry Anderson, live in Golden, Colorado.

Martha Oliver Withjack

In 1977, I received my PhD degree from Brown University, only the fourth woman to complete the doctoral program in geology from the ivy-league school. After graduation, I wanted a change from academia and opted to work in the petroleum industry—mind you, just for a few years. So, I gathered my belongings, drove to the oil patch of Tulsa, Oklahoma, and became the first woman geologist to join the research laboratory of Cities Service Oil Company. It was a big change for a young woman from New Jersey. I had to adapt to a new culture—clean up my "salty" language a bit, lessen my Jersey accent, and learn to appreciate Aggie jokes and the importance of football. I also needed to convince my male colleagues that, although I was a woman, I was a geologist just like them. Occasionally, I was denied opportunities considered too unpleasant for a woman or my ideas were not heard until repeated by a man. But, I am happy to say that most of my colleagues were wonderful and accepting. I'll never forget their mentorship and friendship.

Figure 13. Martha Withjack, 1989, field trip in Colorado. (Photo: Martha Withjack, Piscataway, New Jersey.)

I worked hard at the job, and within a few years, I was asked to give a technical presentation to senior management. It was an incredible opportunity, and I was very nervous. The talk was a great success and, afterwards, I was invited to join the managers for lunch at the Petroleum Club. There was one big, unanticipated problem—the Petroleum Club didn't allow women in the main dining area. To avoid further embarrassment, our group was escorted to a small adjoining dining room to have our lunch. Thankfully, times have changed, and women have become an accepted, and critical, part of the petroleum industry. It's hard to believe that less than forty years ago, women geologists were forbidden to become members of the Petroleum Club or, in fact, to even dine there. (Fig. 13)

In 2000, I did eventually return to academia after a long and enjoyable 23-year career in the petroleum industry. To my surprise, I discovered the academic world had not progressed as rapidly as the petroleum industry with respect to the acceptance and promotion of women. Fortunately, times are changing in academia too, and more women are becoming full professors and department leaders.

Martha Withjack was born in New Jersey in 1951. She earned her B.S. in 1973 from Rutgers University, her M.S. in 1975, and PhD in 1977 from Brown University. She lives with her husband, Jim in Piscataway, New Jersey.

Penny Webster-Scholten

Being a non-traditional student, returning to college after raising my family, I never expected that an oil company would find my maturity to be an asset. I had enrolled in my first geology course a few years before only because I needed a hard science on my class list. Suddenly, I was infatuated with the subject and enrolled in every geology course that was offered at both the community college that I first attended, Yavapai College, and later at Northern Arizona University (NAU).

Nearing completion of my master's degree in geology education, I began interviewing with the companies that visited the campus in search of new geologists. With one exception, this was a great experience. The one exception was a service company recruiter who was brutal in the interview, and I immediately realized what he was doing—trying to ruffle me! He started asking rapid-fire questions so I replied with rapid-fire answers. He was startled. He remarked that I'd be expected to have a few beers after work with some of the workers on occasion, and I said that I didn't see any problem with that. Besides, I liked beer.

At one point, he said, "Your grades are AWFULLY good. Why?"

I replied, "Because I worked AWFULLY hard."

He had no response to that but I could tell he was taken aback. I heard that a job offer was coming from them, but I had accepted a job by then, so I had no further contact.

I selected an offer from Cities Service Company after several on-site interviews with other companies. I was thrilled at the entire process of travel and the wining and dining; the feeling that they were interested in talking with me was a bonus I had not even imagined. If a brass band had been playing as I disembarked the plane in Tulsa, Oklahoma, I would not have been more thrilled at the future that lay ahead. I'll always remember the absolute joy I felt as I walked down the concourse toward my career in the petroleum industry.

Joining the training program at Cities Service in September 1982, I was eager to learn all I could yet concerned that my age might still be an impediment. As it turned out, the only real impediment arose with the imminent sale of Cities Service to Occidental Petroleum. The six-month training program was cut back to a four-month program, and the last day of training was the last day of employment! Two training programs that had been running nearly simultaneously were cancelled and all the trainees were terminated. All 42 of us were suddenly forced onto the interview circuit once again, and the competition was extremely intense because the industry slowdown had manifested itself in full force. Occidental only kept employees with 3 years of experience.

Before learning our fate, however, I had volunteered for a week of fieldwork in Nevada for the Basin Studies department at Cities Service. Participating in a soil-gas survey, my job one afternoon was as a lookout, watching for any sign of a strange man with a rifle who didn't want anyone near his property. Rumor had it that he had shot at people previously, but my field partner knew that samples we *definitely needed* were nearby. We parked our vehicle to serve as a bullet barrier between the man's front door and the sample locations a few hundred feet away. My job was to yell if I saw the front door move, so my partner could duck behind the vehicle if a gun barrel were pointed in our direction. My training hadn't really offered much in the way of crime prevention or avoidance, but I took my task seriously and watched and trembled ever so quietly! Eventually we emerged from the site, unharmed, samples intact, and drove off with a relieved satisfaction that we had done our job, albeit with trepidation. When I heard that geology was an exciting career, who would have thought how exciting it really could be?

As the final day of training approached at Cities Service, the job hunt continued. Fortuitously, the American Association of Petroleum Geologists (AAPG) advertised for a *Bulletin* editor, and when I was offered the job, I found myself ensconced as a scientific editor instead of as an industry petroleum geologist. My degrees and the training I had received at Cities Service became the basis for critiquing the writings and research of other geologists. Though not what I had planned originally, I found this new position to be a valuable learning process as the papers I was examining added new dimension to my geologic knowledge.

Nearly three years later, I learned of an opening for a technical editor/writer at Lawrence Livermore National Laboratory (LLNL) in California's Bay area. Accepting their offer, I left AAPG and continued my editorial efforts at LLNL until a geologist position opened in their Environmental Protection Department. I acted quickly and got the job.

Figure 14. Penny Webster-Scholten (1982) returned to college after raising her family, then entered the oil business with Cities Service. (Photo: Penny Webster-Scholten, Cedar City, Utah.)

I worked as a geologist, but was classified as an engineer at LLNL and prepared reports for various regulatory agencies, describing LLNL's status on environmental contamination issues related to our classification as a Superfund site. My field work included drilling water wells, collecting soil samples, performing soil-gas surveys, and preparing the resultant regulatory reports. And, when I became a project manager, I coordinated preparation of a 6000-page, 15-volume report defining our progress on environmental contamination and remediation at LLNL's high explosives test site near the San Joaquin Valley. The report has become a frequently cited, key compendium of data for the environmental industry, in general and LLNL's continuing environmental investigations, in particular.

What started as fulfilling a curriculum requirement at a community college detoured me into a career in the petroleum and environmental industries. When I retired in 1996, I've never regretted taking my first geology course so many years before, and I continue to marvel at the resulting opportunities that were available to m. The fact that I began my career 20 years after the average geologist, suggests that age need not be a deterrent to landing a career with exhilarating, pulse-pounding, yet satisfying adventure (Fig. 14). (See Betsy Campen, Chapter 13.)

Penny Webster-Scholten was born in 1940 in Los Angeles, California, and was awarded her bachelor's degree in geology from Northern Arizona University in 1982.

Marsha A. Green

I must admit, entering the oil business in 1975 was good timing. Upon graduating from Duke, the oil boom in Texas and Louisiana was taking off and the large oil companies were under increased pressure to add female geologists to their rosters. After numerous interviews and not any offers of a job, it was suggested to me by a peer that maybe I should try and get a job as a secretary at an oil company, you know, "just to get my foot in the door." Disappointed, and slightly offended, I soon was rewarded with offers from four major oil companies. I chose Gulf Oil Corporation in Houston, Texas, a good choice!

Starting at Gulf was quite an adjustment. Working for a business in a multi-generational setting, after a lifetime of academia is quite a transition. In addition, I was a "Yankee" from New York and a female, one of three in the Houston office. My first day of work, I'll never forget, I was informed in the nicest southern accent, "You're never really a Texan until you've been here two or more generations."

It was not meant to be insulting, just a statement of fact. Welcome to Texas.

I honestly don't even remember how I learned to do the job of exploration for new oil and gas reserves. I certainly didn't learn how to correlate a log at Duke. I was fortunate to be mentored by the elders of the department, more so than by my peers. The long-established geologists showed me patience and guidance, and reflecting on this connection, many years later, when I changed careers and became a physical therapist, I think the respect and comfort I felt with this generation led me to my preference for geriatric patients and their health issues.

Within the first six months at Gulf I was sent out to "sit a well" to "run" drilling samples and make a geologic sample log. It was a program for all new hires designed to introduce us to field operations and the whole scope of exploration. I learned about the "possum belly," a chambered metal container that slows the flow of drilling fluid before the shale shaker screen so the drill cuttings can be collected, the "monkey board" where the derrick man stands above the rig to pull pipe out of the hole, making a "trip" to pull the pipe out of or run it back in the hole, and acronyms like WOO – waiting on orders and never to cause a WOG – waiting on geologist because time is money.

The drive out to the rig was also an adventure. Of course, there was no GPS and no cell phones back then, just a map and instructions from the home office. Luckily, with Texas being so flat and nothing but wide open spaces, you usually could see the rig from a long way away. Then, for Gulf Coastal Plain wells there was the drive on the seemingly endless board road to get to the rig, hoping not to drive over a nail out in the middle of nowhere. The opportunity to go out on the rigs during the drilling and logging was an educational experience for someone like me, unfamiliar with the oil business in general. It made creating an oil or gas prospect a reality—the people involved, the equipment, the landscape affected, and the money spent.

As time went on, I found I really loved drawing maps. I loved reconstructing paleo-geomorphology and recreating environments of the past. Turning highs into lows, and lows into highs. Maximizing the potential acreage for the prospect, stacking multiple pay zones, and then calculating how much money it could be worth. It was like having a lottery ticket—until the lottery drawing! Meaning, until the well was drilled and logged—anything was possible.

I was meticulous about correlating every well log, mapping every potential sand, and scanning every scout card for clues of overlooked "shows." In the end, however, it seemed like all the management or investors wanted to see was the seismic line over the prospect and the telltale hot spot or anomaly. I was a good map maker. I was more artist than salesman and you needed to be a good salesman to seal the deal—not a personal strength, I admit. I remember presenting one prospect to potential investors and hearing the comment, "that's a pretty map." I doubt my male counterparts were complimented in those terms, but I took it as a positive. The decision to drill or not to drill seemed to rely more on economics at times, which is understandable. I had to remind myself that I was asking the company to invest thousands, upwards to millions, of dollars to drill a well based on an idea.

I am most grateful to Gulf Oil for providing me the opportunities it did as an exploration geologist. They were always respectful and supportive. They were generous with continuing education opportunities as well. I studied fluvial deposits in Fort Collins, Colorado; delta deposits in New Orleans, Louisiana; and turbidites in coastal California. One specific opportunity of note was when I was asked to go out on an offshore drilling well in the Gulf of Mexico. The situation called for a paleontologist to run samples (describe lithology and identify key fossils), and because Gulf's paleontologist was a female, and Gulf wouldn't send her out solo, I was asked go to along and while there, to make a geology sample log.

The trip out in February, by boat in choppy seas, was pretty rough to say the least. Upon arriving at the rig (hours and hours later), the only way up onto the drilling platform was on what I called "the donut." The donut was suspended down to the boat on a cable; we stood on the OUTSIDE of the donut and we were hoisted up by the rig's crane—I can still see the big grin on the crane operator's face. Anyway, we made it. The crew couldn't have been nicer to the novelty females on board. We were given the captain's quarters and served liver and onions for dinner

Figure 15. Marsha Green, 1978, in a Gulf Oil advertisement published by Time Magazine, *as well as many other magazines that year. (Magazine cover:* Time Magazine, *October 9, 1978, copy provided by Marsha Green.)*

(my first and last time for that). Luckily, the weather improved and we took a helicopter back to land. Unfortunately, it was a dry hole, but a memorable experience none the less.

Perhaps my most memorable experience during my years with Gulf, involved their ad campaign: "Gulf people: meeting the challenge." I was fortunate to have a small gas discovery right around the time Gulf was having their diversity campaign. They chose me and my story to run in a variety of national magazines and newspapers. (Fig. 15) My family was thrilled, as was I. My 15 minutes of fame came, and went, at an early age and I could check that off my bucket list (also see Susan Cage, Chapter 12).

I left Gulf after about five years to continue my profession with a small independent oil company and eventually ended up consulting on my own. I was still enjoying the creativity of searching for that perfect prospect but was well aware of the reality of the future. The shift towards computerized mapping (no fun in that for me) and the increased demand for expensive seismic confirmation precluded my continuation in the business as a consultant. But, all's well that ends well. I made a very successful transition to physical therapy, specializing in geriatrics, and retained fond memories of my earlier sixteen years as an "explorer."

Last year, 25 years after I had drawn my last contour map and colored my last cross-section, I decided to purge my old files and destroy most of my exploration files. I had kept them for years—just in case. It made me heartsick. Those maps were like old friends, some were works of art. The countless hours spent collecting the data, analyzing it, and creating an idea, most of which were never even seen by anyone, will always be a source of pride. I did keep a few though—just in case.

Marsha Green was born in Otisville, New York, in 1951. She earned her bachelor's degree in geology from the State University of New York at Oneonta, followed by a master's in geology from Duke University in 1975. She retired from physical therapy in 2013.

Janet Bauder Thornburg

My career is distinguished by some unorthodox diversions. Between 1973 and 2016, I worked a total of 17 years as a petroleum geologist and took career breaks on three occasions. During the 1980s, I took a break to earn a PhD because I wanted to work as a research geologist in the petroleum industry. In 1995, I chose to become a full-time mother following the full-term stillbirth of my first daughter in 1993 and the birth of my second daughter in 1994. After the death of my husband in 2000, I shifted my focus to pastoral care by volunteering as a lay minister at St. Luke's Hospital in Houston. Thanks to an effective professional network, I secured satisfying jobs in petroleum geology after each of these breaks!

My career began as I was finishing my master's degree at Stanford University. The combination of the 1973 Affirmative Action measures and the 1974 oil embargo created extraordinary opportunities for women. I interviewed with five oil companies (Chevron, Mobil, Conoco, Amoco, Exxon) during the on-campus job fair in Fall 1974. All five recruiters were male geologists. Two of them were memorable because of the inappropriate questions they asked,

Exxon recruiter, "If Exxon hires you, will you quit after you marry and start a family?"

Conoco recruiter, "Imagine that you're a contestant at the Miss America Pageant. How would you respond when asked to describe your career aspirations?"

I confess that I actually enjoyed answering the second question because my childhood girlfriend and I liked to play Miss America. We each assumed the roles of semifinalists and took turns winning the pageant. I thought, "I've got this!"

All five companies flew me to their headquarters for final interviews and subsequently offered me jobs in the city of my choice, Denver. I accepted Conoco's offer because their one-year training program provided on-the-job training in geophysics and geology, as well as numerous in-house training courses—not because I thought I would be Miss America.

Shortly after I accepted Conoco's offer in January 1975, the chief geologist, Max Pitcher, invited me to attend their Modern Carbonate Field Course in Belize in April 1975. Although I was still a full-time student at Stanford,

I jumped at the opportunity. A geology student from Rice University and I were the only women and the only pre-employees who attended the course. The other 16 participants were all men who had finished their master's degrees and were working at Conoco. Some of the men questioned the fairness of graduate students attending a highly desirable field course before even starting employment at Conoco. However, I was grateful for the opportunity and took advantage of it to collect carbonate sediment samples for the Marine Geology course I was currently taking at Stanford. This project earned me a perfect score on the resultant term paper, "Texture and Composition of Sediments from Columbus Reef, Belize."

Early in my Conoco experience (1976-77), I worked for ten months in their Production Office in Casper, Wyoming. The Casper office had a large contingent of petroleum engineers and only three geologists: two men and me. The three of us monitored the drilling wells and took turns going to rig sites to determine core points, orient cores as they emerged from the wellbore, and sample and describe the cores onsite. It was hard work at all hours of the day and night. As a female geologist, I occasionally benefited from preferential treatment at the wellsite. The "roughnecks" (rig workers) often rinsed cutting samples for me before bagging them, and then delivered the samples to the doorstep of the tool-pusher's trailer for me to describe. The male geologists had to retrieve and rinse the cutting samples themselves.

Another distinctive Conoco experience was my selection as their "poster child" for Affirmative Action. They wanted to include photos of a female geologist in their publications and sent a professional photographer to shoot photos of me working at a wellsite in the Powder River Basin. The two male geologists in the Casper office teased me good-naturedly about the special attention I received. The resultant photos appeared in two Conoco publications: the 1976 Annual Report and a 1979 booklet, "Conoco: A World of Energy."

Early on, I realized the importance of role models and the setbacks which one could encounter without them. Growing up in Oakland, California, I didn't know any college graduates, men or women, who worked for corporations. My parents and most of their friends were high school graduates at best. My father was a linotype machinist, and my mother was a housewife who raised five children. I was a senior in high school before I met anyone with a PhD. Hence, I grew up without role models for the geology career that I pursued.

All my science professors at Stanford University were males. Although I became acquainted with some female PhD candidates, they were not oriented toward industry. Instead, they aspired to and achieved careers in academia or at the U.S. Geological Survey. When I took summer field geology in 1973, five of the 15 students were women and only two of us became petroleum geologists. During my onsite interviews with oil companies in 1974, the only female geologists I met were recent graduates in the initial year of their careers; there were no older female "mentors" or "role models."

I still believe the absence of female professional role models presented a challenge during those early career days, for me and for other women. I know I made strategic errors because I didn't know the unwritten rules for prospering in a corporate environment. Less important, but equally mystifying, I had no clue how to "dress for success." In an attempt to distinguish myself from the secretaries in the Denver office, I bought a suit comprised of a prim white blouse, a black ribbon bow tie, a navy-blue skirt, and a matching blazer. Within a week of my purchase, another young female geologist in our office wore the identical blouse, tie, and suit to work. Our fledgling attempt to mimic male professional attire was especially awkward on days when we both wore the navy-blue suit.

Although I worked with no well-established female geoscientists at Conoco, I eventually encountered two memorable role models, Esther Magathan and Robbie Gries (Chapter 13), in the late 1970s through RMAG (Rocky Mountain Association of Geologists). In the 1980s, I became aware of Doris Curtis' illustrious career through AAPG and the Houston Geological Society(HGS). I was so grateful to Doris Curtis (Chapter 10) for responding to my request for résumé help when I wanted to reenter the work force after finishing my PhD. She graciously agreed to meet with me in Houston and provided invaluable guidance. Later in the 1990s, I was fortunate to work with Emily Stoudt and Susan Longacre (Chapter 12) at Texaco's research lab in Houston. Both had raised families while remaining fully engaged in their careers as petroleum geologists. Finally, I could see that role models were being developed. The next generation would have them. (Fig. 16)

Figure 16. Janet Thornburg, an instructor for Clastics field trip for Texaco, near Mineral Wells, Tx. 1991. (Photo: Janet Bauder Thornburg, Ann Arbor, Michigan.)

My international work for Texaco was scientifically satisfying and culturally intriguing. Most studies were conducted in Houston, where I applied my expertise in sedimentology and petrography to evaluate sandstone samples from South America and Southeast Asia. However, my most memorable assignments took me to exotic foreign locations: Paraguay and China. The cultural exchanges during the China trip were especially fascinating. In 1991, Texaco sent me to China with two male colleagues - a reservoir engineer and a facilities engineer - to evaluate a proposed joint production venture with the Chinese National Oil Company (CNPC). The trip included one day in Beijing to meet with officials from CNPC and seven days in Panjin to gather data on Gao Sheng, an onshore oil field in Liaohe Basin. I recorded my impressions and adventures daily in a journal. These entries provide a snapshot of China during the early stage of oil and gas trade and investment with the West. The following excerpt from the journal typifies my rewarding experiences.

July 22, 1991

I've spent the last two days describing core, and have one more day to go. The core storage facility is far better than the Quonset hut in Paraguay. However, the set-up for describing core is worse. They don't have tables to set the core boxes on; hence they lay the boxes in rows on the floor. Bending, stooping, or kneeling all day is tiring. The weather has been humid and warm; hence I get pretty sweaty and dirty. One more day of this is all that I can handle.

A very nice Chinese geologist stays at the core facility while I work. Although he doesn't speak English, we can communicate to some degree with "sign language." Yesterday when I finished work, he insisted upon giving me a ride back to the hotel on his bicycle! I couldn't explain to him that I like to walk; so, I accepted his kind offer. People carry passengers on their bikes by having a flat metal frame attached to the rear wheel. The passenger sits sideways on the bike. The two of us must have been quite a sight...the sweaty, dirty American lady with a sweat headband and backpack, perched behind a Chinese cyclist. The breeze as we rode was quite refreshing.

Today an interpreter, Madame Duan, accompanied me to the core facility. Late in the afternoon she came over to chat as I worked. I was tired by then, so welcomed the break. She confided to me that after the first official meeting in Panjin, several of the Chinese scientists commented about the way I speak: "Mrs. Janet speaks English like a bird; it sounds so pretty." I'm pleased that they like the sound of my English; heaven knows I butcher their Chinese names when I try to pronounce them. In retrospect, I can understand why my English sounded pleasing. The other four Texaco [people] include three Chinese (Randy, Y.M., and Heidi) who speak English with heavy Chinese accents, and Charlie who has a classic Texas drawl.

The tendency for the Chinese to call me Mrs. or Madame Janet probably is due to their way of writing names. On a Chinese business card, the surname appears first and the given names second. For example, the interpreter, Madame Duan, is named: Duan (last name) Zhi Hao (first names). The Chinese have remained quite formal when it comes to names; they even refer to one another as "Mr. Wong" or "Mr. Chang." Hence, I'm beginning to wonder if they think my last name is 'Janet.'

The Chinese are very likable people. I will miss their cheerful, smiling faces.

My interactions with foreign nationals sometimes led to misunderstandings because of our cultural differences. Indonesian geoscientists came regularly to Texaco in Houston for advanced training. In all but one instance, these Muslim male professionals seemed quite comfortable having me as their mentor and/or teacher. The exception was a gentleman who attended the Clastics Field Course that I co-taught with two male colleagues. This Muslim man never looked me in the eye, and he addressed his questions to the male instructors. At the time, I thought that his behavior showed low regard for a woman's professional abilities. However, I subsequently learned that avoidance of eye contact can signify a Muslim man's respect for women who are not members of his family. Learning about other cultures is the best part of working internationally!

Life sometimes delivers unexpected events which change your career. For me, such occasions did not end my career, but altered the course and added rewards when rewards were sorely needed.

Until my mid-30s, career goals took precedence over starting a family. When I finally felt ready to have a child, I had difficulty becoming pregnant. My first pregnancy ended in stillbirth at 37 weeks in August 1993; this inconceivable loss forever changed my priorities. When I gave birth to a healthy baby girl 16 months later, I chose to leave Texaco to fully savor motherhood. Most of my co-workers understood and supported my choice. However, several colleagues (male and female) implied that my decision to be a fulltime mother was a waste of education and/or a betrayal of the feminist movement.

While my daughter was my greatest joy and first priority, I still enjoyed geology and wanted to make professional contributions. During the late 1990s, I volunteered with AAPG and the Association for Women Geoscientists (AWG). When my daughter was in preschool, I worked two days weekly as a geologic consultant for Cossey & Associates in Houston.

I disengaged from geologic activities in 1999 when my passion shifted from geoscience to spirituality and psychology. Shortly thereafter, my husband was diagnosed with terminal cancer and died in 2000. The spiritual and psychological resources that I had begun to develop helped me to cope after his death. As part of my healing process, I felt a desire to help others in extreme need. In 2003, I completed a 14-week training program to become a volunteer lay chaplain at St. Luke's Episcopal Hospital in Houston; for the next five years, I had the privilege of providing pastoral care to patients.

The recession in 2008 prompted me to return to the work force. Rather than seek a job in petroleum exploration, I sought an industry position which would better utilize my newly-acquired interpersonal skills. Fortuitously, my close friends, Gillian Apps and Frank Peel, helped me to land the ideal job by critiquing my résumé and introducing me to Nautilus World Ltd., a U.K.-based company that provides training in petroleum geoscience and engineering. Coincidentally, the three Nautilus managers who interviewed me had children the same age as my daughter. These fathers appreciated my choice to take time as a fulltime mother and enabled me to work part-time with full benefits. I could return to work and be available for my teenage daughter before and after school.

From 2009 to 2015, I was a Senior Geologist at Nautilus in Houston where I identified topics that were needed in petroleum training programs, recruited experts to teach courses, assisted instructors with course development, and, especially fun, helped to run field courses. It was a joy to reconnect with geologic acquaintances, and I had delightful interactions on field trips with geoscientists from throughout the world. The timing of my retirement in January 2015 was perfect; it came at the onset of the precipitous drop in oil prices and the resultant reduction in Nautilus courses.

Yes, my path has been unusual, but the constancy has been geology, personal growth, family, and friends. A full and satisfying path, indeed.

Janet Bauder Thornburg was born in Oakland, California in 1953 and received her bachelor's and master's degrees from Stanford University in 1975 and 1976, respectively. She earned her PhD from the University of Colorado Boulder in 1990. She is retired and lives in Ann Arbor, Michigan.

Miriam Israel Winsten

Miriam Israel, born in New York City, spent her summers on the New York City beaches where the tides and ever-changing shoreline profiles impressed upon her the dynamic nature of earth's systems. She was working on the high school newspaper when a friend told her about the University of Iowa program for high school students to learn about geology. Miriam thought it sounded "cool" and applied for and was accepted to the highly competitive six-week program. She left the Northeast for the first time, got to see the Rockies, learned about geology, and did water and soil field work. The experience prompted Miriam to choose a major in geology, even though at that time everyone thought she was not so much "cool" as "crazy."

Miriam pursued her undergraduate degree at Binghamton University. The first, best career advice Miriam Israel received was in her junior year. A Texaco recruiter was at the department to interview prospective students. The over six-foot tall Texan was a caricature of a Texas oil man clad in sport coat with suede patches on the sleeves, big belt buckle, and cowboy boots. He advised an impressionable Miriam, "I'd offer you a job right now but if you go to graduate school, you'll have more opportunity and make more money in two years."

Miriam listened to the advice, graduated with her B.A. in 1980 and enrolled at Bowling Green State University, Ohio, for her masters in low temperature geochemistry.

Looking back at an industry in which geochemistry has played a critical part in unconventional resource plays, Miriam marvels at the foreshadowing of that Texaco career advice to continue with graduate school. She still receives calls about the research published with faculty and fellow graduate students on "The Geochemistry of the Dakota Sandstone and Adjacent Shales" in the San Juan Basin.

Figure 17. Miriam Israel Winsten started her career with a handful of women in college and now works for a company as diverse as New York City, where she was born, Schlumberger. (Photo: Miriam Winsten, Houston, Texas.)

Miriam interned with Marathon Oil in Casper, Wyoming, and received offers to work with Marathon in Houston, Texas. She graduated the year after the first open Gulf of Mexico (GOM) lease sales when all the oil companies were beefing up their offshore GOM groups. Miriam seized the opportunity to work with Marathon's newly-formed GOM group and was with the first wave of women to go offshore to work on exploration rigs. She took the obligatory, offshore survival school, but it was the Professional Information session that gave her real insight to offshore hazards. Again, it was a long-tall Texan who would provide the advice, "There's a laundry you can use, but, little lady, don't send your pretty underthings to the laundry because they'll never come back."

Once on the rig in the 1980s, Miriam recalled, "I went to the galley for something to eat and, of course, I was the only woman. The guy sitting next to me commented, 'I see you're married. Does your husband know you're out here?' (Fig. 17) Without skipping a beat, I replied, 'No, I sneak out here for a good time.' After that, everyone on the rig knew I was okay."

Figure 18. Miriam on the Diamond M. Hunter rig, 1984, Gulf of Mexico. (Photo: Miriam Winsten.)

Miriam's husband also worked with Marathon and after eight years they were transferred back to Findlay, Ohio, with two young children in tow. There were no upstream technical people in this location, so she started a second career—teaching, and in an entirely new aspect of geology and chemistry, hazardous materials management. She was an adjunct faculty member at the University of Findlay, and a consultant. The opportunity to teach and inspire the next generation has been dear to her.

Miriam and husband eventually made their way back to Houston where she would again work the Gulf of Mexico, this time, the "Deep Water" of western shelf regional geology where the next big plays were to be. Her reintroduction to the petroleum industry was during the era when companies had made or were making the leap from paper to workstations for geologic and seismic interpretation. Miriam went from her Mac SE30 for personal use to learning workstations, the geology of the "Deep Gulf", and all the technology that went with it.

The third phase of her career began when Schlumberger offered Miriam an opportunity to use her geology and geophysical skills globally with the challenging "Deep Water" environment. She quickly moved from technical to supervisory to management roles and served as DCS North Gulf Coast Operations Manager with a diverse team of experts in geological, geophysical and engineering consulting, data services, geomechanics, borehole seismic, and engineering solutions.

Outreach and education reentered Miriam's career when she developed Schlumberger's intern program with the University of Houston's Bauer School of Business Program for Excellence in Selling. She also managed a team to develop an interactive exhibit at George Bush Presidential Library and Museum called "Offshore Drilling: The promise of Discovery" that highlights the evolving processes and technology used to explore and produce oil and gas in the offshore environment. This display is currently housed at the OceanStar Rig Museum, Galveston, Texas.

As the Director of Global Social Responsibility and Principal Geologist for Schlumberger, she reflected on her career, "This company has employees from 140 nationalities and operates in 85 countries around the globe. The diversity is terrific. It is remarkable how you start your career with a handful of women in college and progress to working with a company as diverse as the city you were born in." (Fig. 18)

Miriam considers her current boss, Dan Domeracki, as the best mentor in her career. Dan stands out in his support of women and diversity in the geosciences. She said, "Working for Dan and a company like Schlumberger, you learn to think "outside the box." It is creativity and innovation that can take you to the next level."

Miriam Winsten and Dan Domeracki have enjoyed representing Schulumberger and being a part of AAPG's Imperial Barrel Award and the Women's Networking Reception at the Annual Conference and Exhibition. Miriam Israel Winsten is an AAPG Certified Petroleum Geologist, and a licensed Professional Geoscientist in the State of Texas. She is active in i-Educate USA, and the greater Houston Partnership.

Miriam Israel Winsten was born in New York City in 1958 and earned her B.A. from Binghamton University (1980) and M.S. from Bowling Green State University (1982). Miriam Winsten married her college sweetheart, lives in Houston, Texas, and has two children.

Denise Mruk Cox

I had my astrological chart read when I was in 11th grade as part of a class on "Near and Far Eastern Studies." I can still see the woman's cursive handwriting in light blue ink that said, "You enjoy working with the Earth." At the time, I thought, "That makes sense." My sisters and I enjoyed helping our mom create terraced rock gardens on the hill behind our house. I didn't know then that those field trips to collect interesting fossil laden (Devonian) rocks from the Finger Lakes region of New York would turn into a career as a geologist.

Earth science was not an elective in our schools and I had no idea that geology could be a career. I remember while trying to choose a college major, a nursery rhyme kept repeating in my head, "...doctor, lawyer, merchant, thief..." None of those seemed quite right, so I sought out the advice of a high school teacher. Mr. Rainer taught geography and was as passionate about the subject as he was about teaching. He clearly loved his work. He suggested I take classes that would get me involved with the Middle East because of its growing role in global economics. I graduated in 1976; OPEC was gathering strength and the oil embargo was soon to follow.

I attended the State University of New York at Binghamton (now Binghamton University), and having always done well in science and math, I signed up for those prerequisite courses and, as recommended, took Arabic as one of my electives. After my first year, I was fortunate my Arabic professor recognized that I was still searching for direction and told me I should take a geology class because "the Middle East means oil" and geologists are needed to develop the resource.

Dr. Paul Enos taught introductory geology and his lectures demonstrated that geology is a blend of science and art. The physical principles that control sedimentation could be explained either by flow velocity equations or artistically drawn as a fining upward sequence; data points could be contoured by triangulation or the art of "drawing wispy lines." I discovered geology is a science that takes you outside, is intuitive, and doesn't seem like work at all. The spring of my sophomore year, I had found my major.

I had no idea what I would do with a degree in geology until I heard a presentation by Binghamton alumna and AAPG Visiting Geologist Susan Landon (this Chapter). Susan was an Amoco (now BP) exploration geologist and in her tailored tweed suit was the model of a late 70s career woman. She gave a talk about petroleum exploration geology. As she defined a prospect—paleontology, petrology, and sedimentation were no longer lab exercises but useful tools for exploration. The next semester I signed up for a course in petroleum geology.

I have another memory from that lecture. One of the geophysics professors, known for his lack of tact, asked, "Susan, when you were here in school, I remember you were just a 'bug-picker.' How is it you were able to become so successful?" The audience groaned but Susan handled him with self-assured charm and used the question to explain oil company training programs.

I added a senior thesis to my heavy load of geology courses so I could graduate with a B.S. rather than a B.A. in geology. Despite my late start with geology, I graduated in 1980 with a B.S. with honors and was the recipient of the Glenn G. Bartle Award for Excellence in Geology. At an awards luncheon, that same geophysics professor with no tact said to my brilliant, but very humble father, "You're just a factory worker? How is it Denise is so smart?" My father's eyebrows shot up, my jaw dropped, and my advisor standing near us exclaimed, "How can you even ask that?" I started growing a thicker layer of skin that day.

That spring, one of the professors in the department said he would set up an interview for me with an acquaintance of his in Denver. I remember listening to him speak on the phone call, the friendly male banter, and him expressing surprise and repeating the words "Junior Geologist." The interview was set, and I had already planned to be in Denver for AAPG's annual convention.

But when I got there, there was no job. Set back, but determined, I printed out copies of my one-page résumé and knocked on doors. I quickly realized that my condensed undergraduate geology degree qualified me to be a mudlogger, and if I wanted to work as a geologist, I would need a master's degree.

Fate and my fledgling network intervened with my decision to head back to school. A geologist in my apartment complex, who rode the bus to work with a government (OSHA) safety engineer, heard that the U.S. Geological Survey at the Denver Federal Center was hiring. Résumé in hand, I went to the General Administration Office and overheard a woman talking about the need for a geologist for a coring project. I promptly handed her my résumé, did my best to speak more knowledgably than I was about core description and got an interview and the job!

Soon I was a "Physical Science Technician" with the USGS Uranium and Thorium Branch on a nine-well coring project in the San Juan Basin. It was as much mudlogging and core slabbing as it was core description and translation into quantitative fluvial facies units. I had two realizations with that job: first, you could actually see stratigraphic relationships on laterally extensive New Mexico outcrops compared to the vegetated road cuts in upstate New York, and, second, I *loved* wellsite work.

Continuing to look for petroleum opportunities, a year later I went to the Chief of the USGS Oil and Gas Branch, Peter Scholle, and asked to be transferred to his group. He told me about a project in the Guadalupe Mountains in West Texas and the rock work that needed to be done. My enthusiasm and interest in carbonates must have shown and during our discussion he said, "I can't teach what you have" referring to my energy level, or what some would call "passion," for geology. I would hear this from colleagues throughout my career.

He arranged for me to be a student volunteer to work the logistics for an AAPG Field Course he co-taught with Robert Halley to the Guadalupe and Sacramento Mountains. That trip would cement a lasting interest in the Permian Basin and carbonate pore systems.

I went back to school for my master's at the University of Colorado, and finished my thesis in 1985 on the diagenesis of the Capitan Formation in McKittrick Canyon, West Texas. Part of my graduate work included a seminar series on depositional models in petroleum exploration and production. This series brought in world-renowned geologists to lecture on clastic and carbonate depositional models and was offered in the evening so many local oil company people participated. I took the course because I wanted to learn more about applied petroleum geoscience; but the bonus was learning the importance of networking.

My role model for networking was my Aunt Rosie. She had worked as a waitress at the Mark Twain Hotel in Elmira, New York. The restaurant was a popular stopover for businessmen, and she observed that the most successful men (and the best tips) came from those who were the best connected. She would pontificate, "It's not what you know, it's who you know." Then adamantly stabbing the table with her arthritic index finger she would repeat, "I don't care what you say, it's WHO YOU KNOW." I was about six the first time I heard that speech. At that age, I didn't know anyone, so being the precocious child I was, I argued back, "But don't you have to know something to be worth knowing?"

It was networking in the seminar series that lead to my first job working for an oil company. Paul Crevello, a Marathon Oil geologist in the class, was planning to do field work on the Jurassic carbonates in Morocco. He was looking for a field assistant, preferably a carbonate geologist who spoke French and Arabic. Finally, those two years of Arabic paid off! I spent three scorching months in the High Atlas Mountains of Morocco measuring sections, lugging samples, and catering to the whims of an oil company research geologist. I never complained because I was getting a "boots on the ground" education in carbonate stratigraphy. Maintaining a positive attitude and further developing an interest in carbonate diagenesis led to part-time work as a reservoir geologist at Marathon Oil's Denver Research Center. I worked on Gulf Coast Jurassic carbonates by day and my thesis by night.

The Denver Research Center (DRC) had two advantages for a graduate student: interesting cores displayed in the Geological Services Building, and, visiting prominent geoscientists who gave talks, taught short courses, or conducted research. Lloyd Pray was visiting from the University of Wisconsin and we had a spirited discussion about diagenesis and its relation to relative sea level fluctuations in the Guadalupe Mountains. He picked up the phone and called a contact at Exxon Research and said they had to interview me. Alarms went off in my head based on my disappointing undergraduate experience. But the next week, I received a phone call followed by a letter from Exxon that set up an interview. Unlike my previous experience, this time the interviewing company made the travel arrangements—including a travel advance!

My first interview of the two-day process was dinner on Sunday evening with one interviewer. He confessed that he had been in the field all weekend and was tired. I took the hint, kept the conversation light, and asked more questions than he did. At the end, he said, "Thank you for making the interview easy." It was good advice that I pass along to students today.

The next day started with a presentation of my thesis work followed by a full day of interviews. Unsure of how conservative to dress, I donned my tailored suit and low heeled shoes, twisted my long hair into a bun, put on my glasses, and went to the talk. The talk and the interviews went well. Feeling emboldened, the second day I let my hair down, wore my contacts, and was more casual. In retrospect, being myself and "making the interview easy" probably had as much to do with getting the offer to work at Exxon Research as my technical knowledge.

Soon after the Exxon interview, Marathon's Research Center had their annual review with corporate management. I didn't know any of the Houston management but tried to introduce myself and talk about the fascinating reservoir geology of the Yates field, Marathon's "Crown Jewel." I was standing near the bar set up in the conference room—this was 1985 and liquor could still be served in the office—talking with a Houston geophysicist and he introduced me to Bill Stenzel. He told Bill, "We can sure use a girl like this in the company." Stenzel was William K. Stenzel, the Yates Field geologist who testified during the unitization hearings! We talked Yates geology, and that summer when I obtained my master's, I was made a fulltime offer at Marathon's Research Center. Exxon's offer came at the same time. I chose to stay in Denver with my colleagues at Marathon.

After I was hired fulltime, the DRC got a new Assistant Director from Wyoming. He called all the geologists in for interviews about our research. When I entered his office, he was leaning back in his chair—his large belt buckle competing with his girth, his cowboy boots on the oversized management desk—and smoking a cigar. His opening statement was, "You're a pretty girl, (inhales deeply on the cigar) and I don't like pretty girls. I'll be watching you." He proceeded to talk more about himself than DRC research and I left not knowing if I was on probation or if my colleagues were playing a practical joke on me. I discovered later he made similar statements about physical appearance to some of the men, too!

The DRC also had some of the petroleum industry's most respected geoscientists and engineers, many who became valuable mentors for the new employees. The one mentor who stands out for me was John Steinmetz, a Gulf Coast micropaleontologist (and future State Geologist of Indiana). He explained corporate policies, monthly reports, trip reports, performance reviews, and performance planning. I would discover later that keeping a written record of my work goals and accomplishments would make a significant difference in my career.

Unfortunately, there were a few who were not as kind or helpful. One well-published male geologist was particularly caustic, and spoke openly with demeaning language about one of the established female geoscientists. She assured me that his words simply meant she was doing a good job, and that he must feel threatened. He was equally rude to younger geologists. As an example, we were in the auditorium listening to a project presentation by a young woman. When she asked for feedback on her presentation he said, "I don't know, I couldn't listen, I was too busy looking at you."

Figure 19. Denise Mruk Cox, dressed for success in the field or in the office. (Photo: Denise Cox, Panama City, Florida.)

Six months after I was hired, oil price plummeted to $10 a barrel and I faced my first round of layoffs. I watched as the ranks of the DRC were decimated. I told myself I kept my job because I was working on one of Marathon's biggest fields. But looking back, it may have been because my work was well-documented.

In 1988, I asked for a transfer to the Midland, Texas, production office to work in "development." I had been traveling to West Texas for field work and core runs in the heart of the oil patch. I wanted to learn more about field operations, and to apply new technology to development projects.

My first meeting with the Midland Exploration Manager was intimidating. He sat in his enormous leather chair, which had a seat that defied any proper posture, and spoke with a clenched jaw, "Coming from the Research Center, I expect you to hit the ground running." I sat there in my 1980s "dress for success" suit and felt a pang of fear. I was knowledgeable about reservoir rocks and fluid flow through porous media, but still quite naïve about exploration and production operations (Fig. 19).

I ramped up my learning curve by "making rounds." I asked the development geologists and engineers what they were working on and made notes of the maps, cross sections, seismic, reserves, budgets, and AFE's. I discovered people loved to be asked about their work; to use an oil patch term, they "kicked off flowing" with information. I also went out on every core and logging job I could. It made me very popular during holidays. In addition to on-the-job training, I had developed an understanding of the skills of the other geoscientists.

I became what is now termed a "connector." I knew what person "A" was doing and how it might help person "B", if only "C" would provide data. This knowledge became very important as the late 1980s ushered in reservoir characterization projects using multidisciplinary teams. Many 80s era oil companies were very militaristic, with hierarchical chains of command. Geologists reported to geologists and engineers to engineers; they did not have cross-discipline working relationships. Multidisciplinary teams were a major change. Being recognized as a "connector" led to me being selected as one of the team leaders for Midland's first multidisciplinary reservoir characterization project.

I loved my new job, especially working with engineers as I had done at the Research Center. But I was unaccustomed to being called "Sugar," "Honey," and "Dear." I certainly never before had heard anyone say, "You're the type of person who should be having babies!" Conversational sexism was more blatant in comparison to Denver, but I was in West Texas. To get along, I chose to interpret their speech and mannerisms as compliments rather than affronts.

There were, however, actual instances of harassment. The first was unwanted notes and comments from an individual to several women in the office, including me. Everyone said he was harmless and to ignore him. We went out of our way avoie him and and minimize contact. We were acutely aware of harassment because of the Anita Hill sexual harassment hearings when Clarence Thomas was being confirmed for the Supreme Court. I was on a coring job at Yates Field and parked on the north side of the location in the shade and listened with rapt attention to the hearings in my car, as well as later that evening in the camp house. I remember thinking, "I know how she feels." Things are said, but you want to keep in good favor for your career, so you laugh and go along. At some point, it goes too far and then you're in a bind. Certain behaviors were unacceptable, but you didn't report them because, in the early 90s, it would have harmed the accusers' reputation and career more than the offenders'.

Another instance was not sexual, but psychological. An individual sniped at women behind their backs and when management was not present, openly made derogatory comments about them at meetings. He referred to women he did not like as stupid, dismissed their work, and made them miserable; several quit. Job assignments took us to different groups, and years later one of the men who worked with us asked why we put it with it. I could only reply, "Why did *you* let him get away with it?"

Where I didn't experience any discrimination was on the wellsite. From the company man to the rig hands, there was mutual respect. My wellsite mentor said to always bring food and soft drinks to share on location, and I did. If I was staying on location, I would be invited to join their breakfasts—I enjoyed some of the finest home-made breakfast burritos and fresh salsa imaginable.

Overall, my 15 years in Midland were some of the best times of my career. The West Texas outcrops, subsurface geology, and the people who worked it were exceptional. We worked with the West Texas Geological Society and Permian Basin SEPM to organize symposia, field trips, short courses, and core workshops. We participated in some of the first reservoir characterization and enhanced recovery projects, deciphered oil and water co-production from fractured reservoirs, and, witnessed the birth of unconventional reservoirs. I continued to work with the Research Center (renamed the Petroleum Technology Center) and the Bureau of Economic Geology beta testing new logging tools, helping build 3D reservoir models, and introducing remote computer monitoring and 3D visualization of horizontal drilling operations to the Midland office.

Figure 20. Denise and Kurt Cox, Victoria Glacier, Lake Louise, Alberta, Canada. She always knew she would be married in hiking boots and pearls. (Photo: Denise Cox.)

And, Midland is where I met my husband, Kurt Cox. Kurt worked for Chevron, and we had an agreement that we would not work the same areas nor would we talk about specific projects of our companies. Kurt and I were both avid outdoors people and were married on the Victoria Glacier, above Lake Louise in Alberta, Canada (Fig. 20). When I returned to the office, the Magnolia Petroleum article, "Help or Handicap?" (see Chapter 12) was posted outside my door. I laughed and changed my name plate to Mrs. Kurt Cox. More telling about perception related to marital status, the wife of an engineer I worked with said, "I'm so glad you're married; now I don't have to worry when you travel with my husband."

Midland is also where I began to develop leadership skills. I was asked to submit my name for a supervisor opening and I said no. There were several factors, but mainly I had doubts about my readiness. I realize now that when someone approaches you with a leadership opportunity, you *are* ready; they see leadership traits in you that you may not. This is another piece of advice I like to share.

Even though I declined the opportunity within Marathon, outside of work I began to take on more leadership roles with local and national geoscience committees. These skills were greatly enhanced when Bill Morgan asked me to co-chair the AAPG Grants-in-Aid (GIA) Committee. Bill was a great mentor and introduced me to AAPG's movers and shakers who in turn helped me expand the committee to increase domestic and international representation. GIA volunteer work led to a chain-reaction of committee chair and manager appointments, and eventually to serving as Secretary on the AAPG Executive Committee. GIA was also the reason I joined the AAPG Foundation and established a grant in honor of my family.

In 2002, Kurt resigned from Chevron and started Storm Energy, Ltd. A Marathon job opening came available in Denver and with Kurt mobile, I applied. In a whirlwind two weeks after interviewing, I was in Denver working the Pennaco coalbed methane acquisition in the Powder River Basin, Wyoming. The contrast of the Pennaco office with the Midland office was striking. The employees were younger, the percentage of women higher, and my new boss expressed that he was happy with my work. The technical team was working 24-7 to understand and develop the coalbed asset and we felt confident we could develop the project. Unfortunately, Marathon's corporate office made the decision to consolidate the production offices in Houston. So, one exhausting year after moving to Denver, we would be faced with a decision to move to Houston. Most the office chose not to. I commuted from Denver for a year before I, too, resigned.

I went to work as a consultant for iReservoir with former Denver Research Center engineers and learned more about building 3D reservoir models for enhanced oil recovery and "unconventional projects." But then Marathon's Aberdeen office called and asked me to consult on a coalbed methane project in the U.K.—it was an opportunity I couldn't pass up.

And, once again, I air-commuted to work: three weeks on, one week off, between Denver and Aberdeen and I observed the differences between offices. When I consult, I work very long hours during the work week; if I'm away from home, I feel that I might as well be working. Long hours did not sit well with some of my colleagues because it was in such contrast to their concept of "work-life balance." But, eventually I found, their concern and friendship helped me reset my own "work-life balance" equation. Another notable difference from the U.S. was on the wellsite. I was teaching another woman coalbed wellsite geology. When we got to the wellsite, we were stopped and somewhat in jest told by rig hands we were "bad luck." In equally good humor, I replied "We are the reason the well is being drilled. If you don't step aside, indeed, it will be 'bad luck' if the operation shuts down because we couldn't work."

While I was commuting to the U.K., Kurt was successful with Storm Energy projects and reasoned that if I was going to be on the road consulting, he should move back to Panama City, Florida, to be closer to family. When the U.K. project ended in 2009, we moved to Florida. There, I answered a call from Vecta Oil and Gas to work on a regional project on the Eastern Shelf of the Permian Basin. I worked remotely with a digital and scanned data set of wireline logs, sample logs, paleo reports, and scout tickets and would meet with partners when Kurt and I were in Houston or Denver. This project would lead to my first discovery working with Storm Energy, The Super Chicken No. 1.

The move to Florida coincided with both Kurt and me following other long-time interests. He began to write his outdoor stories, and has been successful with his initial publishing efforts. I became more active with the Association for Women Geoscientists (AWG), serving first as a delegate for the southeast region and then as President (Elect and Past). I had received one of the first AWG Chrysalis Scholarships when I was in graduate school and wanted to give back to the organization. During that period, AWG restructured, focused attention on outreach activities at national geologic conventions, and increased its membership. Volunteering with AWG's outreach activities and sharing wisdom from my mentors was richly rewarding work.

In 2016, Kurt started to increase the time he spent writing and I assumed more responsibilities for Storm Energy as President. Kurt also started an environmental project to bring awareness to the problem of plastic marine debris. This provided me with some additional "green credentials" in Florida as I began to give talks to legislative and civic groups about the petroleum industry and hydraulic fracturing. We both stay engaged in existing projects with partners in the Gulf Coast, Permian Basin, and Mid-continent. AAPG has been and continues to be the lifeline that keeps us up to date and connected with friends in the petroleum industry. (Fig. 21)

Figure 21. Denise Cox and John Kaldi, both candidates for AAPG office, flexing their muscle, as they share a commitment to the mission of advancing the science of petroleum geology. (Photo: John Kaldi, Adelaide, Australia.)

Denise Mruk Cox was born in 1958 in Elmira Heights, New York. She graduated with a B.S. in geology with honors from the State University of New York at Binghamton in 1980, joined AAPG in 1984, and earned her M.S. in geology from the University of Colorado, Boulder in 1985. She lives with her geologist and writer husband, Kurt Cox in Panama City, Florida, when they are not on their annual sabbatical to Colorado.

Vicki Cowart

I think of my life in themes, one leading to another, but always with the personal goal of doing something for the greater good. I have never been afraid of a challenge or something new, and have always looked for work that allows me to have an impact. Each theme of my life seems to have occurred when I was in a rewarding moment, often supported and encouraged by male mentors but suddenly disrupted by an insecure boss who had a problem with the idea of women being equal.

My love for math and science was an early driver. As I got ready to go to college in 1971, I was given the catalog for Worcester Polytechnic Institute (WPI) by my high school gym teacher in Tucson, Arizona. My father was a truck driver in a copper mine, and I wanted more than the opportunities I saw in Tucson. Worcester, Massachusetts, seemed "far enough away," and filled with possibility. The curriculum at this small engineering college seemed a perfect fit. When I walked into my first class, I looked around the room and wondered, "Where are the other women?" Through independent study I was shocked to learn that women had only been accepted at WPI a few years earlier, most U.S. colleges hadn't allowed women to matriculate until the early 20th century, and women were less than 20% of any engineering school's student body and faculty. Still, I loved my studies and tolerated the weird dynamics of a nearly all-male school. From WPI, I went to Colorado School of Mines, where I got my M.S. in geophysics and continued my self-study of feminism with classics like Betty Friedan's *The Feminine Mystique* and Susan Brownmiller's *Against Our Will*. At Mines, my passion for math and science was fully satisfied and by joining a local National Organization for Women (NOW) consciousness raising group, my feminism began to develop as well.

One day during my first spring at Mines, the department secretary came running down the hall to catch me and insisted, "You've got to go in there and interview for a summer job!" I had no idea what she was talking about, but I followed her instructions. (It's worth noting that the female secretary told me about the opportunity; my male colleagues learned about it from our professors.) Before I knew it, Skelly Oil in Denver had hired me for summer work, which included a long stint in the Tetons of Wyoming. For a few glorious weeks, I lived out of Jackson Hole and did horseback and helicopter fieldwork on their seismic crew in the incredible terrain of northwestern Wyoming. I could not believe I was being paid to do this. Math! Science! And the mountains!

When I finished graduate school in 1977, the oil business was booming. I took a job with Mobil Oil in Denver. At Mobil I thrived under the mentorship of Clyde Kerns. There were several women in exploration, geologists, and geophysicists alike, and the environment proved to be exceptionally collegial for us. Some of the women I met in my early days at Mobil are still among my best friends. I did not go in the field that much as I was a seismic section jockey which meant having tons of seismic sections dumped on my desk every morning, plowing through them, making correlations, mapping, and starting on a new batch the next morning. But occasionally, I had fun visits to the field in Oregon and California. Boom times in the Rockies led me to more positive experiences with smaller companies, especially when my former Mobil mentor, Kerns, hired me at American Quasar, a very aggressive independent with lots of seismic activity in the thrust belt.

I also continued to develop my interest in women's issues. I helped found the Denver chapter of the Association for Women Geoscientists (AWG) becoming the first nationally-elected president of AWG, and promoted the passage of the Equal Rights Amendment (ERA) among women science groups across the West. One of my favorite memories is of a trip to Oklahoma City with members of AWG, the Association of Women in Science (AWIS), and the Society of Women Engineers (SWE) to join sisters from across the country to march around the Oklahoma capital as their legislature considered ratification of the ERA. It failed there, which meant it failed in the nation, but the movement for women's equality came alive for me.

As it periodically does, the oil industry slowed down in the mid-80s. I had switched over to Atlantic Richfield's (ARCO) production company. There, I developed expertise in running and interpreting seismic velocity surveys (aka checkshots). When ARCO announced they, too, were leaving Denver, they offered me the opportunity to move to Bakersfield, California or Midland, Texas. I chose to take my chances in Denver, which worked out well because Schlumberger, the company I'd worked with on several seismic borehole surveys, asked me to join them to further develop that technology for their Western U.S. clients.

Schlumberger was a dream job. I was based in Denver, I was on the cutting edge of a developing technology, and I had a steep learning curve. Even though it was a well-resourced, multi-national company, their flat structure provided great opportunity and rewarded initiative; I loved this company. Because I had good presentation skills, I was placed in a position to offer client education for our new products. My boss, Percy Percifield, and I traveled a great deal, demonstrating our newest tools and processing techniques from California to Texas to Pennsylvania, Michigan, and on. Percy was another one of those great mentors and teachers.

My job was never routine. In addition to client education trips, I also designed vertical seismic borehole profiles, and eventually, offset and 3-D seismic profiles for the company's clients. I was heavily involved in the processing and ultimately in the interpretation of these (then) exotic techniques and I would go to the wellsite for particularly complex operations.

Once, I was the borehole seismic expert on a big, nasty job that took days to accomplish. We were wrangling a couple of vibroseis trucks as the energy sources on a relatively small, well site footprint. The well was a particularly "sticky" one, meaning more than one stuck tool failed, and I was required to call for replacement tools from as far away as Tokyo and Paris. The job took days to complete, and I nervously studied the limited data available in the field, sitting in the Schlumberger "dog house," trying to will the survey to be successful to get the data the client needed. When the job was over, I could barely keep my eyes open as I drove to the nearest town to sleep for several hours. I was feeling pretty bad about all the difficulties we'd had onsite, but learned an important lesson the next day (Fig. 22). Jack Caldwell, my boss (and another great mentor), told me that I'd done a great job keeping the crew and company people calm, making tough but good decisions, and not buckling under the pressure to complete the job. "It's not about how you handle yourself when things go well," he said. "A good job is when you handle yourself well and keep those around you focused on moving forward when things are going wrong or circumstances are particularly tough."

In 1991, Schlumberger promoted me to District Manager with a transfer to Belle Chasse, Louisiana, near New Orleans ("What? Gulf Coast?"). The Denver team was so happy for me to take what was a critically important career step. They gave me a send-off party, cheered for me, and told me how proud they were that "one of them" had made it! Taking over a district in the Gulf, I was flushed with excitement and determination to make good. At the time, there were only two or three women in management in the entire company, and I became one of them.

Arriving in New Orleans, I was immediately challenged by my new boss who said, "I've been all over this globe. I've worked with every kind of person, every color—red, black, yellow—it don't matter, but I have never had to work with a woman!"

Figure 22. Vicki Cowart, 1990, in Utah when logging a difficult well for Schlumberger; unusual problems made for a sleepless week.. (Photo: Vicki Cowart, Denver, Colorado.)

Okay, I thought, I know how to prove myself, I've done it before, I'll do it again.

New Orleans was not nearly as technically creative and inventive as Denver had been, and it turned into a struggle. "We have *always* done it this way. It works. We will keep doing it this way." New ideas and ways of doing things were anathema to them.

It was right around that time when I read, in shock, the words of the Schlumberger CEO in an interview in *The New Yorker* magazine: "Women have no place in this industry." This was followed shortly after by my boss in New Orleans saying directly to me, "I don't promote women because of what's between their legs."

Wow, how do you work hard and circumvent such misogyny? My last straw in New Orleans occurred during Mardi Gras. The company traditionally rented a hotel suite with a balcony to provide a place for clients to enjoy the festivities. I was enjoying the parades with two women clients and suggested that we go to the company suite. Upon arriving, I followed the traditional protocol, which was to yell up to colleagues on the balcony to let us in.

They started bellowing, "Hey, first show us your tits!"

Okay, it was New Orleans and Mardi Gras, but I was an employee,

I was one of them. In fact, as a District Manager, I outranked several of them. Embarrassed, my clients couldn't believe what was happening. I was determined they should let us in, without having to show anything, but their boorish behavior continued. After a long unpleasant discourse, finally one of the "good guys" came downstairs and let us in. But, I decided then that the entire environment was not for me. This was 1993, I had been in the South only two years.

Out-of-the-blue, Jeanne Harris, my friend in Denver, called and mentioned that Colorado was looking for a new State Geologist. She thought my résumé fit the job description perfectly. I applied. In the meantime, I asked Schlumberger to relocate me back to Denver. I had found their treatment unacceptable, and I wanted to be made "whole again." I hired a lawyer who helped me get a settlement, which facilitated the move. Fortuitously, Schlumberger agreed to a negotiated settlement on the very day the state offered me the position of State Geologist. I had been so hurt and disillusioned, it felt especially good to inform my colleagues in my farewell fax of my upcoming appointment – after I deposited the settlement check.

Thus, the second theme of my life began. State Geologist and Director of the Colorado Geological Survey (CGS) was another dream job, working with a great staff with the flexibility to create programs that supported and educated the citizens and resource industries of Colorado. I was the first woman to be named state geologist in Colorado and only the third in the United States. Again, I enjoyed the friendship and mentorship of some great guys, notably the State Geologists of Wisconsin (Jamie Robertson), Nevada (Jon Price), and Utah (the late Lee Allison). Within a few years, I became the first woman selected to be an officer of the Association of American State Geologists (AASG), and by 2001, I was the first female president of the AASG. I was thrilled to work on the intersection of science and policy not only on the state level, but on national efforts through activities with the U.S. Geological Survey, the American Geophysical Union, and the National Research Council of the National Academy of Sciences. (Fig. 23)

Because state surveys are part of the state government, they can be somewhat political, to say the least. After six years at the Colorado Geological Survey (CGS), a new Colorado Governor was elected from a different party, which had a huge impact on the Department of Natural Resources (DNR). Though I was nonpartisan in my job, I was known to be a Democrat. New obstacles arose. When the recently appointed Republican DNR director called a meeting, I was surprised to find that my name plate was no longer at the table as it had been and I, the only woman previously at the leadership table, was relegated to the back row. Soon, my travel was cut, I was no longer allowed to speak to groups around the country or state about geologic hazards or resource development. I did not find the job rewarding any more, and began to think about next steps. I hired the very capable Vince Matthews to become the (acceptably male) face of the CGS. Vince took the lead on interactions with the DNR and State political staff. When I left, he became the State Geologist and continued the agency's good work.

Figure 23. Vicki held the position of State Geologist for Colorado and was the first woman to chair the Association of State Geologists, 1993-2000. (Photo: Vicki Cowart.)

Almost magically, the third theme of my life presented itself. Across the years, even as I loved my work in the sciences, I continued to grow as a fierce advocate of women's equality, women's rights, and women's health. At a related fundraiser, I learned that Planned Parenthood of the Rocky Mountains (PPRM) had announced a search for a new President and CEO. My husband, who had stood by my side through all of these career changes and moves, whispered to me, "That's your next job!" Believing vigorously in the truth of Margaret Sanger's quote, "No woman can call herself free who does not own and control her body," I had been a volunteer, contributor, and board member for years of the Colorado Chapter of the National Abortion Rights Action League (NARAL). My experience in leading the state agency, working with the Colorado legislature, and fundraising for AWG and NARAL, turned out to be what the PPRM Board was looking for. I took the

Figure 24. As spokesperson for women's rights, Vicki has been especially effective in her position as director of the Planned Parenthood of the Rocky Mountain region. (Photo: Vicki Cowart.)

position in 2003 and have enjoyed it with the same passion I did the science phases in my life. I still get up every morning hoping to have a positive effect. I love the people I work with, am inspired by the people we help through our health care and sex education, and, above all, I am driven by our advocacy to champion a woman's right to be a full and equal part of our world. (Fig. 24)

Mentors, passion for my work, and strong communities of women have helped my career feel both successful and worthwhile. I have enjoyed every period in my life and however difficult the transition to a new stage might have been, it has been the right thing, at the right time, and richly rewarding. Or, as my hero, Hillary Rodham Clinton says, "Never stop believing that fighting for what's right is worth it."

Vicki Cowart was born in Tucson, Arizona, and earned her B.S. from Worcester Polytechnic Institute in 1975, and her M. S. from Colorado School of Mines in 1977. She lives in Denver with her geologist/lawyer husband, Chris Hayes, and still enjoys the great outdoors.

Chapter 16 Sources and References

Anderson, Donna Schmidt, Golden, Colorado. 2016. Personal autobiographical writings and source of photograph as cited in figure caption.

Brownmiller, Susan, 1975, *Against Our Will*, Simon & Schuster, New York, New York, pp. 472.

Cowart, Vicki. Denver, Colorado. 2017. Personal autobiographical writings and source of photographs as cited in the figure captions.

Cox, Denise Mruk, Panama City, Florida, 2017. Personal autobiographical writings and source of photographs as cited in figure captions.

Darnell, Nancy. Boulder, Colorado. 2016. Personal autobiographical writings and source of photograph as cited in figure caption.

Friedan, Betty, 1963, *The Feminine Mystique,* W. W. Norton and Co. New York, New York, pp. 239.

Green, Marsha A., 2016. North Kingston, Rhode Island. Personal autobiographical writings and source of image as cited in figure caption.

Landon, Susan M. Golden, Colorado. 2016. Personal communication, 10/2014; source of photographs as cited in figure captions.

McPeek, Larry, Evergreen, Colorado. 2017. Personal communication, 2/07/2017.

Sheldon, Ruth. 1941. "The Ladies Find Oil." *Scribner's Commentator*, vol. 10, pp. 28-32.

Taylor, Ione, Kingston, Ontario. 2016. Personal communication, 6/2016-10/2016); source of photographs as cited in figure captions. Video interview, 9/14-15/2016, archived at AAPG, Tulsa, Oklahoma.

Thornburg, Janet Bauder, Ann Arbor, Michigan. 2016. Personal autobiographical writings and source of photograph as cited in figure caption.

Time Magazine, New York, New York, October 9, 1978. Advertisement, Back cover: source of cover of Marsha Green, with her permission.

Webster-Scholten, Penny, Cedar City, Utah. 2016. Personal autobiographical writings and source of photograph as cited in figure caption.

Williams-Stroud, Sherilyn, Pasadena, California. 2016. Personal communication 8/2016-10/2016; source of photographs as cited in figure captions, including website: https://drive.google.com/open?id=0B9M4vehvr56HSzdHOFEySXh4UG8. Video Interview 8/9-10/16 archived at AAPG, Tulsa Oklahoma.

Winsten, Miriam Israel, Houston, Texas. 2016. Interview with Denise Cox; source of photographs as cited in figure captions.

Withjack, Martha Oliver, Piscataway, New Jersey. 2016. Personal autobiographical writings and source of photograph as cited in figure caption.

Chapter 17

Management—Rock Stars

By the 1980s, only a few short years after the Equal Employment Opportunity Commission (EEOC) had changed the hiring practices of oil and gas companies in the United States (aided by the oil boom from the late 70s oil embargo), women who were hired out-of-college had little trouble getting jobs and had a fairly level playing field for opportunities. They, understandably, also had no awareness of the road traveled before them and consequently no appreciation for those trials and tribulations, for those achievements. It was a history destined to be lost.

The new atmosphere generated great possibilities for women. If they wanted to combine a career with a family, there were ways to do it. There was more assistance from the employer, though sometimes not very helpful, as Deborah Pfeiffer discovered; she could go to part-time when she had twins, but still had the same work load. There was accommodation by employers for the employee's needs, as Cindy Yeilding found, when she did not want to uproot her family for any transfers as was the historic practice. The concept of hiring help for childcare was not only embraced by this generation, it was made easier when salaries became equitable for both working parents. Life-work balance, while sometimes a challenge, was readily embraced by many like Susan Cunningham, who said she loved both sides of her life and just embraced them both.

Mentoring for the hires of this generation continued to be mostly male to female, as there were no women in positions of higher management to take on this role. The men who mentored did it well, and the women who benefited were very appreciative. As these women excelled in their profession, they became the missing female mentors. And they were all mentoring both young female and male geologists—never giving it a second thought.

The managerial path was not always smooth and just as there were beneficial mentors, there were also individuals, whether knowingly or not, who impeded advancement. María Antonieta Lorente found ways to turn managerial adversaries into supportive colleagues using humor, frankness, and diplomacy. And these colleagues played a role in her advancement.

Though there are now many examples of women geologists in the vice-presidential role within major companies, the last ceiling to crash, that of president and CEO, continues to be illusive. However, it does happen in smaller, independent petroleum companies, particularly companies that have been founded by geologic entrepreneurs like Susan Morrice and Robbie Gries. Susan Cunningham and Annell Bay's participation on corporate boards herald in a world of opportunity for women in the future. Women in Brazil, Venezuela, and Spain (Sylvia Anjos, María Antonieta Lorente, and María Jesús Simón Granda) forged new leadership paths for the next generation and, they too, combined careers with the family option. And, significantly, this generation could exercise the option to have or not have a family, as it suited them.

Bryce Covert, Economic Editor at *ThinkProgress*, writing about women on corporate boards in December, 2013, says,

> Companies with women on their boards are more likely than those without gender diversity to have added new board directors: Less than 60 percent of all-male boards have added a new director in the past three years, while more than 80 percent of those with at least one women have. Nearly 95 percent of companies with a woman on their board have added a new director over the past five years, compared to 77 percent of male-only ones...The [Ernst and Young] report also finds that more turnover and diversity may be on its way. Twenty percent of the board seats at S&P 1500 companies are held by those who are around age 72, a common age for retirement. Ernst & Young estimates that about 27 percent of board seats could change hands in the next five years. This could be a big opportunity to bring in more women: men account for 94 percent of the seats held by people age 68 and over.
>
> But women still have a lot of ground to make up. They hold just 15 percent of board seats, ... Some industries are worse than others: about 40 percent of oil and gas companies don't have any female board directors. American companies haven't made any significant progress in increasing gender diversity in eight years. Fifty of the largest 500 don't have any women on their boards at all.
>
> ... Having more women on a board is correlated with that company paying less for an acquisition and making fewer of them, which protects shareholder value and firm performance. Three separate studies have found that boards with gender diversity significantly outperform those that don't in stock price, returns, and performance. Women's decisions have been found to lead to better company performance overall.

Women have a much brighter future in the oil and gas industry, and the Managerial Rock Stars contributing to this Chapter are symbolic of 100 years of progress and evolution, regardless of fits and starts along the way.

Susan Cunningham

Susan Cunningham, as a successful executive in the oil and gas business, is frequently asked the question about how she balances work and life. She thinks this concept of "work-life balance" puts undue stress on each of us. It implies that work and life should be separate, and balanced.

"It's all life," she remarks. "It's how we earn a living, how we are fulfilled. It's all life."

Of course, it is easier when a person loves their profession as she does. It is fun and fulfilling. So is being a wife and mother. She asks, "What is to balance?" She just does both, with gusto!

This Canadian-born geologist was hired with her bachelor's degree from McMaster University in 1980 by Amoco Canada. The Canadian education system, similar to that of the United Kingdom, endeavors to have their bachelor-degree students ready for industry with an early undergraduate specialization on a chosen career path. In high school, Susan didn't know what "geology" was, but knew that she had a lifelong curiosity about the physical earth— '

What makes a mountain? Why is that river curved and others are not? How are those rocks made? When she got to college, aimed at physical geography to answer her questions, she found that *geology* was recommended for that degree. Taking geology the first semester, she fell in love with it, scored the highest grades, and was granted a scholarship.

She left her home in Toronto, the only one of her siblings to move far away, and started to work 1700 miles away in Calgary. Susan had developed an early desire to have travel, especially international travel, as part of her life. Her parents had taken the family to Sri Lanka when Susan was eight years old, put the children into local schools, and arranged for them to experience many wonderful and wondrous places.

During her first year with Amoco, Pierre Trudeau nationalized the petroleum industry in Canada and that meant that Amoco Canada had to downsize. For Susan, it was a godsend. Normally, by Amoco rules, she would have had to work for 4-5 years before she could be considered for the international organization, but she was offered a position in that group, located in Houston, after only a year and a half. It was 1985, and it was with some trepidation that she agreed to Houston—known as the "Murder Capital of the U.S."—so, she asked for a temporary foreign assignment. To her surprise, management agreed! Pushing her luck, she decided to ask for Amoco's permission to drive to Houston and take two weeks to get there. She got it! On Expenses! Her reasons? Susan had just bought a Turbo TransAm American Eagle and she wanted see all the geologic wonders of the western U.S. along the way—Glacier, Yellowstone, the Grand Canyon. She learned her first career lesson,

"Don't be afraid to ask for something! You might get it!"

As soon as she was in Houston, she was immediately assimilated into Amoco's international efforts and relished the work challenges, responsibilities, and travel. After initial assignments in the Middle East, she was soon in Africa working in the rift valley (Fig. 1). Susan became camp boss and tested a couple of exploration concepts—resulting in two dry holes, but setting the stage for future exploration in the area.

Figure 1. Susan Cunningham, working in Tanzania in the East African Rift Valley in the 1980s. (Photo: Susan Cunningham, Houston, Texas.)

She was considered next, for Egypt, which she really wanted, and had acquired approval for Amoco's first 3D exploration effort in the Gulf of Suez. 3D was previously not used for exploration; it had only been used for development geology. Unfortunately, the Amoco joint venture with the Egyptian Oil company, GUPCO, was not ready for a woman geoscientist and would not agree to her assignment. She did, however, act as manager during her time there doing "vacation relief" for the Amoco managers residing in Cairo.

On another assignment, she was part of the team evaluating Algerian concessions and much to her surprise, found that this time being a woman was an advantage. When she first arrived, the Algerian staff assumed that she was some kind of assistant or "go-fer" and treated her that way. She decided not to correct anyone, but to just ask smart questions and let their awareness develop. Gradually their opinion changed and soon she found herself in a warm friendship with one of their team. He invited her to meet his wife and mother and they drank mint tea in a courtyard of the *Casbah*, a part that foreigners rarely got to see. More fortunate than that, because they developed a feeling of trust, he began to feel comfortable providing her with data important to the evaluation which he had been reluctant to share with others. Susan supposed it may have been that he saw her as less threatening, less competitive than the men from Amoco. Who knows for sure, but she was very happy to have the data for the assessment.

Back in the U.S., her management position was also not always apparent and led to some humorous moments. Once, when she and four or five of her employees (all male) arrived in Dallas for a meeting with Oryx Petroleum, they rode in a taxi van headed to Oryx's office in the Galleria area. The taxi driver looked at her in the rearview mirror and said, "Lady, you might enjoy me dropping you at the Galleria while these guys are in their meeting. There are some great shoe shops there!" Her colleagues were chagrined and embarrassed, and finally, one said, "Well, er, she's our boss!"

Susan's career has benefited from her life-long habit of studying human nature, psychology, and gender variabilities. When she was first offered a position as "country manager" to Denmark, she thinks she had a somewhat typical female reaction of immediately worrying that she might not be qualified, or might not be *ready*. Fortunately, she talked it over with her husband, Paul Koeller, who said, "Of course, you're ready! Do you think they would have asked you if they doubted you were ready? The men you are working with who have the same experience level would jump at this chance."

She thought of the psychological reading she had done and she realized that she had fallen into a common female trap, where self-doubt could hold her back. She took the job, met the challenge, loved the work, and excelled. Which also goes to another lifelong philosophy,

"Decide to do something and THEN figure out how to make it work. Don't try to get everything all set up before making a decision, or, you can miss the opportunity. Let your decision be guided by your passion, not by convenience."

When she agreed to the Denmark job, she was seven months pregnant. She didn't know exactly how childcare was going to work or how her husband's transfer to Denmark would work (though they had set some guidelines early in their marriage). She just did it! She arrived with a five-week old baby. She took advantage of her Canadian family resources and found a young girl to go with them to Denmark and babysit for the summer until someone in Denmark could be found. Susan found out later that when she had been suggested for the job, one of her bosses said, "No way, she is pregnant, she won't go." But another boss, a new guy, thought it should be her decision, not theirs. Wise man.

Part of her arrangement with Statoil was that, after one year in Norway, she would return to Houston and head up that office. That was supposed to work well with her family plans, notably what her husband was planning to do. At the end of the year, Statoil decided to close down their Houston office. What to do? Simultaneously, she was contacted by another major company with an offer for her to come to Houston and become a vice president of global *Core* exploration. While she had some justifiable qualms about the management structure and her future with them, Susan decided the additional experience and the strength of the new title would be a good career decision. She took the job. And indeed, all the trepidation proved to be real. However, her title and additional leadership experience led to her next job offer—that with Noble Energy, which was, at that time, Noble Affiliates (Samedan Oil) in 2001.

Susan still chuckles at her recollection of the Noble hiring process, where she kept asking for a company organization chart and was put off with verbal descriptions of the organization, but no paper chart. She liked everything about the offer, so she took the job without seeing the chart. The night before she assumed her role in the Houston office, she was finally given the Organization Chart and was surprised to find that she was the only professional woman in management for the company! She later discovered the head of engineering was aghast at having a woman as the new head of exploration and was vocal about "what is the company coming to!" He insisted that everyone refer her to him if there were any questions. The women in the company who were in support roles of administration and land not only were supportive, but when she walked in the first day, they also literally stood and applauded her!

There have been countless career "firsts" for Susan in the companies where she has been employed, and there are also notable ones in her volunteer efforts and giving back to industry. She was the first woman selected to be on the Offshore Technology Conference (OTC) Board in 2003, the largest oil and gas sector trade show in the world with about 50,000 people and 2000 companies in attendance. In 2010-11 she became the Chairman of the OTC, another first for a woman. And, whereas the OTC did not usually attract much publicity in its annual Houston conference, that was the year of the Macondo disaster in the Gulf of Mexico, the worst oil spill in the history of offshore exploration and production. Susan had to address the press repeatedly and with all the knowledge and presence of mind she could muster. It is no wonder that people still talk about her as having been "one of the best" Chairs ever. She facilitated the expansion of the OTC into Brazil. Another OTC effort she participated in was the establishment of the Arctic Oil and Gas conference.

Serving on corporate boards is an area where female geoscientists are very rare, especially the larger boards. In 2005, Susan was approached to join the board of an iron ore and metallurgical coal mining company, Cliffs Natural Resources. The headhunter who approached her told her they were not specifically looking for a woman, but that if they found a woman who qualified, the company would consider that a bonus. She joined the Board, encouraged by that premise. Later, when another one or two women were added to the Board, she realized there was a significant cultural shift that she believes might be applicable to women on other boards.

When there is only one woman, she found that her ideas and her opinion were sometimes not heard, registered, or given attention. Whereas, with more than one woman, they tended to assist each other in being heard. It was not a deliberate dynamic, but a significant evolution.

This Board experience coupled with her 36 years managing men and women, she made her realize that women tend to want to be "really good" before they try to ask for or put their names in for promotions. They can inadvertently project a demeanor of "not being ready."

Women also tend to apologize too much, engendering a lack of confidence in their abilities with the people who work with them. She says,

"Don't apologize. Don't project a lack of confidence."

She had a brilliant young woman working for her who was unconsciously, but frequently, saying, "I'm sorry, I'm sorry." This young woman was having a tough time with the people she was supervising and sought advice from Susan. Susan said, "Quit apologizing! Show your confidence in yourself and in them." Three months later the woman came back to her and said she had taken that advice and her whole department had turned around!

Susan also has advised male managers that work for her,

"Consider women for promotions even if their confidence level is not apparent."

She lets them know that is likely a gender difference and, if he thinks the woman would be good, he should give her the opportunity.

Another piece of advice Susan readily gives,

"Don't burn any bridges."

When Susan quit Amoco, she was not unhappy with the company, she just wanted a new challenge. She had a new boss at Amoco who was known to be a real "up and comer." When she went in to tender her resignation, he started telling her how excited he was to have her on his team and what plans he had for her, so, she had to stop him and tell him that she was resigning. She remembers being very careful to let him know that her decision had nothing to do with him or the company. They remained respectful friends and now he is on the Board of Directors for Noble. Yes, it pays to stay on good terms and not to burn bridges.

She has been with Noble for 15 exciting and wonderful years and has found ways to face and overcome new challenges. There developed a period when she felt she was at a stalemate. She was not having the impact in the company that she could envision. She had followed a lot of rules over the course of her career, and they had brought her a long way. But—ever the introspective woman—she felt her old "rules" were not working any more. Those rules included:

Be one of the boys.
Never be a victim.
Work harder than anyone else.

As she progressed in her career, she added more guidelines:

No wasting time chitchatting.
Only be objective, never emotional.
Grab opportunities.
Never talk about personal problems with a boss, and minimize conversations with them because they are busy.

To address her concerns, as she had done throughout her life, she took a deep look at herself and signed up for some career coaching. While she was at it, she added leadership classes. She discovered many of her lifelong "rules" were not effective or not needed any more. She was willing to make some major changes, which included:

Be "less like a man" and more authentic.
Recognize relationships are very important and deserve the time needed to develop them.
Understand it is okay to show emotions, especially when it includes passion for company growth and strategies.

Figure 2. Susan and her sons climbed to the top of a volcano in Hawaii to see the sun rise, 2003. (Photo: Susan Cunningham.)

Recalling a subsequent meeting with 30-40 company men where she became so emotional about their exploration and performance goals (she wanted to find a billion barrels of oil!), that the entire room went deadly silent. Afterwards, a colleague said, "Boy, I thought I was dedicated to this company and to our growth, but now I realize I have not been nearly as committed as I could be!" She expanded the impact of coaching by providing it to her staff and increased everyone's productivity and confidence—and, amazingly, those "near impossible and outrageous goals" were being met. They surpassed that billion-barrel goal. (Fig. 2)

Susan Cunningham was born in Ottawa, Canada, in 1956. She received her bachelor's degree in geology from McMaster University in 1979. Susan and Paul live and work in Houston, Texas.

Annell Bay

Stereotypes were never part of Annell Bay's family. Her parents instilled a strong love of learning and the value of education in all their children. Her mother was an English-psychology major who received a master's degree in psychology and taught and tutored children for over 50 years. Her father was a petroleum geologist with a career spanning over 40 years, including 28 years at Shell Oil Company. While her mother created a love of literature, music and philosophy in their lives, her father demonstrated his love of math and science. With all three of her siblings being well-rounded, strong students, her two brothers chose to study history and English, and Annell and her sister chose to study math and science.

While growing up in Texas and on annual family vacations throughout the western United States, her father often stopped at road cuts and talked to four sleepy children about outcrops, fossils, and sedimentary layers. At home, there were many opportunities for Annell to see her father working on geologic maps and cross sections at the dinner table. Even Annell's eighth grade science project was a father-daughter venture; together they created a three-dimensional wooden model of Galveston Island showing the water depths of Galveston Bay, the Houston Ship Channel, and the Gulf of Mexico. Annell's science project is currently an "art installation" in her brother's home.

When it came time for college selection, Annell had two goals: go to school in a cool place and study science. With her knack for negotiating, she approached her father with two options.

Annell: "Dad, I really love forestry and understand the importance of agricultural science. So, I want to go to Oregon State."

Father: "Stephen F. Austin in Nacogdoches, Texas, has one of the best forestry schools in the nation."

Annell later made a second attempt: "Dad, I have decided that I love oceanography even more than forestry and I know how important it is, so I want to go to Scripps Institute in La Jolla, California."

Father: "Texas A & M in Galveston has one of the premier oceanography departments in America. I'm sure you'll love it."

Figure 3. Annell Bay, with Shell Oil in 1982, core workshop. (Photo: Annell Bay, Austin, Texas.)

Realizing that negotiating without the power of the purse left her with few options, Annell began surveying the schools in Texas. She selected Trinity University in San Antonio and chose to study biology. During her sophomore year at Trinity, in an environmental biology class, a geology professor was asked to give a guest lecture. Dr. Robert Freed's lecture was entertaining and fascinating. His stories and his enthusiasm about geology captured Annell's imagination. She decided that day to switch her major to geology. In 1977, Annell received a bachelor's degree in geology from Trinity and next attended The University of Texas at Austin (UT) where she received a master's degree in geology in 1980. She also met her future husband, Robert Suchecki, at UT as he was finishing his doctorate in geology.

Upon graduating, Annell took a job with Shell Oil in New Orleans (Fig. 3). At Shell, she found that oil exploration was "puzzle-solving detective work" with interesting people in an intellectually stimulating environment. She especially enjoyed working with geologists her father's age who mentored the incoming geologists and geophysicists. Soon after starting her career with Shell, she married Robert who was working for Chevron Oil Field Research Company in La Habra, California. Annell resigned from Shell and accepted an offer from Chevron in applied research in La Habra—she had finally found her way to California, just north of La Jolla! (Fig. 4).

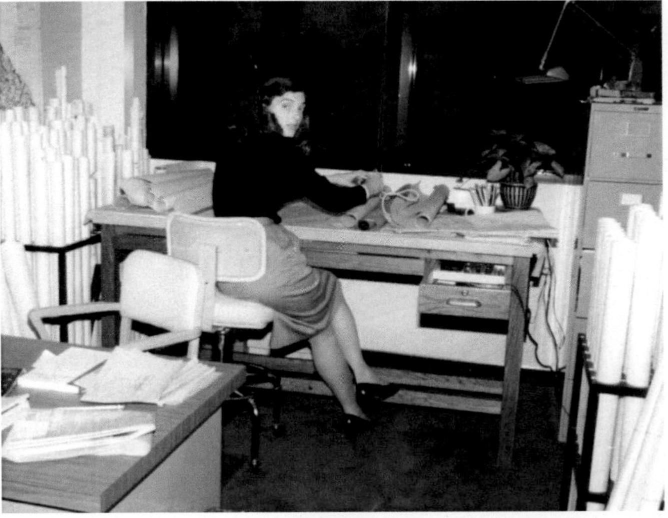

Figure 4. Annell with Chevron Oil in 1981. (Photo: Annell Bay.)

In 1984, Annell and Robert moved to Dallas, Texas, where he took a job with Arco Research and she with Sohio Oil, which was later bought by BP America. In 1988, she took a job with Sun Company, but when Sun spun off the independent, Oryx Energy, she went with Oryx. Annell was happily back into exploration assignments for these companies and these were important years for developing her technical skills—building new exploration play opportunities, recommending and drilling many wells, learning risked pre-drill well economics, and gaining operational and well-site experience. After four years at Oryx, Jerry Box, Executive Vice President of Exploration and Production, created a key turning point in her career. He seemed to seek out opportunities to promote men and women alike. Annell was surprised and flattered when Jerry told her that someday she would be Vice President. Jerry made her a special assistant and told her that she had to agree to three things. He said, "One, don't ask if I have time to speak to you; I always have time for you so just come on in. Two, don't pound on my desk! And, three, don't come in here and cry!"

Jerry's mentoring of Annell included taking her along to all the executive meetings, "otherwise, how will you learn?"

Sometimes her inclusion in meetings was frowned upon by his superiors, but he persisted and provided Annell with an extraordinary training opportunity. Jerry encouraged her, at his Vice President meetings, to fully participate, to acquire information for him, and to reprioritize or redirect the work that was being done. In this role, she learned how to diplomatically work with both peers and senior management, improve organizational productivity, and analyze fundamental company financials.

From 1993-2001, Annell moved from Special Assistant to Exploration Manager at Oryx, and then to Director of International Operations at Kerr McGee. Kerr McGee had acquired Oryx in 1999. It was a very productive and inspiring eight years. In 1994, her initial role in management was overseen by another extraordinary mentor, M.E. "Eddie" Anglin, the Vice President of International Exploration. Eddie had business savvy, was skilled in technical evaluation and oversight of prospects, and, was an intuitive judge of character and ability. Eddie took his job seriously, but also had fun and made sure those around him did the same. One of his favorite sayings was, "In God we trust and everyone else we check on." Again, Annell felt very fortunate to have a mentor and a trainer like Eddie ,and throughout her career she tried to emulate his style.

In her first role in management, Annell learned a key lesson:

Geologists from around the world do not approach risk analysis and risk taking in a uniform and consistent manner.

For example, an international geologist on assignment in the U.S. brought her a prospect where 400 feet of sand was defined on one side of the profile and another 450 feet of sand was defined on the other side of a profile. Because there was a data gap between the two sections, the geologist would not project the two sand bodies in the data gap. Annell asked, "Don't these sands likely connect where the data is missing and you can select a well location between them?"

The geologist resisted because he was unsure of which direction the channel sands meandered, and therefore was not comfortable recommending where to drill a well. She tried to encourage him, "But which direction do you *think* best fits the data? You understand this basin and, as long as you don't violate the data, your interpretation will be acceptable."

"Oh, no" he said, "it is not ok for me to be wrong!" This discourse helped her realize that the capacity to take risks and to measure risks was often dictated by the culture in a country and that she needed a broader and different leadership style to ensure consistency in risk analysis to drive successful international exploration programs.

Figure 5. Annell Bay, Board of Directors, Apache Corporation. (Photo: Annell Bay.)

Annell thinks of her career in three phases:

Phase 1: Her technical skills phase with Shell, Chevron, Sohio/BP, and Sun/Oryx;

Phase 2: Her leadership phase when she was promoted to Exploration Manager with Oryx and Director of International Exploration with Kerr McGee; and,

Phase 3: Her executive management phase as Vice President years, with Kerr McGee from 2001-2004, with Royal Dutch Shell for exploration in the Americas from 2004-2008, and finally Marathon Oil from 2008-2014.

Under her leadership as an exploration vice president, significant new oil and gas resources were added at competitive finding costs in Australia, Ecuador, Brazil, Kurdistan, North Africa, West Africa, the North Sea, the Gulf of Mexico, and onshore U.S. For exploration decision-making and risk/resource portfolio balance, she ensured that exploration teams used standardized probabilistic evaluation tools for subsurface assessment and above ground screening criteria to risk, compare and rank opportunities within a global portfolio. In addition, Annell initiated and led career development programs to identify and develop leaders within each company. As a vice president and member of the executive Exploration and Production (E&P) leadership teams, she shared responsibility for business delivery of oil and gas goals, monthly Profit/Loss statements, technical personnel resource management, and delivery on targets for safety, drilling, financial, and economic metrics.

In 2014, Annell retired from Marathon and joined the board of directors of Apache Corporation (Fig. 5). In 2015, she joined the board of Hunting PLC, and, in 2016 joined the board of Verisk Analytics. Annell also serves on the Advisory Boards for the Jackson School of Geology at The University of Texas at Austin, the American Association of Petroleum Geologists, and in the Independent Petroleum Association of America's Energy Education Center for the Petroleum and Technology Academies in Houston high schools. In 2012, Annell was named in the 100 Women Leaders in Science, Technology, Engineering, and Math. In 2013, she received the BioHouston award for Women in Science. Annell continues to coach and advise talented men and women in the oil and gas industry.

Annell and Robert have two children who are following in their footsteps: their daughter has a master's degree in chemical engineering from Northwestern University and their son, two bachelor's degrees, one from Trinity University in philosophy and the other from Western Colorado State in business and petroleum land management; both work in the oil and gas industry. Annell adds in closing, "Most of the statements in this biography are factual; some might be tall tales—because I was born in Midland and grew up in Houston where Texas tall tales still flourish!"

Annell Bay was born in Midland, Texas, in 1955. She received her bachelor's degree in geology from Trinity University in 1977, and her master's from The University of Texas at Austin in 1980. Annell and Robert live in Austin, Texas.

Michelle Judson

My greatest moments of professional and personal satisfaction came from embracing unforeseen events that challenged me to grow and alter my path. My story highlights those events and the people who influenced my career.

My mother told me she knew I would be a scientist from a young age. I remember watching Jacques Cousteau and Diver Dan on TV as a child and being captivated. I learned to scuba dive at 13 and was filled with wonder. My elementary school science projects covered a broad range of topics from making food from seaweed to Antarctic geomorphology. I am grateful to my parents for encouraging me to explore options and find my own path.

During high school, I followed a strong math and science curriculum even though guidance counselors tried to dissuade me from doing so. One summer, I attended a four-week program in oceanography organized into chemistry, biology, geology, and physical oceanography sessions. During the geology session, I remember the instant, as if it was yesterday, of discovering that I could figure things out on my own—that I had an intuitive understanding of something. I wanted to be a marine geologist.

I took Introductory Geology and a four-week field camp my freshman year at St. Lawrence University. I was hooked. Following my undergraduate degree, I pursued a M.S. at the University of South Carolina. My thesis investigated fluctuation of the Antarctic ice sheets during the Miocene. The knowledge I gained about ocean processes, deep-sea sediments, and integrating data would prove invaluable throughout my career as an exploration geologist. I had discovered my passion for geology (Fig. 6).

Figure 6. Michelle Judson collecting samples for her B.Sc. Thesis in the Susquehanna Quarry, Ogdensburg, New York, 1978. (Photo: Michelle Judson, Lummi Island, Washington.)

My first job was with Sohio Petroleum Co. in 1981. It was boom time in the energy business and I had 25 job offers. I chose Sohio because the offer was in San Francisco, California, versus Houston or Amarillo, Texas, or New Orleans, Louisiana. I also enjoyed the people I met at Sohio and the small-company culture.

This is where my next big adventure began. I defended my master's thesis on a Friday and presented myself at Sohio's office in San Francisco on the following Monday, ready to start work—only to discover that plans had changed and my job would be in Anchorage, Alaska! (Fig. 7). I was a little taken aback, and in my youthful naivety called several of the companies that I had turned down to see if I could get their offer back. Over the next 24 hours, I came to the realization that this would be a once-in-a-lifetime opportunity and a great adventure. I made the decision to go. Later that same week I was on a plane to Anchorage. The next week, I was on the Sohio charter to Prudhoe Bay and a helicopter ride to the exploration rig camp at Endicott. On the helicopter ride out to the rig, the first words out of the Company Man's mouth when he met me were ,"not another goddamn female on my rig."

An experienced wellsite geologist, Connie Zarndt, was my mentor during this time. She was a remarkable woman who commanded huge respect in the North Slope community. She taught me how to do the job, and more importantly, role modeled how to behave as a woman in a rig camp with 60 men. Upon hearing that my nickname on one rig was "BB"—short for "Boom Boom"—and that the guys generically referred to women as "split tails," I decided to ignore it all, develop a thick skin, and pick my battles. To blow off steam I blasted Helen Reddy's "I Am Woman" in the core trailer and sang along.

Figure 7. Michelle working with core samples on the rig floor, North Slope of Alaska, 1982, the SOHIO Nechelik #1. (Photo: Michelle Judson.)

You had to work hard to earn the respect of people working and living in a remote rig camp. I remember the day when I felt I had earned the respect of the rig floor crew. As a part of the coring process, I had to carry core collection boxes up to the rig floor and then take them down to the core trailer to describe after the samples were collected. This pushed the limits of my physical capabilities. After doing this for a few weeks, I got up from a sleep break one day to begin the process and discovered that someone had taken the core boxes up to the rig floor for me—I had earned my first notch of respect.

Much of the telecommunications equipment didn't work brilliantly back then, so you had to rely on your own judgment and often make big decisions. I learned about data quality and its vulnerability. During my week in town, I worked on prospects, taking information from the senior geologists, writing up well proposals and well completion reports, and learning from others how to integrate information into the bigger picture. Those first two years were all about building my geologic skillset.

I worked a weekly rotation for two winter drilling seasons on the North Slope. It was exciting times with the drilling of the Niakuk, Pt. Thompson, Oliktok Pt., Nechelik and Mukluk exploration wells. It was the perfect job to build a solid technical foundation for a career. I also learned to work as part of a team and developed relationships that lasted my whole career.

When drilling activity slowed down in 1983, I had my first introduction to organizational change. The Alaska Exploration Team was consolidated in San Francisco for a couple of years before being further consolidated in Houston.

In 1993, I was working in London at BP's Exploration Headquarters on the Commercial Planning Team. It was a wonderful opportunity to learn about and contribute to the bigger picture of the business. A reservoir engineer and I built a world oil supply model to support future oil price forecasting models. This role gave me an understanding of the economics of the global upstream energy business.

When it was time for me to rotate to a new position, I jumped at the opportunity to see another part of the world and accepted the role of Senior Development Geologist for BP's emerging business in Azerbaijan. My primary task was to coordinate the BP/Statoil Common Field Development Feasibility Study for the multi-billion barrel Guneshli-Chirag-Azeri (GCA) Field. We created a subsurface to pipeline business focused plan and delivered a detailed appraisal strategy for the field, positioning BP to take a lead negotiating role within the Foreign Oil Company consortium.

As the team was getting ready to go to Baku to start negotiations, we were in a meeting when one of the Exploration vice presidents told me, in a public forum, that he did not want me going to Baku to lead a portion of the negotiations, because I was a woman and I was an American. When my line manager, who was already at the airport getting ready to fly to Baku on a BP charter heard this, he refused to leave without me as I was technically prepared for the reserves negotiations. It all ended with me making a mad dash to Heathrow to catch the charter, which I missed. It is not every day someone gets a 737 waiting on the tarmac for them. I flew out the next day. In retrospect, I can appreciate the concern that someone from the U.S. representing British Petroleum might have been confusing. I believe that the "woman issue" was not relevant as there were several senior women on the state oil company of Azerbaijan Republic (SOCAR) team, and my participation ended up being an advantage.

I have some wonderful memories of this time. The negotiations could get difficult and edgy at times. I was the only woman on the Foreign Oil Company subsurface negotiating team and there was a woman, Elmira Veliyeva, who represented SOCAR. We were both accountable for the reserves determination element of the discussion. I will always carry the memory with me of a very difficult day with many strong words. During one of the breaks, Elmira came in with a beautiful bouquet of roses from her garden for me. The whole team sat around the table, drank sweet tea, and ate sweet cherries and chocolate. It was a lovely interlude.

Another wonderful memory was the day I visited SOCAR's office with a female translator. I usually had a young man with me. The SOCAR women I had been working with instantly started asking lots of questions about my personal life, questions they would never ask through a man. It ended with them wanting to find me a nice Azeri man to marry. It was a wonderful experience being in a different culture and getting business done.

Then the price of oil went down, the project pace slowed down, and my next position would be back to Houston.

At the time of the BP Amoco merger in 1998, I got a call from Ian Conn, a fabulous leader, who offered me the job as Resource Manager for the Mid-Continent Business Unit in the North American Gas Business Unit. One of the first things we needed to do was transition the existing Amoco team from Denver to Houston. Only 15% of the team decided to move, so we had to build a new team, staffed with people from the far corners of the BP Amoco organization. During this time, I was dealing with a medical issue and needed to have surgery to discover if it was ovarian cancer. At one of the most vulnerable times in my life, I learned the power of trusting and believing in others.

The first time I got the Mid-Continent Resource team together in Houston was the day before my surgery. I literally said hello to everyone, told them what was up, shared a project plan of what needed to be done, suggested who should take the lead on various items, and left. When I returned two weeks later, the team had come together, accomplished everything and more. Upon reflection, the team did it better than if I'd been there.

I learned how to set direction and to create space for people to deliver.

I learned to listen and drive growth based on the knowledge and capability of the team. One of our outcomes was reversing the production decline in the Arkoma Red Oak Field. We did some meaningful work together.

Barry (my now husband) was wonderful in his support during this time. He demonstrated that I could trust someone to be there for me through the good and the bad times. I saw a different choice for prioritizing my work and personal life balance. Six months later, we decided that I would move from Houston to Austin so Barry and I could spend more time together. He had two teenage children, so our options were continuing to commute on weekends or me moving to Austin.

One of Barry's favorite statements is *"people get out of the way of someone who knows where they are going."* After making the decision to move to Austin, I meet with Ian Conn and told him that I was moving to Austin and would like to propose a scope of work that would allow me to remain a BP employee while telecommuting from Austin. After a few rounds with Human Resources (HR), I signed a performance contract to co-lead an Innovation Project for the Mid-Continent Business Unit to improve production performance across the organization. We had been challenged to explore how to "*operationalize* innovation in pursuit of delivering sustainable extraordinary production performance." Working collaboratively with my co-lead, Lauren Segal, was fantastic. The way we seamlessly worked together was a multiplier of each other's capabilities. We created a buzz and people called us from all over the BP organization to find out more about what we were doing. We created a language and a framework for innovation and developed processes designed to foster the creation and exchange of great ideas. We realized success!

I had moved to Austin with the full belief that I had ended my career. That was far from the truth. A couple of years later Dennis Roemmich, the Canada Gas Business Unit Leader, asked me to lead the Growth Performance Unit. Taking that risk had opened new opportunities. Barry and I were married by that time and we took this opportunity to honestly look at our careers and what each of us wanted to do. Barry decided to step away from his job as a statistician in the semiconductor industry to become a professional maker of fine stringed instruments and bows. We moved to Calgary.

In 2003, the company decided to change the strategic direction of the business in Canada from "growth" to "sustain." This meant downsizing the business which included eliminating my job. My final role in Canada was to lead the organizational change project and look for my next role.

Jim Farnsworth, the Global Exploration Vice President, asked me to lead the newly formed Subsalt Imaging Technology Leadership area. This was a new approach to technology development in BP and they were looking for someone who could bring all the stakeholders together to deliver new technology solutions in support of a critical business need.

The initial challenge was to create a strategy that aligned business needs and technology solutions along with an implementation plan. A key player in the decision process was BP's external Group Technology Advisory Committee. I will always remember the day John Etgen (a brilliant geophysicist) and I flew to London to meet with the Technology Advisory Committee. We had developed our Subsalt Imaging Strategy and needed to secure funds (a lot of funds) to run multiple at scale field trials of new technologies whose proof of concept was based on computer modeling. I knew our geophysicists had found possible solutions—leadership now needed to find the courage to test these ideas in the field.

John was his usual, brilliant self and simply communicated complex technical issues. The end result was resounding support for our proposal and a challenge to do more. I will never forget the look on the faces of the team when we returned to Houston and told them that we had secured program funding. I don't think that they ever thought it would happen. Their expressions were somewhere between incredulous, thrilled, and sheer terror. I remember going into the office of the scientist who did the 3D Finite Difference Modeling (Carl Regone) looking him in the eye and asking, "This is going to work, isn't it?" He paused, slowly smiled, looked me in the eyes, assured me it would, and it did.

This was one of the most extraordinary times in my career. I discovered the joy of taking a big risk and believing in other's ideas. Together, we delivered a program of new, multiple wide-azimuth acquisition and processing techniques that changed the way deep-water subsalt seismic data was acquired by the entire industry. My role in the project created follow-on roles as the Geoscience Technology Unit Leader and as the Vice President Paleogene Technology Flagship.

In 2009, I was leading the multi-disciplinary Paleogene Technology Flagship, a program to deliver the subsurface and engineering technology to economically develop this emerging play in the Deep Water Gulf of Mexico. Part of this project was to understand the role of the Paleogene discoveries within BP's global asset portfolio. This was also the time when unconventional resources were becoming an increasingly significant component of the portfolio. It was early days in the industry's understanding of the comparative value of conventional and unconventional resources and how to derisk resources through the appraisal and development cycle.

After digging into the comparison for the Paleogene, I wrote a position paper defining the appraisal needs of BP's increasingly complex portfolio of appraisal assets. This was at the time when BP was transitioning from an asset organization to a functional organization. Historically, the Exploration Function transitioned assets to the Projects Function immediately following a discovery. As a part of the organizational changes, a decision was taken to move Resource Appraisal into the Exploration Function. In January 2010, I was appointed to a newly created position of Vice President of Resource Appraisal in the Exploration Function. In this role, I was a member of the Exploration Function Leadership Team accountable for managing BP's Upstream Resource Appraisal portfolio of conventional and unconventional assets.

It was my dream job. The role provided me the privilege of seeing new geology and traveling the world to interact with regional teams. To be successful I needed to leverage a lifetime of experience. This role called me to utilize them all.

Content. Technical strength and knowing my craft is a core foundation of my personal brand. Being credible is a core tenant of who I am. Early in my career this meant being the best geologist I could be. As I progressed through my career, I expanded my understanding of other disciplines and learned to understand how all the technical elements of the business came together in pursuit of a shared goal.

Figure 8. Michelle Judson, 1993, when she joined the Commercial Planning Team, BP Exploration Headquarters, London, England. (Photo: Michelle Judson.)

Ethics. I always tried to speak the truth and to create an inclusive environment where diverse individuals could come together in high-performing teams. These skills were valuable in this role as I was influencing key decisions that would impact the future of BP's portfolio.

Relationships. I was able to leverage a career of relationships with people across the world of BP and industry. Many of the people I had worked with in previous roles were in key leadership roles; the track record we had established of working together enabled us to have honest, direct conversations and quickly reach alignment on critical business issues.

Leadership is about knowing where you want to go. I learned over my career how to set a strategic direction, create a delivery plan, and enroll others.

I am privileged to have worked with several extraordinary women such as Cindy Yeilding, Barbara Yilmaz, Lauren Segal, and Kerry Inman over my career. This network was a source of strength, fun and enduring friendships. (Fig. 8)

I retired from BP in March of 2014. It was time for Barry and me to create a home and build roots in a community. I had accomplished more and seen more of the world than that young geologist starting her career 33 years earlier thought possible. It makes me smile to know that I still have a passion for geology and desire to see more of the world.

One of the greatest joys over my career was motivating people to reach out beyond what they thought possible and embrace challenge in pursuit of an idea. I am currently applying this skill to enable students to find their passion and working with local educators, businesses, and government leaders to connect careers and education.

Michelle Judson was born in New York City in 1957. She acquired her B.Sc. in geology in 1979 from St. Lawrence University and her M.S. in geology in 1982 from the University of South Carolina.

Pinar Oya Yilmaz

In 1977, I chose the Taurus Mountains in southwest Turkey for my field work toward my master's degree at Bryn Mawr College and later for my PhD at The University of Texas at Austin (UT). Little did I know that decision was going to propel me into a job with an oil and gas company.

To acquire permission to work the Taurus Mountains, I had to pull together all my self-assurance and persistence to gain access to the area. I walked to the Geologic Director's office with letters of recommendation and greetings from U.S. geologists. His secretary wouldn't let me in, because I did not have an appointment nor did I look important enough. I told her that I had personal messages for the Director from U.S. geologists and insisted that she announce me. She relented.

Director Sadrettin Alpan was impressed enough with my field work proposal that within 30-minutes, he agreed to allow me to do field work in Finike/Antalya. He gave me logistic support including a room at the base-camp, a Jeep, a driver, and topographic maps. (Fig. 9)

My resolve and determination were tested throughout three summer field seasons by poisonous snakes, conservative Moslems in local villages, and politics within the Turkish geological community.

After spending two unpleasant weeks as the only woman at the base-camp the first summer, I rented a room in a neighboring town. I arrived in this town wearing field boots and pants, where women on the streets were always covered with head scarves and big coats. When I walked down a street curtains would be pulled aside as people gazed at me, their faces carefully hidden in the shadows. Many nights as I came back from the field, men would try to follow me home. This was a very conservative part of the country. But I persisted.

Figure 9. Pinar Yilmaz in the Taurus Mountains, Turkey, doing field work in 1978. (Photo: Pinar Yilmaz, Houston, Texas.)

During my first year at UT in 1978-79, Mobil Oil offered me a job. I had never thought of working for the oil and gas industry, but they were interested in my knowledge of Mediterranean geology and acquired a work permit for me. Before accepting the offer, I asked a Saudi Arabian with Aramco what he thought of the offer. He encouraged me to accept the job offer, praising the company, but suggested that I negotiate for a larger salary and more vacation days. I did and found that was good advice, indeed. I began working for Mobil in 1980 and finished my PhD a year later. I was now learning what it means to be an exploration geologist!

My first well site work was offshore Cook Inlet, Alaska. Mobil had assured me that I would have a separate bedroom and bath. The rig manager was told I was from Turkey and I learned I was the first female geologist on

Figure 10. Pinar near Tripoli, Libya. Geologic field trip, 2008, at the Leptis Magna archeological ruins. (Photo: Pinar Yilmaz.)

that rig. I didn't think much of it but was surprised at the large number of men around the helicopter pad when I arrived. This was followed by men crowding into the break room when I was there. I soon realized they were checking me out.

The male geologist on the rig was upset about losing his single room. He tried to embarrass me by taking me on a tour of the rig facilities while the crew was changing, which entailed them undressing for showers. My instincts kicked in, not trusting him, and, also, noticing the horrified expression on the radio man's face when the tour was offered. I declined his offer. That incident was relayed around the rig and I was quickly accepted by the workers and managers. My fellow geologist was relegated to a room above the diesel engines.

Once, we experienced an emergency on the rig and I was put in charge of the radio. When I answered the radio at first, a male voice at the other end hung up saying, "I must have the wrong number!" After four tries, he finally asked, "When did the rig acquire a receptionist?" I explained I was the geologist, and he finally got it!

For the next four weeks, I was under the protected wing of the managers on the rig, all watching out for me. They later told me they had expected me to get off the helicopter in a veil and black abaya! From there I went to production drilling in Kansas, Oklahoma, and the Texas panhandle participating in the drilling of 72 wells, all the while working with wonderful crews.

Working internationally, I had a variety of experiences related to gender. My first visit to Saudi Aramco's Shaybah field operations required having two female engineers and a geophysicist accompany me where there were no facilities for women. Another great memory was traveling with Petrobras up the Amazon to the Urucu gas operations, where not only were women in charge of field operations, but the boss was also a woman. What a pleasant surprise. Field work in Turkey, Tunisia and Sinai always required male escorts, and, when field work was finished, I was declared *unmarriageable* because I had been in the field with men. (Fig. 10)

It is through some interesting coincidences that my career evolved to include a unique role in relationship building across industry. In the mid-1980s, I was in Houston at the Turkish Consulate's residence helping them get ready to host the Turkish Prime Minister, Turgut Ozal, for a dinner reception. They were personal friends and he had asked me to assist them. Many industry guests were invited who were doing business in Turkey. As the doorbell rang, I happened to answer, and who should I greet but my own company president and his wife! He looked a bit surprised when I introduced myself, but was more surprised later in the reception when I was asked to translate his conversation with the Turkish Prime Minister. Mr. Ozal knew English but I was asked to provide translation for only a phrase or wording he couldn't remember. Mr. Ozal asked me to be the intermediary with correspondence between Mobil and him in the future. This led to an invitation to be a liaison for ongoing work between Turkish Petroleum and my company.

Figure 11. Pinar in the Rub Al Khali desert, Saudi Arabia, 2008. (Photo: Pinar Yilmaz.)

My work has been in research, exploration, and production over the last 35-years working for the same company. I traveled the world working with National Oil Companies (NOCs), academicians, and government agencies. I have made a great network with friends from high school, college days, and work colleagues which cuts across geopolitical boundaries, cultures, and scientific disciplines. They are my friends around the world. I know them and their families—learning from them and growing with them. Some of these friendships resulted in creating a new position in

1997 for me within Mobil as external technology coordinator, where I was to liaise between the company and academia, consultants, and research centers. (Fig. 11)

My early volunteer work started with the Geological Society of America (GSA), Houston Geological Society (HGS), and American Association of Petroleum Geologists (AAPG). Later I worked on technical program committees of the National Science Foundation (NSF), European Association of Geoscientists and Engineers (EAGE), Society of Petroleum Engineers (SPE), International Petroleum Technology Conferences (IPTC), and World Petroleum Council (WPC). I have met wonderful people in these committees and have expanded my network year after year. For example, in 1997, while I was at the World Petroleum Congress in Beijing, I got to know Petrobras friends as they were promoting Rio de Janeiro., which helped laterk when I worked in Brazil as Co-Chair of the 1998 and 2009 AAPG international conference program with Petrobras. This was followed with similar work with some of the other companies, including Saudi Aramco and geologists from Bahrain, Colombia, Malaysia, and the Chinese National Petroleum Company. I enjoy building relationships while managing interfaces between professional societies and my company. (Fig. 12)

Figure 12. Doha, Qatar, 2015, Pinar with Amin Al Nasser, CEO Saudi Aramco on the right and Mohammed Saleh Al Sada, Industry of Qatar. (Photo: Pinar Yilmaz.)

In 1984, I joined Exxon Production Research Company where I served in a variety of technical positions and transferred to Exxon Exploration Company in 1995. Today I am the advisor for external upstream projects at ExxonMobil Exploration Company and serve as World Petroleum Council's Vice President of Finance representing the U.S. National Committee.

Pinar O. Yilmaz was born in Izmir, Turkey, and earned her B.S. in geology in 1976 from Kirkland College (now Hamilton College). She has her M.S. from Bryn Mawr (1978) and Ph.D. from the University of Texas at Austin (1981). She has been honored for her work and service by Hamilton College, ExxonMobil, the Nigerian Association of Petroleum Geoscientists, Brazilian & Venezuelan Associations of Petroleum Geologists, Houston Geological Society, IPTC and AAPG.

Sylvia María Alves Couto Anjos

Geology was a late arrival in the college curriculum in Brazil. Sponsored by Petrobras, the first class graduated in 1961 at the Universidad Federal de Ouro Preto. Sylvia Anjos graduated in 1978 from The Federal University of Rio de Janeiro and was the second female geologist to go to work in Petrobras—the only company operating in Brazil. She felt fortunate to be one of the two women who could join Petrobras when she was just 21 years old. (Fig. 13)

Figure 13. Sylvia María Alves Couto Anjos, 1980, on the Petrobras winning table tennis team. (Photo: Sylvia Anjos.)

Sylvia was anxious to do all the work the other geologists did, including well-site work, but women were not allowed to sit wells. Her opportunity came one day when one of the guys was assigned to a well but did not have a driver's license. Desperate, they called Sylvia at home on a Saturday night and asked her to drive him out to the well. She signed out the company vehicle and started driving them to the location. When they got away from the office, her colleague insisted that she turn the car over to him to drive because he "knew the way."

Reluctantly, she gave him the wheel—whereupon he almost killed both of them in the traffic. After that big scare, they stopped. Deep silence. Then she took the wheel again and admonished herself for having let him drive knowing that the vehicle, and their lives, were her responsibility! The good part of the experience was that once she was out on the location, the company decided she might as well learn how to do wellsite work and take her turn sitting wells. Their decision and her work opened the door for women to go out on rigs for wellsite work in the future.

Sylvia recalled an early wellsite incident that was a result of having no bathroom facilities. She still laughs about her extra efforts to walk far enough from the drilling rig so the crew on the racking platform, who were tripping pipe out of the hole, could not see her. She walked and walked—stopped and turned to see if she could see the guys on the rig—yes, she could. So, she kept walking and turning, kept walking and turning. Finally, she found a bush and was completely shielded from the view from the crown of the rig. She was fully in process of her private business when suddenly a truckload of rig workers came driving up on a nearby, unseen road, shouting and pointing at her. Welcome to the world of well sitting.

When Sylvia was assigned to sit an offshore rig, they would helicopter her back and forth every day because there were no overnight facilities for women on the rigs. A terrible waste of resources, but finally the offshore rigs were altered to accommodate women staying overnight and doing their tour of duty properly. Geologists in Brazil actually loved to pull offshore duty because for every day they spent offshore, they got a day off back onshore. Whereas, with onshore wellsite work, a geologist had to spend three days out on the rig to earn one day off.

It was also a coveted assignment to be sent to the United States for graduate school; Petrobras had never sent a woman and Sylvia wanted to go. She watched carefully as many of her colleagues took the tests (the Graduate Record Exam, or GRE) to gain entry to U.S. graduate schools and often failed. She decided to take the initiative and try the test on her own. She studied in her evenings and weekends and spent a considerable amount of money to take the exam and passed it. She was assigned four months of training at the University of Illinois and she excelled. The professors told her they wished she could stay for a master's program, but to attend graduate school "requires a good score on the GRE." She produced her GRE results and they were all surprised, and agreed to let her work on a master's.

By then Sylvia was married, but she was determined to go on to the University of Illinois. A great misfortune was that her supervisor, Dr. John Howers, committed suicide before she completed her master's degree. However, Professor Albert Carozzi stepped in and, not only supervised the completion of her master's, invited her to study with him for a PhD.

At that time, she became pregnant with her first child and little Debra was born a month before Sylvia started her coursework for her doctorate. Ordinarily, in Brazil, pregnant women would take off four months with each pregnancy, but Sylvia just kept working, not wanting to risk losing the opportunity for her advanced degree. As she worked toward her PhD, she once again got pregnant, and again, just kept working. She had her second baby in September of 1986, and finished her PhD coursework in October. When her boss at Petrobras saw she was pregnant, he declared that he hadn't sent her to school to get pregnant. Sylvia never let that hold her back and returned to Brazil with two degrees and two children, never having taken the maternity leaves she was entitled to.

Becoming a manager was not on Sylvia's radar for years as she worked in the Research Laboratory at Petrobras. She had observed that the financial incentive was really negligible for these positions. However, there was a societal push from the wives of many of the men to get into management for the increase of status. Whereas, rarely did the husbands of female employees want them to become managers. She had been asked to take on a management position in 1988 and declined. Despite her preference for research, she was made the substitute or "acting" manager for several years. After this happened several times, Sylvia decided she might as well take the management position since she was already doing the work. And thus began her journey to becoming Geoscience General Manager for Petrobras Exploration & Production. The first woman to do so.

Figure 14. Sylvia took the initiative to get into graduate school and became the first female Exploration Manager for Petrobras. (Photo: Sylvia Anjos.)

Sylvia ultimately moved away from the Research Lab and into exploration; it was at a most fortuitous and exciting time. It was 2006 and Petrobras had just finished drilling the pre-salt discovery well in the offshore Santos Basin. Suddenly, the company which had been focused for decades on turbidite reservoirs, needed to get up to speed with carbonates and microbial carbonates. Sylvia assumed this challenge with her staff and led an intense ten years retraining staff so they could apply a new model to the geologic and geophysical evaluation and development of the pre-salt reservoirs. Petrobras' production in the Pre-salt achieved over one million barrels of oil per day in 2016.

Though Sylvia Anjos could retire now, the work at Petrobras continues to be too exciting and fulfilling to leave. She has had, and continues to have, a very wonderful career in petroleum geology (Fig. 14).

Sylvia María Alves Couto was born in Rio de Janeiro, Brazil, in 1957. She earned her B.S. degree in geology from the Universidad Federal de Rio de Janeiro, in 1978. After joining Petrobras, she returned to school and earned her M.S. degree from the University of Illinois in 1984, and her PhD in1986. She was married to Luis Anjos and has three daughters, Debora, Maríana, and Fernanda.

María Antonieta Lorente

In 1983, Maraven, an affiliate of Petróleos de Venezuela, South America (PDVSA) originated from Shell Oil, awarded me a scholarship to work toward a doctorate at the University of Amsterdam in Holland with Professor Thomas van de Hammen. The company wanted me to research and fine-tune existing palynological zonations and adapt them for high resolution biostratigraphy for exploration in Venezuelan basins. (Fig. 15)

Figure 15. María Antonieta Lorente, 1996, field trip to see the Querecual Formation, with its spectacular nodules, planning a field trip for the 1997 AAPG meeting. (Photo: María Antonieta Lorente, Houston, Texas.)

As I worked on this problem, I decided it would be good to quantitatively characterize organic matter—like what we do with clastic sediments—which would be useful to characterize paleoenvironments. In 1983, digital image analysis was a very new technology still in the development stage, and there were only two places in Europe (United Kingdom and the Netherlands) that had the equipment. Professor van de Hammen got permission for me to use the equipment that was in The Soil Institute in Wageningen.

For two months, I traveled daily from Rijswijk to Wageningen—four hours daily by train and on foot. I was in the middle stages of pregnancy but managed to analyze about 500 samples. When I finished, the total amount of data captured was so huge that we had to do the first-ever remote transfer from the Soil Institute to the University of Amsterdam. Once I had the data and started the statistical analysis, I realized it had been corrupted—I could not separate the true data from the noise. Going back to the Soil Institute, they said that they had no defects and that I must have made some mistakes that caused the data corruption. I had to repeat the work. Now in my 8th month of pregnancy, I made those four-hour round trips again and reanalyzed at least half of the samples and, again, remotely transmitted the data. Same problem.

Now desperate, I decided to use only the data that could be filtered which left me only 150 samples instead of the 500 I had prepared. At one point, my friend, Berend De Vries, thought we needed to go to the University of Amsterdam Math Institute to look at the integrity of my data. Eight months pregnant, I climbed on the back of his bicycle, and he arduously pedaled us across town without grumbling all the way. Only a real friend would do this.

Even with those limitations, I could demonstrate the usefulness of this type of technology for the textural characterization of organic matter with digital image analysis. Finally, after defending my doctorate, and in the solemn Oude Luterse Kerk (a Lutheran Church built around 1633 in downtown Amsterdam that the University used in the 1960s to 90s for important ceremonies, including the public defense of a PhD thesis), the Soil Institute laboratory manager approached me and offered his apologies. My work had forced them to realize they DID have a problem with the equipment. The corruption was from their side and was in the digital storage part of the system. They only became aware of the problem through my work because no one else had used the equipment so intensively before. He essentially admitted that they could not bring themselves to believe that a young Latin woman from South America could find an error on such a sophisticated piece of technology!

I was awarded my PhD with Cum Laude honors. This was quite an achievement from a University that had only distinguished 25 women with Cum Laude honors in their 355-year history; and most of those honors had been in Humanities, not Mathematics and Natural Sciences!

In 1987, when I returned to Maraven in Caracas, I aspired to have a "friendlier" setup for the digital image analysis technology. I wanted to install the program to work on our desktop computers which were just beginning to populate our offices.

Maraven had an entire floor in the main office dedicated to IT—full of computer engineers, electronic engineers, physicists, and the like. One day, determined to find help with my vision, I took the elevator down to the 7th floor. Uncertain how to approach this department, since I did not know anyone there, I was presented with "a miracle" when the elevator doors opened. There stood a former classmate of my sister from computer engineering school. I had not seen her in many years so I had to reintroduce myself to her. I told her what I was hoping to accomplish. Less than a year later, the first prototype of our new Digital Image Analysis in Stratigraphy (ADIE) was up and running on our desktop computers!

I was so excited and happy with what my team had accomplished that I became very emboldened at the 1987 Christmas party a few weeks after ADIE was up and running. I saw the President of the company at the reception and gathered all my courage and approached him,

"Mr. Castillo, our team has developed a new technology and we would really like to show it to you."

Surprised, he looked at me for a minute, then said, "Very well, then I'll see it tomorrow at 9 am."

"Perfect!" I answered, "tomorrow, 7th floor, 9 am, we will introduce you to ADIE. I will pick you up in your office."

I turned around and rushed to find my team, Orlando Morean, Jenny Rincon and Terry Wright to give them the good news. They almost had heart attacks—in those days the president of the company never came to anyone's office to see something! Quickly, every IT person knew of the president's visit the next day to learn about ADIE. And, I was in trouble. IT management summoned me, whereupon I was reprimanded for talking to the president without prior authorization. I must confess, that reprimand did not worry me much.

The next day I arrived in the office very early in the morning and was greeted by all my colleagues with worried, desperate faces and dark circles around eyes. ADIE had stopped working during the night. They tried everything—disassembled the equipment, changed the processing card—but nothing seemed to work. At 8:50, I decided that whatever had happened, it was my fault for being so enthusiastic. I decided to face the music with Mr. Castillo and accept any consequence for me and for my career.

I went to his office and, as promised, he was waiting for me. I told him, "It is with great shame and remorse, that I have very bad news, ADIE does not work today."

Frowning seriously, he asked, "Are you sure that ADIE ever worked?"

I said, "Yes, it has been without problems for a couple of months."

He was thoughtful for a moment and then said that he wanted to see it anyway. As we walked onto the IT floor, all the IT staff was lined up along the hallway. It was the most embarrassing moment of my life. He greeted them and we went into the ADIE office where our team was looking totally defeated. Mr. Castillo asked them to explain what had happened. They said that the night before everything was fine, but when they tried early that morning, it just did not work. They had changed all the parts with the other prototype, but still it does not work.

So, Mr. Castillo looked at us and said, with extreme seriousness, "Have you tested the electrical outlet this morning?"

We all looked at each other incredulously, then Orlando switched the plug to another source and the whole setup started working normally.

Mr. Castillo, with his eyes twinkling, laughed, and told us, "You created it, but I made it work." A great relief spread throughout the hallways and everyone celebrated!

Two years later, ADIE became the first U.S. patent granted for a combination of hardware and software for this kind of digital image analysis. The team names were included into the INTEVP (Instituto de Tecnología Venezolana para el Petróleo) inventor's mural and Maraven took a booth, for the first time ever, at AAPG's Annual Meeting to promote the proprietary technology.

One of my favorite career stories occurred in 1976 when I was doing my first field work for a month with other colleagues from the Central University of Venezuela in Churuguara, Edo Falcón, Western Venezuela (about 140 miles west of Caracas and deep in the country). As soon as we arrived, we were warned not to talk or get into fights with anyone in town because everybody had a machete and did not hesitate to use them. There were four women in the field party and we were also warned that women could not enter the bars in town. We thought this was a bit of exaggeration to prevent us from getting crosswise with the locals.

Our field party was divided into teams of two, and assigned our areas for mapping and sampling. I was paired with my colleague, Arturo Lara, who happened to be black, and our assigned area was about 18 miles from the basecamp. Our work day began at 5 am going into the field and returning at about 4 pm. After bathing and dining, we worked further on our sample descriptions and prepared them for transport, then updated the geological columns, maps, and cross sections. We usually finished around 10 pm every night.

Very soon, all the locals were talking about the "black and the blonde" working all day long in the field. Of course, people were already curious about what we were doing and the word spread that we were looking for gold. Several tattered peasants approached us saying that they knew where the gold was, but it was always pyrite. Usually, we laughed it off, but we finally got tired of the story and told them we were looking for oil.

It did not take long for everyone in the area to know us, and for us to know everyone there. For me, having been raised in the modern and cosmopolitan city of Caracas, it was a shock to be faced with the extreme poverty in the desolate part of the country, and yet, I found an unbelievable contrast between city and country hospitality. As poor as the country people were, they were always generous hosts. Every time we ventured close to a shack, the children ran to hide behind the mother's skirts and the father came out with the machete in his hand to defend the family. But as soon as they saw it was the "black and the blonde," they always invited us into their homes made of bajareque (posts and cane and a kind of adobe mud). They would share with us whatever they had at their table, almost always a cup of weak coffee or, if there was no coffee, water and cassava. (Fig. 16)

Figure 16. María Antonieta with her colleagues, Enrique Puche, and Oscar Odreman, from the Ministry of Energy and Mines, on a field trip to the La Luna Formation, 1993. (Photo: María Antonieta Lorente.)

One day when we came back to basecamp extremely tired, we learned that we needed groceries for dinner that night and the next day. We had only one vehicle in the camp, an old Jeep CJ5. Very few of us could drive the 4X4 and I was the only woman who could. That night, I was the only one in camp who could drive the CJ5, so I was asked to go to the small grocery store and buy the supplies. Two of my female colleagues volunteered to come with me and I drove into town and to the small store. We bought groceries, but the last item we needed to buy was beer, and the store had run out. The grocer said we needed to return to the basecamp and bring one of the men back to buy beer at the bar. With lots of concern on his face, he warned us not to go to the bar ourselves. We, of course, drove straight to the bar. When we arrived, my two companions got out of the car and proceeded into the bar, while I waited for them in the jeep. I was still dressed in my field clothes, with sturdy field boots and my field belt equipped with canteen, field knife, and Brunton compass. After a few minutes, my two companions were expelled from the bar followed by an outraged chorus of male voices shouting, "In this village women do not enter the bar!"

Shocked, furious, and without thinking twice, I got out of the car and entered the bar alone. Inside the bar, I was met with a very deep and dense silence and astonished faces staring at me. For a second, I got a bit worried, but, determined to stand up to these rough locals, I headed straight to the bartender and ordered 12 beers to take away. The stunned barman looked over to the owner of the bar and began the same mantra, "Here, we do not serve women."

Much to his surprise, the owner shouted, "Give her the beers, *she is the Blonde*, and she is here looking for oil."

The bartender scowled but gave me the 12 beers, and I very proudly turned around and defiantly looked at each one of the men sitting there. Then, I walked slowly out of the bar, jumped into the CJ5, and drove away.

That night we celebrated the first time in history a woman entered a bar in Churuguara and was served beer.

In the 90s, my much-admired and respected colleague, Hans Krause, chose a team for a technical meeting with Exxon in Houston that was 100% women: a petrophysicist, a sedimentologist, a biostratigrapher, and an interpreter.

We were in a hotel close to Exxon's offices so the four of us decided to walk over for our first meeting. When we arrived, the very elegantly dressed, front-desk male receptionist looked at us, and, with a twinkle of curiosity in his eyes, asked what we wanted. We responded, "We are from Maraven, Venezuela, and are here for a meeting with the Exploration Team."

He went on to ask, as usual, for our identification and the name of the persons who we were going to meet, and told us to sit and wait. We waited quietly for about 15 minutes and then became worried because we were kept waiting past the start time of the meeting. We were a little bit upset about being kept waiting. So, when it was five minutes past the meeting time, we asked the receptionist why we were kept waiting so long—perhaps our hosts had not arrived to work yet? He stared at us in surprise and replied he was waiting for the rest of our team to arrive. We got upset and dryly told him that we *were* the entire team.

He looked shocked and immediately proceeded to call our hosts and let them know the Maraven Team was downstairs at the reception. After a few seconds, we were invited upstairs to the meeting room. When the four of us reached the meeting room, we faced about ten geoscientists, all male, impatiently waiting for Maraven. Of course, we noticed they seemed astonished when we entered and thought it was because of our "late arrival." We greeted our hosts and started being introduced but noticed they kept looking toward the door as if expecting more people.

After a few minutes of niceties, the head of their team openly asked us when we were expecting the rest of our group to arrive, no doubt meaning the men. We told him that nobody else was coming and we were late because their receptionist, rudely kept us waiting downstairs. We were ready to begin.

Immediately after we began our presentation, a female geologist entered the room and was introduced as the sedimentologist of the team. We greeted her and continued with the presentation. Later, during the coffee break, she confessed to us confidentially that she had not been invited to this meeting until after it began. Someone had rushed to her office with instructions for her to immediately join the meeting. That was humorous for us; we laughed and understood the purpose of including a woman on their side!

Another story from my professional experiences occurred in 1994 when I was the first female President of the Venezuela Geological Society. I was scheduled to deliver the opening speech at the International Geological Congress we hosted, the "Simposio Bolivariano de Exploracion Petrolera de las Cuencas Subandinas" in Puerto La Cruz, Eastern Venezuela. About a half hour before the opening session, I was called into a reception with the VIPs attending the Congress. I was a bit upset by this last-minute request, as I was preparing for the opening ceremony and time was precious. I was already stressed about facing the big gathering, as I tend to get nervous before these presentations.

I arrived at that informal meeting, and to my surprise, the PDVSA Exploration Business Unit VP sitting at my side very subtly requested that I show him my speech and get his approval before my delivery. Though caught by surprise, I just smiled and whispered back, "No Sir, you are my boss at the office, but not here. In this Congress, you are my guest, so, I invite you to sit and patiently wait a few more minutes and you can hear my speech with the rest of the attendees."

About two years later, I was the first female geologist promoted to the Executive Level (Group 30) in Maraven Exploration, and about a year later I was trusted with managerial duties in the geological laboratories of PDVSA Exploration Business Unit, *with* the Exploration Business Unit VP's support and approval!

Close to the end of 1996 when the PDVSA Exploration Business Unit was undergoing merger turmoil with three affiliates (Lagoven, Corpoven and Maraven), I was given the responsibility to merge all the Geological Laboratories. Our new boss was convening a series of meetings with the managers of the affiliates for the transition to the new structure.

As one of the two Maraven managers, I arrived at the meeting within the corporate building. Our new boss began the meeting, looked at me and said, "I want a manager for this position not a Miss Venezuela."

I was astonished at this insult. But, I kept my cool, looked around, and then retorted, "I don't know what you are talking about; I don't see any Miss Venezuela around, neither in this office nor in the corridor."

The first months working with him were a nightmare.I was distraught. I even sought advice from several high-level manager colleagues during one of the Annual AAPG meetings, but cultural differences between them and my situation rendered their advice useless. After carefully considering all the options, which included resigning, I decided to stay with my job and go ahead with what I call the "old Latin way."

"Be resilient; never give up on ideas and remain cool and calm throughout any difficult situations."

I must do this, even when my blood was boiling and I had to hold my breath, and not show my fists. We continued to clash in our management meetings, especially when he expressed different views as to how the Geological Labs should be operated. I would remain calm and very professionally explain my perspective. This was put to the ultimate test in a countrywide management meeting when he embarrassed me in front of everyone by saying, "Of course, whatever I say, Dr. Lorente will not agree because she thinks she knows more than I do."

All eyebrows were raised at that comment, and they turned to me. I put on a nice smile, and calmly but firmly said, "That is what you say, but it isn't exactly the case. I disagree about this specific matter related to the Laboratories and wish you would accept that Laboratories are my specialty, and I am obligated to provide you with my recommendations. I think we could settle this if you would accompany me on a tour around our major Geological Laboratories and Warehouses all over the country, so you can see with your own eyes what I am talking about. We could then eliminate pointless discussions about who is right or wrong."

Immediately, he accepted the challenge in front of everybody, and in the next weeks we visited all the facilities. About a year later, he said in another managerial meeting, "María Antonieta was very smart in dealing with me, choosing to *show* me her points, rather than to have endless discussions about which strategy was best for her labs."

After a year of difficult experiences, our professional relationship changed from confrontation to trust, and he sought my advice in many different matters, even after I retired from PDVSA Exploration Business Unit. He knew that I was always going to tell him the truth as I saw it and would never just agree with him to climb the corporate ladder. In the end, we became good friends and still are. My advice:

"Stick to your guns, but be professional."

María Antonieta Lorente began her career in the oil business in 1980 with Maraven S.A. (formerly Shell de Venezuela). During her career, she has broken many "glass ceilings," starting in 1987 when she became the first woman to be recognized as an Exploration Specialist with Holding Director Potential—her first breakthrough. In 1996, she was the first woman in Maraven to be promoted to the Executive Level, and in 1997, was the first woman in PDVSA with countrywide responsibilities as Unit Chief of Laboratories and Geological Services. In 1998, she became the Leader for all Stratigraphers in the Business Unit, another first for a female, and by 2001, was the Planning and Strategies Manager for PDVSA Exploration Business Unit.

María Antonieta took retirement at the end of 2001. From 2002 to 2007, she and two other female colleagues created and ran their own consulting company in Spain (Geoambio, S.L.). She had an interesting project with the Wine Industry at the Group Fuertes--Bodegas Luzon and, in 2008, they obtained the first Ecoefficiency Award granted to a Winery in the Murcia Region. In 2011, she returned to the oil industry as a consultant and continues as such today.

María Antonieta has broken a few glass ceilings as well with her volunteer association work, first as President of the Venezuela's Geological Society (SVG) 1993-1997, as a member of the SEPM Board of Directors (International Councilor) 1998-2000, President and founder of the Latin America Section SEPM, 1998-2001, and in 2002, as Professor of the post-graduate program in geology, she developed a 100% online teaching program in Stratigraphy for the Central University in Venezuela.

María Antonieta Lorente, was born in Caracas, Venezuela, in 1954. She earned her Geological Engineering and master's degree from Universidad Central de Venezuela in 1978, and 1983, respectively, and her PhD Cum Laude from the University of Amsterdam in 1987. She married her life-long partner, Jose Luis Perez in 1978, and they have one child. María Antonieta is still working as Stratigraphic Services Manager at ALS Oil and Gas-Reservoir Laboratories, and lives in Houston, Texas.

Cindy Yeilding

Cindy Yeilding knows from experience that one of the greatest drawbacks to success can be a person's adherence to "dogma." She has often discussed how this has impacted her career, relating her experiences when she has challenged dogma and biases. She professes,

"Dogma is defined as a prescribed doctrine proclaimed as unquestionably true. Dogma is not the same as truth. It describes simply an accustomed way of thinking, or "conventional wisdom."

John F. Kennedy once likened dogmatic thinking as, *"the comfort of opinion without the discomfort of thought."* Though it is often associated with religion, we find dogmatic thinking throughout our everyday lives. Cindy has made a career out of challenging these conventional "wisdoms," such as finding oil in a "dead sea," creating value from castoff discoveries, and helping to disprove the myth that women can't be scientists and/or leaders.

Cindy's path into geology began in preschool and was strongly influenced by her mother, who had a compulsion to pick up rocks, shells, and fossils (crinoids for necklaces) on all their family vacations out of their hometown of Dallas, Texas. She insisted, when Cindy was trying to select her college courses, that she at least register for "Rocks for Jocks"—and that did it, Cindy fell in love with geology. However, her sixth-grade teacher had predicted her path long before she arrived at Southern Methodist University. Cindy says her teacher wrote in her autograph book that she was "*A very nice girl...*" (Cindy interjects here, "I was chubby, buck-toothed and wore thick glasses, what else would she say?") then the teacher went on "*...and an excellent geologist!*" Apparently, her rock and fossil collection was memorable; it was donated to the school as a teaching guide for future classes. By middle school, Cindy shed the glasses, got a decent haircut, braces, contact lenses and parlayed her gymnastic skills (she could do 27 back handsprings in a

Figure 17. Cindy Yeilding displays her skills at "splitting" her time and balancing her life at an early age as a Junior High School cheerleader in 1975. (Photo: Cindy Yeilding, Houston, Texas.)

row) so that she was elected to the cheerleading squad. Indeed, she was known in high school as "the cheerleader who was great at math." (Fig. 17)

She loved her academic work at SMU, where she got her B.S. in geology in 1982. She continued her education at the University of North Carolina, where she studied Appalachian carbonates with John Dennison, Dan Textoris, Conrad Neumann, and Walter Wheeler. After graduating with her master's degree in 1984, Cindy's plan was to earn a PhD and become a college professor. But first, she thought, spending five years or so in the energy industry would be good for her, so in 1985, she took a job with Sohio (now BP) in Houston, Texas. As it turns out, she still loves her work 32 years later.

Her arrival at Sohio was apparently a surprise; she wasn't expected to arrive for a few more months. She was placed in onshore subsalt exploration—a foreshadowing of her future. A few months later, almost everyone in her team was let go. She was told, "You would have been gone, too, but HR wouldn't let us fire someone with less than six months' experience."

Cindy quickly moved into the pool of operations geologists supporting onshore and offshore Gulf Coast drilling wells, and spent much of the next three years as a drilling rig (wellsite) geologist. Cindy's new career path took her across the U.S. Gulf Coast, which was where she experienced one of her earliest brushes with a rather striking dogma: *Women are bad luck offshore.*

That might be partially correct, because in her first few years on wellsites, BP found very little oil or gas! Eventually, she figured out that what most bothered the all-male rig crew was not that she was a woman, but that she was a *geologist*. Here's what a crew full of engineers thought of geologists, "They want to halt all drilling progress just to look at tiny rock samples. They think they understand drilling but they don't. In short, geologists just get in the way."

In the eyes of the rig crew, being a woman was far less vexing than being a geologist. To buck this thinking, Cindy had to develop relationships with the crew members and then share her understanding of each well's objectives and geology. She was teaching. The crew began to understand her insights, and when men on the rig started throwing around terms like "stacked channel complex" and "Miocene nannofossils," she knew she had become a part of the drilling team. That she was the only woman for hundreds of miles didn't matter—to most people. She remembers just one fellow that she had never won over. While she worked offshore with him for five weeks, every day he would ask, "When are you going to leave?" She would always answer, "Not soon enough." To which he would spit on the rig floor as she walked past. Okay, you cannot win them all.

Overcoming that, she was soon known as "Cookie" on several offshore rigs. Not because she was female, but because she could not resist the freshly baked chocolate chip cookies on the rigs. They would typically have a batch waiting for her upon arrival. In turn, Cindy spent hours running hundreds of laps around various rig heliports trying to work off the effects of four meals (and countless cookies) a day.

Three years and no social life later, Cindy transferred into BP's offshore Gulf of Mexico appraisal, development, and production team. One of her favorite dogma-busting experiences occurred when she was assigned to relinquish a Gulf of Mexico federal lease block, which included a sub-economic discovery, back to the government. Learning that new seismic had been shot over the block, she asked not only for some time to reevaluate it, but also to be allowed to assemble a technical team including Mac Beggs from BP's research lab, reservoir engineer, Tom Morrow, and, geophysicist, Wayne Wilson. Though permission wasn't completely granted, they managed to build the team and integrate the existing wells with the new seismic data. At first assessment, the seismic appeared to have too many migration "smiles" to be of any use, but collaboration between the geophysicist and geologist resulted in the discovery that these were not migration smiles at all—they were in fact shelf margin deltaic clinoforms. Though the team was limited in experience, most having only four or five years in industry, they created detailed reservoir maps, reduced the geologic uncertainty, and asserted that this was an economic field, even if just barely.

Then another breakthrough occurred. The facilities engineer, Thyl Kint, also young and inexperienced, challenged the current assumptions around the production facility, eventually demonstrating that a tension leg platform was not required and that a fixed platform would work. This further improved the economics and enabled

BP to move the Amberjack field into production, and the revenue from the field helped "keep the lights on" for the Houston office for many years. Leadership was thrilled with the teamwork and technical excellence and that they did not have to release the block back to the government.

Probably her most satisfying work has been in the Deepwater Gulf of Mexico. She loves working in exploration because all projects begin with some new concept or technology. So, almost by definition, exploration involves dogma-busting. Unique ideas, and developing the technical and business case to justify pursuing them, create opportunity, and make explorers a unique combination of scientist, artist, and marketer.

Cindy's early career had been peppered with annual or, sometimes more frequent, layoffs. After she completed her appraisal/development assignment, she was transferred to a short-lived Gulf of Mexico shelf exploration team. A few months later, and during a particularly difficult downsizing, her line manager stopped by to share "good" news: She was being moved to the deepwater Gulf of Mexico team and she still had a job.

The deepwater move turned out to be a good news/bad news story. Companies had been secretive about letting geologists view seismic lines from the deepwater "tight holes." Geologists might see only one line across the landmark Shell/BP "Mars" discovery or just a *cartoon* drawing of what had been seen on the line, which led to misinterpretation of deepwater success factors. Cindy's new assignment was a prospect that was already being drilled, one that was the last of seven ill-fated industry geophysical bright-spot "syncline" dry holes. The exploration school of thought, at the time, was to search for oil in synclines, exploring from "the top down." This meant starting at the top of the section and, working downward, looking for geophysical attributes, which had led to the previously mentioned dismal well failures.

Old Dogma – "This type of exploration was like 'shooting fish in a barrel.'"

It was difficult to find anyone who wanted to hear about the well results that lacked any sort of technically viable trap or charge mechanisms, but her team did notice there were astonishingly well-developed middle and lower slope sands. However, working with the old model, the team's well reviews and updates were virtually ignored. This disappointing phase of exploration soon propagated a new dogma.

New Dogma – "The Gulf was finished as a major hydrocarbon basin."

Only BP and Shell remained in the Gulf—most of the major companies were already gone. But, BP leadership believed in the potential of the *deepwater* Gulf of Mexico, and instead of letting the team go, they implemented a major regional review of the basin. The team, led by Barbara Yilmaz, included Houston-based explorers as well as several UK-based technical experts and leaders. The technical excellence brought from BP's global headquarters in London added significant value, and BP changed its exploration strategy for the Gulf of Mexico.

The explorers fell back on basic geology and reevaluated their entire exploration model. And, the team hunted for "elephant" prospects that could yield over 500 MMBOE and which would have the potential to open a new play and support stand-alone infrastructure to get the hydrocarbons to market. While working on this, they soon found their maps stopped at the edge of salt layers where no data was coming through (salt famously contorted data so it was useless for interpretation). The team was encouraged to use their imagination to interpret where they previously would have been stymied. This created some high-grade "sweet spots" in the deepwater Gulf of Mexico and led to a remarkable prospect inventory of potential "elephants." The next step was to figure out where to drill, but, again, seismic imaging related to near-surface salt hampered the selection of drill sites.

Cindy believes she has probably worked as many or more offshore lease sales than any geoscientist at BP and has always found it to be exciting — and often humbling. Though the team had built a significant prospect inventory, their new geophysical imaging for salt proved so complex that many leases expired before they could drill all their lease inventory. Billions of barrels of oil have been found on the old BP leases by other companies who leased after BP had to relinquish the leases.

Overcoming that frustration, Cindy was charged with drilling the prospect inventory of "elephants." The advances in 3-D depth imaging had been applied and the prospects were high-graded. Taking over from Michelle Judson, Cindy managed the team who delivered the Thunder Horse, Thunder Horse North, and Blind Faith fields, delivering more than one billion barrels net to BP, along with a few more dry holes. The joint exploration/drilling team won another Innovation Award after the Thunder Horse discovery.

In 2001, Cindy moved into a leadership role in global technology, as head of over 200 scientists and engineers in BP's research and development (R&D). Again, improving seismic imaging offered the most business promise. Many of BP's high-graded exploration basins worldwide, were covered by a massive and complex canopy of salt which, like in the deepwater Gulf of Mexico, distorted normal seismic imaging. "Simpler" salt geometries had been imaged through the application of conventional 3D (Kirkoff) depth migration at scale, but the more complex salt bodies required a breakthrough. BP (and the industry) had hit a brick wall—they needed a geophysical breakthrough.

When the R&D teams initially discussed the need for higher density seismic data to image around salt, they concluded that just was not a solution. Eventually, John Etgen, one of BP's top research scientists, came back with a bit of dogma-busting. He said he thought the problem was solvable–the technology to acquire and process this data was within reach. It was only the logistics, simultaneous operations by a flotilla of boats to acquire the data—that made it appear prohibitive. Cindy asked John, "Well, it might be hard, but is it do-able?"

John thought so and developed a focused program with a different offshore geophysical acquisition setup. He brought in Michelle Judson to lead the program. The new design was called WATS for "wide-azimuth towed streamer seismic." The great thing about WATS was that it was not *really* new technology. It was a *new way of using existing technology*. They could now get a clearer picture of the geology below the salt. All of industry quickly applied these new methods. Simultaneously, Cindy applied this same innovative thinking to the geological challenges in the company's portfolio, and soon the R&D budget went from $5 million to $80 million.

Cindy's first international experience was in 1994 when Venezuela opened exploration blocks to foreign companies. Her role was to lead the joint BP/Amoco team in western Venezuela, and she jumped into some of the most rewarding technical field work and team work she's ever experienced. The team's remit included three weeks of work in the western Andes, supported by a local academic geologist—who didn't realize Cindy was "the boss" until he had uttered a few disparaging remarks about women. Soon he came to her and apologized profusely, stating that he didn't mean anything negative, and that he respected women as leaders in business.

But then he said, "Everything is going to be fine, as long as we don't have women going into the field with us."

She replied, "I'm heading to the field with you tomorrow for three weeks. See you then!"

He also didn't realize she spoke some Spanish and made daily derogatory comments in Spanish. At the end of the trip she told him, "*Ya sabes, he entendido todo lo que dijo.* (I understood everything you said.)" He was completely embarrassed, and to compensate, he offered to carry her backpack full of rocks. She accepted. (Fig. 18)

Figure 18. Cindy, always drawn to the Carboniferous, seizing the opportunity to examine an outcrop near Knoxville, Tennessee on a GSA "vacation" field trip. Note the hot pink boot laces acquired right after her corporate feedback about wearing colors that were "too bright." (Photo: Cindy Yeilding.)

Back in Houston and now leading the Western Hemisphere geoscience technology team, Cindy's group could begin putting their innovative 3-D pre-stack depth imaging migration at scale, on all of those intriguing sub-salt prospects. They won another of BP's Innovation Awards for their achievements. With her newfound passion for advanced geophysical imaging, Cindy soon found herself back in Gulf of Mexico exploration.

Cindy spent the next ten years in Gulf of Mexico (GoM), most of this time in the role of Vice President, GoM Exploration, and Appraisal. After this she moved into the leadership role for new plays and global access. In her role as BP's Vice President of Global Basin Analysis, she and her team combed the world's basins seeking to uncover new play concepts, encountering new dogmas, and identifying new opportunities. What is fact and what is fiction has yet to play out, as many of these basins are still untested and their "heretical thinking" remains "unbusted"— for now! Cindy is currently Senior Vice President for BP America, where she serves as an internal and external ambassador and leader for BP's U.S. businesses and holds multiple board roles.

About ten years into her career, Cindy was thrown in a quandary when she was sent to a week-long Leadership Assessment class to be evaluated on her potential as a leader. Her analysis came back with very good reviews and some valuable comments about where she could improve technically and corporately. Then, there was an added piece of advice regarding her physical appearance; her hair, though naturally blonde, and her stylish clothes were thought to be distracting. The recommendation she received was to tone down her appearance to "fit in" better. She left the seminar worrying about how to deal with this, and after mulling it over, went to her boss, Jim Farnsworth, to tell him about the advice and what she had decided to do, "I won't be myself if I make these kinds of changes, so I just want you to know that I accept that my career will be dampened. And, furthermore, if I change, what happens to the next blonde, slightly trendy female geologist?"

He said, "I don't care what you look like—you're one of the best deliverers I've ever worked with. The bottom line is the quality and impact of your work."

Relieved, she headed out to Neiman Marcus and bought two new "cute and colorful suits."

Despite this type of experience, Cindy's career progressed and being female never played a significant part in her mindset. But, Cindy became aware of "gender" when she was asked to give a talk at a 2005 AAPG luncheon regarding the status of women in the industry. Allyson Anderson (Book), then with ExxonMobil, asked her to deliver "something provocative." Cindy thought, "Oh, I think everything is fine—this could be the shortest talk in history!"

Being a scientist and loving research, she delved into the challenge, reconstructing her peer group and where they were now. The short answer not—working nearly as well as she had thought! Looking at statistics, and trying to gather information from other companies led to a pivotal change in her thinking; she discovered that the numbers were, in fact, not so good. Not because women weren't hired, but because they didn't stay in the business. She has since made a large effort to understand why women leave the workforce, what individuals and companies can do to change that, and how can she help industry not only attract, but retain women in geoscience. Cindy's vision is a world of true meritocracy, where all people can succeed based on their performance and qualifications. *She also found that being an advocate for improving the ratio within a company for gender, race, and culture, in fact, improves the company's business performance.* Mentoring and sponsorship of others became a new mission for her, and her company is wholly aligned with the concept.

Cindy's career has provided her incredible opportunities for making a difference and she had felt it to be gender-blind, but occasionally, odd gender-related comments would surprisingly appear. When she was awarded the role as head of global geoscience research and technology, she was thrilled and couldn't wait to get started. Ian Vann and Kenny Lang, who recruited her for the position, pointed out that her experience in operations and exploration, coupled with her multiple technology awards and international experience, were precisely the qualities they wanted. But she was deflated when one of her close friends said, "You only got that job because you're a female." The comment made her even more determined to prove herself.

In 2011, Cindy was appointed as the AAPG board member on the Offshore Technology Conference (OTC), succeeding Susan Cunningham, who was the first female OTC board member. Susan challenged Cindy to continue to shake up the board's thinking. The board is quite innovative and progressive, but when Cindy suggested to the all-male group that they host a women's networking event at the next meeting, a dead silence overtook the room. Then one of the fellows said, "I think that's a great idea."

Soon others chimed in and agreed. OTC planned it for about 50 attendees and 125 showed up! It was a great success; more than 300 people attended the following year And, organizers had to turn away an additional 100 people due to space limitations. The event has since become a core part of OTC's agenda as the conference contin-

Figure 19. Cindy with her husband and progeny, two budding geologists, Tyler and Zack, have spent many vacation days examining rocks. Thanksgiving at Enchanted Rock, Llano, Texas, 2006. (Photo: Cindy Yeilding.)

ues to build inclusion and diversity into the meeting content.

Cindy challenged another strongly dictated career advancement dogma.

"You must be mobile in the energy business."

Generally corporations projected the dogma that a person must move about, move their family, and take assignments wherever the company deems necessary. If you don't do it, your career will dead end. She knew, early on, that with her husband's career needs, their two children Tyler and Zack, and, aging parents on both sides of the family, mobility could not be part of her career equation. But, as others have said,

"If you ask for what you want and make sure you perform, you can shape your own destiny."

Thus, she and her family planted roots in Houston and have lived and worked there very successfully through both domestic and international opportunities. (Fig. 19)

AAPG has been a major part of Cindy's career and has offered her many opportunities for personal and professional development. Cindy joined AAPG as an undergraduate. While the prestige of belonging to such an august society was a compelling reason to join, one of the biggest bonuses was that AAPG sent so much mail that her undergraduate campus mailbox was never empty. Service to AAPG came early for Cindy, when she served as a student chapter officer at SMU. Over the years, Cindy delivered multiple talks and poster sessions, chaired panels and took courses, honing her skills as a geoscientist. Cindy and her colleagues gave the first public presentation of the Gulf of Mexico Thunder Horse discovery at AAPG's Annual Convention to a packed audience, and Cindy was thrilled to be selected by Paul Weimer as an AAPG Distinguished Lecturer in 2002-2003 (Fig. 20). The Distinguished Lecture tour was a career highlight, and while Cindy wasn't the first female AAPG Distinguished Lecturer, she believes she was probably the first to deliver many of her lectures while pregnant. AAPG offered Cindy a platform and opportunities to be provocative, including encouragement of her talks "*Is the Workstation Killing Geology?*" and "*All that's Certain is Uncertainty.*"

Figure 20. Cindy Yeilding, BP's Vice President of Global Basin Analysis, Board member for the Offshore Technology Conference. (Photo: Cindy Yeilding.)

Cindy Yeilding was born in Dallas, Texas, in 1960. She earned her B.S. in geology at Southern Methodist University in 1982 and her M.S. at the University of North Carolina in 1984.

Julia Ann Downey Garvin

I was born in Fort Smith, Arkansas, in 1960, and it wasn't until I was older that I realized that there was a logic to me being born in Fort Smith, my brother in Tulsa, and my sister in Oklahoma City—it was all related to petroleum geology. I had the grand tour of the Anadarko Basin before I was three years old while my dad, Marlan Downey, worked in Shell's field offices when we were little. We grew up immersed in geology, driven by the passion my father had for the science. We didn't go to Disneyland, we went to the Grand Canyon. Family road trips to see the grandparents in Nebraska took several days, as we traversed through Utah, Arizona, and New Mexico. Family photos of us growing up always had us rock climbing, or along a creek bed. So, I thought everyone grew up licking rocks and had a chemistry set in their garage with commercial grade chemicals.

I entered The University of Texas in 1978 to pursue a degree in mathematics or physics. For the sheer fun of it, I enrolled in geology courses as my elective since I enjoyed the opportunity to be outdoors and had grown up with a fascination for the science. One of the biggest benefits of the geology department was the camaraderie of the students. No other department had as many field trips, student organizations, and opportunities to socialize. The male/female ratio was quite high, which I admit, I enjoyed. The real turning point in my degree choice came when Dr. Bill Fisher, who was the current department chair, pulled me aside and suggested I earn a degree in geophysics which would combine all my math and physics credits with my geology credits. At the time, geophysics majors could opt for an industry internship in lieu of the six-week summer geology field camp. So, I had to make a choice—six weeks in the grueling West Texas desert, or eight weeks in a highly-paid petroleum industry internship. I interned with Marathon Oil Company, and thus began my twenty-four-year career with them.

In the 1980s, there were several women geoscientists at Marathon, but none in supervisory or management roles. I set this as a goal, as my parents had always instilled in me that I could do and be anything I wanted if I worked hard and set my mind on it. But first, I had a technical mind-set to challenge at Marathon. When I first started, Marathon had separate geology and geophysics teams that worked on exploration projects. I was never content with only providing seismic interpretations and maps, preferring to interpret the logs myself and integrate them into my interpretation. This gave me the chance to see the big picture, I developed a talent and passion for generating new plays and prospects, and an ability to clearly convey my ideas.

While my exploration skills flourished, my career growth was hampered by not having experience in operations. Operations assignments generally were not given to women, especially to women for offshore work. I lobbied hard to get on that logging rotation so that I could go out to offshore rigs for both logging and coring runs. What a thrill when I finally received notice that I was to fly out to one of the jack up rigs. The helicopter pilot was very friendly, and suggested that we could make a stop on the beach for a quick six-pack if I wanted. He smiled and winked, and proceeded straight to the rig.

The only women that had been on this Marathon-operated rig were the galley hands, so they didn't quite know what to do with me. They arranged for me to use the company man's cabin and we shared a bathroom, using bungee cords as a lock. (I don't think the company man appreciated this switch.) The rig hands were actually excited to have me there, and I spent countless hours in the galley listening to their troubled love lives, giving them my perspective. I never had to eat alone.

My career took off with the guidance and assistance of many great colleagues and mentors at Marathon. Tom Fanning, who was the Exploration Vice President at the time, recognized my potential and provided me with the opportunity to work as his staff geologist and later ,as the first female exploration supervisor. Paul Gucwa later moved me into the appraisal team for Marathon's deepwater Gulf of Mexico Troika and Petronius projects in the Lafayette, Louisiana office—where I would meet my husband. I returned to Houston, now married to a drilling engineer, and became the first female exploration manager overseeing Marathon's Gulf of Mexico deepwater exploration team.

After the birth of my two children, I began to question whether there really was such a thing as a balanced work and home life. Instead, it was clear to me that it was about choices. Do I get a full-time nanny? Do I work part-time? Do I try to do it all myself? I had a promising career path ahead of me, but I also had an option to join my dad at the small family business he had started, Roxanna Oil (named as a tribute to the original Shell Oil company,"Roxana", set up in the U.S.) (See Chapter 1.) At the time, Roxanna had no debt and was successful with a few projects as well as having acquired consulting contracts. I was only six years from full retirement benefits with Marathon Oil, when I made the choice to leave a large amount of money on the table and join Roxanna for a fraction of what I was making at Marathon. No regrets. (Fig. 21)

Figure 21. Julie Ann Garvin, became President of Roxanna Oil, Houston, Texas in 2005 and founder of Roxanna Associates. Prior to joining Roxanna Julie was Geoscience Advisor, Worldwide Exploration for Marathon Oil Company. (Photo: Julie Garvin, Houston, Texas.)

Today, Roxanna holds several hundred thousand acres of working and royalty interests in the United States and internationally. Our consulting group is continuously under contract to provide expertise in exploration and development programs for Majors and Independents. Paul Gucwa has become Roxanna's Exploration Vice President, and one of my most trusted advisors. Most of all, I thoroughly enjoy coming to work each day, working with my Dad, five brothers and sister who all are involved in the company. I get an adrenaline kick every time we develop a new play idea, every time we close on a deal, and every time I smell oil in the samples. (Fig. 22)

Being a woman in this business has had its benefits, in my estimation. It caused me to not simply follow an established career path, but instead to create my own.

As women, we can have such insight to others perspectives, that it helps us to create win-win partnerships through thoughtful negotiations.

As a business owner, I truly understand the work/life balance issues for both male and female employees and work hard to provide a work environment that allows for flexibility. I am one of the lucky ones who has enjoyed an exciting, successful career as female geologist. But, "luck favors those who are prepared."

Figure 22. Julie with her father and Chairman of the Board of Roxanna, Marlan Downey, reviewing their leasehold acquisition in 2008 in what is today the prolific "Stack Play" of Oklahoma. (Photo: Julie Garvin.)

Julie Downey Garvin is President of Roxanna Oil with over 35 years as an exploration geologist. She received her bachelor's degree in geophysics from The University of Texas at Austin, with honors, in 1982. She is a member of AAPG, SEG, and several geological societies, and is on the Advisory Board of the UT Jackson School of Geology. Married to Mike Garvin, they have a son and a daughter. Julie is a regular guest speaker at industry conferences and geologic society luncheons.

Deborah Susan Robinson Pfeiffer

Although I was born in Arlington, Virginia, I spent my formative years in Omaha, Nebraska. We did not have a lot of money but my parents always had books in the house. In 1970, when I was in the 2nd grade, Mom and Dad bought a complete set of the World Book Encyclopedia. Over the next few years, I read every volume cover to cover. As I got older, I bought books or borrowed them from school or public libraries. I read classic novels, biographies and, occasionally, science related material. When I was in the 9th grade, I checked out a Physical Geology book from the public library and suddenly, I knew what I wanted to do for the rest of my life.

I started working in industry right after I graduated from The University of Texas at Austin (UT) with my master's degree in geology in August, 1988. I went to work for Shell in New Orleans as a geological engineer, even though I did not have a degree in engineering. The title was given to all the geologists in the production group. I worked in what was known as the Coastal Division and provided geologic support for eight different fields my first year. This was a heavy workload for a new hire and was due to an unexpected resignation in the team.

After about a year with the company, I was given a petrophysical field assignment but also kept my office workload. The field assignment was required of all production new hires and consisted of traveling offshore to be the company representative during logging activities. I had many adventures traveling from New Orleans to Venice, Louisiana, to catch a boat out to the offshore rigs; most of the 15 logging jobs I went to were on platforms, jack up or barge rigs. The field assignment was six months long and it never failed that I would be requested, usually at the last minute, to drive down to Venice in the middle of the night. Since this was during the winter months, there was more than one occasion when I was driving in heavy fog and could not see much beyond the front hood of the car—something my older self would never do!

One time, I had a boat captain take me out to the rig during a particularly foggy night and the company man said to me, "I can't believe you made it in this weather. That boat captain is the only one crazy enough to bring you out here. In January 1991, I was assigned to the Gulf of Mexico deep water Auger development project, which had an interdisciplinary team of geologists, geophysicists, and subsurface engineers. Auger was Shell's first Tension Leg Platform project and I was very excited to be a development geologist on the team.

Shortly after getting this assignment, my husband, Ron, and I found out I was pregnant with our first child. As soon as the first trimester of my pregnancy had passed, I decided to tell my supervisor as a courtesy and thought the news was of no importance as I planned to continue working after the baby was born. However, in those days, most professional women at Shell who had children did not stay with the company very long for a variety of reasons—not the least of which was the lack of benefits, demonstrated by a maximum of only six weeks' maternity leave. As soon as I told my supervisor the news, he said, "We have to go tell Dave."

Dave was his boss—and I was totally perplexed by his reaction. Later that day, I found myself in Dave's office with my supervisor talking about my pregnancy. During the conversation, I kept thinking to myself, why does Dave need to know about this, and what difference does it make? I never found out why we had to have the conversation with Dave, but I assume it had something to do with the fact that I had just been assigned to a high-profile project and they wanted to know if I was planning to stay or not. I stayed.

Six weeks after Lauren was born, I was back at work. Ron and I both managed to each hold down fulltime jobs and take care of a baby without any family support in Houston (Ron is also from Nebraska). I continued to work on the Auger project, interpreting 3D seismic data, maturing development well locations, and supporting well operations. In late 1993, my husband and I found out that we were having twins. This is when things got interesting. In April of 1994, Katherine and Kristin were born. Again, after a six-week maternity leave and with an additional week of vacation, I went back to work. This time it was much more difficult to juggle both work and babies. All three were in diapers for a while and the twins did not sleep through the night for the first six months. I got to the point where I would come to work, sit down at my desk, turn on my computer, and just stare at the screen for a few minutes because I was so sleep deprived. To Shell's credit, they accepted my request to work part time, but I found that I was doing the same amount of work for half the pay so I went back to work fulltime after a few months.

I had many supervisors during my early years with Shell and all but one of them had attitudes that ranged from neutral to supportive of professional women balancing a career and children. The outlier was a supervisor that I worked for over an 18-month period who told me that he did not think women who had children should work and that I would never be promoted beyond the discipline level. He was wrong.

The most frustrating aspect of working and raising children was finding good quality day care in the New Orleans area. When Lauren was nine months old, we moved from the West Bank to the Northshore which for those who are not familiar with the area, is a difference of more than 40 miles. However, we loved our babysitter who had taken care of Lauren since I had gone back to work, so we continued to take Lauren to her even though it meant doubling back to the Shell building downtown each morning and driving the wrong direction to pick her up every afternoon. My friends at work used to rib me that I needed to invest in a helicopter to get Lauren back and forth from the West Bank. After the twins were born, we hired a series of nannies (I had to fire three in a row until I found one I liked) until all three children were old enough to go to a local daycare in Mandeville (Fig. 23).

After working on the Auger project for three years, I was ready for a different assignment. I like variety and being challenged, so I talked to my supervisor about other opportunities. After more than a year, I was interviewed and accepted for a job as the development geologist for Mensa, another Shell deep water project in the Gulf of Mexico (GoM). It was only after I had been in the job awhile that I found out that the chief geologist had played a hand in my being selected for the role—all because he had seen one or more presentations I had given while I was working on the Auger team. This was the first time I realized,

Figure 23. Deborah and Ron Pfeiffer, with their oldest daughter and twins. (Photo: Deborah Pfeiffer, Houston, Texas.)

"You never know how or when someone in a position of influence can impact your career."

Soon after joining the team, the deep-water division was reorganized geographically, instead of by value chain, so I found that I was now responsible for both exploration and development in the Mississippi Canyon protraction area. This gave me the opportunity to work exploration for the first time. I worked on several GoM lease sales while at the same time drilling development wells at Mensa. In 1999, I was asked to consider a planner role. However, in addition to lease sales and development work at Mensa, I started to mature a lead called Princess because I was convinced that it would be a discovery. As I have done for most of my career, I listened to my inner voice to help determine which opportunity was right for me. I turned down the planner role and went on to drill the discovery well at Princess finding, 200 MMBOE.

In September 2000, I left Shell and joined BHP Billiton (BHPB) in Houston. When I first arrived at BHPB, I was assigned to the GoM exploration team. There were only 250 people in the office when I joined, so I could get to know many people in a short period. Within a year, I started my first supervisory position and first international assignment. Over the next 3 1/2 years, I was the Subsurface Manager for the Angostura project offshore Trinidad and Tobago and led the subsurface effort from first appraisal to first production. As Angostura neared first production, I knew that it was time to move on to another role. Because there were no other management roles available, the Exploration President asked me to spend a year studying appraisal best practices and determine lessons learned from a number of BHPB appraisal projects. I could make good use of what I had learned and subsequently took on the role of GoM Appraisal Manager and then the global role, Director for Near Field and Appraisal.

One of the biggest lessons of my career came when I was demoted from Director to a Senior Manager Exploration role in 2008. I spent the first two weeks feeling sorry for myself before making a decision,

"Make the best of the situation and learn everything you can.

Figure 24. Deborah Pfeiffer, with BHPB, now VP Geoscience Operations. (Photo: Deborah Pfeiffer, Houston, Texas.)

Over the next six years, I led international projects in several countries including Trinidad and Tobago, Barbados, South Africa, Colombia, Falkland Islands, Brazil, and India. In late 2013, I was promoted to my current role as Vice President Geoscience Operations which covers all safety critical geoscience activities (e.g. pore pressure prediction/detection, shallow hazards prediction/detection, well formation evaluation, and seismic acquisition project management) (Fig. 24). In this latest role, I have leveraged my varied experiences over many years in operational work such as drilling wells and acquiring 2D and 3D seismic data.

In summary, over my career, I have learned many lessons.

Be your own advocate. Know what you want to do and lay the groundwork to make it happen.

Build your network so that you have a voice in the room when talent management decisions are made.

Get to know people that you admire and seek their advice either through formal or informal mentoring.

Listen to your inner voice to help you decide whether an opportunity is right or not.

Be patient and flexible." This is especially important if you are also raising children. Sometimes things do not go according to plan and you must be resilient when dealing with difficult people or situations.

Take time for reflection. Request and take feedback constructively.

Ask for a coach if you have something you need to work on. I have had a coach twice in my career and both times, it was a fabulous opportunity for self-discovery and I benefited greatly.

Finally,

Be curious and be willing to take on roles where you will need to stretch your skill sets.

Deborah Susan Robinson Pfeiffer was born in Arlington, Virginia, in 1961. She earned her B.S. in geology at University of Nebraska in 1984, and her master's at The University of Texas at Austin in 1988. She and Ron Pfeiffer were married in 1985 and reside in Houston, Texas.

María Jesús Simón Granda

After I graduated in Geology from the Universidad Complutense de Madrid, Spain (UCM), in 1987, I began working for CEPSA (Compañía Española de Petróleos SA) in February, 1988, with a scholarship from the Industry Ministry. Although Spain is not an "oil country," CEPSA has been involved in the upstream sector since its origin in 1929. The former CEPSA Exploration & Production (E&P) subsidiary (CIEPSA) was created in 1940, a pioneering exploration effort for Spain. When I joined CEPSA, the Exploration & Production (E&P) team was composed of about 30 people including non-technical personnel. The small Geoscience Department was staffed with five male geoscientists and myself. Today, the company has 900 employees and the Geoscience Department has around 100 employees.

After working with geologists and petrophysicists of the group for seven months, in September I was sent out as a wellsite assistant geologist to the Cordoba C-1 well. It was being drilled in the Guadalquivir basin, South Spain, very close to a small village that we used as basecamp. When I arrived, a child from the village approached us and with a funny Andalusian accent asked me in front of the whole team, "Are you one of the *oil men*?"

Over the laughter of the staff I answered him, "Yes dear; I am one of them."

A year later, geophysicist, Ramon Romero, requested that as part of my on-the-job training, I perform a reinterpretation of the large seismic program acquired in the Guadalquivir Basin where the company had just had a gas discovery. Upon completion of this task—my first experience as a seismic interpreter—I began assisting him in the interpretation of several seismic campaigns of the Berkine Basin in eastern Algeria. Ramon was promoted to Exploration Manager and I gradually assumed more responsibility. My "temporary office" during those months was the boardroom of the company, where there was a 15- meter long conference table—ideal for the seismic interpretation on paper. Our seismic sections were tens of meters long and the paper prints were very difficult to handle. I rolled and tied them hundreds of times while interpreting the selected horizons—coloring with my Stabilo pencils.

Ten different 2D seismic surveys had to be integrated over the Rhourde Yacoub Block 406A Exploration License in the Berkine Basin, Algeria. With more than 100 milliseconds (ms) of misties between them, those were the days when we needed to apply manual corrections over the entire data set and the measured two-way time. It was tedious and time-consuming, but had to be done. Next, we created structure maps for the prospective formations and identified a closure of less than 20 ms in the southern part of the Block. We named it the "Rhourde El Khrouf (RKF)" prospect.

Proud of our work, we travelled to Algiers in 1990 to present the work to our partner, Sonatrach. At the first meeting in their offices, I was asked, "And then—you are the wife of whom?"

"No, no sir, I'm not married yet!" I responded timidly to the audience. Surprised, they looked at me for a minute, then said, "So, you're the secretary?"

Figure 25. María Jesús Simón Granda, 2003, finalizing an Ecopetrol contract, in Madrid Spain. (Photo: María Jesús Simón Granda, Madrid, Spain.)

In those days, it was unheard of to find women in the E&P technical teams in Algiers, and it seemed logical to them that I must be the wife or the secretary of some executive in the team. Ramon explained to them that I was the geophysicist who had interpreted the maps to be discussed in our meetings. In the early 1990s, I was always the lone female in our many partner meetings.

Our partner approved our RKF prospect and we started preparing the RKF-1 well proposal. It was very difficult because it was the first well to be drilled in that part of the Berkine Basin and was in a remote area with no infrastructure. However, for me, it was very exciting because everything was new.

In July 1992, I travelled to the RKF-1 wellsite in the middle of the Sahara Desert. I was approaching the rig, I noticed the workers were leaning against the railings of the rig floor—dangerously close to breaking the railing—staring at this woman approaching the drill site! It was the first time they had seen a woman in the desert, but after the initial surprise, and within a few days I felt perfectly integrated into the team. (Fig. 25)

Figure 26. María Jesús Simón Granda was involved in CEPSA's first discovery in Algeria, the RKF-1, opening the Rhourde field in the Berkine Basin. (Photo: María Jesús Simón Granda.)

The RKF-1 well resulted in an oil discovery and I spent the next three years traveling between Algiers and Madrid, working nonstop, including weekends. At that time, the total CEPSA geoscience team was comprised of only two people, me and my boss, Ramon. We had a huge responsibility for preparing and monitoring the back-to-back drilling of the RKF appraisal wells, and at the same time, designed a seismic campaign for RKF, and a nearby Ourhoud prospect, which resulted in the second largest oil field in Algeria.

After the discovery of RKF field, the Sonatrach/CEPSA Association acquired three seismic surveys over Block 406A, and I spent some weeks in the desert with the seismic contractor with each of those surveys. The contractors, again, were surprised to see a woman as representing the operating company, but I felt perfectly accepted by all the staff from the very first minute. (Fig. 26)

Figure 27. Seismic work in the Berkire Basin prior to the Ourhoud discovery where María Jesús was a surprise to the locals, but was well integrated into the fieldwork. (Photo: María Jesús Simón Granda.)

In the mid-1990s, we didn't have workstations in our offices in Madrid and I was sent to Denver, carrying as my hand luggage the magnetic tapes from the seismic processing center. I spent several months at International Reservoir Technologies, Inc. (IRT) offices and worked with Dan Stright (who had been working with us since the discovery in 1992) and Scott Haberman (a former Chevron geophysicist) who introduced me to workstation new technology for interpreting the seismic. Both were great friends to CEPSA and to me, and worked well in our behalf. (Fig. 27)

I consider myself a privileged person to have been part of the very beginning of what is now the CEPSA E& P Division and for having directly participated in the discoveries of very important fields. More than 28 years of professional life have provided many anecdotes with very diverse characters from all corners of the world. I am sharing this contribution as a tribute to Ramon Romero, who was my teacher, my mentor, and my boss from the beginning of my career. He had an undeniable intuition for exploration; he taught me and everyone to work hard, to maintain a positive attitude in the face of adversity, and to stand up for our team against any obstacles. Tragically, he died a few years ago, but he was responsible for the pioneers at CEPSA E&P to come to love the oil and gas exploration side of this business.

María Jesús Simón Granda was born in Spain in 1964. After her Geology bachelor's degree from Universidad Complutense de Madrid she completed a Post Graduate degree in Information Systems at the Universidad Pontificia de Salamanca in 1991. She has been in the E&P division of CEPSA since 1988 and was the first woman to become Exploration Manager; she has been the Asset Manager for CEPSA Colombia (2001 to 2016) and she is currently the CEPSA Geosciences Manager. She was Vice-President of the AGGEP between 2006 and 2008. Married since 1990, she has two children.

Susan Morrice

There are very few people who get a chance to make a big difference in a country and maybe fewer geologists. Susan Morrice is one of the rare few. It all started with a phone call. Susan was working in her Denver geological consulting office one morning in 1984, when an old friend from near her native Ireland, Sir Ian Rankin (who owned Rankin Oil), called and said in his very British accent, "I say, Susan, do you know if there is any oil down here?" (Fig. 28)

Figure 28. Susan Morrice, newly arrived from Ireland in Denver, longing to be an entrepreneur. 1976. (Photo: Susan Morrice, Denver, Colorado.)

She said, "Where in the world is 'down here?'"

He said, "Oh yes, here in British Honduras, but I guess they call it Belize now."

Susan replied honestly, "I don't know, but I'll see what I can find."

Soon she was at the U.S. Geological Survey (USGS) library at the Federal Center in Lakewood, Colorado, asking the librarian about any geologic publications ranging from Mexico, Honduras, British Honduras, and Guatemala. Fortuitously, J. A. Peterson and others had just released an open file report that sorted out the stratigraphy for the entire area and tied in the productive strata of the Mexican Gold Coast throughout the region down to Guatemala (Peterson, et al, 1983).

She delved into the study and was soon convinced that the same productive horizons in Mexico could extend south to Belize. She called Rankin back and let him know what she had found. He asked her to hop on a plane and meet him in Belize. Susan was 30 years old at the time; a petite 5 feet 4 inches, blue-eyed blonde with a typical Irish ruddy complexion. She exuded boundless energy and enthusiasm. She still does!

Susan Morrice was born in 1952 and raised in Belfast, Northern Ireland, in the height of the ethno-nationalist conflict known as, "The Troubles." She went to Trinity College in Dublin for her bachelor's in geology (1976) and headed to the United States for her first job. She had read about the American entrepreneurial spirit and was determined to become an entrepreneur herself!

She landed her first job describing rock samples at American Stratigraphic Company in Denver, happy to be putting her degree to work. Later, she went to work for Knight Royalty Company as a Frontier Geologist and found herself at the leading edge of the new plays emerging in the Rocky Mountains, such as the Overthrust Belt from Montana to Arizona, the Columbia River Basalt gas play, the Michigan basin Niagara Reef play, and the Californian Salton Sea play. She also had the experience of being involved in bringing Knight Royalty public on the Stock Exchange. These experiences fed her desire "to go it alone," so, she set up S. Morrice and Associates in 1982, and said yes to all the consulting work she could get. Working in Belize was her favorite consulting and very soon she had to hire seven people to keep up with all the work (Fig. 29).

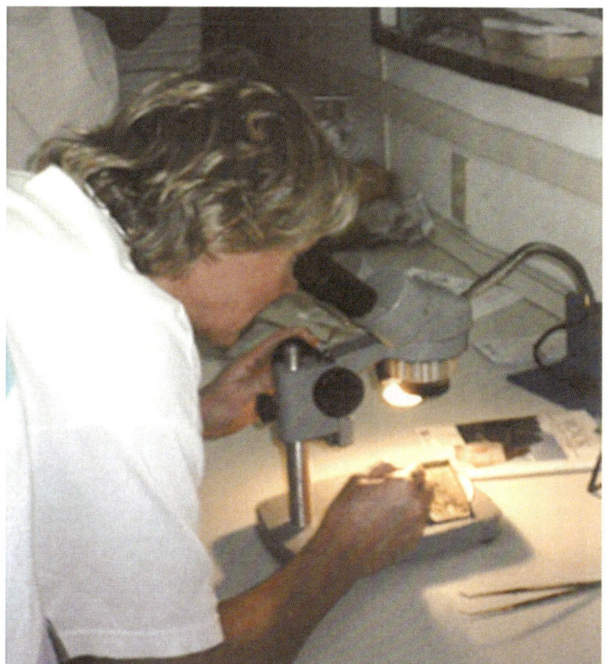

Figure 29. Sample descriptions for drilling wells was part of Susan's first job with Amstrat, and she still does it today for her own wells. (Photo: Susan Morrice.)

Rankin and another partner, based on her recommendations, took some leases onshore Belize, and continued to employ her as a consultant. However, the partner ran out of money and could not pay her consulting fees. The only asset he had was his interest in the leases. Never having imagined herself as a working interest partner—as a real oil company exploring international leases—she was soon doing just that in partnership with her friend, Ian.

One of many bizarre experiences Susan had in three decades of exploration was when she and Ian had completed their seismic on their onshore leases and Susan took a contingent of Dallas oilmen into the Belize jungle to see the exploration territory. Susan and Ian were trying to interest the Texans in investing in the project. Miles into the interior of the country, near the Guatemalan border, the Dallas oilman, who insisted on driving even though he was not used to those challenging roads, hit a muddy dip in the tree-logging road and made the mistake of gunning the vehicle. This, of course, caused their jeep to dig in and, soon, they were sunk into mud over the axle.

After several attempts to get out by digging and pushing, Susan said, "Well, we'd better start walking as we have many miles to go before dark."

And, off they went. After several miles, they suddenly heard another vehicle approaching and soon saw a battered pickup truck with armed drug runners/guerillas. They seemed totally shocked to find a bunch of gringos in the jungle. Susan quickly decided the best course of action was to humor them and "pretend" they were just good neighbors and she enthusiastically approached them with a big smile and said, "Oh, do help us with our wee problem. We are stuck back a couple of miles and need help getting our car out!" She convinced them, and back they went to the jeep, where the guerillas proceeded to pull it out.

Suddenly, they heard a roar coming from the jungle and looked up to see two British tanks emerging with their gun barrels leveled and very threatening. An officer popped up out of the turret and asked, "What the bloody hell are you all doing here?!"

Again, Susan, did not hesitate, but ran forward with her very Irish accent and said, "I'm just wishing I was back at home in Belfast instead of stuck here in the jungle!"

The officer, who three days before had left Belfast, was shocked. After an awkward stand-off, which included a very quick exit of the drug runners, the soldiers got out their chains and used a tank to pull the vehicle out of the mud. They then confessed to Susan that they were, in fact, lost. Susan, having supervised seismic in the area, possessed the best maps of the region and taking them out said, "Follow us! We'll take you right to your camp at Holdfast."

When they dropped off the soldiers and made their way back to asphalt road, the Dallas oil man turned to Susan and said in his deep Texas drawl, "Suz-annnnn? Did you jes set up this whole dang thang for us?"

Suffice it to say, they did not invest, and she never heard from them again.

In fact, Susan and Ian found they could not engage any partner to invest in drilling at that time. The political climate in the newly born country of Belize was under threat of invasion from Guatemala (Guatemala had maintained for decades that "British Honduras" was their territory and even after Belize's independence in 1981, the territorial dispute was unsettled.) Belize requested and required help from the British armed forces to guard their borders. That political situation, plus the negative history of earlier unsuccessful drilling efforts, helped to defeat the project. Reluctantly, they let the leases go. But Susan had fallen in love with Belize and their people.

In 1988, she was introduced to a young Belizean employee of CGG, a geophysical company, in Denver. A mutual friend contacted her and said, "I know you love Belize and we have a Belizean working for us in Denver whom I think you should meet."

This was Mike Usher, working as a seismic surveyor. He came from a well-known Belizean business family. As they talked, they discovered they both shared a vision of finding oil and gas in Belize and using it to completely transform the country for the good. Over the next 15 years, they explored both onshore and offshore licences and managed to find partners to join in exploration and drilling to the tune of $12.5 million—but with no success.

Susan continued with other projects which included exploration with Robbie Gries and Denver-based Priority Oil & Gas, to look for shallow onshore natural gas in the cross-border area of Ireland and Northern Ireland. Susan hoped that a discovery in the broader region of Northern Ireland would bring economic prosperity and help in the reduction of "The Troubles." As they met with county officials in Country Fermanagh, a bomb was being planted in their hotel and was detonated the next day. Fortunately, no one was killed in that incident, but the "peace" that had "broken out" in Ireland in 1995 was definitely not a given. The cross-border natural gas exploration venture was disappointing. The six wells on their million-acre block were drilled and had gas shows, but the hydraulic fracturing necessary to develop the tight sands was constrained by limited onshore choices for equipment and even more limited time to experiment and optimize frac'ing techniques. It was an engineering and economic failure and the project was dropped.

In 1994, when Robbie Gries was Chair of the AAPG Annual Meeting in Denver, she asked Susan to chair the "International" convention activities. Susan said, "What do I do in that job?"

Robbie answered, "I have no idea—the position has recently been created because the organization is growing with international members faster than with U.S. members and it seemed like a good idea."

Susan came back to Robbie shortly thereafter and said, "Robbie! I have a brainstorm! What if we invite the oil ministers from all the petroleum countries of the world to come to the Annual meeting and show their oil and gas potential and licenses? Companies can see everything in one place!"

It sounded like an amazing idea, and Robbie took it to the AAPG staff and Executive Committee, only to face an enormous amount of skepticism and negative reactions.

"It will cost so much!"

"It could take so much Exhibition space!"

"How about the security of the ministers?"

"Do you think they will even come? What if it is a dismal failure!"

"What about our reputation?"

The fears were endless. But, Robbie convinced them that the Denver contingent would raise a half a million dollars to cover costs, that the volunteers could be found, and that Susan would make it happen. AAPG gave them a deadline of January for the money to be raised. When the deadline was faced, Susan and Robbie had only raised half what was needed. They hemmed and hawed and, without totally lying, made it "appear" the money had been secured. And, in fact, they did raise the necessary funds by convention time.

Believe it, build it, and it will come!

In June 1994, the first AAPG International Pavilion was born (Fig. 30). Fifty countries were represented, from Brazil's large Petrobras and Indonesia's Pertamina to tiny Liberia and newly born Eritrea. Denver geology families took in many of the high-level Ministers and their teams. Denver geologists met every delegation at the airport. A last-minute field trip into the Denver Basin was offered to showcase natural gas production into combined cycle combustion electrical generation using waste water for hydroponic tomato production. The International Pavilion was wildly successful and has become an institution at the AAPG Annual Meeting for over 20 years. More importantly, it has been said that billions of barrels of oil have been discovered because of the relationships and partnerships spawned in the International Pavilion! Susan was Awarded the Distinguished Service Award by the AAPG and described as a global visionary.

Figure 30. Susan in front of the Denver Convention Center where the AAPG International Pavilion was born in 1994. (Photo: Susan Morrice.)

Susan's devotion to supporting young geologists with similar creative ideas is demonstrated by her support of Mary Beth Hatteberg, her young employee who came to her with an idea for a Student Exposition where students would be invited into S. Morrice Associates' office to present poster sessions of their work to potential employers. Morrice would invite industry representatives to attend and meet the students, and review the posters. Shortly before the event unfolded someone thought to invite AAPG staff to the exposition to see if it might be a concept that AAPG could embrace.

Crowded into the small office, the Exposition was a big hit and the next year AAPG sponsored it in Houston at Rice University, as the "AAPG Student Expo." The event became a successful employment platform for students from all schools—especially schools that only had the rare visit from a petroleum industry recruiter. Having been in place for over 20 years, it has provided a win-win situation for students needing exposure to industry opportunity and for companies to evaluate excellent students in a very professional setting. The Expo has been duplicated in Laramie, Wyoming; Norman, Oklahoma; Bakersfield, California; and Morgantown, West Virginia.

Meanwhile, Susan's work in Belize continued. Susan did a lot of soul searching about how she wanted to continue in exploration and how much she wanted projects that would benefit the people of a country without just "taking all the oil money and running," as was the model for many historical international projects. She wanted to develop a new model, a holistic business model (holistic is defined as treating something as a whole, not a part) She anticipated that if oil was found in Belize, it would not be an "external" part of the country's business, but integrated into the whole economy of Belize. Wallace Pratt's phrase intrigued her, "Oil is found first in the mind." While in the middle of a seminar about how to fully develop a person's mental potential, her friend, Mike Usher, called, "Susan, a farmer was drilling a water well in the Cayo area and is very disappointed because the water is contaminated with oil!"

Susan told Mike that Cayo was where she believed the oil migration pathways would be most prospective. They both got excited and could again envision discovering oil in Belize, transforming Belize, and creating a holistic model for oil development. They formed Belize Natural Energy (BNE) and acquired 500,000 acres of onshore leases. But, there had been 50 dry holes drilled in the area with no success, and they could not find a partner to fund the drilling. They decided on a new tact, and went to Ireland where 76 small Irish investors embraced their concept and became shareholders in BNE. This time, all the stars aligned—they acquired drilling partners and drilled the first wildcat well. The selection of the location for this first well can only be attributed to "a leap of faith!"

The huge acreage block had only limited 2D seismic data available at the time and the odds were not great. Like finding a needle in a haystack! But, EUREKA! The first well came in! It was the Mike Usher #1, testing 1000 barrels of oil a day at 3000 feet! A play can commonly require 10 to 15 wildcats to discover oil, especially with only 2D seismic, so this was fortunate indeed (Fig. 31).

BNE got the oil to market in record time which created cash flow to drill five more wells in a row—all successful. The heartbreaking part of this tremendous accomplishment was that Mike did not live to see the success. The first oil discovery in Belize occurred on the first anniversary of Mike Usher's death. (His wife, Patty Usher, continues to serve on the BNE Board of Directors.) Over the next ten years, BNE continued to develop the field and experienced the highest production rate at about 5000 barrels of oil a day. BNE turned around the fortunes of the entire country saving it from a very difficult financial crisis in the Great Recession of 2008-2012.

Belize Natural Energy is the largest revenue generator in the country. They have employed up to 400 people, 98% Belizean. Ancillary businesses around their exploration and development increase that economic impact by thousands of people. The company successfully faced the further challenge of creating an entire petroleum infrastructure—pipelines, storage tanks, transport tanker trucks, computer monitoring, port facilities, etc. In 2015, BNE celebrated 10 years of production and 10 million barrels produced. Susan reached back to her old friend, Sir Ian Rankin, after the discovery and presented him with some shares in the company—a small gesture of thanks for introducing her to Belize. This kind of unrequired generosity is almost unprecedented in the business.

Figure 31. It can be tense, watching a display of downhole data on a screen as a well is logged—will it be a discovery? A dry hole? (Photo: Susan Morrice.)

BNE regards the people of a country as part of the "true natural resources of any country." Susan calls it "the oil within" at BNE. BNE has won international recognition for its focus on education, community development and sustainable, environmentally responsible production. In 2012, they won the GetEnergy Education Award based on their "new holistic model," a global

Figure 32. Susan Morrice continues to have meetings with cabinet members in the Northern Ireland government showing them the importance of exploration and development for Ireland. (Photo: Susan Morrice.)

competition involving 40 other energy companies, and countries most of which had multiples of BNE's staff and revenue. Oil is the limited asset, but the open creativity and energy of the employees of the company is unlimited and exemplifies the real potential and value of any company and country. Another unique aspect of Susan's relationship with Belize was that when she negotiated the leases with the government, she requested and got a percentage of the royalties to go toward a non-profit Foundation "The BNE Trust," which has contributed over $8 million to educational and environmental work throughout the country.

On October 1, 2015, in New York, the holistic reputation of BNE was celebrated at the United Nations (on its 70th Anniversary), when a ground-breaking East-West, country to country partnership was signed between BNE/Belize and the United Arab Emirates (UAE) all based on BNE's people-centric approach. Susan's early vision for discovering oil and making a real difference in Belize could become a model for other countries to emulate and replicate. A dream come true!

Susan is often found back in Ireland where her roots run deep and she can pass on her exploration and life model to young entrepreneurs. Today she enjoys her two daughters, Hannah and Clare, and granddaughter, Jace, who remind her how important it is to make a lasting difference in the world they will inherit (Fig. 32).

Susan Morrice was born in Belfast, Ireland, in 1952. She earned her bachelor's degree in geology from Trinity University in Dublin in 1976. She moves between Belize, Denver, and Northern Ireland on a regular basis.

Chapater 17 Sources and References

Anjos, Sylvia Maria Alves, Rio de Janeiro, Brazil. 2016. Personal communication, 9/2016-12/2016; source of photographs as cited in figure captions.

Bay, Annell, Houston, Austin, Texas. 2016. Personal communication; 10/2016-12/2016; source of photographs as cited in figure captions. Video interview, 9/15-16/2016, archived at AAPG, Tulsa, Oklahoma.

Covert, Bryce, 2013, "Having More Women on Boards Sparks Even More Diversity", bcovert@thinkprogress.org, November 25.

Cunningham, Susan, Houston, Texas. 2016. Personal communication, 8/2016-01/2017) and source of photographs as cited in figure captions. Video interview, 9/13-14/2016, archived at AAPG, Tulsa, Oklahoma.

Garvin, Julia Ann Downey, Houston, Texas. 2016. Personal autobiographical writings and source of photographs as cited in figure captions.

Granda, Maria Jesús Simón, Madrid, Spain. 2016. Personal autobiographical writings, personal communication and source of photographs as cited in figure captions.

Judson, Michelle, Lummi Island, Washington. 2016. Personal autobiographical writings and source of photographs as cited in figure captions. Video interview, 8/8-9/2016, archived at AAPG, Tulsa, Oklahoma.

Lorente, Maria Antonieta, Houston, Texas. 2016. Personal autobiographical writings, personal communication and source of photographs as cited in figure captions.

Morrice, Susan, Greenwood Village, Colorado. 2016. Personal communication and source of photographs as cited in figure captions. Video interview, 8/7-08/2016, archived at AAPG, Tulsa, Oklahoma.

Pfeiffer, Deborah Susan Robinson, Houston, Texas. 2016. Personal autobiographical writings and source of photographs as cited in figure captions.

Yeilding, Cindy, Houston, Texas. 2016. Personal communication and source of photographs as cited in figure captions. Video interview, 9/16-17/2016, archived at AAPG, Tulsa, Oklahoma.

Yilmaz, Pinar Oya, Houston, Texas. 2016. Personal autobiographical writings and source of photographs as cited in figure captions.

Epilogue

Anomalies—Pioneering Women in Petroleum Geology: 1917 – 2017 is a celebration of individual courage, fortitude, and professionalism; it is also a timely reminder of 100 years of historic efforts that began with post-Victorian social attitudes and basic inequities in a male-dominated profession.

The main objective for this book was to uncover the history of women in the science and business of petroleum geology, to appreciate their lives, their struggles, their successes, and their failures. I wanted to better appreciate the building blocks they provided to our generation and future generations. I wanted to know these early pioneers as intimately as I could; a task inherently difficult from the distance of so much time and so much social change. It was an impossible goal, even if I could have talked to the earliest of our petroleum geologists, but I went as far as I could, and have personally realized a rich appreciation for these women and for their careers.

The success of our pioneering women over formidable odds has been the driver in this effort to preserve their legacy. I want to give them a voice, to preserve their records, and to broadcast their accomplishments. As I celebrate these women who made positive impacts on the petroleum industry, I also mourned the loss of so many from this exciting profession due to the perceived role for women in the household and the archaic rules about their working outside the home. I anticipate this book will bring more stories and more heroines out of the dark and, no doubt, additions and corrections to the stories now written.

I, more fully, recognize the powerful advantages that women of the Affirmative Action generation, including myself, enjoyed by having more equitable working conditions that provided options to a family and to women within the family. I know our era benefited from having legal recourse to counteract would-be career spoilers. Our generation also had household conveniences beyond imagination for women of the 1920s and 1930s, which truly made it easier for a woman to combine domestic responsibilities with working outside the home. And, significantly, our generation benefited from the breakthrough advances in birth control that gave us more options to combine a career with family planning.

Our petroleum pioneers, if they were to stay in the industry, had to find a way to "live within their situation" and those who were successful were, no doubt, formidable. But, where we found personal records, we learned that the challenges did drain the spirit and nurture self-doubt. Women who said, "What else could I do?" were right, they had no recourse. Publicly, they often said, "Oh, I always got along very well and have no complaints." But privately, many would confide their discontent over the lack of equal pay, recognition, and promotion.

Women in the workforce today, when they have good jobs, great mentors, and exciting geologic assignments might not look back to embrace this history, but I believe their careers would be greatly enriched by finding empathy for these early petroleum geologists. Tough times in today's careers will be easier to withstand knowing others before them found ways to overcome difficulties. Many women today might carry the illusion that success is mostly about rewards for good performance. But it was not always that way, and for many, it remains a struggle today.

Anomalies

Looking at the women "on top" of their professions today, who have had greater options and choices to design their own career paths; I understand how drastically the world needed to change for that to be possible. The changes for women between "then" and "now" are revolutionary—women have been freed to pursue their passion for geology, encumbered only by the same twists of fate that affect the men in our industry.

When I started this project, I did not realize how many heroes I would encounter and come to adore. I met real oil finders, business women with interests in the wells they drilled, women who were philanthropists, women who developed personal wealth, and women of science who made an economic difference to the industry. Our pioneering women in petroleum geology were indeed "anomalies," different from their male cohorts in countless ways, and they brought increased value to an entire industry.

--RRG

Women in the field in 1909, collecting fossils near White Mound, Oklahoma. (Photo: # 5130, Western History Collections, University of Oklahoma, Norman, Oklahoma.)

Glossary of Some Terms Used in This Book

These definitions were written for the layperson and are not intended as a comprehensive resource for a petroleum industry professional.

Aero magnetic survey	Magnetism in the earth varies tremendously. From my yard to my friend's home across town, the pull of the earth's magnetic force is different. Geophysicists can measure this with airborne equipment and interpret how the basement rocks under various data points cause these differences.
Alidade	Surveying instrument for mapping, which has a telescope for sighting and measuring angles.
Anticlinal theory	Early geologists were convinced that an anticline would capture oil and gas if it had an impermeable layer covering it to prevent buoyant natural hydrocarbons from leaking to the surface.
Anticline	When rocks are folded, as occurs in "mountain building" the folds that warp upward (convex) from the axis are called anticlines while the folds that warp downward (concave) from an axis are called synclines.
Balcones Escarpment	A large prehistoric fault traverses through the Austin, Texas area and created the "hills" on the northwest side and left the "plains" on the southeast side. The old fault line can be seen in many areas and is called the Balcones Fault.
Barge rig	A drilling rig set up on a barge that can drill wells in shallow water.
Bedding plane	Sedimentary rocks are deposited in layers in most cases by water or wind. Each layer of rock is laid down as a "bed" of sediments, the break between one layer and the next is called the bedding plane.
Benthic	Bottom dwelling sea life and the ocean bottom itself.
Biostratigraphy	Bio means life, strata means layer. In geology, biostratigraphy is identifying and correlating the fossil life found in layers of rock.
Blow out valve	The equipment (valve) used to shut off the fluids circulating up or flowing from a well during drilling or completion.
Blowout preventer	The preventer has both automatic and manual values to shut off fluids from rising to the surface from a wellbore with too much force or pressure. Otherwise, the well might "blow out" or be a "gusher."
BOPD	Barrels of oil per day. A well might produce 200 barrels of oil per day or 200 BOPD.
Borehole seismic	A process, with special tools made to go into a wellbore, that creates sound waves and measures how the rocks respond to those waves, such as how fast or slow the sound is carried.
Brachiopods	A sea animal similar to a clam, with two halves or two valves. The valves don't mirror each other like clams do.
Brunton compass	A compass to help a field geologist with precise measurements of direction (quadrant or degree) and angle that rocks are oriented and sloping (strike and dip).
Bug-picker	A nickname for people who work with identifying microfossils. A micropaleontologist.
Calcareous	Calc, meaning calcium, is often combined with carbon trioxide ($CaCO3$) to form calcite. Calcite will react to acid by "fizzing" like the bubbles when you open a bottle of soda pop. Calcareous rocks contain calcite.
Carbonate	A rock made mostly of calcium carbonate(limestone) or calcium-magnesium carbonate (dolomite).
Carbonate stratigraphy	Carbonate stratigraphy is the study of what controls the layered sequences of limestone ($CaCO3$), dolomite ($CaMgCO3$), and associated rocks.
Carboniferous	The rocks deposited during the Paleozoic Era, 345 to 280 million years ago (mya). It was sometimes called "The Age of Coal" as many coal layers were identified in that rock sequence. Coal is a form of carbon from plant matter, hence "carboniferous" was the description.
Cartographer	Cart means 'map' in Latin, and a cartographer is a map maker. Petroleum geologists are prolific map makers.
Casing	Casing is defined as a "shell" that protects something. Well casing is steel pipe that protects the layers of rocks around an oil well bore-hole from any of the fluids that are produced…whether oil, gas, water.
Casing collars	The end of each length of casing (pipe) is thicker and contains the threads to screw two pieces of casing (pipe) together. This thicker part of the casing were the lengths of pipe join is called the collar.
Casing head gas	Gas is produced from a hydrocarbon-rich rock layer at depth up through a drilled well's casing. At the top of the casing, referred to as the "head," the gas goes into equipment to be measured and transported. All gas coming up the pipe to the casing head is called casing head gas.

Cast off discoveries A discovery is made when oil and/or gas are encountered in anticipated economic quantities. If it is not economic to produce, meaning it costs more to produce than can be made by selling the hydrocarbons, a company may choose to not develop the discovery. It can be referred to as "cast off." At some later date, higher prices or better technology might make the discovery economic.

Cenozoic The youngest of the geologic eras, 66 mya to the present.

Chain tongs A type of large wrench that clamps or releases easily when used to connect and disconnect (break) drilling pipe.

Chambered tool A tool that can be lowered into a wellbore, which has a chamber that can collect debris or sand from the bottom of the wellbore and bring it back to the surface. Used to clean out a wellbore.

Chaotic bedding A bed of rock is a layer of rock. Sedimentary rocks have usually been deposited by water or air and if not disturbed, will lithify, turn into rock, with simple flat layering. If the soft sediments are greatly disturbed before being lithified, the result might be "chaotic" rather than simply layered.

Circulate Mud-weighted fluid is pumped down the center of the drill pipe and flows up the outside the drill pipe while drilling. This "circulation" keeps the drill bit cooled as it cuts the rocks at the bottom of the well bore. The muddy fluid also captures the pieces of cut rock and carries them back to the surface. The driller controls the circulation of the fluid while drilling. When the geologist wants to see the cuttings from the bottom of the hole, the driller holds off the downward drilling and just circulates the mud and therefore the samples to the surface.

Clastics A clast is a piece of rock mostly small or tiny fragments of rock. Sandstone, conglomerates, and shales are made of "clasts" of rocks or per-existing minerals. "Clastics" is also a term that geologists use to describe rocks that are not chemically precipitated like limestones or salts.

Comanchean Cretaceous age rocks, about 140 to 125 million years old.

Completion If a well is drilled, and an oil or gas bearing horizon is located, it is determined to be "commercial," or worth producing to be sold. The drill well is then "completed", meaning it is equipped to safely produce by putting steel casing in the hole, and putting production equipment on the surface to gather, measure, and store or transport the hydrocarbons.

Conditioned To condition a well bore, the driller circulates muddy fluid through the drill string of pipe which coats and builds up a "mud cake" on the sides of the wellbore so that the walls do not easily cave in.

Conductivity The ability of rock types to conduct electrical current can be measured and used to identify the type of rocks and fluids they contain. Saltwater-bearing rocks are more conductive than oil-bearing rocks.

Contour maps Contours maps are made by drawing lines of equal value (contours) based on data points posted on a map. One kind of contour map is a surface topographic map where elevations are measured and contours are drawn to tie together the same elevation all over the mapped area. Contour maps can be made for anything that involves measurements, such as barometric maps for weather purposes, or if one is looking for oil and gas, a contour map is made of the depths to drill to the oil or gas layer, the prospective rock layers.

Core When a well is drilled, if the geologist wants to see more of the subsurface rocks and the fluids they contain, than the tiny "cuttings", a doughnut-shaped "coring" bit will be used to drill a cylinder of rock and retrieve it in one whole piece. Geologists can see and collect much more data with the whole rock sample, but it is very expensive, so an entire well is rarely cored.

Cosmoline Waxy brown material used to prevent rust.

Crinoids A class of animals that live on the sea floor in both shallow and deep water, these sea creatures often look like flowers growing on the sea floor. They have a mouth surrounded by feeding arms which gives them a plant like look.

Cross sections A diagram along a line of interest that represents a vertical slice of the earth and illustrates what a geologist interprets lies beneath the earth's surface.

Crustal deformation The earth's "crust" is the outer layer of many layers that make up the earth. The crust is made up of "plates" that slowly move about the crust. When these plates collide they can buckle or "deform" the crust where they make contact often building mountains.

Cuttings The small pieces of rock that result from the drill bit chipping, grinding, and "cutting" down through rocks while drilling a well bore; also called samples.

Deltas When a river meets a body of water such as the Gulf of Mexico, all the flowing energy changes and sediment that the river has been carrying settles out and drops to the ocean floor. This can create a triangular-shaped body of sediments. Delta means triangle in Greek.

Denali Fault System Mt. Denali, also known as Mt. McKinley, is the highest peak in North America. The Denali fault system runs through this area and was named after Mt. Denali, like the San Andreas fault in California is named after the San Andreas valley.

Derrick The frame work of the oil rig that has the hoisting tackles and other equipment to lift drill pipe in position and apply weight and rotate to drill a borehole. It is the tall, four-sided structure that one sees as a well is being drilled. After drilling is finished, the derrick is moved off location.

Devonian Part of the Paleozoic rock sequence that were deposited 405 to 345 mya.

Diagenesis All the physical changes (like compaction) and chemical changes (like precipitation of mineral cements) that occur after sediments are deposited and are being lithified, or turned into rock. Examples include grains being deformed by compaction from burial and calcite mineralization forming between sand grains.

Diamond-bit drill holes Wellbores that have been drilled with diamond encrusted drill bits. Diamonds are the hardest minerals on earth and are used to drill rocks that are very hard and have very low penetration rates with conventional metal-toothed bits. . The diamonds are "man-made" industrial diamonds.

Dip meter A tool that measures the orientation and slope (strike and dip) of rock layers. These measurements help the geologist or operator understand the angle from horizontal of the rock layers that will affect thickness and depth calculations. The data can be displayed with symbols plotted with depth and summarized on graphs. As an example, the dip meter tool measurement might indicate the rocks are dipping 15° southeast.

Doghouse The small cabin on a rig floor used as an office and storeroom, with gauges, tools, and supplies. It houses the geolograph.

Drawworks The equipment that hoists the drill pipe.

Drilling foreman The person who supervises the actual drilling operations of the well.

DST	DST is the acronym for a Drill Stem Test. A tool is lowered into a drill hole to test the rock for fluids, pressure, and permeability.
Embayment	An indentation into the shoreline, larger than a cove, but smaller than a gulf.
Estuarine	An estuary is the widened mouth of a river where fresh water and sea water meet and mix. One might study the plants or animals or sediments that are found in the "estuarine" environment.
Evaporites	When water evaporates, the residue that remains from minerals previously held in solution by the water, are called evaporites. Salt is formed in this manner.
Facies	The rock characteristics that reflect how the rock was deposited and formed, such as in a sand dune, in a tidal flat, in a river margin.
Farmed in	If an oil operator wants to participate in another operator's drilling project, he can propose to pay for part of the land and drilling costs in exchange for any revenue, if the well is good. This is called a farm in.
Farmed out	If an operator wants another company to pay for part of their drilling project (lowers their risk and capital investment) they might "farm out" a percentage of the costs in exchange for giving the partner an interest in the well (percentage of production).
Faults	A fracture in the rocks of the earth's crust where there has been displacement; one side, or both sides of the fault have moved in relation to each other. Can be up and down, or , or both.
Fauna	Fauna is Latin for "animal life", whereas flora is Latin for "plant life".
Field mapping	Geologists go to areas that have rocks exposed at the surface to understand their deposition and vertical/lateral relationships. Collecting samples and recording the information on measured sections and maps are part of field mapping. Field mapping can be done in areas where there is a need to understand the surface geology or in well known areas to learn about the geology.
Fishing	In the oil business, this is when pipe or tools have become stuck in the drill hole. The operator must "go fishing" to get the equipment or tool that is stuck.
Fluvial systems	Fluvial means river in Latin. A fluvial system, in geology, means any rocks formed from sediments deposited by river processes.
Folding	Folding usually refers to layers of rocks that have been bent or curved under pressure (squeezed). Convex folds can be anticlines; concave folds can be synclines.
Foraminifera	The single-celled marine animals that have lived on earth for over a billion years and still live today. They form microscopic shells that are very distinct and different from other species. Paleontologists have found that they evolved so fast that different species can be found in different layers of rock and can be used to determine geologic age. They are great for "correlating" rock layers that are far apart and because of their small size for age dating and correlating subsurface samples (cuttings).
Formation	Geologists identify a rock layer that is distinctive, and that they might be able to recognize over large areas, and give it a formal name based on its depositional environment and regional extent. As an example: the Dakota Formation is predominantly a sandstone deposited in association with the Late Cretaceous Western Interior Seaway. .
Fossil mollusks	A mollusk is a group of soft bodied animals that usually have a shell like clams and mussels. When buried and citified (turned to rock) they are fossil mollusks.
Fossil plates	Some fossilized animals have external skeletons that are identified as having various "plates", like the plates that make up part of a trilobite, or a crinoid or parts of a dinosaur's armor.
Fracture networks	Fractures are cracks in the rocks. There may be more than one set of fractures, formed at different times in geologic history when pressures caused the rocks crack. One set of fractures might form an open network of cracks while another set is closed from the cracks being filled with calcite crystals or silica cements.
Gastropod	A snail type animal.
Geochemistry	The study of the chemistry of rocks. What are the organic or inorganic chemical elements that make up each type of rock and how they change through time and various earth environments of deposition.
Geode	A round or nodular rock that is hollow inside and sometimes may be filled with beautiful crystals.
Geological survey	The United States and most countries have a bureau of scientists that study the geology of that state or country. They are called a Geologic Survey; for example the Geological Survey of Ireland. Surveys study the geology to try to understand the natural resources (how much gold, silver, oil, gas, phosphate, coal, etc.) or natural hazards within that state/country.
Geolograph	A recorder, formerly with pens and paper, that makes a log of the rate per foot that the drill bit penetrates rock when drilling. Today many geolographs are computerized.
Geomechanics	Geo is earth, and mechanics is the study of rock behavior under pressure and temperature changes.
Geomorphology	Morph is form, so the study of earth forms is recognizing and classifying the various surface features seen every day: mountains, valleys, mesas, plateaus, landslides, volcanos, and many more examples.
Geoscientist	A scientist who studies the earth; earth scientist. Geoscientist is synonymous with geologist but may include other earth scientists, like geophysicists and geochemists.
Geothermal Maturity	In geology, the history of temperature changes affecting the rocks over time is an important aspect of determining if a rock has had enough time, pressure, or high temperature to change plant and animal material into hydrocarbons (oil and gas).
Gravel Packers	A downhole screen filter filled with appropriately sized sand to provide wellbore stability and prevent formation sand grains from being produced. A common procedure in Gulf Coast wells/s.
Gravity oil	Oil has various densities, respective to water. As one may observe oil is less dense than water and can float on it. But not oils have the same density. The gravity is an inverse measure of the oil density relative to the density of water. "Light" oil has a gravity higher than 31° and "heavy" oil has a gravity in the 10° to 20° range. If the gravity is less than 10° it will not float.
Horizon	The drilling objectives or the prospect or anticipated pay zone can be referred to as a horizon.

Hydraulic fracturing — Hydro means water, a combination of hydrogen and oxygen (H2O). Water is used to fracture rocks deep in the subsurface through the wellbore. Added to the water is a small percentage (usually less than 10%) of sand and thickening agents like clay. The clay makes helps the water to carry sand. Once the water is pumped into the rocks with enough pressure to fracture the rocks, the sand is left behind in the cracks of the rocks when the operator stops pumping the liquid. Sand serves to keep the micro fractures open after the fracturing is completed. Why do this? Some rocks are so "tight", meaning do not have natural paths for oil or gas to flow into the wellbore. By fracturing them the oil and gas can then flow into the pipe in the wellbore and up the pipe to the surface to the production facilities.

Hydrocarbons — Compounds of hydrogen and carbon. All organic bodies are made of some mixture of these compounds; oil and gas are complex mixtures of hydrogen and carbons, resulting in compounds like methane, propane, ethane, etc.

Hydrology — Hydro means water in Latin, and hydrology is the study of water and its flow in many forms: above ground in rivers and oceans; underground in aquifersand petroleum reservoirs.

Ichthyology — Ichthys means fish in Latin, so an ichthyologist studies fish!

Invertebrate paleontology — In animal life, there are vertebrates--animals with vertebrae or backbones; there are also invertebrates--animals without backbones, such as mollusks, slugs, snails, flies, spiders, etc. Invertebrate paleontology is the study of fossil animals without vertebrae.

Iron ore — The rocks that are rich in iron minerals. Most minerals like iron, copper, zinc, etc. occur dispersed in rocks. To take the mineral out of the rocks, they must be crushed and processed to separate the mineral, like iron, from the surrounding rock that is not iron. The basic rock holding pockets or veins of iron is called iron ore.

Isopach — Iso mean equal. The term can be used to describe a map that displays lines of equal thickness of a rock layer. Some rocks like chalk beds cover hundreds of miles with very little change in the thickness, while others, like a river bed deposit, or a fossilized reef have significant changes in thickness over short distances. The isopach (map) shows the thickness of that body of rock over a specific area.

Jack up — A jack up rig is a drilling vessel that is floated out to a spot in the ocean and then the legs of the platform are stationed securely to the seafloor bottom while the derrick is elevated into a position to drill a well. They are used in shallow water up to 350 feet deep.

Jug-hustlers — The people on a geophysical crew who layout (and collect) cable and plant the "geo phones" in defined patterns to detect the seismic recordings.

Jugs (Geophones) — Geophones record the ground movement. For petroleum geology, it is recording artificially induced movement, either by "thumping" the ground with a hammer device, or moving the ground by setting off dynamite.

Kelly — The heavy square or hexagonal tool suspended from the top of the derrick that screws into the topmost joint of drill pipe to turn the drill string as the rotary table turns.

Landman — A person who leases land, either private or public, for a company to drill or who researches ownership records.

Lineaments — The core of this word is "line" and geologically this is a linear feature on the surface of the earth, such as a fault line, a line of volcanoes, a line of sink holes -- anything that can be mapped with the appearance of "lining up."

Lithologic logs — Lith means rock; a lithologic log is a record a geologist makes of each layer of rock that is being investigated (like a diary or a ship captain's log of a sea crossing). It usually results in a vertical display or a "log" of descriptions with depth .

Lithologies — Lithologies describe the general physical characteristics of rocks like sandstone, shale, conglomerate, limestone.

Macropaleontology — Macro means large. Macropaleontology is the study of fossils large enough to be visible without a without a microscope.

Magnetic data — The data collected by a magnetometer shows the magnetic force across an area. Geophysicists can map this data and make predictions about which rocks in the subsurface like basement rocks might be causing the variation in magnetic readings.

Magnetometer — An instrument to measure the earth's natural magnetic field.

Marginulina — A type of foraminifera, microscopic one-celled animals.

Marine gravity survey — Gravity surveys measure the earth's natural gravity pull. A marine survey takes gravity readings over the oceans. The readings vary depending on the rocks in the subsurface and geophysicists can use this data to interpret physical properties and anomalies in the subsurface.

MCFD — M is a symbol for a thousand, C stands for cubic, F stands for feet and D for day. This is the acronym for thousands of cubic feet of gas produced in one day. A gas well might produce 10,000 cubic feet of gas per day (MCFD).

Miocene — The geologic time (epoch) with rocks of a "young" age compared to all the rocks on the earth's surface, ranging from 5 to 23 million years old.

Microbial — Microbes are bacteria or other micro-organisms that can cause disease or fermentation. In the oil and gas business, microbial can refer to a texture in rocks from these processes.

Microfauna — Fauna is "animal" life and microfauna would be that animal life which requires a microscope to identify and study.

Micropaleontology — Micropaleontology is the study of fossils that are so small they need to be viewed with a microscope for identifying and studying.

Migration "smiles" — A term used to describe a particular display of a seismic record. When sound waves are plotted as a seismic cross section some will artificially bend upwards into a "smile" if the data is not processed correctly or when the rocks greatly vary in composition (velocity).

Mineralogist — A person (geoscientist) who studies minerals.

Miocene — A part of the youngest rocks on earth, from about 5 to 23 mya.

Miocene biostratigraphy — The study of the fossil life in the rocks that are 5 to 23 mya.

Mississippian — The age of Paleozoic rocks that range from 345 to 310 mya.

Nannofossils — Fossil remains of the tiniest single cell organisms, like algae, which have calcareous structures that can be seen with a microscope.

Oil & gas interests — Having a financial contract (lease) for a percentage of oil and gas production. Perhaps a percentage of the income and expense for certain wells.

Oil scout — A person who is looking for information about other companies' activities in oil and gas exploration and development. A "spy" for a company, who will watch courthouses to see who is taking oil and gas leases, or will watch a well drilling from a distance to see how deep they are drilling. This information is reported back to the scout's company or client so that no one is surprised by activity.

Oligocene	The geologic time (epoch) with rocks that have been identified as between 23 and 34 mya.
Ostracods	Tiny aquatic animals (crustaceans) that live on the sea floor or sometimes in lakes. Most are as small as 1-2 millimeters in size, but they can be as big as 30 millimeters. They have chitinous (hair like) or calcareous valves, like a clam and when fossilized, are used by geologists to correlate from one layer to another in the same way the foraminifera have been used for biostratigraphy.
Outcrop	Rocks on the earth's surface that are visible, meaning not covered with vegetation or man-made structures like parking lots or cities. Road cuts rocks showing on the sides of a river, and cliffs along coastlines provide particularly good outcrops for geologists to study. In desert areas, where there is little vegetation, outcrops abound.
Packers	A device that has a hydraulic mechanism that can expand within a wellbore and can be put in a well bore to seal off a part of the wellbore. Typically used to isolate a zone for testing.
Paleoecology	Ecology is the study of relations of organisms to each other and their environment. Paleoecology is the study of fossil animals and plants in the rocks or geologic record.
Paleoenvironments	The reconstructed environment where sediments were deposited millions of years ago, using clues preserved in the rocks.
Paleogene	The older rocks of the Cenozoic era, Paleocene, Eocene and Oligocene, ranging from 66 to 23 mya.
Paleogeographic	Geography is studying the physical features of the earth's surface—rivers, mountains, oceans, hills, shorelines, etc. Paleogeographic studies are conducted by geologists to learn what those features were in the past. Over 60 million years ago there was a seaway from Canada to Mexico; geologists have reconstructed how the earth looked then from clues in the rocks.
Paleontology	The study of life in the past, based on fossil plants and animals.
Paleozoic, Mesozoic, Cenozoic	The three eras of rock layers from almost 600 mya to present, which have very distinctive fossils and types of rock that make them identifiable to geologists.
Paleo-magnetism	The earth has a magnetic field that changes over time and is preserved in the rock record. The current magnetic field causes the needle on a compass to point "north." Over the history of our earth, the magnetic pole has changed. Paleomagnetic information is extracted from rocks and reveals the location of ancient magnetic poles.
Palynology	The study of pollen or other plant grains, like spores. Most plants living today or that have lived in the past, can be identified by studying these microscopic grains.
Palynological zonations	Plants, like animals, have evolved and changed through time. Just as micropaleontologists study a foraminifera zone in rocks and correlate it to other rocks distant from their sample, so palynologists have developed knowledge of what pollen correlates to a certain ages of rock. This is very useful in non-marine environments that do not have foraminifera in them.
Paraffin oils	A waxy solid mixture of hydrocarbons that is flammable.
Pay zone	Pay is the term the petroleum industry uses to describe a layer of rock that can produce oil or gas, because it will "pay" for the expense of drilling the well and make a profit. The rock layer that yields the oil or gas is the pay zone.
Pectinidae	The family of sea creatures that have two valves, like clams and mussels.
Pennsylvanian bioherms	Pennsylvanian is the age of the rock (280-310 mya), and bioherms are the fossilized reefs or mounds. They contain fossils of corals, snails, clams, sea urchins, etc. Because of the mounded shape, they can make excellent petroleum reservoirs.
Perforators	To perforate a well is to make holes in the casing pipe so that fluids from the "pay" zone can flow into the cased wellbore and ultimately be produced to surface tanks or pipelines. A perforator is a type of specially built gun that can be lowered into the hole to the correct zone and fire shots into the casing to make perforations or holes in the casing.
Permeability	The capability of a rock layer to allow fluids to flow through it. If it has low permeability, it is difficult for water, oil, or gas to flow. If the rock has high permeability it is easier for fluids to flow through it.
Permian	Rocks deposited on earth between 280 and 230 mya.
Petrographic	Petro means rock, and with the term graphic means to "picture" the rock. All rocks are composed of minerals. A petrographic display, often under a microscope, shows all of the various minerals that compose that rock.
Petrography	The study of minerals and textures in a rock, usually with a petrographic microscope, scanning electron microscope, X-ray fluorescence, or many other tools.
Petrophysicist	A person who studies the physical and chemical properties of rocks—how they react to nature's processes and what minerals and chemicals are in the rock. In oil and gas, a petrophysicist commonly uses geophysical well logs to ascertain these properties.
Photomicrograph	A photograph taken with a microscope. The microscopic magnifies objects so that the components can be better identified.
Physiography	The part of geography that is most concerned with studying the physical aspect of land and sea; whereas cultural geography is concerned with human effects.
Planktonic	Characteristic of "plankton", which are tiny organisms that float in the sea or in a lake, like foraminifera, algae, tiny crustaceans. They provide food for many aquatic animals like whales.
Plate tectonics	The earth's crust is made of many major plates including the African, Antarctica, Eurasian, Indo-Australian, Pacific, North American, and South American plates. These plates move about the surface of the earth. Tectonic is from a Latin word meaning "building" and, through the collision of the plates, mountains are built. The intersection of two plates, like the Pacific plate and North America plate, can cause earthquakes and sometimes volcanic activity. It is exciting activity, even if it is in slow in geologic time.
Plays	For a petroleum geologist, this is the study that defines where a trend of potential oil and gas reservoirs might exist. Trend plays can have a large geographic area that has potential. When the geology is detailed enough to pick specific drill sites, then one would have "prospects" within the play.
Pleistocene	The geologic time (epoch) from about 2.5 mya to around 12,000 years ago.
Pliocene	The geologic time (epoch) prior to the Pleistocene, from 2.5 mya to 5 mya.
Plugging	In petroleum geology, when a wellbore is drilled and fails to find commercial oil and gas, the well will be plugged, meaning cement is pumped into the casing to prevent any fluids from coming to the surface. Oil and gas wells that were successful are also eventually plugged, and filled with cement, when the zone no longer produces.

Poor man's 3D (2D swath)	Typical three dimensional (3D) seismic is recorded with shot points and sources for sound waves covering the area in a dense, typically rectilinear pattern. It is very expensive for a small company. However, two dimensional seismic might lay out all the lines to cover an area, but only every other line will record data, with no sound sources at those points. It is much less expensive than true 3D data.
Porosity	A measurement of the void space in a rock. For petroleum geology, porosity is a measurement sued to determine the volume of fluids or gases to occupy.
Porous	Having void spaces called pores between the grains or minerals of a rock. Oil, gas, and/or water can collect in the pores.
Precambrian	The geologic time (Supereon) for rocks older than 570 mya, mostly not sedimentary.
Precambrian, Paleozoic, Mesozoic, Cenozoic	The layers of rock covering the earth are divided into four Major groups called Eras. The Precambrian is from 4000 million years ago (mya) to about 540 mya, the Paleozoic era ranges from about 540 to 252 mya, the Mesozoic ranges from 252 to 66 mya, and the Cenozoic is from 66 to less than one mya.
Pre-salt	Large bodies of salt in the sediments along the Gulf Coast cause the layers over them to fold or form "salt domes". The layers deposited under the salt are called the pre-salt layers. Geophysical tools recording data over and around a salt deposit had very difficult time recording sound waves for the layer of rock under the salt.
Prospect	A prospect in the oil and gas business relies on data interpretations and "educated guesses" about what might lie beneath the surface. Geologists study all the well logs from nearby wells and seismic surveys around the area to look for a possibility of finding oil and gas stored in certain layers. These become "prospects" for drilling.
Pyrite	Pyrite is commonly known as "fool's gold" because it is shiny, metallic, and brassy-yellow that an amateur might mistake for gold. It is an iron sulfide mineral that grows in beautiful, square crystal forms.
Quadrangle	A rectangular surface mapping area. The US Geological Survey has mapped all of the US, one quadrangle at a time.
Radiolarian	One-celled animals with a spherical skeleton made of silica. Quartz is a mineral is made of silica.
Rare-earth elements	Rare earth elements are 17 unusual elements that are actually not rare. In fact, they are abundant but very difficult to separate out of the mineral ore. They are often finely dispersed in the ore but may concentrate into large nodules.
Rathole	A rathole is a shallow drill hole about 30-35 foot deep that is used for storing the kelly, a rotating shaft of pipe that transfers torque from the kelly bushing to the drill string during drilling operations. It is similar to the "mouse hole" where drilling pipe is stored when not in use. Also, after drilling the entire wellbore, the driller will often drill a "rat hole," meaning to drill deeper to allow more room downhole for the well logging tools to record the entire thickness of the "pay zone." They can also be drilled to use for a latrine on a location.
Reserves	Estimates of the amount of oil or gas in place in a pay zone are called reserves. The volume is calculated by knowing the area covered by the oil and gas trap, the porosity of the rock, the thickness of the rock, the water saturation, and other factors.
Reservoir	A reservoir is an area of rock that has enough porosity to contain sizeable amounts of fluid such as water, oil, gas. The fluids fill the pore space between grains or minerals and can be microscopic to grain sized or larger. Larger voids caused by fractures or the dissolving of limestone can be found in some reservoirs.
Resistivity	The ability of rocks to impede the flow of electrical current can be measured as resistivity. Resistivity can be used to identify the type of rocks and fluids they contain. Porous oil- and gas-bearing rocks typically have high resistivities.
Rhodocrosite	A beautiful rose red mineral (manganese carbonate), considered a gem stone; also, the state mineral of Colorado.
Rig hand	A person who works on a drilling well.
Rod and transit	Surveying equipment which has a telescope and measuring accessories used for surface mapping.
Rotary drilling	Rotary drilling was invented when oil and gas explorers wanted to drill wells deeper than possible with "cable tool" rigs. A cable tool drilling operation employed a heavy tool strung up on a cable and allowed to fall into the wellbore, to crack and chip the rock. Rock samples were "bailed" out of the hole using a cylindrical bucket. It was a very slow process used to drill shallow water wells, and early on, the first oil wells. The rotary technique utilized a drill bit on the end of the drill pipe going and turned by a clockwise revolving "rotary" table. This method could cut the rock faster by the cutting action of the drill bit and could keep fluid circulating to remove the rock pieces more efficiently.
Roughneck	A roughneck is a "rig hand" who helps add new lengths of pipe to the drill string to continue drilling and helps to bring the string out of the hole when the drill bit needs to be changed, or when the well needs to be tested or logged. When not doing this work, they are often tend to the rig maintenance.
Royalties	When oil and gas companies lease the mineral rights to drill wells either on private, state, or federally owned land in any country they agree to give the original owner of the rights a "royalty" as a partial percentage of the revenue earned from the sale of any oil or gas discovered, if there is any. Sometimes oil and gas companies give the geologist or the originator of the prospect a "royalty" to repay them for their hard work and creativity.
Saline deposits	Saline basically means salty water. When saline water evaporates, it leaves a residue or deposit of salt.
Salt dome	Large deposits of salt can concentrate beneath the sediments on the sea floor, and the weight of the thick overlying sediments will sometimes cause the salt to "flow." As the salt flows and accumulates into a large concentrated bodies, the overlying sediments are draped and folded over it, creating a dome. Sometimes the domes are visible on the surface above it. Early oil explorers looked for these "domes" because many were also good places for oil and gas (which are lighter than water) to accumulate in the fold. It is basically a round anticline created by salt accumulation.
Salt plugs	Salt can be pumped down a wellbore to temporarily plug off a zone while it is being completed or treated. When the procedure is complete, it can be removed by just flushing with water.
Salt structure	Similar to a salt dome.
Samples	Samples as used in this book, refer to the small pieces of rock (cuttings) that are brought to the surface and collected while drilling through the rock. The cuttings are forced up to the surface with circulating drilling mud. These "samples" of what is being drilled are important to the wellsite geologist for identifying the rock layers and the fluids they contain.
Scout	See oil scout.
Scout data	Information gathered by an oil scout about drilling or leasing activities by other companies.

Scout ticket	Information about each well that is being proposed for drilling, or is drilling, or has been drilled. In the early days, independent scouts would sell or trade this data. They called the paper with the date a "scout ticket." Most states now require that all of this data is reported to the state, and made available to the public.
Sedimentology	The study of sediments and the processes that result in their formation, transport, and deposition.
Seismic	Pertains to the vibrations or shaking of the earth that occur naturally with an earthquake or artificially with a truck that "hammers" the surface to create a record of the rock layer's reactions to shaking. Small amounts of dynamite can also be used to "shake" the surface to create a "seismic data point," a record of the layers beneath the surface.
Seismograph	A recording of the movements of the ground, such as when an earthquake occurs. Oil and gas explorationists use a mechanical thumper or dynamite to vibrate or jiggle the earth's surface in an area they are exploring and record the data on a special truck-mounted seismograph.
Seismometers	Same as a seismograph, it can measure the direction, intensity, and duration of an earthquake, natural or the smaller man-made shaking that can occur in oil and gas geophysical exploration.
Serpentine	A group of rock forming minerals, usually green in color and found in nature.
Shale shaker	A vibrating screen that is adjacent to the rig floor. When drilling mud comes up the hole to the rig floor it is deposited on the screen, where the shaking makes the drill mud fluid fall through the screen to be re-used in drilling. The cuttings or samples from the bottom of the hole are collected from the top of the screen. These samples are examined by the geologist.
Shales	A very fine grained sedimentary rock, often found in very thin layers. Frequently shale is grey or black when it has abundant organic material in it, that has been converted to carbon though the lithification process.
Shelf margin deltaic clinoforms	The continental shelf is the area adjacent to a continent that is covered by the ocean. At the margin of the shelf, where the sea bottom rapidly gets deeper and becomes the ocean floor many sedimentary processes are active, such as sediments flowing into the ocean from river deltas. Many unique deposits form at the shelf edge, where the slope intensifies. This sloping surface results in a type of bedding or layering called a clinoform.
Soft rocks	Soft rocks are those formed mostly by sedimentary process; tiny grains of sand, mud, and minerals being deposited and formed over time into rocks. They are considered "soft" as opposed to "hard" rocks that form when the magma deep in the earth's crust cools and develops rocks like granite; or, when the magma explodes to the surface as a result of volcanic activity and the molten rock cools on the surface, like lava.
soundings	Recordings of the depth from the ocean surface to the floor of the ocean. When these measurements were put on a map and contoured, the resulting map depicted the topography of the ocean floor. This facilitated the discovery of mid-ocean ridges and the identification of ocean floor spreading
Spectrographer	During WWII, it became important to detect underwater sounds and identify what caused them, especially trying to locate submarines. A sound spectrograph was developed by the Bell telephone labs which would record the sounds and plot them on paper. A spectrographer would interpret the signals—was it a submarine, a whale, a surface ship?
Spudding	Spudding means to initiate the drilling of the well. The rig is moved in, the drilling equipment put into place, and the rotary tools start drilling the hole. That is spudding the well.
Squeeze job	Injecting a cement slurry into a layer of rock through openings (perforations) in the drill pipe to isolate a zone.
Stable Isotope Geochem istry	An isotope is an element in nature, with equal numbers of protons and different numbers of neutrons. Stable isotopes are not radioactive; unstable isotopes are radioactive.
Stacked channel complex	Rivers flow and carry sediment. Sediment deposited in the river channel is called a channel deposit. Geologists find evidence of channels in the rock records that have, over time, been deposited one on top of another. These are stacked channel complexes.
Stenography	Stenography was the act of a secretary taking notes using shorthand; rarely used any more, it was a rapid way to write what someone was saying. At a later time, the stenographer (secretary) would type the shorthand into words.
Stopes	The open space in a mine after the ore has been extracted.
Straddle test	The use of two inflatable packers in a drill stem test to isolate a hydrocarbon bearing zone for testing.
Strata	Layers of sedimentary rock, mostly of one rock type, such as sandstone or limestone. (Singular stratum)
Stratigraphic correla tions	Strata that are related, usually by age of deposition, are "stratigraphically correlated" to each other. If I am in Fort Collins, Colorado, and I drive south to Pueblo and look closely at the rock, I can "correlate" similar rocks from one place to the other. Sometimes fossils are used to make better correlations because they can provide a geologic date for when the strata were deposited, before the strata became rock.
Stratigraphy	Strata means layers of rock. When you look at rock outcrops along the highway, you see that layers have different characteristics: some layers are a different color, some layers have a different size of sediments like pebbles, sand, or clay, and some layers have different thicknesses. Each noticeably different layer is a stratum, many different layers are strata. Stratigraphy is the relationship of the strata to the geological time scale.
Strikes	Strikes, in geology, are not like Union strikes. Geologic strikes refer to the way rocks are oriented. If a rock layer is dipping and you walk across it staying at the same level--which way are you walking? Northeast, southwest south? This direction that you "strike out on" is called the strike of the dipping bed. If you walk down the dipping bed, 90° from the strike, that is the dip direction, again it can be described as north, south, etc., so many degrees from direct north. Then, the amount of dip is measured with the Brunton compass, such as 15°.
Subsalt	Strata that lie beneath a layer of salt.
Sub-thrust	The rocks that underlie a thrust fault. A thrust fault is a low angle structural feature that results when a block of rocks is pushed and overrides (slides or drags over) another block.
Sub-volcanic	Rocks that lie beneath volcanic flows or volcanic deposits.
Sucker rods	Equipment in a completed well which includes a steel rod, attached to a pump jack that helps pull up the oil and other liquids from the wellbore.
Suffragette movement	A suffragette is a woman seeking the right to vote through organized protest. A movement would be many women joining together to demand the right to vote. Often the suffragettes had marches in their cities; universities had suffragette clubs for young women students.

Sumps	A low place to collect water or other liquids.
Syncline	A fold in rocks where the sides rise upward from the axis of the fold. Similar to the shape of a bowl (concave).
Tailings	Rock that is mined which does not appear to be ore, and are usually dumped adjacent to the mining operation.
TCF	Trillion cubic feet of gas.
Tension leg platform	An oil and gas production facility for offshore use. It is buoyant (floats), and the entire platform is moored to the seafloor.
Tertiary	The geologic time (period) of younger rocks in the geologic column, less than 65-66 million years old.
Tidal influences	Sediments that are influenced by the rising and lowering of shoreline waters as a result of tides, such as ripple marks or the angle that small beds of sediment are deposited.
Tight	"Tight" in the oil and gas business has several meanings. First, the rock might be considered tight when it has very little pore space in it; when it can hold very little fluid. Another use of the term is to describe withholding information about a well, if you are not allowed to talk about it, you are keeping the information "tight." Some might call the wellbore a "tight hole", when information is not released to the public or to competitors until regulations dictate the release. Also spelled "tite."
Time-synchronous sandstone deltas	If more than one delta is forming along a coastline at the same time, they are time synchronous.
Tintina Fault System	A long fault that extends from British Columbia, Canada into central Alaska.
Toolpusher	The person who supervises the actual drilling of the well; he can also be called the drilling foreman.
Topotypes	A fossil that is found in an area where that species was originally discovered and formally named.
Transgressive-regressive sedimentation	When sediments are deposited on a coastal shoreline as the sea-level rises, they are called transgressive. When sediments (like beach sands) are deposited on the shoreline as sea-level drops, they are regressive.
Trilobites	An animal now extinct, that lived in the ocean and had three "lobes" the length of its body, hence, tri-lobe. There are more diverse types, over 20,000 species, than any other extinct species; first found in rocks 521 mya, but were extinct by 250 mya.
Tripping out	Bringing the drill pipe out of a wellbore, usually in two or three lengths of pipe at a time or about 60 or 90 feet, respectively.
Tubing	Tubing is string of pipe that goes down a cased well bore and serves as a conduit for oil and gas to be brought to surface.
Tungsten	A heavy metal that is hard, steel-gray, and used in projectiles. It is often used in combination with steel to increase toughness.
Turbidites	Sediment-laden(turbid) water flows down the continental shelf and when the flow stops, the sediments drop out with recognizable coarse to fine grained pattern. When the sediments are lithified, they are called turbidites.
Turritella	A variety of sea snails with a tightly coiled, elongated cone.
Twinning (dry holes)	To twin another well, is to drill right next to them. A dry hole is a well that did not or was not produced.
Type localities	Geologists have given names to almost all the visible layers of rocks around the world. In studying them, they determine they have notable characteristics that make them a candidate to have a formal geologic (stratigraphic) name,. The formal name is usually assigned using a geographic location where the rocks are described, like the Pierre Shale after Pierre, South Dakota.
Unconventional shale gas play	New technology has created the ability to extract gas from fined-grained (shale) rocks, which are considered "tight" due to low porosity and permeability, hence "unconventional." A "conventional" type of reservoir can be drilled and produced using long established traditional methods.
Vertical uplift	Mountain ranges are formed from the uplift of the rocks, most often associated with plate tectonic movements. Vertical uplift implies the rocks moved directly upward with pressure mainly from directly below the mountain. When forces have a horizontal component of pressure, the rocks might be squeezed together and thrust over and under one another.
Weevil	A new person to drilling operations, a "newbie."
Wellbore	The hole that is drilled to find oil and gas.
Well cuttings	Well cuttings are like "samples" --the small pieces of rock that are brought to the surface and collected while drilling through the rock. The cuttings are forced up to the surface with circulating drilling mud. These "samples" of what is being drilled are important to the wellsite geologist for identifying the rock layers a and the fluids they contain.
Well log	Wells that are drilled have "logs" made of the descriptions of lithology (the rock types) or other characteristics, like the amount of natural radiation, the resistance of the rock to electrical flow, or the speed that sound (acoustic waves) travel through the rock. Each of these characteristics are measured for the full depth of the drilled hole and is called a well log.
Wide-azimuth	An azimuth is the horizontal angle or direction of a compass bearing. In the acquisition of seismic data, some new technology using variations in azimuth setups can enhance data recovery.
Wildcat	A well drilled some distance away from producing wells on a new idea or a new prospect to find oil and gas. In contrast, a well drilled in a field to add to existing production is a "development" well and carries much less risk that it will be a "dry hole".
Wireline logging	When an oil well is drilled, the operator will hire a service company to "run logs" on the well to help determine if the well will produce economic quantities of hydrocarbons. The service company will lower the measuring tools down the hole on a "wire line" or cable. The logs measure many different characteristics, such as resistivity and density. They may also measure natural radioactivity, travel times for sound to penetrate rocks, and many other aspects inherent in rocks.
Working interest	A person or company who is paying a percentage of the cost of the well for a percentage of any oil or gas found in that well.
Worms	The person on a drilling crew with the least experience who gets all the menial chores and often is asked to collect the samples and label them for the geologist. They grab the sample, usually with a kitchen strainer, wash it, bag it, and mark it.
Zone	Zone is a common name for a rock layer of interest; such as a "pay zone", high pressure zone, or simple a "trouble zone".

Abbreviated Index

A

B

C

H

I

J

K

L